Contents

Preface

Publication users

This essential health and safety guide provides an excellent reference for those who have responsibility for or involvement in construction activities. The guide provides an understanding of the health and safety risks affecting this important sector of work and assists those responsible to manage them effectively.

The practical and informative approach of the publication will provide managers, health and safety practitioners and others who work in the construction industry with a perspective of the significance of health and safety risk in construction activities and an understanding of the control measures that can be applied to manage risk. This publication would be particularly useful for clients, designers, principal contractors, CDM co-ordinators, contractors and site managers. Those working in facilities and event management industries will also find the guide useful, as many of the risks they encounter are similar.

The guide is an excellent source of information for those undergoing the following learning programmes:

- To meet the requirements of the NEBOSH National Certificate in Construction Health and Safety syllabus, this award meets the key knowledge indicator when assessing Stage 1 competence for CDM co-ordinators referenced in the Approved Code of Practice for the Construction (Design and Management) Regulations 2007.

- To develop the knowledge of managers and supervisors working in construction.

- To develop and enhance competency and skills needed for facilities managers.

- To develop and enhance competency and skills needed for those who construct and disassemble temporary structures for outdoor events, music or theatre production and trade or other exhibitions.

Reference is made to the harm that construction hazards may have and the prevalence of injuries they cause in the construction industry. The publication contains an emphasis on practical solutions to construction workplace health and safety issues. Full colour photographs, tables and sample documents are provided to enable an understanding of how these risks can be managed. The publication contains a sample report from a questionnaire that may be used as a basis of a health and safety review for organisations.

Scope and contents

Syllabus

The Essential Health and Safety Guide focuses on construction hazards and related losses, risk control measures and core management of health and safety principles as they relate to construction activities.

The 3rd edition of this publication has been thoroughly revised and updated to embrace the May 2010 specification of the syllabus for the NEBOSH National Certificate in Construction Health and Safety award. Though the publication will suit all those interested in the topic in general and studying for other awards, it has been structured to reflect the order and content of the NEBOSH National Certificate in Construction Health and Safety syllabus in particular. In this way, the student studying for this award can be confident that the Essential Health and Safety Guide reflects the themes of the syllabus and forms an excellent Study Book for that purpose. Each element of the Essential Health and Safety Guide has an overview that sets out the learning outcomes of the element, the content and any connected sources of reference and relevant statutory provisions.

All statistics shown throughout this publication are the latest available at time of going to press.

Assessment

In order that users may check their understanding of the topic expressed in the Essential Health and Safety Guide and in particular the syllabus for the NEBOSH National Certificate in Construction Health and Safety award, a number of assessment questions have been included.

In addition, the publication contains a sample health and safety review questionnaire that may be used as a basis for an evaluation of an organisation's performance. The questionnaire has been produced by NEBOSH as part of their practical assessment of the above award, their origination and copyright is acknowledged. In order to understand how the questionnaire may be used and the type of report produced by candidates studying this award, a completed questionnaire and report is provided.

Legal requirements

The Essential Health and Safety Guide has at its heart the fact that health and safety should be managed as a risk. However, as one of the risks to a business is the risk of prosecution, care has been taken to relate topics to current legislation. The level of treatment is targeted to cover the interests of those developing their skills in health and safety management and in particular those following a course of study. Legislation is referred to in context in the various elements that comprise the Essential Health and Safety Guide and reflects the certificate level syllabus of the NEBOSH award.

Photographs and users

We have taken particular care to support the text with a significant number of full colour photographs and schematics. They are illustrative of both good and bad working practices and should always be considered in context with supporting text. Readers will find this a useful aid when trying to relate their background and experience to the broad based construction activities that may be encountered.

Where photographs, diagrams and text extracts are known to be drawn from other publications, a clear source reference is shown and RMS wish to emphasise that reproduction of such items within the Essential Health and Safety Guide is for educational purposes only and the original copyright has not been infringed.

Acknowledgements

Managing Editor: Ian Coombes

Member of the Safety Groups UK (SGUK) Management Committee. NEBOSH Trustee, member of NEBOSH Council and former NEBOSH examiner. Former member of the IOSH Professional Committee and Chair of the Initial Professional Development Committee. Member of the Construction Dust Partnership.

RMS Publishing Ltd wishes to acknowledge the following contributors and thank them for their assistance in the preparation of The Management of Construction Health and Safety Risk publication:

Geoff Littley, Principal Consultant ACT, CMIOSH, CSPA; experienced health and safety advisor, including in manufacturing and transport industries. Lead tutor for NEBOSH Certificate level courses, in particular for the NEBOSH National Certificate in Construction Health and Safety award. Provides training and mentor support for CDM Coordinators.

Barrie Newell, Director ACT, FCIM; current member of the NEBOSH Certificate Panel, former senior manager in the chemical industry with over 20 years experience of the management of toxic chemicals, waste disposal, energy recovery and recycling.

Julie Skett, senior project development and co-ordinator. Nick Attwood, Kris James and Andy Taylor layout and formatting.

Publications available from RMS:

Publication	Edition	ISBN
A Study Book for the NEBOSH National General in Occupational Health and Safety	Seventh	978-1-906674-28-1
The Management of Construction Health and Safety Risk	Third	978-1-906674-15-1
A Study Book for the NEBOSH Certificate in Fire Safety and Risk Management	Fourth	978-1-906674-20-5
The Management of Environmental Risks in the Workplace	Third	978-1-906674-24-3
The Management of Health and Well-being in the Workplace	First	978-1-906674-14-4
A Guide to International Oil and Gas Operational Safety	First	978-1-906674-19-9
A Guide to International Health and Safety at Work	Third	978-1-906674-18-2
Study Books for the NEBOSH National Diploma in Occupational Safety and Health:		
■ (Unit A) Managing Health and Safety	Fifth	978-1-906674-25-0
■ (Unit B) Hazardous Agents in the Workplace	Fifth	978-1-906674-26-7
■ (Unit C) Workplace and Work Equipment Safety	Fifth	978-1-906674-27-4
Study Books for the NEBOSH International Diploma in Occupational Safety and Health:		
■ (Unit IA) International management of health and safety	Third	978-1-906674-29-8
■ (Unit IB) International control of hazardous agents in the workplace	Third	978-1-906674-30-4
■ (Unit IC) International workplace and work equipment safety	Third	978-1-906674-31-1
Controlling Skin Exposure (BOHS)	First	978-1-906674-00-7

Foreword

With the continued poor record of the construction industry in regards to health and safety, it is of the utmost importance to make those within the industry aware of procedures to change both standards and culture.

This essential health and safety guide complements training with a structured approach to give managers and others the tools to allow positive health and safety management within the construction industry.

After many years within the industry, I have seen major improvements but there is always a need for step-change action. This Essential Health and Safety Guide to The Management of Construction Health and Safety Risk will assist construction personnel in achieving such a step-change.

John Lacey, C.F.I.O.S.H., F.S.I.A.. H.F.A.P.S, M.A.S.S.E
Chair of IOSH Construction Specialist Group and past president of IOSH.
Has been involved in and led by example construction health and safety,
in both the UK and other areas of the world for over 30 years.

Figure List (including tables and quotes)

List of abbreviations

LEGISLATION

CAOR	Control of Artificial Optical Radiation at Work Regulations 2010
CAR	Control of Asbestos Regulations 2012
CDM	Construction (Design and Management) Regulations 2007
CER	Control of Explosives Regulations 1991
CHIP 4	Chemicals (Hazard Information and Packaging for Supply) Regulations 2009
CNWR	Control of Noise at Work Regulations 2005
CLAW	Control of Lead at Work Regulations 2002
COSHH	Control of Substances Hazardous to Health Regulations 2002
CSR	Confined Spaces Regulations 1997
DSEAR	Dangerous Substances and Explosive Atmospheres Regulations 2002
EPA	Environmental Protection Act 1990
EWR	Electricity at Work Regulations 1989
EPDOC	Environmental Protection (Duty of Care) Regulations 1991
EPS	Equipment and Protective Systems Intended for Use in Potentially Explosive Atmospheres Regulations 1996
FSA	Fire (Scotland) Act 2005
FSSR	Fire Safety (Scotland) Regulations 2006
FAR	Health and Safety (First-Aid) Regulations 1981
HASAWA	Health and Safety at Work etc Act 1974
MRRA	The Health and Safety (Miscellaneous Repeals, Revocations and Amendments) Regulations 2013.
IRR	Ionising Radiations Regulations 1999
LOLER	Lifting Operations and Lifting Equipment Regulations 1998
MHOR	Manual Handling Operations Regulations 1992
MHSWR	Management of Health and Safety at Work Regulations 1999
NRSWA	New Roads and Street Works Act 1991
PPER	Personal Protective Equipment Regulations 1992
PSSR	Pressure Systems Safety Regulations 2000
PUWER	Provision and Use of Work Equipment Regulations 1998
RIDDOR	Reporting of Injuries, Diseases and Dangerous Occurrences Regulations 2013
RRFSO	Regulatory Reform (Fire Safety) Order (RRFSO) 2005
RTA	Road Traffic Act 1988 and 1991
RVCUR	Road Vehicles (Construction and Use) Regulations 1986
RVLR	Road Vehicles Lighting Regulations 1989
SMSR	Supply of Machinery (Safety) Regulations 2008
SSSR	Health and Safety (Safety Signs and Signals) Regulations 1996
SWMP	Site Waste Management Plans Regulations 2008
TWA	Transport and Works Act 1992
WAH	Work at Height Regulations 2005
WHSWR	Workplace (Health, Safety and Welfare) Regulations 1992

GENERAL

3D	Three dimensional
AA	Automobile Association
ABI	Association of British Insurers
ABS	Active Braking Systems
AC	Alternating Current
ACMs	Asbestos Containing Materials
ACOP	Approved Code of Practice
AFAG	Arboriculture and Forestry Advisory Group
AIDS	Acquired Immune Deficiency Syndrome
APF	Assigned Protection Factor
APS	Association of Project Supervisors
BMGV	Biological Monitoring Value
BSI	British Standards Institution
CAD	Computer aided design programmes
CAT	Cable Avoidance Tool
CCDO	Scheme for the Certification of Competence of Demolition Operatives
CCTV	Closed Circuit Television
CE	Conformité Européene
CECA	Civil Engineering Contractors Association
CEN	European Standards
CIOB	Chartered Institute of Building
CLP	Classification, labelling and packaging of chemical substances and mixtures
CPR	Cardio Pulmonary Resuscitation

CTS	Carpel Tunnel Syndrome
DC	Direct Current
DNA	Deoxyribonucleic Acid
DSD	Dangerous Substances Directive
DSE	Display screen equipment
DVLA	Driver and Vehicle Licensing Agency
EU	European Union
FLT	Fork Lift Truck
FRA	Fire Risk Assessment
H_2S	Hydrogen Sulphide
HAVs	Hand-arm Vibration Syndrome
HEPA	High Efficiency Particulate Air
HGV	Heavy Goods Vehicle
HIV	Human Immunodeficiency Virus
HML	High, Medium and Low
HPA	Health Protection Agency
HSE	Health and Safety Executive
HV	High Voltage
ICE	Institute of Civil Engineers
IIRSM	International Institute for Risk and Safety Management
IOSH	Institution of Occupational Safety and Health
IT	Information Technology
IEE	Institute of Electrical Engineers
LEV	Local Exhaust Ventilation
LFS	Labour Force Survey
LGV	Large Goods Vehicle
LPG	Liquefied Petroleum Gas
LTEL	Long Term Exposure Limit
LV	Low Voltage
MCWP	Mast Climbing Work Platform
MDI	Methylene Bisphenyl Di-isocyanate
MEWP	Mobile Elevated Work Platform
MSD	Musculoskeletal disorder
MSF	Manufacturing, Science and Finance Union
NASC	National Access and Scaffolding Confederation
NEBOSH	National Examination Board in Occupational Safety and Health
NNLW	Notifiable Non-Licensed Work
NVQ	National Vocational Qualification
ORSA	Occupational Road Safety Alliance
PAT	Portable Appliance Testing
PCV	Passenger Carrying Vehicle
PPE	Personal Protective Equipment
PPM	Parts Per Million
RCD	Residual Current Device
RMS	Root Mean Square
RPA	Radiation Protection Adviser
RPE	Respiratory Protective Equipment
RTFLT	Rough Terrain Fork Lift Truck
SDS	Safety Data Sheets
SNR	Single Number Rating
STEL	Short Term Exposure Limit
SWL	Safe Working Load
SWI	Self-reported Work-related Illness
TDI	Toluene Di-isocyanate
TWA	Time Weighted Average
UKAS	United Kingdom Accreditation Service
UKCG	UK Contractors Group
UN GHS	United Nations' Globally Harmonised System
UV	Ultraviolet
VCM	Vinyl Chloride Monomer
VWF	Vibration White Finger
WBV	Whole Body Vibration
WBVS	Whole Body Vibration Syndrome
WEL	Workplace Exposure Limit
WRULD	Work Related Upper Limb Disorder

Construction law and management

Learning outcomes

On completion of this element, candidates should be able to demonstrate understanding of the content through the application of knowledge to familiar and unfamiliar situations. In particular they should be able to:

1.1   Identify the scope, definition and particular issues relating to construction activities.

1.2   Outline the legal, moral and financial consequences of failing to manage health and safety within the construction industry.

1.3   Outline the scope and application of the Construction (Design and Management) Regulations 2007.

1.4   Identify the nature and main sources of external construction health and safety information.

Content

Sources of reference

Health and Safety in Construction (Guidance) (HSG150), HSE Books ISBN 9780717661824

Managing Health and Safety in Construction CDM ACOP, L144 ISBN 978-0-7176-6223-4

Successful health and safety management (HSG65) HSE Books ISBN 978-0-7176-1276-5

The Management of Health and Safety at Work (ACOP) (L21), HSE Books ISBN 978-0-7176-2488-1

Relevant statutory provisions

Construction (Design and Management) Regulations (CDM) 2007

Health and Safety at Work etc Act (HASAWA) 1974 - Sections 2, 3, 20-25, 33 and 39-40

Management of Health and Safety at Work Regulations (MHSWR) 1999 - Regulation 5

1.1 - Scope, definition and nature of construction activities

Types of work

BUILDING WORKS

Building works involve most trades within the construction industry such as ground workers, steel erectors, brick layers, carpenters, plasterers, etc all working closely together with the common goal of creating a new finished building or structure.

RENOVATION

Renovation work involves restoring an existing building or structure to a condition that is representative of its original condition or improved by repair and modernisation using more up-to-date materials and practices. As with new building works, this also involves most of the common trades normally used within the construction industry.

ALTERATION

Alteration works are required when the layout of an existing building, structure or premises no longer suits the use for which it was originally intended. This can include elements of both new building works and renovation works. Alterations can comprise an extension to an existing structure or demolition and removal of sections of the internal structure to make premises more spacious. Alternatively, an alteration may involve dividing the existing structure into smaller, separate sections by the introduction of partition walls of various materials (block-work, brick-work or studding and plasterboard).

MAINTENANCE OF EXISTING PREMISES

Maintenance work is an essential element to ensure that the condition of an existing building, premises or structure does not deteriorate and that it remains in as good a condition as is possible. Work is normally carried out on a regular scheduled basis to deal with issues of wear and tear, but can also be required when a problem suddenly occurs that requires urgent attention, for example, loss of roofing materials following a storm. Maintenance can be carried out on all components of existing premises, including the building, services, and any final building finish and furnishing.

Occupied premises

Careful planning of maintenance work should be given when the building or premises are occupied. Hazards from paint, dust, falling masonry and excavations should be considered; suitable and sufficient risk assessments should be made and controls implemented.

Unoccupied premises

Unoccupied premises/buildings can pose other hazards, with unstable groundwork, footings, walls, beams supporting floors and roofing. In addition unoccupied buildings are likely to be infested with vermin or suffer intrusion by pigeons in rafters where roof integrity may have failed, presenting the risks of biological hazards. Again these hazards should be highlighted, suitable risk assessments should be made and controls implemented.

CIVIL ENGINEERING AND WORKS OF ENGINEERING CONSTRUCTION

Civil engineering and engineering works normally relate to heavy construction activities requiring large items of plant and equipment such as cranes and excavators. This work will require specialist knowledge and experience in order to undertake civil engineering activities such as highway construction, bridge construction, piling works, large foundations, large concrete structures, excavations and utility projects. Engineering construction activities include the building of power stations, wind farms, chemical process plant and vehicle assembly plant.

DECOMMISSIONING

Decommissioning is concerned with the preparation necessary to take (permanently or temporarily) a piece of equipment or plant out of use. For example, the decommissioning of an air compressor that requires replacement or a building for a change of use (a warehouse into a manufacturing unit). Decommissioning also applies to taking a production site out of service, for example, a nuclear electrical power generation plant. The decommissioning process will include removal of mechanical, electrical, gas, compressed air, hydraulic, telecommunications, computer or similar services, which are normally fixed within or to a structure. In addition, it will include the safe disposal of any product or waste resulting from decommissioning.

DEMOLITION

The term demolition refers to 'breaking down' or 'removing'. In construction activities, demolition is carried out on buildings and structures that are no longer required or are possibly derelict and unsafe.

Account needs to be taken of potential hazards that may arise from demolition, for example the risk of premature collapse, presence of live services, asbestos dust and falling debris. Demolition must be carried out in a well-planned and controlled manner in compliance with a safe system of work.

The arrangements for demolition should be written down before the work begins. This safe system of work may be in the form of a safety method statement identifying the sequence required to prevent accidental collapse of the structure.

A safe system of work may include:

- Establishing exclusion zones and hard-hat areas, clearly marked and with barriers or hoardings.
- Covered walkways, to protect pedestrians if materials should fall from above.
- Using high-reach machines for mechanical demolition.
- Reinforcing machine cabs so that drivers are not injured from falling debris.
- Training and supervising site workers, in site rules and incident reporting.

Any project that involves any element of demolition (full or part demolition) falls under the control of the Construction (Design and Management) Regulations (CDM) 2007.

DISMANTLING

The term dismantling refers to taking things apart, often for reuse in another location. In construction, this is applied to parts of buildings and structures that are no longer required where they are located, such as temporary structures used for outdoor events, for example, concert staging or temporary athletic tracks/stadiums.

In a similar way to demolition, arrangements for dismantling should be written down before the work begins. The safe system of work may be in the form of a safety method statement identifying the sequence to be followed to prevent accidental collapse of the structure and any temporary supports necessary to maintain stability.

Range of activities

SITE CLEARANCE

Site clearance consists of preparing the site prior to the works being undertaken. This may involve removal of hazardous waste, obstructive trees, unwanted scrub and landscaping. Demolition activities may also be required as part of site clearance prior to construction works beginning. Where there are high levels of contaminants it may also be necessary for ground remediation.

Following completion of construction works site clearance will involve removal of all waste associated with the construction activities to a licensed waste disposal site, for example, brick and timber off-cuts, packaging and spoil. It will also include the removal of all plant and equipment used on the construction project, with the aim of leaving the site in a clean and tidy state ready for its intended use.

EXCAVATION

Excavation consists of digging below ground level to various depths in order to create a cavity that can be used for exposure of buried utility services, trenching for installation of utility services, casting building foundations or ground investigations. Methods of digging used for excavation work include the use of hand tools (pick, fork, shovel), and also by using a mechanical excavator. Major excavations for basements, sub-structures etc, remain as a permanent part in the construction operation.

LOADING, UNLOADING AND STORAGE OF MATERIALS

Construction sites use a host of different materials in the construction process that will require loading or unloading by mechanical or manual means. These can be broken down into materials that are used or removed immediately at site (i.e. excavation spoil, concrete mix, mortar mix) and materials that are stored at site and used or removed at regular intervals as required (bricks, cement, sand, timber, sundries, waste disposal skips). Loading and unloading should be undertaken using the correct procedures that comply with site safe systems of work and wherever possible avoiding the need for manual handling. Storage requirements should be identified and planned for the whole project. This will need to consider security, safe position and suitable ground condition; protection from adverse weather and potential for falls from a height or into an excavation.

SITE MOVEMENTS

Construction sites contain various types of heavy mobile plant and equipment and large numbers of site workers. Construction site projects should be well planned to take into account vehicles moving around the site. In particular, consideration to safe access and egress would include issues of adequacy of space for manoeuvring and ensuring operator visibility. Routes for both vehicles and pedestrians should be provided and be suitably surfaced, clearly defined and separated.

FABRICATION

Fabrication at site can include steel erecting, welding and form-working. Quite often it can involve working at height (where specialist work platforms and fall arrest equipment should be used) and adequate control is essential to prevent the falling of materials and tools. A variety of specialist equipment may be required and only be used by competent persons, for example, welding machine, bolt gun, or nail gun.

DECORATION

Decoration consists of applying various coatings, for example, paints, wallpaper, and artex, necessary to create the final finished appearance to a building or structure. The tools involved with decoration are often handheld and not powered. Various access systems including mobile elevating work platforms are required for this type of work.

CLEANING

Cleaning involves applying water, steam or various abrasive or chemical agents to the surfaces to be treated, for example, walls, windows, floors, fabric. The method of application can require the use of various types of equipment ranging from vacuum cleaners, floor polisher through to high pressure jets. Consideration should be given to the correct disposal of waste materials.

INSTALLATION, REMOVAL AND MAINTENANCE OF SERVICES

Various utility services are required on both existing and new construction sites and are usually buried underground, for example, electricity, gas and water. In new installations this involves a great deal of liaison with the planning authority, utility companies and the designer concerning the route the services will take and will involve excavation with heavy plant, loading and unloading of materials. New services are often connected to their source at a location that is situated outside the construction site boundary. Where this occurs, additional hazards to the general public present themselves and suitable precautions will be required. For example, traffic control (by means of signing and lighting) as well as guarding and protection of the public by the use of barriers and warning signs. Removing or maintaining utilities can present other hazards. Utility services should be isolated correctly prior to any work commencing, as this may require involving the utility companies so proactive planning is essential.

LANDSCAPING

Landscaping usually takes place during the final stages of the construction phase when there is little or no construction plant travelling around the site. Landscaping may include altering site levels and the introduction of trees, shrubs, grass turf/seed etc. The works generally consist of loading and unloading of materials, manual handling, and cleaning work (footways and roads). Note that care should be taken to avoid planting trees close to underground services or near to building footings.

Meaning of construction terms

MEANING OF 'EXCAVATION'

CDM 2007 defines 'excavation' as including any earthwork, trench, well, shaft, tunnel or underground working, but does not include the exploration for or extraction of mineral resources or activities in preparation for any place where exploration or extraction is to be carried out.

MEANING OF 'STRUCTURE'

CDM 2007 defines 'structure' as any building, timber, masonry, metal or reinforced concrete structure, railway line or siding, tramway line, dock, harbour, inland navigation, tunnel, shaft, bridge, viaduct, waterworks, reservoir, pipe or pipe-line, cable, aqueduct, sewer, sewage works, gasholder, road, airfield, sea defence works, river works, drainage works, earthworks, lagoon, dam, wall, caisson, mast, tower, pylon, underground tank, earth retaining structure or structure designed to preserve or alter any natural feature, fixed plant and any structure similar to the foregoing.

The definition of structure also includes any formwork, falsework, scaffold or other structure designed or used to provide support or means of access during construction work, and any reference to a structure includes a part of a structure.

Particular construction issues

TRANSITORY NATURE OF WORKERS

The construction industry is characterised by its intermittent, temporary, transitory nature. Generally, building and construction contractors hire a work force on a project basis. Thus, workers in the construction industry are accustomed to travelling from areas where work is not plentiful to fill short-term labour shortages created by expansion and contraction of local construction activity elsewhere.

TEMPORARY NATURE OF ACTIVITIES AND THE CONSTANTLY CHANGING WORKPLACE

Construction sites constantly change through the build phase, as the trades that are associated with the construction vary greatly at each stage. Consideration needs to be given to site induction for new workers as appropriate.

The safe systems of work, risk assessments, site safety procedures and site inductions will need to be updated regularly to suit the most current situation. A construction site will always be an unfamiliar workplace with new hazards and dangers posed as each phase moves to the next.

TIME PRESSURES FROM CLIENTS AND PRINCIPAL CONTRACTORS

Clients have one of the biggest influences on the health and safety of those working on a construction project. Their decisions have substantial influence on the time, money and other resources available for the project. Because of this, the Construction (Design and Management) Regulations (CDM) 2007 make them accountable for the impact their decisions have on health and safety. In the same way, the principal contractor may exert pressure on contractors to fulfil tasks within time limits. This is a natural part of the efficient organisation of a construction activity where a number of contractors work together to achieve the goals. Each activity may depend on the timely completion of another. However, if the time available to complete the overall project becomes limited, possibly due to delays or underestimation of the necessary time for completion of an activity, the principal contractor may put contractors under pressure to complete work on time or early. This can lead to less planning time and the potential for risks to be taken in order to save time.

WEATHER CONDITIONS

For those working outdoors, adverse weather can create numerous problems. Short term exposure to the sun can cause excessive sweating, dehydration and fatigue. There are fears that prolonged exposure can cause skin cancer. Strong wind increases risk when working at height and can cause unexpected movement of loads suspended on cranes. Heavy rain may cause soft ground conditions which can increase problems with site traffic and undermine the stability of scaffolds and excavations. Extreme cold leads to snow and ice which increases the likelihood of slips and falls. It may also increase the risk of brittle failure of equipment.

LEVELS OF NUMERACY AND LITERACY OF WORKERS

Poor levels of literacy and numeracy can significantly impede the progress of workers at a workplace. The level of understanding and critical information retention required, for example, when attending a health and safety induction, can be significantly reduced. Where numbers and the written word are utilised instead of a pictographic approach, then the meaning can be marred regarding written critical safety instructions or directions that may need to be followed could be unintentionally ignored. Weights and measures, dates and times critical to processes could also be misconstrued or overlooked if workers are innumerate.

NON-ENGLISH SPEAKING WORKERS

Regulation 10 of the Management of Health and Safety at Work Regulations (MHSWR) 1999 requires employers to provide information to employees which is comprehensible and relevant, i.e. capable of being understood by the person for whom it is intended.

For employees with little or no understanding of English, or who cannot read English, employers may need to make special arrangements. These could include providing translation, using interpreters, or replacing written notices with clearly understood symbols or diagrams.

Employers need to consider the following with reference to their non-English speaking employees:

■ Check that prospective workers have sufficient command of English for their role.
■ Check worker understanding of instructions and health and safety related notices.
■ If other members of staff are available who can speak the employee's native language, then they may be able to help the employee understand the working culture and environment in the UK.

The employee's previous experience should be determined. This can show whether they have relevant experience to carry out the work required.

1.2 - Consequences of failing to manage health and safety

General argument

There are three good reasons for preventing accidents in the workplace:

MORAL

Injury accidents result in pain and suffering for those affected. Though the actual numbers vary, each year construction activities in the UK typically result in an average of one fatality for each week worked. Clearly, it is important that employers and employees do everything that they can to avoid this.

LEGAL

It is a legal requirement to safeguard the health and safety of employees and others that might be affected by an organisation's operations.

FINANCIAL

Accidents at work cost a great deal of money, especially when damage is added. Costs resulting from construction accidents can be enormous and can be many times larger than could initially be perceived. The effect of an accident on construction work could lead to delays and possibly penalty charges being laid against those causing the delay.

Size of the construction health and safety 'problem'

Although there have been significant reductions in the number and rate of injury over the last 20 years or more, construction remains a high risk industry. The Health and Safety Executive (HSE) report that the Labour Force Survey (LFS) in 2012/2013 confirmed that though construction accounted for 5% of the employees in Britain it accounted for 27% of the fatalities, 10% of the major and 5% of the over 7 day injuries.

There were 39 fatal injuries to workers in construction in 2012/13, and of these fatalities 12 were to the self-employed. This compares with an average of 53 over the previous five years, including an average of 18 to the self-employed. In 2012/13, 26% of all workplace fatal injuries were in construction and the industry accounts for the greatest number of fatal injuries of the main industry groups. The rate of fatal injury per 100,000 construction workers in 2012/13 was 1.9, compared with a five year average of 2.3. The all industry rate for the period 2012/13 was 0.5 per 100,000 employees. During 2012/2013 the main causes of worker fatalities in construction were falls at 59% then being hit by a moving vehicle at 10%.

NUMBER AND RATE OF FATAL INJURY TO WORKERS 1993/94 - 2012/13

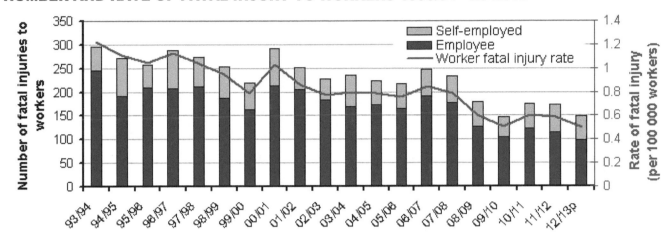

Figure 1-1: Number and rate of fatal injuries in construction activities in 2012/13.   *Source: HSE.*

NUMBER AND RATE OF REPORTED MAJOR INJURY TO EMPLOYEES

There were 1,913 reported major injuries to employees in 2012/13, compared to 2,298 in 2010/11 and an average of 2,815 over the previous five year period. The corresponding rates of major injury per 100,000 employees were 156, compared with 173 in 2010/11 and a five year average of 192. The all industry rate for the period 2012/13 was 78.5 per 100,000 employees.

NUMBER AND RATE OF REPORTED OVER 7 DAY INJURY TO EMPLOYEES

There were 3,133 reported over 7 day injuries to employees in 2012/13, compared to 4,784 over 3 day injuries to employees in 2010/11 and a five year average of 5,986. The corresponding rates of over 7 and 3 day injury per 100,000 employees were 255.4 in 2012/13 compared with 360.5 in 2010/11 and a five year average of 405.6. The all industry rate for the period 2012/13 was 233.1 per 100,000 employees. Under Reporting of Injuries, Diseases and Dangerous Occurrences Regulations (RIDDOR) 2012, the legal reporting requirement changed in April 2012 from over 3 days' incapacitation to over 7 days.

INCIDENCE OF ILL-HEALTH

The Labour Force Survey (LFS) estimated over the period 2009/10 to 2011/12 for 'self-reported illness caused or made worse by current or most recent job for people working in the last 12 months' was reported to have a prevalence of 74,000 people suffering from ill-health in the construction industry and a rate of 3,270 per 100,000. This compares similarly with the all industry average rate of 3,200 per 100,000. An estimated 818 thousand working days were lost due to ill-health in 2011/12.

The HSE also reported that the Cancer Burden Study, 2012, showed that the construction industry had the largest burden of occupational cancer amongst the industrial sectors, over 40% of the occupational cancer deaths and cancer registrations were from construction. About, 3,700 occupational cancer cases are estimated to arise each year as a result of past exposures in the construction sector.

HSE reported in 2011/12 that an estimated 1.4 million working days were lost, 818,000 due to ill-health and 584,000 due to workplace injury, making a total of 0.7 days lost per worker.

Accidents and ill-health are costly to workers and their families. They can also impact significantly on organisations because, in addition to costs of personal injuries, they may incur far greater costs from damage to property or equipment, and lost production.

1.3 - Construction (Design and Management) Regulations (CDM) 2007

Scope and application

The Construction (Design and Management) Regulations (CDM) 2007 are intended to focus attention on planning and management throughout construction projects, from design concept onwards. The main aim of CDM 2007 is to integrate health and safety into the management of the project and to encourage everyone involved to work together to:

- Improve the planning and management of projects from the very start.
- Identify hazards early on, so they can be eliminated or reduced at the design or planning stage and the remaining risks can be properly managed.
- Target effort where it can do the most good in terms of health and safety and to discourage unnecessary bureaucracy.

CDM 2007 applies to all "construction work". The term "construction work", as defined in Regulation 2 of CDM 2007, means the carrying out of any building, civil engineering or engineering construction work and includes:

The construction, alteration, conversion, fitting out, commissioning, renovation, repair, upkeep, redecoration or other maintenance (including cleaning which involves the use of water or an abrasive at high pressure or the use of corrosive or toxic substances), de-commissioning, demolition or dismantling of a structure.

The preparation for an intended structure, including site clearance, exploration, investigation (but not site survey) and excavation, and the clearance or preparation of the site or structure for use or occupation at its conclusion.

The assembly on site of prefabricated elements to form a structure or the disassembly on site of prefabricated elements which, immediately before such disassembly, formed a structure.

The removal of a structure or of any product or waste resulting from demolition or dismantling of a structure or from disassembly of prefabricated elements which immediately before such disassembly formed such a structure.

The installation, commissioning, maintenance, repair or removal of mechanical, electrical, gas, compressed air, hydraulic, telecommunications, computer or similar services which are normally fixed within or to a structure.

CDM 2007 is divided into five parts:

Part 1 Deals with matters of interpretation and application.

Part 2 Covers general management duties which apply to all construction projects, including those which are non-notifiable.

Part 3 Sets out additional management duties that apply to projects above the notification threshold (projects lasting more than 30 days, or involving more than 500 person days of construction work).

Part 4 Applies to all construction work carried out on construction sites, and covers physical safeguards that need to be provided to prevent danger.

Part 5 Covers issues of civil liability, enforcement in respect of fire, and amendments and revocations of other legislation.

Duties

THE CLIENT

The client is an organisation or individual for whom a construction project is undertaken. Clients only have duties when the project is associated with a business or other undertaking (whether for profit or not). An organisation or individual can be, for example, a local authority, school governors, insurance companies and project originators on private finance initiative projects. Domestic clients are people who have work done on their own home or the home of a family member that does not relate to trade or business, whether for profit or not. Domestic clients are a special case and do not have duties under CDM 2007.

Clients' duties

For *all* projects, ensure that:

- Work can be carried out safely.
- Adequate welfare facilities are provided.
- Any workplace complies with CDM 2007 Part 4.
- Make relevant pre-construction health and safety information available.

Where a project is notifiable, the client must:

- As soon as practicable appoint a competent CDM co-ordinator.
- Then appoint a competent principal contractor.
- Promptly provide the CDM co-ordinator and principal contractor with pre-construction information.

- Not allow work to start until the construction phase plan and adequate welfare facilities are in place.
- Provide the CDM co-ordinator with information for inclusion in the health and safety file.
- Keep health and safety file available for inspection and revised as necessary.

THE DESIGNER

Designers are those who have a trade or business that prepares drawings and specifications for new construction work or modifications to existing structures or buildings. Typically they will prepare drawings, design details, specifications, bills of quantities, specification (or prohibition) of articles and substances, as well as the related analysis, calculations and preparatory work for their employees or others under their control to prepare designs relating to a structure or part of a structure. A designer could be an architect, structural engineer, building surveyor, landscape architect, other consultants or manufacturing and design practice contributing to or having overall responsibility of any part of a design.

Designers' duties

For *all* projects, ensure that:

- The client is aware of their duties.
- Take account of other design considerations.
- Design to avoid foreseeable risk during construction, use and maintenance of the building.
- Give priority to collective measures over individual measures.
- Ensure where it is not possible to avoid risks that they are minimised.
- Provide adequate information about materials used in the design that could affect the health and safety of persons carrying out construction work.

Where a project is notifiable:

- Must not commence work (other than initial design work) in relation to a project until a CDM co-ordinator has been appointed.
- Provide the CDM co-ordinator with information for inclusion in the health and safety file.

THE CDM CO-ORDINATOR

The CDM co-ordinator is appointed by and assists the client with health and safety risk management matters and the appointment of competent contractors. Another important feature of the CDM co-ordinator is to advise on the adequacy of management arrangements of the health and safety provisions, facilitate good communication and co-operation between project team members and preparation of the health and safety file.

CDM co-ordinators' duties

CDM co-ordinators should:

- Be in a position to give advice to clients.
- Ensure co-operation between persons involved in the project.
- Ensure that designers include among the design considerations the principles of prevention.
- Liaise with principal contractor regarding information for the health and safety plan and health and safety file.
- Identify and collect pre-construction information.
- Ensure that designers comply with their duties.
- Ensure co-operation between designers and principal contractor in relation to any design change.
- Prepare a health and safety file.
- Ensure that a health and safety file is delivered to the client.
- Notify the Health and Safety Executive (HSE).

THE PRINCIPAL CONTRACTOR

The principal contractor is the lead or main managing contractor responsible for properly planning, managing and coordinating work during the construction phase, in order to ensure that the risks on site are properly controlled, which allows the management of health and safety to be incorporated into the project.

Principal contractors' duties

The principal contractor should:

- Plan, manage and monitor the construction phase to ensure that it is carried out without risk.
- Liaise with the CDM co-ordinator.
- Ensure adequate welfare facilities are provided.
- Draw up site rules.
- Display the notification details.
- Prevent unauthorised access to the site.

Ensure that every contractor is:

- Informed of the minimum amount of time allocated for planning and preparation.
- If necessary, consulted about the health and safety plan.
- Given access to the health and safety plan.

- Given any relevant information.
- Informed about the information that may be required for inclusion in the health and safety file.

Ensure that every worker is provided with:

- Site induction.
- Information that has to be provided by a contractor (see below).
- Any further information that might be necessary.

CONTRACTORS AND THE SELF EMPLOYED

The contractors and the self employed (sub contractors) are workers who are engaged in the project but have a duty to co-operate with the principal contractor in planning and managing the work to ensure that risks are properly controlled. Contractors can be engaged to conduct specialist work such as utility provision and special trades.

Contractors' duties

For *all* projects, ensure that:

- They do not start work unless they are aware of their duties.
- Plan, manage and monitor work to ensure that it is carried out without risk.
- Every contractor that the contractor appoints is provided with relevant information.

Every worker under the contractors control is given information and training which should include:

- Site induction (if not provided by the principal contractor).
- Results of risk assessments and control measures.
- Site rules.
- Emergency procedures and the persons involved in implementing the procedures.
- They do not commence work until unauthorised access to the site has been prevented.
- Ensure that adequate welfare facilities are provided.

Where a project is notifiable the contractor must:

- Not start work unless the contractor knows the names of the CDM co-ordinator and principal contractor, has been given access to the health and safety plan and the project has been notified to the HSE.
- Provide relevant information to the principal contractor on the health and safety risks created by their works and how they will be controlled.
- Identify any contractors they have appointed to the principal contractor.
- Comply with directions given by the principal contractor and any rules in the health and safety plan.
- Provide the principal contractor with any Reporting of Injuries, Diseases and Dangerous Occurrences Regulations (RIDDOR) 2013 reports.

Appointment and competence required of relevant parties

Where a project is notifiable, the client must appoint a CDM Co-ordinator and a principal contractor as soon as is practicable after initial design work or other preparation for construction work has begun.

No person, who is a duty holder under CDM 2007, is allowed to:

- Appoint or engage a CDM co-ordinator, designer, principal contractor or contractor unless the person to be engaged is competent.
- Accept such an appointment unless they are competent.
- Instruct a worker to carry out or manage design or construction work unless the worker is:

1) Competent.
2) Under the supervision of a competent person.

To be competent an organisation or individual must have knowledge of specific tasks and the risks that may arise.

"An appropriate health and safety qualification such as the NEBOSH construction certificate will demonstrate that the person has adequate knowledge of health and safety, but this will need to be coupled with a second stage assessment to demonstrate that they have experience in applying this knowledge in the construction environment".

Figure 1-2: Assessing the competence of individual CDM co-ordinators.   *Source: CDM 2007 ACOP, Regulation 4.*

Notification of projects

CDM 2007 applies to all construction projects. However, construction projects with a construction phase longer than 30 days or involving more than 500 person days of construction work are notifiable to the Health and Safety Executive (HSE).

Notification by the CDM co-ordinator must be in writing and can be made using the form F10 (rev). A copy of the notification should be posted at the place where the work is to be carried out.

Preparation of pre-construction information

PURPOSE OF PRE-CONSTRUCTION INFORMATION

The purpose of pre-construction information is to provide information to those bidding for or planning work and for the development of the construction phase plan. Pre-construction information is essentially a collection of information about the significant health and safety risks of the construction project that the principal contractor will have to manage during the construction phase.

The pre-construction information will mainly come from:

- ■ *The client* - who has to provide information relevant to health and safety to the CDM co-ordinator. This could include existing drawings, surveys of the site or premises, information on the location of services, etc.
- ■ *Designers* - who have to provide information about the risks which cannot be avoided and will have to be controlled by the principal contractor and other contractors. Typically this information may be provided on drawings, in written specifications or in outline method statements.

The pre-construction information serves three main purposes:

- ■ During its development the plan can provide a focus at which the health and safety considerations of design are brought together under the control of the CDM co-ordinator.
- ■ Secondly, the plan plays a vital role in the tender documentation. It enables prospective principal contractors to be fully aware of the project's health, safety and welfare requirements. This will allow prospective principal contractors to have a level playing field as far as health and safety is concerned on which to provide tender submissions.
- ■ Thirdly, the plan provides a template against which different tender submissions can be measured. This helps the CDM co-ordinator to advise the client on the provision of resources for health and safety and to assess the competence of prospective principal contractors.

The CDM co-ordinator is responsible for ensuring that the pre-construction information is prepared. This does not mean that the CDM co-ordinator must produce the information directly, but the CDM co-ordinator must ensure that it is prepared.

CONTENT OF THE PRE-CONSTRUCTION INFORMATION PACK

The contents of the pre-construction information will depend on the nature of the project itself. However, the following areas should be considered:

Description of project

- ■ Project description and programme details.
- ■ Details of client, designers, CDM co-ordinator and other consultants.
- ■ Whether or not the structure will be used as a workplace; therefore the need to comply with the Workplace (Health, Safety and Welfare) Regulations (WHSWR) 1992.
- ■ Extent and location of existing records and plans.

Client's considerations and management requirements

- ■ Arrangements for planning and managing the construction work.
- ■ Structure and organisation.
- ■ Health and safety goals for the project and arrangements for monitoring and review.
- ■ Communication between duty holders.
- ■ Site security and welfare.
- ■ Requirements for health and safety of client's employees and customers, including vehicles, permits to work, restrictions and emergency procedures.
- ■ Activities on or adjacent to the site during the works.
- ■ Site delineation and security arrangements.

Environmental restrictions and existing on-site risks

a) Safety hazards, including:

- ■ Boundaries and access, including temporary access.
- ■ Restrictions on delivery, storage or removal of materials.
- ■ Adjacent land uses.
- ■ Existing storage of hazardous materials.
- ■ Location of existing services - water, electricity, gas, etc.
- ■ Ground conditions.
- ■ Existing structures - stability, or fragile materials.
- ■ Difficulties and damage to structure, for example, height restrictions or fire damage.

b) Health hazards, including:

- ■ Asbestos, including results of any surveys.
- ■ Existing storage of hazardous materials.
- ■ Contaminated land, including results of surveys.

- Existing structures, hazardous materials.
- Health risks arising from client's activities.

Significant design and construction hazards

- Design assumptions and control measures.
- Arrangements for co-ordination of on-going design work and handling design changes.
- Information on significant risks identified during design (health and safety risks).
- Materials requiring particular precautions.

The health and safety file

- Description of its format.
- Conditions relating to its content.

FORMAT OF THE PRE-CONSTRUCTION INFORMATION PACK

If the pre-construction information is to be effective in helping to select a principal contractor, the CDM co-ordinator and any other professional advisers who put together the tender documentation will need to determine what the most suitable format for the plan is. Clearly the way the pre-construction information is included in the tender documentation and is structured is essential if responses on health and safety are to be made by prospective principal contractors.

The pre-construction information does not have to be a separate document. If the project is a large and complex one, a separate document which ensures that the key information is highlighted, makes sense. However, on small projects, some of the information outlined will already be in existing tender documentation. In this case, the key information can be highlighted in a covering letter or by use of an index pointing to which information should be considered.

The construction phase plan

PURPOSE OF THE CONSTRUCTION PHASE PLAN

The purpose of the construction phase plan is to set out how health and safety is to be managed during the construction phase. The plan is developed by the principal contractor and is the foundation on which the health and safety management of the construction work is based. The contents of the construction phase health and safety plan will depend on the nature of the project itself and be proportionate to the risks involved in the project. Many of the items in the construction phase plan reflect the information considered at the pre-construction phase, but with further consideration for the construction phase.

CONTENT OF THE CONSTRUCTION PHASE PLAN

Description of the project

- A description of the project and programme, which will include details of important dates.
- Details of other parties involved in the project and the extent and location of existing records and plans.

Management of the work

- The management structure and responsibilities of the various parties involved in the project, including the client, CDM co-ordinator and other members of the project team, whether based at site or elsewhere.
- The health and safety standards to which the project will be carried out, including health and safety goals. These may be set in terms of statutory requirements or high standards that the client may require in particular circumstances.
- Means for informing contractors about risks to their health and safety arising from the environment in which the project is to be carried out and the construction work itself.
- Means to ensure that all contractors, the self employed and designers to be appointed by the principal contractor are properly selected (i.e. they are competent and will make adequate provision for health and safety).
- Means for communicating and passing information between the project team (including the client and any client's representatives), the designers, the CDM co-ordinator, the principal contractor, other contractors, workers on site and others whose health and safety may be affected.
- Arrangements for reporting and identification of accidents, including passing information to the principal contractor about accidents, ill-health and dangerous occurrences that require to be notified by the HSE under RIDDOR 2013.
- Arrangements for the provision and maintenance of welfare facilities.
- Arrangements for health and safety induction and training.
- Arrangements that have been made for consulting and co-ordinating the views of workers or their representatives.
- Arrangements for site rules and for bringing them to the attention of those affected.
- Arrangements for risk assessments and written systems of work.
- Emergency arrangements for dealing with and minimising the effects of injuries, fire and other dangerous occurrences.

- Arrangements should be set out for the monitoring systems to achieve compliance with legal requirements; and the health and safety rules developed by the principal contractor.

Arrangements for controlling significant site risks

- Arrangements of controls safety risks', including preventing falls, control of vehicles and safety when working with services.
- Arrangements for control of health risks, including removal of asbestos, manual handling, noise and vibration.

The health and safety file

- Layout and format.
- Arrangements for collecting information.
- Storage of information.

Provision of appropriate and relevant information to all parties

Relevant information must be provided to appropriate parties to ensure the health and safety of persons affected by the project, and, to assist the persons to whom information is provided under CDM 2007. In order to perform their duties under CDM 2007, every client must ensure that:

- Every person designing the structure that may be bidding for the work (or who intend to be engaged), is conversant with the project-specific health and safety information needed to identify hazards and risks associated with the design and construction work.
- Every contractor who has been or may be appointed by the client is promptly provided with pre-construction information in accordance with the CDM 2007 regulations.

The pre-construction information shall consist of all the information in the client's possession (or which is reasonably obtainable), including:

- Any information about or affecting the site or the construction work.
- Any information concerning the proposed use of the structure as a workplace.
- The minimum amount of time before the construction phase which will be allowed to the contractors appointed by the client for planning and preparation for construction work.
- Any information in any existing health and safety file.

Preparation of the health and safety file

PURPOSE OF THE HEALTH AND SAFETY FILE

The purpose of the health and safety file is to provide a source of information needed to allow future construction work, alterations, refurbishment and demolition, including cleaning and maintenance, to be carried out in a safe and healthy manner.

Clients, designers, principal contractors, other contractors and CDM co-ordinators all have legal duties in respect of the health and safety file:

- CDM co-ordinators must prepare, review, amend or add to the file as the project progresses, and give it to the client at the end of project.
- Clients, designers, principal contractors and other contractors must supply the information necessary for compiling or updating the file.
- Clients must keep the file to assist with future construction work.
- Everyone providing information should make sure that it is accurate, and provided promptly.

PREPARING THE HEALTH AND SAFETY FILE

The CDM co-ordinator is responsible for ensuring the health and safety file is prepared. Putting together the health and safety file is a task which should ideally be a continual process throughout the project and not left until the construction work is completed. Early on in the construction project the CDM co-ordinator may find it useful to discuss the health and safety file with the client. This will help determine what information the client requires and how the client wishes the information to be stored and recorded. When the client's requirements are known, procedures may need to be drawn up by the CDM co-ordinator so that all those who will be contributing to the health and safety file (for example, designers and contractors) are aware of:

- What information is to be collected.
- How the information is to be collected, presented and stored.

The CDM co-ordinator may find it useful to detail in the pre-tender stage health and safety plan requirements on how and when the information for the health and safety file is to be prepared and passed on. The principal contractor may also find it useful to include similar procedures in the health and safety plan for the construction phase.

Throughout the project those who carry out design work (including contractors) will need to ensure so far as is reasonably practicable that information about any feature of the structure which will involve significant risks to health and safety during the structure's lifetime are passed to either the CDM co-ordinator or to the principal contractor.

Providing this information on drawings will allow for amendments if any variations arise during construction. It will also allow health and safety information to be stored on one document, therefore reducing the paperwork. The principal contractor may need to obtain details of services, plant and equipment which are part of the structure from specialist suppliers and installers, for example, mechanical and electrical contractors and pass this information on.

Contractors have a specific duty in CDM 2007 to pass information for the health and safety file to the principal contractor, who in turn has to pass it to the CDM co-ordinator. This information could include 'as built' and 'as installed' drawings as well as operation and maintenance manuals.

At the end of the project the CDM co-ordinator has to hand over the health and safety file to the client. In some cases it might not be possible for a fully developed file to be handed over on completion of the project. This may happen because the construction work was finished rapidly to meet a tight deadline and completion of the health and safety file was impossible. Clearly a common sense approach is needed so that the health and safety file is handed over as soon as practical after a completion certificate or similar document has been issued.

CONTENTS OF THE HEALTH AND SAFETY FILE

The contents of the health and safety file will vary depending on the type of structure and the future health and safety risks that will have to be managed.

Typical information which may be put in the health and safety file includes:

- A brief description of the work carried out.
- Any residual hazards that remain and how they have been dealt with (for example buried services).
- Key structural principles (for example, bracing or sources of stored energy).
- Hazardous materials such as lead paint or pesticides.
- Information regarding the removal or dismantling of installed plant and equipment.
- Health and safety information about equipment provided for cleaning or maintaining the structure.
- The nature, location and markings of any significant services such as underground services; fire fighting services, etc.
- Information and as-built drawings of the structure, its plant and equipment.

Exemption of domestic clients

Domestic clients are people who have work done on their own home or the home of a family member, that does not relate to a trade or business, whether for profit or not. If the work is in connection with the furtherance of a business attached to domestic premises, such as a shop, the client is not a domestic client.

Local authorities, housing associations, charities, landlords and other businesses may own domestic property, but they are not domestic clients. Similarly, a company formed by independent leaseholders of flats to undertake maintenance of the common parts of a structure is not a domestic client, and will have duties under CDM 2007.

Domestic clients have no client duties under CDM 2007, which means that there is no legal requirement for the appointment of a CDM co-ordinator or principal contractor when such projects reach the notification threshold. Similarly, there is no need to notify the HSE where projects for domestic clients reach the notification threshold. However, designers and contractors still have their normal duties as set out in Parts 2 and 4 of CDM 2007, and domestic clients will have duties under Part 4 of CDM 2007 if they control the way in which construction work is carried out.

Designers and contractors working for domestic clients have to manage their own work and co-operate with and co-ordinate their work with others involved with the project in order to ensure the health and safety of all involved in the project. The requirements in Schedules 2 (welfare facilities) and Part 4 (regulations 25-44) of CDM 2007 still apply to the work they do for clients.

1.4 - Sources of external construction health and safety information

Sources external to the organisation

MANUFACTURERS' DATA

Section 6 of the Health and Safety at Work Act (HASAWA) 1974 requires manufacturers to provide information. There are a wide variety of regulations, for example the Control of Substances Hazardous to Health (COSHH) 2002 and the Supply of Machinery (Safety) Regulations (SMSR) 2008, that assist and reinforce this requirement.

Where products are delivered to site there should be information readily available related to weight, specialist handling, storage, preservation, where applicable, along with other identified hazardous properties. Manufacturers' data should also provide a source of information regarding the scale of risk related to the use of construction work equipment, in particular with regard to noise and vibration exposure.

LEGISLATION

Details of Acts and Regulations are available from the website of the National Archives. New statutory instruments are published on the internet within 15 days of the printed publication (http://www.legislation.gov.uk). As the website is a record of current and past legislation care has to be taken to ensure data being viewed has not been amended by subsequent legislation. Acts and Regulations are prime sources of information; they give the precise legal requirements that are to be complied with. They can, however, be difficult to read without some legal understanding. It is also easy to miss changes and amendments unless an updating service is used.

HSE PUBLICATIONS

HSE Books publishes both HSE approved codes of practice (ACOPs) and HSE guidance documents. While failure to follow an ACOP is not in itself an offence, a defendant would have to show that the steps they took were equally effective. This has the effect of transferring the burden of proof of complying with the ACOP onto the defendant. This makes ACOPs a particularly important source of information. Guidance notes, and other advisory literature, are persuasive in a court of law. Lists of both priced and free publications are available from HSE Books (http://www.hsebooks.com).

TRADE ORGANISATIONS

The *CITB-Construction Skills* is the sector skills council for construction. It provides initiatives and programmes relating to its sector skills role, providing support and guidance to the construction industry. Organisations such as the CITB-Construction Skills provide publications, videos/DVDs and CDs to help deliver effective training and development across most subjects within the construction industry.

The Construction Industry Research and Information Association were founded in 1960. In recent times the organisation's name was shortened to *CIRIA.* Today, CIRIA is now known solely by its abbreviated name. CIRIA's mission is to improve the performance of those in the construction and related industries.

CIRIA works with the construction industry, Government and academia to provide performance improvement products and services in the construction and related industries and currently engages with around 700 subscribing organisations. Activities include collaborative projects, networking, publishing, workshops, seminars and conferences. Each year CIRIA runs about 40 projects, holds over 90 events and publishes 25 best practice guides.

INTERNATIONAL/EUROPEAN/BRITISH STANDARDS

The British Standards Institute (BSI) provides some high quality advice, which is usually more detailed than that set out in legislation and may express good practice that is more that the legal minimum standard. There is a distinct trend towards linking British Standards with legislation, for example, with the Health and Safety (Safety Signs and Signals) Regulations (SSSR) 1996 and BS 5499-10:2006, which is the British standard that sets out requirements for safety signs. Many other British standards are not linked to specific legislation, but set out good practices that the construction industry should follow, for example BS 8534:2011 "Construction procurement policies, strategies and procedures. Code of practice". The BSI has also introduced a health and safety management system standard called "BS OHSAS 18001:2007 Occupational health and safety management systems". There is also progressive harmonisation to European Standards (CEN) and the use of CE Marking, standards that conform to European requirements are identified by the addition of EN, for example BS EN 12649:2008+A1:2011 "Concrete compactors and smoothing machines. Safety". Similarly, where standards are determined to be applicable internationally they are recognised by the International Organisation for Standardisation and are identified by the addition of ISO, for example BS EN ISO 19432:2008 "Building construction machinery and equipment. Portable, hand-held internal combustion engine driven cut-off machines. Safety requirements and testing".

IT SOURCES

There are many information technology sources of information. These include a variety of websites, manufacturers' software and BSI standards. Information via IT is widely available from utility companies, Government Agencies (HSE, EA, etc.), the International Labour Organisation, Local Authorities and the Department of Trade and Industry.

PROFESSIONAL BODIES

Institute of Civil Engineers (ICE)

The ICE was founded in 1818 and was granted a royal charter in 1828. The ICE's declared aim is to "foster and promote the art and science of civil engineering" and it has 80,000 members worldwide. The ICE is one of the organisations that establish the standards for civil engineering courses run by universities in the UK, and some overseas. The ICE has formed a health and safety expert panel to facilitate best practice in the delivery of health and safety risk management. As part of this process it has established a register for those members who wish to demonstrate a defined level of competency in health and safety within the construction process. The register has two levels of membership:

1) CDM co-ordinators.

2) Designers, clients and contractors - for those that take a lead in health and safety matters.

Chartered Institute of Building (CIOB)

With over 42,000 members the CIOB is the international voice of the building professional, representing a body of knowledge concerning the management of the total building process. Chartered Member status, represented by the designations MCIOB and FCIOB, is recognised internationally in the construction industry.

With its increasing international membership and growing profile in the UK, the CIOB makes an influential contribution to the construction industry.

Civil Engineering Contractors Association (CECA)

The Civil Engineering Contractors Association was established in November 1996 at the request of contractors to represent the interests of civil engineering contractor companies registered in the UK. CECA's current membership is in excess of 350 civil engineering companies that range in size from large and well-known national names to the medium and smaller sized companies. CECA members account for 75 - 80% of the civil engineering workload undertaken in Great Britain. The association establishes annual health and safety priorities that it wishes to achieve, for example providing representation on strategic health and safety committees and groups, such as Working Well Together SHAD working group.

UK Contractors Group (UKCG)

The UK Contractors Group (UKCG) is an association of contractors operating in the UK. The UKCG has over 30 members, who between them deliver £36 billion of construction turnover - a third of total construction output. UKCG has two main objectives, to:

■ Promote the interests of the construction industry.
■ Take leadership to raise standards within the industry.

The UKCG works closely with the CBI Construction Council on its first objective and with supply chain partners to meet the second. The current main priority is promoting the case for infrastructure investment and working with government to improve the efficiency of public sector construction procurement.

Association of Project Supervisors (APS)

The APS provides a forum and sets standards of excellence to promote, encourage and advance the continuing education of persons providing the services of CDM co-ordinator pursuant to the Construction (Design and Management) Regulations (CDM) 2007. The APS is a member led organisation, represented through Regional Committees, then through Council to the Board of Directors. Amongst APS members are the country's leading architectural, engineering, health and safety, project management and surveying professionals.

Institution of Occupational Safety and Health (IOSH)

Founded in 1945, IOSH is the Chartered body for health and safety professionals. With more than 39,000 individual members, IOSH is the largest professional health and safety organisation in the world. IOSH is the voice of the profession, and lobbies governments on policy and law. IOSH accredit qualifications for their members, provides guidance, develops resources, runs courses and organises events to further health and safety. IOSH has a specific construction group that focuses on health and safety issues that affect the construction industry.

International Institute for Risk and Safety Management (IIRSM)

The IIRSM was established in 1975 as a professional body for health and safety practitioners. It was created to advance professional standards in accident prevention and occupational health throughout the world. Over the last three decades IIRSM has grown from a collective group of UK health and safety professionals to an established international institute in over 70 countries.

Sample assessment questions

1. **Identify** the duties of the client for projects that are notifiable under the Construction (Design and Management) Regulations 2007(CDM). (8)

2. **Identify** the duties placed upon the principal contractor under the Construction (Design and Management) Regulations (CDM) 2007. (8)

3. **Identify** the designer's duties during a notifiable project under the Construction (Design and Management) Regulations 2007 (CDM). (8)

Please refer to back of assessment section for answers.

Construction site - hazards and risk control

Learning outcomes

On completion of this element, candidates should be able to demonstrate understanding of the content through the application of knowledge to familiar and unfamiliar situations. In particular they should be able to:

2.1   Explain the factors which should be considered when carrying out an initial assessment of a site to identify significant hazards and their risks.

2.2   Explain the appropriate general site control measures needed in setting up and organising a site.

2.3   Identify the health, welfare and work environment requirements on construction sites.

2.4   Explain the hazards and appropriate control measures for violence at work.

2.5   Explain the hazards and appropriate control measures for substance misuse at work.

2.6   Explain the hazards associated with the movement of people on construction sites and the control measures for pedestrians.

Content

Sources of reference

Driving at work, Managing work-related road safety, INDG382, HSE Books, ISBN 978-0-7176-2740-0

Essentials of health and safety at work, HSE Books ISBN 978-0-7176-6179-4

Health and Safety in Construction (Guidance) (HSG150), HSE Books ISBN 9780717661824

Managing Health and Safety in Construction CDM ACOP, L144 ISBN 978-0-7176-6223-4

Safe use of work equipment (ACOP) (L22), HSE Books ISBN 978-0-7176-6295-1

Work at Height Regulations 2005 (as amended)- A Brief guide, HSE Books (INDG401rev1) ISBN 978-0-7176-6231-9

Workplace Transport Safety – Guidance for Employers, HSG136, HSE Books, ISBN 978-0-7176-6154-1

Relevant statutory provisions

Construction (Design and Management) Regulations (CDM) 2007

Health and Safety (First-aid) Regulations (FAR) 1981

Health and Safety (Safety Signs and Signals) Regulations (SSSR) 1996

Personal Protective Equipment at Work Regulations (PPE) 1992

Provision and Use of Work Equipment Regulations (PUWER) 1998

Work at Height Regulations (WAH) 2005 (as amended)

Site Waste Management Plans Regulations (SWMP) 2008

2.1 - Initial site assessment

Factors to consider in site assessments

PREVIOUS/CURRENT USE

The previous and/or current use of a site may present many hazards that need to be identified in an initial assessment before construction work starts. If, for example, it is a "green field" (undeveloped) site, it may provide public access/right of way to members of the public or a recreation area for children. The site could be private and used for agriculture or grazing of livestock. If a "brown field" (previously used, developed) site, it could contain occupied or unoccupied buildings/ premises. Occupied premises will mean regular traffic on the site whilst unoccupied premises may be in a state of disrepair and dereliction. Any existing premises that are either occupied or unoccupied will, more than likely, be or have been connected to various below ground or overhead services that may require further investigation.

Figure 2-1: Site assessment - previous use. *Source: RMS*

Figure 2-2: Site assessment - access. *Source: RMS.*

HISTORY OF SITE

It is important to take into account the history of a site, as the site may present hazards in the form of asbestos or chemical contamination which requires specialist waste removal and land reclamation services. There may be mineshafts present or other types of underground voids, such as abandoned cellars, manhole chambers or large diameter drains. Action should be taken to make site surveys and obtain current and/or historic plans that may identify any or all of the above circumstances.

AREA OF SITE AND RESTRICTIONS

The location or area of the site should be considered and any possible restrictions noted, for example, there may be trees that are protected and unable to be felled or other natural obstacles that could cause problems to the works. If a site is bounded by a main railway line or other premises, then the available space to store or operate any construction related plant and equipment may be restricted once work begins.

TOPOGRAPHY AND GROUND CONDITIONS

Topography relates to the physical surface conditions of the site and is an important factor to be considered along with the ground conditions below the surface. The landscape may be flat and even or is it made up of banks, dips and hills therefore making any operations on site far more difficult to carry out. The ground conditions may be soft soil, clay or rock, each condition presenting its own individual problems and hazards. The site could have a high water table or be susceptible to becoming flooded or waterlogged.

OTHER (NON-CONSTRUCTION) ACTIVITIES ON SITE

When a site is acquired, it may be necessary for other non-construction activities to be carried out prior to any construction works being authorised to begin. This could be site reclamation and clearance, installation of security fencing, lighting and signs, ground investigations, piling operation, site surveys and installation of essential utilities (power, water and gas). Other non-construction activities usually continue when construction has started, consisting of delivery of plant, equipment or materials, site security and development of a utility network around the site.

NATURE OF SURROUNDINGS

Roads

Roads and highways that surround a site boundary can be a significant source of additional hazard and are a main area for consideration as access to any site is primarily via some form of roadway. Factors such as the type of road (dual carriageway, main road, one-way system, country lane), road speed encountered, volume of traffic (high all day, cyclical, rush hour), type of traffic using the road (agricultural plant, cars, heavy goods vehicles (HGV's), well lit or unlit, and capacity of road (weight, height or width restrictions). It may be that special requests or notifications are to be made with the local authority regarding access and site traffic proposals. If the site is within a residential area or in close proximity to a school, permissions or restrictions may be enforced regarding when or if surrounding roadways may or may not be used. In any of the above situations, there is a potential for danger.

Figure 2-3: Roads.   *Source: RMS.*

Figure 2-4: Footpaths.   *Source: RMS.*

Footpaths

Footpaths are a means of providing pedestrians with a safe means of travelling by foot usually alongside a highway. It should be identified how the footpath is used (for example, for a school journey by children or by people queuing for a bus). The risk of injury may be increased at the entrance to a construction site where pedestrians cross the access opening and might encounter heavy site mobile plant or goods vehicles delivering materials to site. Footpaths may also skirt the construction site boundary, where pedestrians may also become at risk due to the activities within the site (for example, falling objects from a scaffold structure, flying objects from cutting, drilling or hammering operations, fumes, dust, chemicals).

Railways

Railways present the hazard of heavy, high speed trains (up to and in excess of 125 mph) that do not have the ability to respond to dangerous circumstances that may arise as other transport modes are able to, i.e. quick emergency stopping, avoidance by changing direction. In addition to these hazards, there may be overhead cables carrying 25,000 volts or rails carrying 750 volts. Work near to railways requires suitable planning, as any clash between a travelling train and site equipment, plant or vehicles could, and most likely would, lead to disastrous consequences. Rail authorities have laid down strict procedures that are to be followed and any party working on railways should be in possession of a 'Personal Track Safety' certificate. High-visibility clothing that is worn on or near to a railway line should be of the correct standard and colour (high-visibility orange). Restrictions on colours worn on or near to a railway should be strictly followed and nothing that is red or green be worn due to the fact that it may be mistaken as a signal by a train driver. Communications should be maintained with the rail authority and notification given of any works being carried out on or near to the railway in order that all issues can be complied with correctly.

Figure 2-5: Railways.   *Source: Welsh Highland Railway.*

Figure 2-6: Waterways.   *Source: RMS.*

Waterways

Waterways located on or near construction sites present a risk of drowning; the water does not have to be fast flowing to cause a worker to get into difficulty. Other factors to consider if waterways are in close proximity to a construction site are: the likelihood of floods occurring, environmental pollution of the waterway, damage to associated wildlife by site activities. Conversely, it is necessary to consider exposure of site staff to hygiene hazards through contaminants or disease (chemical pollutants, Weil's disease) within the waterway.

Waterways are used by a considerable number of boat operators that may be affected by the activities on site (for example, falling objects from a scaffold structure, flying objects from cutting, drilling or hammering operations, fumes, dust, chemicals). Boat operators may equally affect site safety, for example, collision of the boat with a scaffold structure.

Residential/commercial/industrial properties

Construction can take place in local or immediate proximity of residential, industrial or commercial property that may be either unoccupied or occupied and fully operational. Construction traffic will generally add significantly to the normal traffic loading in the area, which may result in congestion, for example, during the 'school run' period and lunch times. This may well be exacerbated by vehicles queuing near the site entrance to gain access. The increase in large goods vehicles (LGV's) in the area will lead to increased engine noise, vehicle exhaust fumes and the risk of collisions with other vehicles, pedestrians. Young children and the elderly may be particularly at risk, as they may choose to weave through semi-stationary traffic and may not be visible to large construction vehicle drivers when they decide to move their vehicles. There are additional risks where work is carried out in commercial property (shops, offices) as the work may take place in busy areas where members of the public and staff are present. In the case of industrial properties (factories, workshops), people may be at work when construction activities take place and the premises can present additional hazards from machinery, plant, equipment, chemicals, etc. being used. Construction workers may not be familiar with the hazards presented, which could increase the risk of personal injury.

Figure 2-7: Commercial properties. *Source: RMS.*

Figure 2-8: Industrial properties. *Source: RMS.*

Schools

Schools are very busy areas and accommodate children of various ages that may have no or little perception of danger or risk and by their nature are often very inquisitive of their surroundings. In addition to children, parents or carers that deliver children to and collect children from the school create pedestrian and vehicular traffic hazards around the immediate area. Children are frequently tempted to try to gain access to construction sites and normally achieve this when site security is poor and consideration has not been given to access through small openings. Sites often underestimate the size of openings, which some small children are able to fit through, particularly when compared with that which is required to restrict adult access.

MEANS OF ACCESS

Access to a construction site should be through a controlled point and requires adequate planning to take into account the surrounding area. Restrictions and hazards relating to safe access to a construction site may include the conditions of the highway from which access is being gained (size, speed, use). The traffic that will operate on the site needs to be considered (size, type, frequency, volume).

Figure 2-9: Means of access, overhead restrictions. *Source: RMS.*

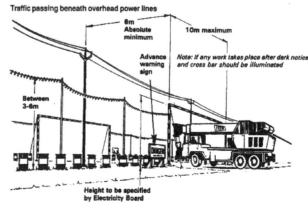

Figure 2-10: Safe distance barriers for overhead services.
Source: HSE, HSG144.

PRESENCE OF OVERHEAD AND BURIED SERVICES

Overhead services in the form of electricity cables present the obvious risk of electrocution through either making direct contact with the electricity cable or where arcing (discharge by spark 'jumping' to a near earth point) occurs. Overhead cables should be identified prior to site works and the risk factors determined. Construction sites may involve the use of various pieces of large, mobile plant and equipment (cranes, excavators, etc) and steel scaffold systems near to power supplies. If such equipment is allowed to come too close to an overhead cable it may provide a sufficient level of earth for the power to 'leap', making the particular item of plant live. If this occurs, subsequent 'arcs' are possible to other people or plant within close proximity of the original earth point.

Buried services (electricity, gas, water, etc) are not obvious and the likelihood of striking a service when excavating, drilling or piling is thus increased without a site survey to identify any service present. The results of striking an underground service are varied, and the potential to cause injury or fatality is high. Incidents can include shock, electrocution, explosion and burns from power cables, explosion, burns or unconsciousness from gas or power cables, and impact injury from dislodged stones/flooding from ruptured water mains.

2.2 - Appropriate general site control measures

Site planning

Following an initial site assessment that has identified hazards and risks associated with the works, control measures should be implemented to ensure the safety and well-being of all those who are affected by the construction site and its activities. A plan must be assembled to take into consideration the following factors.

ARRANGEMENTS FOR SITE ACCESS

Access to a construction site must be planned to minimise any hazards identified during the initial assessment. When a suitable location for site access has been identified, this must be controlled at a point or points that are designated as authorised access point/s and the remainder of the construction site boundary must be secure against unauthorised access. Site safety information should be displayed at access points to inform all attendees of contact names, rules and emergency procedures. Barrier systems are normal on complex undertakings, accompanied by procedures for admittance and exit of people and plant. Special rules for site safety induction and issue of any site security identification are often used to maintain control.

Figure 2-11: Site access. *Source: RMS.*

Figure 2-12: Site controls - access and roadways. *Source: RMS.*

ROADWAYS

Public roadways often extend or continue into construction sites and are subject to pedestrian and vehicular traffic. Construction site roads should be subject to site safety rules such as speed limits, safety restraints (seat belts), direction of flow (one way systems where possible), and there should be segregation of pedestrian and vehicular traffic similar to that used on the public highway. Adequate space should be provided for parking and to allow vehicles and plant to manoeuvre safely and the area should be well lit as required. Vehicles and mobile plant should never be allowed to block roadways or access points as this may prevent emergency vehicles and crews gaining access in the event of a major incident. Site slurry/mud on the road surface that can create skid hazards for site plant and vehicles should not be allowed to accumulate and there should be a system for inspection and cleaning of the surface and vehicles' wheels.

STORAGE

The storage requirements are dependent on the type of material to be stored. Different material types should be stored separately, to avoid cross contamination and the potential for a harmful adverse chemical reaction. If combined storage is permitted, it is advisable that different materials be kept separated for easy identification and retrieval. In addition to authorised access of site operatives, the storage area should be designed to allow safe access by forklift trucks and for the use of suitable mechanical lifting aids to eliminate the need for manual handling where possible.

Housekeeping should be of a good standard and kept clean and tidy with suitable lighting and ventilation. There should be appropriate fire precautions and provision of correct fire extinguishers. Storage areas should be restricted to authorised site staff only and have the correct safety information signs that warn of any dangers or mandatory signs enforcing the wearing of personal protective equipment (PPE). They should be used for solely that purpose and must not be used for any other purposes such as mixing operations or as a rest or smoking area.

Storage of flammable substances

Substances should be stored in such a way that they cannot

- Escape and contaminate personnel or the environment.
- React with other substances causing explosion, fire or toxic fumes.

Requirements for storage

- Store small quantities only in the workplace.
- Small quantities of flammables should be stored in clearly marked flameproof metal containers.
- Non-compatible chemicals should be stored apart.
- Chemicals giving off fumes should be stored and used only with suitable respiratory protection.
- Chemicals should be stored away from sources of heat, possibly refrigerated.
- Bulk storage should be outside away from other buildings and sources of heat, including sunlight.

Features of a bulk flammable substance store

- Single storey, light construction in non-combustible materials.
- Flame proof electrical equipment.
- Door sill and perimeter bunding for containment of up to 110% of the maximum storage container of the chemical. If more than one container is stored, the system must be capable of storing 110% of the biggest container capacity or 25% of the total tank capacity within the bund. Whichever is the greater must be adopted.
- Interceptor pits for spillage.

Figure 2-13: Misuse of storage.   *Source: RMS.*

Figure 2-14: Loading/unloading.   *Source: RMS.*

LOADING/UNLOADING

Construction sites are constantly changing with a variety of tasks all happening at once, including continuous staff, vehicles and material movements around the site. With this in mind, it is very important that any loading and unloading of materials used on the construction site is carried out in its own dedicated area/zone under competent supervision. The delivery of materials or equipment to a construction site should be scheduled and planned to minimise the volume of traffic at site at any one time, and drivers/operators of delivery vehicles given a site specific induction to ensure an awareness of hazards, site safety rules and procedures.

Loading and unloading of materials or equipment should be planned and organised. Materials should not be allowed to be placed too high or to lean over creating a potential risk of collapse with the possible result of major injury or a fatality. A number of people have been killed on construction sites due to carelessness in handling. Generally, loads should be kept small with goods on pallets that are in good repair. Lightweight boxes that offer no strength and can be crushed or bags of free-flowing solid (gravel) should always be palletised and never be stacked on top of each other. Different types of container should be stacked separately.

Loads should not block or be placed near emergency exits, fire points/extinguishers, vehicle routes or block light or visibility. They should be placed on firm, solid ground or floors that are strong enough to provide adequate support. Workers should be trained in the correct way to handle loads and also in the dangers associated with unsafe practices/or incorrect loading methods. Site staff should be instructed never to climb up or stand on top of racking or palletized material.

OFFICES

There should be an office available on site to house first-aid facilities and equipment, emergency procedures, health and safety information, site induction documentation, health and safety plan (if the Construction (Design and Management) Regulations (CDM) 2007 apply), construction drawings and specifications. General site office equipment and records are also stored in the site office, for example telephone, fax, training records, visitor personal protective equipment and filing facility.

LIGHTING

Adequate lighting should be provided that allows safe access and egress into and around the construction site along roadways, vehicle and pedestrian routes. Special consideration should be made to areas such as scaffold structures, excavations, flammable stores or fuel bunkers/tanks. Signs warning of dangers at site should be clearly lit to allow approaching people advance notice.

SIGNS

The provision of suitable signs is an important factor in making people aware of the hazards and precautions that relate to construction work. The entrance to a construction site should have an information board that provides details of the client, architect, supervisor, contractor and any other important parties. It will also include mandatory health and safety signs such as those requiring the use of hard hats or ear protection. Other information could include a basic site layout plan and details of where to report upon arrival at the site.

REMEDIATION WORKS

Remediation works may need to be carried out prior to the development of a new site or the modification to an existing structure. Remediation can be necessary due to the effects on the site of its prior use, which may lead to contamination of land, water and structures. Former sites that may need remediation include fuel stations, gasworks, chemical storage facilities, industrial factories (for example, wire, rubber and chemical manufacture). The substances forming the contamination can represent significant health hazards. They may include benzene, hydrocarbons, acids, cyanide and metals, for example, arsenic, nickel, cadmium and chromium.

Remediation work can vary from removal of contaminated soil, for example, with the redevelopment of a brown field site to the identification and establishment of controls for building contaminates, such as asbestos prior to an extension being made to an existing structure. The work may involve removal of hazardous materials left over from prior processes, excavation of contaminated soil, removal of contaminated surface water, cleaning of contaminated soil/water, stabilisation of land, treatment of invasive species of weeds, building temporary bunds to control water runoff and the recovery, movement or protection of human or infected animal remains.

Site preparation/remediation work that involves the removal of topsoil that is contaminated with heavy metals or other hazardous substances will require specific arrangements in relation to personal protective equipment requirements and practices to be carried out. The work is likely to require the provision of gloves, overalls, eye protection and respirators. Additionally, the work will necessitate campaigns of awareness training to ensure good levels of personal hygiene are maintained, with emphasis on ensuring that open cuts are covered with waterproof dressings whenever required.

Consideration will need to be given to specific welfare facilities provision, for example, a decontamination unit may be needed, which has a dirty area where contaminated clothing can be removed after work, an area with a shower or other means of washing and a clean area where normal clothes could be kept while employees are working on site. There should be arrangements in place in order to prevent contamination when eating and smoking. First-aid and emergency decontamination facilities should be located near to the place of work.

PROVISION OF UTILITY SERVICES

The planning of the provision of utility services to the site will involve consideration of the initial needs of the site, further needs as the site becomes established and the long term needs of the client who will take over the site. This may initially involve the use of portable, self-contained services, for example, water stored in a mobile tanker, electricity supplied by generators and portable welfare facilities with contained waste.

As the site develops, demands for utility service may increase and a more robust provision may be required. It may be possible to utilise the services that have to be put in place for the benefit of the client on completion of the construction work or it may be necessary to establish alternative sources. The identification of utility services required for the site should be determined in liaison with local supply companies before work commences, at the planning stage.

Certain utilities, such as gas or fast internet broadband, may not be available. Other services may be limited, such as water supply (particularly pressure), drainage or electrical capacity. Limitations in the water supply may need to be addressed by the provision of storage tanks, particularly if there is an identified need for a water sprinkler system or other fire fighting provisions.

Drainage may need to be provided through the use of septic tanks or other means, such as organic reed bed installations. Electrical supply may require the organisation and suitable location of an additional electrical sub-station to increase the capacity of supply.

Preparation of site waste management plans

RESPONSIBILITY OF CLIENT AND PRINCIPAL CONTRACTORS

The Site Waste Management Plans Regulations (SWMP) 2008 require any client intending to carry out a construction project on any one site in England with an estimated cost greater than £300,000 to prepare a site waste management plan before construction work begins. This includes projects involving new build, maintenance or alteration/installation/removal of services.

If a project is started without a site waste management plan both the client and principal contractor will be guilty of an offence. The SWMP 2008 is enforced by the Environment Agency and the local authority.

A site waste management plan must identify:

- The client.
- The principal contractor.
- The person who drafted it.
- The plan must describe the construction work proposed, including:
  - The location of the site.
  - The estimated cost of the project.

A record of any decision regarding the nature of the project, its design, construction method or materials employed in order to minimise the quantity of waste produced on site, taken before the site waste management plan was drafted, must accompany the plan. In addition, the plan must:

- Describe each waste type expected to be produced in the course of the project.
- Estimate the quantity of each different waste type expected to be produced.
- Identify the waste management action proposed for each different waste type, including re-using, recycling, recovery and disposal.
- Contain a declaration that the client and the principal contractor will take all reasonable steps to ensure that:
  - All waste from the site is dealt with in accordance with the waste duty of care in section 34 of the Environmental Protection Act 1990 (Part 1 pollution control) and the Environmental Protection (Duty of Care) Regulations 1991(regulation 2 transfer notes).
  - Materials are handled efficiently and waste managed appropriately.

If a client intends to use one or more contractors for any project that SWMP 2008 applies to, they must appoint a contractor as the principal contractor. If a client does not use a contractor, all obligations placed on the principal contractor under SWMP 2008 must be carried out by the client.

The site waste management plan must be updated by the principal contractor. This includes recording details of waste whenever it is removed from the site and monitoring of the plan. If it is necessary to deviate from the plan this should be explained. Where the project is greater than £500,000 the plan must accurately reflect progress of the plan, including a record of the types and quantities of waste produced, reused, recycled, recovered or disposed.

The principal contractor must ensure that the site waste management plan is kept available at the site and that every contractor knows where it is. The waste management plan must be retained by the principal contractor for two years after completion of the project.

Additional duties are set out in SWMP 2008 for the client and principal contractor, to assist with the smooth management of waste. The client must support the principal contractor by providing reasonable direction to the principal contractor. The principal contractor must ensure:

- The co-ordination and co-operation of contractors during the construction phase of the projects.
- Every worker receives an induction, information and training related to the site waste management plan.
- Waste produced during construction is re-used, recycled or recovered.

Both the client and principal contractor must:

- Review, revise and refine the site waste management plan as necessary.
- Ensure roles and responsibilities are communicated.
- Take reasonable steps to ensure site security to prevent illegal disposal of waste from the site.

Site preparation for specialist activities

LIFTING

Lifting operations on construction sites can vary widely dependent upon the size and weight of the load required to be lifted and the lifting equipment required to carry out the lift. Specialist lifting equipment on construction sites is usually either mobile crane or tower crane type. Prior to undertaking lifting operations with any piece of lifting equipment, vital preparation is required to ensure the safety of all those affected. This includes thorough planning of the lift to include a safe system of work, method statements, risk assessments, permits to work (if required) and competent authorised persons assigned to manage the lifting operation.

The ground on which the lifting equipment is to be situated should be firm and level and suitable load spreading decking provided to ensure stability. Depending on the nature and frequency of the lifting operations, it may be necessary and appropriate for the ground to be made up with hardcore or concrete to ensure strength and stability in all weather conditions.

Consideration should also be given to surrounding structures and overhead power cables, ensuring the minimum safe working distances from them. Access to the area below the lifting area should be controlled or restricted to protect people at site from items falling during the lift. The equipment used for the lift must be inspected prior to use and regularly as per the specified frequencies and all test certificates made available. The Lifting Equipment and Lifting Operation Regulations (LOLER) 1998 are specifically related to mechanical lifting and associated equipment.

PILING

Piling is a method of creating long, straight underground cavities that are used for stabilising/strengthening the ground and providing foundations for a building or structure. This is performed by either using drilling or by compacting force. The most common method of piling involves the use of a guide 'tube' in which a heavy solid 'driving piece' supported by lifting equipment is released down the guide tube causing the material it strikes to displace upon impact and thus create a cavity when withdrawn. This operation is repeated until the required depth of bore is achieved.

Another method involves a steel liner being mechanically 'hammered' into the ground to the required depth. Preparations for piling works may include identifying buried services, hidden voids, the density of the material being piled and ground stability for equipment, water table levels and any local buildings or structures that may be affected by vibrations. Piling is a very noisy operation and consideration should be given to surrounding areas.

Figure 2-15: Site signs.   Source: RMS.

Figure 2-16: Steelworks.   Source: RMS.

STEELWORKS

Steelwork is often used to form the basic 'skeleton' on which a structure is built. The majority of steelwork is designed and manufactured off site and is then assembled using the various pre-fabricated sections and steel beams during the build. Associated activities usually involve working at height with materials that are very heavy and difficult to manoeuvre. Site preparation involves the creation of large, level concrete surfaces, on which the steelwork stands and is fixed. The erection of steelworks requires thorough planning to include safe systems of work, risk assessments, method statements and permits to work where required. Where practicable, risks should be eliminated or reduced to the minimum possible level by combating hazards at source (for example, use of mobile elevated work platform for access, cranes for lifting). Any lifting equipment or access equipment should only be used on firm and level ground.

Site security and means of protecting the public

Regulation 22 of CDM 2007 places a duty on the principal contractor to ensure that:

> *"(6) No contractor shall begin work on a construction site unless reasonable steps have been taken to prevent access by unauthorised persons to that site".*

Figure 2-17: Regulation 22 of CDM 2007.   Source: Construction (Design and Management) Regulations (CDM) 2007.

Regulation 27 of Part 4 of CDM 2007 deals with good order and site security, it requires that:

> *"(2) Where necessary in the interests of health and safety, a construction site shall, so far as is reasonably practicable and in accordance with the level of risk posed, either:*
>
> *(a) Have its perimeter identified by suitable signs and be so arranged that its extent is readily identifiable.*
>
> *(b) Be fenced off".*

Figure 2-18: Regulation 27 of Part 4 of CDM 2007.   Source: Construction (Design and Management) Regulations (CDM) 2007.

PERIMETER FENCING

Construction sites must be contained within a perimeter fence. The main purpose of fencing is to keep out unauthorised persons (for example, members of the public including children) and to prevent injury or death. Perimeter fencing also provides security against theft of materials, plant or equipment from the site. Fences should be adequate and suitable and installed at a reasonable distance from the structure to allow unrestricted movement on site of people and mobile plant, and prevent any activities being undertaken affecting the environment outside the fence. The fence should be regularly inspected to ensure there is no damage, breaks or gaps to allow unauthorised entry. When one piece of fencing is fixed to another, the fixing should face into the protected site, where possible, so as to impede tampering and removal of the fences by unauthorised persons.

Figure 2-19: Unauthorised access.   *Source: RMS.*

Figure 2-20: Perimeter fencing and signs.   *Source: RMS.*

SIGNS

Signs should be fixed at regular intervals on the perimeter fence to warn of the dangers within the site and instruct people to 'keep out'. Quite often, the name of the security company that is responsible for 'out of hours' security will also be displayed with a telephone number for emergency contact or to report any trespass.

SAFE VIEWING POINTS

Members of the public are quite often intrigued by construction sites and can be attracted to the perimeter fence to see for themselves what is going on. This may result in injury from flying particles, dust, fumes or splashes, even though the person is outside the perimeter fence. This can be avoided by arranging for a pre-planned viewing point that consists of a wire mesh panel integrated into the fence that allows members of the public to view the site's activities. The viewing point will be planned and situated in an area that is not exposed to hazards.

MEANS OF SECURING PLANT, CHEMICALS, ETC

Plant, equipment, materials or chemicals should be suitably secured to prevent injury by unauthorised access. Plant should be locked up at all times when not in use and keys held in a secure location (site office, safe). It may be practical to house plant in an additional internal site compound. In order to improve security certain items of heavy mobile plant are provided with steel sheets or shutters fitted around the cab and padlocked in position.

MEANS OF CONTROLLING DANGERS ON PUBLIC HIGHWAYS

Areas that surround a construction site are subject to mud and debris from the tyres and chassis of vehicles that frequent the site, which creates additional hazards to other road users as highway surfaces become slippery and create skid hazards. This can be controlled by the implementation of regular highway cleaning with road sweeper vehicles. Action can also be taken at site exits prior to vehicles leaving the site by routing site traffic through a tyre and undercarriage cleaning system, which assists in preventing mud and debris leaving the site.

Controls need to be in place to avoid vehicles entering the site queuing back onto the public highway; these will include the close monitoring of delivery schedule arrangements. A banksman may be needed to direct the vehicles and other traffic, particularly if the site entrance is restricted and a number of forward and backward movements of delivery vehicles are necessary to enter the site. If work continues in the hours of darkness, additional lighting may be necessary at site entrances and exits to improve the delivery drivers' general perception of hazards and pedestrian visibility.

Arrangements with client/occupier of premises

SITE RULES

Site rules will vary at different sites or premises due to the wide range of activities that may be undertaken. Site rules provide instructions that must be followed by permanent site staff and visitors and also other important information relating to site/location specific hazards. Occupiers of premises or clients may have different standards of site rules and some may enforce them more stringently than others. Contractors should always enforce their own site rules in addition to client/occupier rules.

CO-OPERATION

Co-operation between client, contractor and occupier is a very important factor. The occupier of a premises or site will have a detailed knowledge of any site specific hazards that may or may not be obvious to a contractor undertaking construction works and this may impact upon the works. In addition, the client or occupier has the authority to place controls and restrictions on the site. The contractor should be experienced in the activities that will be carried out and will have assessed any hazards related to the activities that are to be carried out at site. It is vital that all parties co-operate and communicate in order that this knowledge and information can be assessed to determine any new hazards that may arise and to enable appropriate information to be cascaded to other people at risk on the site. Co-operation will also be required where site activities need to be controlled or access restricted or where a shared knowledge is required to undertake a task, for example, decommissioning or removal of machinery.

SHARED FACILITIES

Occupied premises will quite often have various facilities available for existing workers/occupiers, for example, hot and cold water, toilets and rest facilities. It may be acceptable, with the agreement of the party in control of the premises and its facilities, for these to be shared for mutual benefit. CDM 2007 establishes a duty on the client contractors and the principal contractor to ensure that welfare facilities are provided. Therefore, where CDM 2007 applies and the client occupies the premises where construction work is to take place, it is in the interests of both the client and contractors to agree what facilities are required and what can be made available to the contractors.

Figure 2-21: Protection of others.   *Source: RMS.*

Figure 2-22: Sanitary conveniences.   *Source: RMS.*

First-aid and accidents

It is the duty of the employer (this could be the main contractor), under the Health and Safety (First-Aid) Regulations (FAR) 1981, to provide first-aid provisions and to inform the employees of these arrangements. These facilities should be in a clean environment, probably sited in a separate site office or portacabin. The Reporting of Diseases and Dangerous Occurrences (RIDDOR) Regulations 2013 require a record of prescribed accidents to be kept on site. All reportable injury accidents and dangerous occurrences must be recorded, deaths being additionally notified by telephone directly to the Health and Safety Executive (HSE).

Protection of other employees/visitors

Construction related activities that are carried out at a client's premises, while the premises are occupied, must take into account the lack of knowledge of construction hazards of the client's employees and visitors using the premises. This lack of knowledge may put them at risk from the hazards. This may require site rules to be amended and be supported by induction, personal protective equipment issue, signs, barriers, lighting or verbal instruction.

Arrangements for site inductions

All new or transferred employees, sub-contractors, including utility suppliers, architects' and surveyors should receive a site induction. This should be tailored to the site concerned and follow a formal structure, with documentation signed and logged. The following subjects should be covered (as a minimum):

- Welfare provisions (toilets, showers, rest areas).
- Site rules.
- Fire fighting equipment and assembly points.
- Use of personal protective equipment (PPE) and any training requirements.
- Traffic management plans.
- First-aid provision.
- Permits to work and any specific work restrictions.
- Emergency procedures.
- Reporting procedures for incidents, accidents, unsafe conditions, shortcomings in the employer's controls.

- Access and egress, for example, signing in and out.

Specific hazards and controls:

- Electrical.
- Plant and equipment.

- Work procedures.
- Method statements.

- Hazardous substances.
- Manual handling.

Working in occupied and unoccupied premises

OCCUPIED PREMISES

Careful planning of construction or maintenance work should be taken prior to work commencing on occupied premises. Hazards from paint, dust, falling masonry and excavations should be considered, suitable and sufficient risk assessments should be made and controls implemented. Factors to be considered include establishing controls to segregate contractor workers from the occupier's employees. This may include establishing separate parking, traffic and pedestrian routes. Where this is not possible, particular attention will need to be given to assessing where the contractor - occupier interface presents a risk. Risks will increase when a high volume of the occupier's employees interact with the construction work, such as at the start of work, lunch period and close of work. Where there is a risk from the construction work, such as falls of materials from a height, walkways will need to be covered to protect pedestrians. Arrangements for welfare facilities and first-aid will also need to be determined.

UNOCCUPIED PREMISES

Unoccupied premises/buildings can pose other hazards, with unstable groundwork, footings, walls, beams supporting floors and roofing. In addition, unoccupied buildings are likely to be infested with vermin or suffer intrusion by pigeons in the rafters where roof integrity may have failed; this can increase the risks of biological hazards. Unoccupied premises may have been used by itinerant trespassers sleeping rough and the potential risk of needle stick injuries from discarded syringes will also need to be assessed. Again, these hazards should be highlighted, suitable risk assessments should be made and controls implemented.

2.3 - Health, welfare and work environment requirements

Provision of health and welfare facilities

The CDM 2007, Regulation 9, establishes a duty on the client to take reasonable steps to ensure that Schedule 2 of CDM 2007, regarding welfare facilities, is complied with. A similar, but stronger duty, so far as is reasonably practicable, exists for contractors under Regulation 13 and the principal contractor has an absolute duty under Regulation 22 to ensure that Schedule 2 is complied with throughout the construction phase.

Generally, on construction sites temporary welfare facilities are provided so that they may be relocated as the build phase of the work is carried out. If the work involves refurbishment or extension to an existing building, separate facilities may be required to segregate construction site workers from the occupiers. This may be a requirement of the contract with the client, but often is necessary to maintain the required number of facilities, such as sanitary facilities, for the extra number of people on site. Other reasons may be to meet specific legal requirements, such as the Control of Asbestos Regulations (CAR) 2006, where there will be a requirement to provide separate washing and clothing facilities for those working with asbestos or its removal.

DRINKING WATER

Schedule 2 of CDM 2007 requires that an adequate supply of wholesome drinking water must be provided.

The supply needs to be accessible. If not provided in the form of a fountain, then drinking vessels must also be provided. The supply outlet from taps should be labelled, 'Suitable for drinking', or 'Unsuitable for drinking' as appropriate.

WASHING FACILITIES

Schedule 2 of CDM 2007 requires suitable and sufficient washing facilities, including showers where necessary because of the nature of the work or for health reasons. Where work is particularly dirty or workers are exposed to toxic or corrosive substances, showers may also be necessary. They must be provided at readily accessible places. In addition, washing facilities must be provided:

- In the immediate vicinity of every sanitary convenience.
- In the vicinity of changing rooms required by Schedule 2.

On all sites, a suitable number of wash basins big enough to allow a person to wash their hands, face and forearms should be available. There must be a supply of clean, hot and cold or warm running water, so far as is practicable, soap or other means of cleaning, towels or other means of drying and the rooms that contain these facilities must be kept clean, ventilated, lit and maintained.

Other than facilities for washing hands, forearms and face separate washing facilities must be provided for men and women, unless provided in individual rooms that may be locked from the inside.

SANITARY CONVENIENCES

Schedule 2 of CDM 2007 requires that readily accessible, suitable and sufficient sanitary conveniences must be provided. The conveniences must be adequate for the numbers and gender employed, lit, kept clean and maintained in an orderly condition. Separate conveniences for male and female workers must be provided except where the convenience is in a separate room and the door is capable of being locked from the inside. Provision should be made for regular cleaning and replenishment of consumable toilet items.

Figure 2-23: Washing facilities. *Source: HSE, HSG150.*

Figure 2-24: Temporary showers. *Source: RMS.*

FACILITIES FOR CHANGING CLOTHING

Schedule 2 of CDM 2007 requires that where special clothing must be worn at work or for reasons of health or propriety a person cannot change in another room then suitable and sufficient changing facilities must be provided. Separate facilities or separate use of facilities for male and female workers must be taken into account. The changing rooms must be provided with seating and, where necessary, include facilities to dry work clothing, personal clothing and personal effects.

The ACOP to the Workplace (Health Safety and Welfare) Regulations (WHSWR) 1992, which has similar requirements, recommends that changing facilities should be readily accessible to workrooms (and eating facilities if provided) and should contain adequate seating arrangements. The facilities provided should be sufficiently large to enable the maximum number of workers to use them comfortably and quickly at any one time.

ACCOMMODATION FOR CLOTHING

Schedule 2 of CDM 2007 requires suitable and sufficient accommodation must be provided at readily accessible places to enable workers to lock away their personal clothing not worn at work, clothing worn at work but not taken home and personal effects.

Clothing accommodation must be suitably secure; it must be suitable for the work clothing and would typically be separate from personal clothing where it was necessary to avoid health risks due to contamination or damage. Clothing accommodation should be in a suitable location near to changing facilities and drying facilities for work clothing, personal clothing and personal effects.

REST AND EATING FACILITIES

Schedule 2 of CDM 2007 requires readily accessible, suitable and sufficient rest facilities to be provided or made available at readily accessible locations. Such rest facilities must be provided in one or more rest rooms (new and modified, etc. workplaces) or in rest rooms or rest areas (existing workplaces).

Schedule 2 of CDM 2007 sets out specific requirements that the rest rooms or rest areas must conform to:

"(a) Include suitable arrangements to protect non-smokers from discomfort caused by tobacco smoke (though other legislation relates to the prohibition of smoking in workplaces this may be necessary to consider if rest facilities are made available in domestic premises.

(b) Be equipped with an adequate number of tables and adequate seating with backs for the number of persons at work likely to use them at any one time.

(c) Where necessary, include suitable facilities for any person at work who is a pregnant woman or nursing mother to rest lying down.

(d) Include suitable arrangements to ensure that meals can be prepared and eaten.

(e) Include the means for boiling water.

(f) Be maintained at an appropriate temperature".

Figure 2-25: Schedule 2 of CDM 2007.   *Source: Construction (Design and Management) Regulations (CDM) 2007.*

Canteens, restaurants etc. may be used as rest facilities providing there is no obligation to buy food.

Figure 2-26: Accommodation for clothing.   *Source: RMS.*

Figure 2-27: Rest and eating facilities.   *Source: RMS.*

SEATING

Suitable seats should be provided for workers who have to stand to carry out their work and occasionally have the opportunity to sit down. Seats should be provided for use during breaks. Rest rooms must have sufficient seats with backrests for the number of workers who may use them at one time. Seats in the work area can be counted as eating facilities provided the place is clean and there is a suitable surface to place food. There should also be facilities for pregnant and nursing mothers to lie down if required.

VENTILATION

Regulation 42 of CDM 2007 requires:

"(1) Suitable and sufficient steps shall be taken to ensure, so far as is reasonably practicable, that every place of work or approach thereto has sufficient fresh or purified air to ensure that the place or approach is safe and without risks to health.

(2) Any plant used for the purpose of complying with paragraph (1) shall, where necessary for reasons of health or safety, include an effective device to give visible or audible warning of any failure of the plant".

Figure 2-28: Regulation 42 of CDM 2007.   *Source: Construction (Design and Management) Regulations (CDM) 2007.*

The principal features of a ventilation system are:

■ Provision and maintenance of the circulation of fresh air in every occupied part of a workplace.
■ The rendering harmless of all potentially injurious airborne contaminants, for example, welding fumes and gases.

HEATING

Regulation 42 of CDM 2007 requires:

"(1) Suitable and sufficient steps shall be taken to ensure, so far as is reasonably practicable, that during working hours the temperature at any place of work indoors is reasonable having regard to the purpose for which that place is used.

(2) Every place of work outdoors shall, where necessary to ensure the health and safety of persons at work there, be so arranged that, so far as is reasonably practicable and having regard to the purpose for which that place is used and any protective clothing or work equipment provided for the use of any person at work there, it provides protection from adverse weather".

Figure 2-29: Regulation 42 of CDM 2007.   *Source: Construction (Design and Management) Regulations (CDM) 2007.*

Workplaces can vary greatly; they may be very cold and exposed, such as at height on a scaffold, or general indoor workplaces at ambient temperature.

The level of heating should be appropriate to provide physical comfort. The nature of the work and the working environment will need to be assessed to achieve the correct level. Several factors should be considered such as personal capability, degree of hot or cold, wind speed and humidity. Whenever possible the individual should be able to adjust their workplace to achieve this objective or be able to use a refuge from time to time against excessive heat or cold weather conditions.

LIGHTING

The basic need is to provide sufficient and suitable light in the circulation areas to allow movement of personnel, materials and equipment between work areas to take place conveniently and in safety. The aim should be to provide conditions that remain comfortable to the eye as it passes from one zone of the workplace to another, and to make available all information relevant (for example, safety signs) to the well-being and safety of the workforce which can be received through the sense of sight. Particular care should be taken when site work is carried out after dark or when work is to be carried out indoors, underground or in any area of confinement not normally accessed by workers.

Each work place should be assessed in relation to the tasks to be carried out. Temporary lighting can be hazardous if not installed correctly and presents the risk of electric shock, fire or explosion.

Attention should be drawn to accident black spots, such as changes in floor level or flights of stairs, with increased levels of illuminance served by luminaires which are carefully positioned to provide good three-dimensional modelling, while preventing any direct sight of the unshielded source, so as to avoid disabling glare. Machinery, which makes fast cyclic movements, should be carefully illuminated to prevent the occurrence of stroboscopic effects.

Sudden changes in lighting levels should not occur between neighbouring zones of the workplace. Levels should be graded to allow time for the eye to adapt. The processes of dark adaptation can take several minutes (more than half an hour in extreme cases) during which time the efficiency of the eye is severely reduced, making accidents more likely.

Differences in the colour characteristics of so-called 'white light' sources are sometimes apparent to the eye and although its ability to colour-adapt is considerable, the occurrence of frequent noticeable changes due to the use of various kinds of sources in the same interior may accelerate the onset of fatigue as well as making fine colour judgments impossible.

Regulation 44 of CDM 2007 requires:

"(1) Every place of work and approach thereto and every traffic route shall be provided with suitable and sufficient lighting, which shall be, so far as is reasonably practicable, by natural light.

(2) The colour of any artificial lighting provided shall not adversely affect or change the perception of any sign or signal provided for the purposes of health and safety.

(3) Without prejudice to paragraph (1), suitable and sufficient secondary lighting shall be provided in any place where there would be a risk to the health or safety of any person in the event of failure of primary artificial lighting".

Figure 2-30: Regulation 44 of CDM 2007.   *Source: Construction (Design and Management) Regulations (CDM) 2007.*

FIRST-AID FACILITIES

The first-aid facilities required for a particular construction site will depend mainly on the risks of the work being carried out and the number of people affected by the risks. The higher the risks and the number of people affected the more facilities are required. Where sites are small and only exposed to general construction risks one first-aider and a first-aid box may be adequate. Where the site has a significant number of people exposed to a wide range of risks it may be necessary to provide a specific first-aid facility in the form of a first-aid room. First-aid facilities of this type should contain essential first-aid provision and equipment, including:

- Sink with hot and cold running water.
- Drinking water and disposable cups.
- Soap and paper towels.
- A store for first-aid materials.
- Foot-operated refuse containers, lined with disposable yellow clinical waste bags or a container for the safe disposal of clinical waste.

- A couch with waterproof protection.
- Clean pillows and blankets.
- A chair.
- A telephone or other communication equipment.
- A record book for recording incidents where first-aid has been given.

Inclement weather and extreme temperatures

"Every place of work outdoors shall, where necessary to ensure the health and safety of persons at work there, be so arranged that, so far as is reasonably practicable and having regard to the purpose for which that place is used and any protective clothing or work equipment provided for the use of any person at work there, it provides protection from adverse weather".

Figure 2-31: Temperature and weather protection.   *Source: CDM 2007 Regulation 43.*

INCLEMENT WEATHER

Adverse or inclement weather is a term used to describe unpleasant weather conditions including storm, rain, high winds, snow and abnormal temperatures, for example, very cold, i.e. less than 10°C to below freezing or very hot, i.e. temperatures above 30°C. Both very cold and very hot temperatures are a risk to health. Exposure to inclement weather can have significant effects on a worker's health and safety and those in construction activities can be particularly at risk from the effects.

One of the fundamental mechanisms by which the body regulates its temperature is by perspiration. Important factors that aid or hinder this process are airflow and humidity. *Humidity* relates to the moisture content in the air. Air with a relatively high humidity has little capacity to cool the body by 'wicking' away sweat, whereas low humidity can cause dry skin and cracking. In a similar way, if a worker's clothing gets wet the 'wicking' effect can quickly cause significant heat loss in cold conditions.

In winter, the strength of the wind can significantly affect the air temperature and effectively reduce the ambient temperature by many degrees in exposed workplaces, called *wind-chill*. This can put individuals at greater risk than in still or sheltered conditions at the same temperature.

EFFECTS ON WORKERS OF INCLEMENT WEATHER AND EXTREME TEMPERATURES

Excessive exposure to heat is referred to as heat stress and excessive exposure to cold is referred to as cold stress.

Cold stress

In very cold temperatures, the most serious concern is the risk of hypothermia or dangerous overcooling of the body. Another serious effect of cold exposure is frostbite or freezing of the exposed extremities such as fingers, toes, nose and ear lobes. Hypothermia may be fatal in the absence of immediate medical attention.

When surrounding temperatures drop below 18°C body heat is lost. To maintain equilibrium the body adjusts itself by attempting to conserve heat by decreasing the blood flow to the skin's surface areas (ears, nose, fingers and toes) or by increasing heat production through involuntary muscle movement, such as shivering.

The most dangerous and rapid heat loss occurs when clothing is wet, wind is high, surrounding surfaces are cold, or when the body is immersed in cold water. The body can lose 25 to 30 times more heat when in contact with cold wet objects than under dry conditions or with dry clothing.

Cold stress impairs performance of both manual and complex mental tasks. Also, sensitivity and dexterity of fingers lessen in a cold environment. At lower temperatures still, cold affects deeper muscles, resulting in reduced muscular strength and stiffened joints. For all these reasons incidents are more likely to occur in very cold working conditions. Workers exposed to cold environments are at risk of cold induced injuries occurring in localised areas of the body, for example frost-nip, chilblain, trench foot, and immersion foot:

Frost-nip is the mildest form of a freezing cold injury, occurs when ear lobes, noses, cheeks, fingers, or toes are exposed to the cold and the top layers of a skin freeze. The skin of the affected area turns white and it feels numb.

Chilblains are a mild cold injury caused by prolonged and repeated exposure for several hours to air temperatures from above freezing, 0°C, to as high as 16°C. In the affected skin area there will be redness, swelling, tingling, and pain.

Immersion foot occurs in workers whose feet have been wet (for example, when wearing boots), but not freezing cold, for days or weeks. It can occur at temperatures up to 10°C. The primary injury is to nerve and muscle tissue. Symptoms include tingling and numbness; itching, pain, swelling of the legs, feet, or hands; or blisters may develop. The skin may be red initially and turn to blue or purple as the injury progresses. In severe cases, gangrene may develop.

Trench foot is "wet cold disease" resulting from prolonged exposure in a damp or wet environment from above the freezing point to about 10°C. Depending on the temperature, an onset of symptoms may range from several hours to many days, but the average is three days. Trench foot is more likely to occur at lower temperatures, whereas the immersion foot condition is more likely to occur at higher temperatures and longer exposure times. A similar condition of the hands can occur if a person wears wet gloves for a prolonged period under similar cold conditions as described above. Symptoms are similar to those of immersion foot.

The two most severe cold stress injuries are frostbite and hypothermia.

Frostbite is caused by exposure to extreme cold or contact with extremely cold objects. It occurs when tissue temperature falls below freezing point. The parts of the body most commonly affected are the face, ears, fingers and toes. Frostbitten skin is white and feels 'wooden' all the way through. In severe cases, gangrene may develop.

Hypothermia is caused by a decrease in core body temperature to a level at which normal muscle and brain functions are impaired. This occurs when metabolic heat production of the body is not sufficient to replace heat lost by the body to the environment. Maximum severe shivering develops when body temperature has fallen to 35°C. Lower body temperatures present the following signs and symptoms:

- Persistent shivering.
- Blue lips and fingers.
- Irrational or confused behaviour.

- Reduced mental alertness.
- Poor coordination.
- Poor decision-making.

Hypothermia can occur in relatively mild weather, particularly cool-wet weather, even when physical work is being carried out. It is the most frequent cause of death in water immersion.

Heat stress

In a very hot environment, the most serious concern is heat stroke. In the absence of immediate medical attention, heat stroke may be fatal. Heat stroke fatalities occur every summer. Heat exhaustion and fainting (syncope) are less serious types of illnesses that are not fatal, but interfere with a person's ability to work.

Heat exhaustion can occur when the temperature inside the body (the core temperature) rises to anything between the normal 37°C up to 40°C. At this temperature, the levels of water and salt in the body begin to fall, which can cause a person to feel sick, feel faint and sweat heavily. The symptoms of heat exhaustion can develop rapidly. They include:

- Very hot skin that feels 'flushed'.
- Heavy sweating.

- Being sick (vomiting).
- A rapid heartbeat.

- Dizziness.
- Extreme tiredness (fatigue).
- Feeling sick (nausea).

- Mental confusion.
- Urinating less often and much darker urine than usual.

Heat stroke is far more serious than heat exhaustion. It occurs when the body can no longer cool itself and starts to overheat. When the core temperature rises above 40°C the cells inside the body begin to break down and important parts of the body stop working. If left untreated, it can lead to complications, such as organ failure and brain damage. Severe heatstroke results in death. Early symptoms of heat stroke include:

- High body temperature.
- Heavy sweating that suddenly stops.
- A rapid heartbeat.

- Rapid breathing (hyperventilation).
- Muscle cramps.

The extreme heat that causes heatstroke also affects the nervous system, which can cause other symptoms such as:

- Mental confusion.
- Lack of co-ordination.
- Fits (seizures).
- Restlessness or anxiety.

- Problems understanding or speaking to others.
- Seeing or hearing things that are not real (hallucinations).
- Loss of consciousness within half an hour.

PREVENTATIVE MEASURES FOR WORKERS EXPOSED TO INCLEMENT WEATHER AND EXTREMES OF TEMPERATURE

When considering preventive measures for exposure to inclement weather and extreme temperatures consideration will need to be given to collective controls whenever possible, such as the provision of shelter. However, this will often require the provision of other controls in addition.

Cold environments

Preventive measures for cold environments include:

- Provide a sheeted area to protect workers from wind and rain, for example, the sheeting of scaffolding.
- Provide means to bring tools, equipment and materials that need to be handled and have been stored in cold conditions up to a reasonable temperature before use.
- Provide mobile facilities for warming up, and encourage the drinking of warm fluids, such as soup or hot chocolate.
- Introduce more frequent rest breaks.
- Give consideration to suspending work until the weather improves.
- Educate workers to enable them to be aware of the early symptoms of cold stress.

Ensure the personal protective equipment issued is appropriate:

- Clothing should have a high insulation tog rating (but not hinder flexibility for the movements necessary to carry out the tasks required), prevent absorption of water and be suitably fastened to reduce the effects of wind chill.
- The feet should be insulated to avoid loss through conduction.
- The head should be covered to the maximum extent practicable, to avoid excessive heat loss.
- Clothing should be light in colour to prevent heat loss through radiation.

Hot environments

Preventive measures for hot environments include:

- Introduce shading from the heat of the sun in areas where individuals are working, particularly if the work causes them to remain in position for long periods, for example, when doing brick or block work.
- Reschedule work to cooler times of the day.
- Provide more frequent rest breaks and introduce shading to rest areas.
- Provide free access to cool drinking water.
- Encourage the removal of personal protective equipment when resting to help encourage heat loss.
- Educate workers to enable them to be aware of the early symptoms of heat stress.

Wet environments

Preventive measures for wet environments include:

- Provide a sheeted area to protect workers from rain.
- Re-organise work so that it can be conducted indoors while it is raining or ground is wet.
- Establish areas of made up ground for work to be carried on outside without the need to stand in water or mud.
- Provide suitable breathable fabric waterproof clothing and footwear.
- Provide spare work clothing to enable those affected by wet conditions to change when needed.
- Provide drying facilities for wet clothing, including footwear.
- Encourage workers to remove wet clothing during rest periods.
- Educate workers to enable them to be aware of the effects of working in wet conditions and its link to cold stress.

Windy environments

Preventive measures for windy environments include:

■ Provide a sheeted area to protect workers from wind, for example, sheeting of scaffolds and open areas of partly constructed buildings.
■ Give consideration to suspending high risk outdoor work until the weather improves.
■ Re-organise work so that it can be conducted indoors while it is windy.
■ Educate workers to enable them to be aware of the effects of working in windy conditions, particularly the wind chill factor and its link to cold stress.

EFFECTS ON WORK OF INCLEMENT WEATHER AND EXTREMES OF TEMPERATURE

In addition to the effects on workers of inclement weather, inclement weather can lead to extremes of temperature and other conditions that can have significant effect on construction work. Extreme temperature effects include very hot and very cold conditions.

In hot conditions construction work sites will become dry and dusty and the ground may become cracked or shrink, particularly in clay soils. This may affect the stability of scaffolds, tower cranes and make site roadways difficult to navigate and cause equipment to overheat or seize. Dust will become airborne easily at relatively low wind speeds (3-4k/hr) and will increase the discomfort of workers, affecting their eyes and exposed skin. Some dusts are particularly hazardous if they become airborne, such as cement, which are caustic. Dust will also affect visibility and may increase the risk of site vehicle collisions with other equipment, structures or pedestrians.

Cold conditions are often accompanied by rain, snow or ice. Rain will soften the ground and any mud arising will make the site roadways particularly hazardous, increasing the risk of slips to workers and vehicles sliding out of control. Mud may be transferred from site vehicles onto public highways increasing similar risks to road users. The moisture from wet clothing may condense on the inside screens of mobile equipment resulting in poor visibility. Wet conditions may prevent the use of electrical equipment. Water may also transfer from clothing to hands, increasing risks from the operation of electrical equipment, even when indoors. In addition, porous materials that get wet may increase in weight or other materials may become difficult to handle, leading to increased risk of manual handling injuries.

Severe cold, below zero Celsius, may affect the structural stability of some critical equipment, for example, cranes and lifting accessories exposed to cold and wet weather will have an increased risk of corrosion and brittle failure. All exposed walk surfaces will also be very slippery in wet and low temperature conditions, particularly those on access equipment such as scaffolds, access points to mobile work equipment and the decks of delivery vehicles.

Visibility may be reduced significantly by snow fall or heavy rain, increasing the risks of collision of site vehicles with other equipment or pedestrians, with the added hazard of water or ice increasing breaking distances and reducing driver directional control. Engine fuels, brake fluids and operational hydraulic oils may freeze, resulting in equipment or brake system failure.

Heavy snow fall will alter the landscape, obliterate walkways and may create ill-defined road routes. Drivers of site vehicles may not see hazards such as trenches or open manholes or underestimate the width of waterways, which when frozen and covered with snow appear much narrower, and may drive their vehicles onto and through the ice.

PREVENTATIVE MEASURES FOR WORK AFFECTED BY INCLEMENT WEATHER

Whenever possible outdoor work should be planned to be started and carried out when the weather is temperate, for example, in the spring. Arrangements should be made to monitor weather patterns daily in advance and consider temperature, rainfall, wind speed and direction.

Work areas that may be exposed to severe weather conditions should be sheeted or covered, to provide shelter for workers and protection for the work being conducted. Suitable protective clothing, including footwear, should be provided. Wet conditions may require making available a change of clothing so that wet clothing can be removed and dried. This will necessitate the provision of drying rooms and similar rooms will need to be provided to enable workers to access a warm environment, hot meals and drinks to recover from exposure to inclement weather.

> "(2) Every place of work outdoors shall, where necessary to ensure the health and safety of persons at work there, be so arranged that, so far as is reasonably practicable and having regard to the purpose for which that place is used and any protective clothing or work equipment provided for the use of any person at work there, it provides protection from adverse weather".

Figure 2-32: Outdoor work and weather protection. *Source: CDM 2007 Regulation 43.*

When planning the site layout and its development it is important to establish roads, walkways and drainage of the site. This may require the provision of formal roads and pathways that may be incorporated into the building/structure under construction as the project progresses or they may be set out as a temporary measure. Make arrangements to improve temporary roads using compacted gravel to reduce the formation of mud, there may also be a need for arrangements to prevent site vehicles transferring mud onto public roads such as water jetting of wheels before the vehicle leaves site. Grit bins should be provided for use where there are gradients for vehicles to navigate or pathways that are likely to be exposed to ice. Check the working temperature of any fluids used in vehicles with manufacture specification for working in low temperature environments. In heavy snow identify traffic routes with markers such as flags and establish a similar scheme to identify high risk areas such as trenches and drains.

Where excavations or other subsurface areas of the site may be affected by heavy rainfall arrangements should be made to limit its ingress and for its removal. This may involve the use of sandbags to prevent water entering areas, sheeting and pumps to remove water. Porous materials that may be affected by wet conditions should be covered or stored indoors. Where possible, arrangements should be made to conduct work involving electrical equipment indoors. Work at a height may have to be suspended in windy conditions and roof work may also be stopped while snow and ice are present.

Excavations, mobile equipment and access equipment, such as scaffolding, may require a formal inspection after the effects of inclement weather.

2.4 - Violence at work

Hazards relating to violence at work

Maintenance and construction activities often need to be completed within a fixed timescale and this can result in increased pressure on workers to work quickly and without error. This may lead to an increase in tension between workers, particularly if one worker perceives another to not be working quickly enough to achieve the final goal. Such circumstances might result in violent outbursts between co-workers or other contractors. This may include workers being sworn at, threatened or even the use of physical violence.

> *"Any incident, in which a person is abused, threatened or assaulted in circumstances relating to their work".*

Figure 2-33: Definition of work-related violence.   *Source: HSE.*

Verbal abuse and threats are the most common types of incident. Physical attacks are comparatively rare. The most common risk factors relating to violence are:

- The position a person holds - a worker may hold a position of authority over another person; how they use this authority and the effects on the person can cause disagreement, resentment and could cause the person to be more aggressive.
- The location of the work - if the worker is working isolated from others this may leave them at risk. Some locations may not be secure and third parties may enter perhaps looking to steal or create damage.
- The time of working - work during late evening and early morning may mean there is less supervision and increased irresponsible behaviour, for example, the singling out of a young worker by the more experienced group for teasing or abuse.
- Alcohol and drugs - can make some people more aggressive. Because their perception and behaviour is more unpredictable, it may lead to misunderstandings and violence.
- Visible appearance - violence may arise simply because someone does not like a worker's visible appearance and what this may represent. This can be accentuated if the individual belongs to a minority group and perhaps as a poor understanding of the common language used by co-workers.
- The availability of weapons - if weapons, improvised or normal, are available to be used a sudden outburst that may have been verbal could escalate to involve major personal injury because a weapon was available, for example, bricks, knives, hammers, cartridge tools.

Control measures to reduce risks from violence at work

POLICY

The policy for dealing with violence should be written into the health and safety policy statement so that all employees are aware of it. This will encourage employees to co-operate with the policy and report further incidents.

DETERMINE CONTROLS RELEVANT TO THE RISK

- Identify who might be harmed and how.
- Identify who is most at risk.
- Where appropriate, identify potentially violent people in advance.
- Evaluate the risk.
- Check existing arrangements.
- Train workers to recognise early signs of violence and how they can reduce the likelihood with their behaviour.
- Provide information, for example, on relevant incidents.

- Improve the lighting.
- Improve security, for example, video cameras; maintain site security and control access and egress.
- Check arrangements for lone workers and consider two workers where risks are high.
- Arrange safe transport or secure car parking for people who work late at night.
- Ensure the issue and use of tools and other equipment controlled is and stored securely when not required.

MONITOR

Check regularly to see if the arrangements are working by consulting workers and worker health and safety representatives. If violence is still a problem, review work practices and risk controls.

- Ask workers informally through managers and health and safety representatives.
- Encourage workers to report all incidents and keep detailed records.

- Classify all incidents according to their actual or potential severity of outcome.
- Try to predict what might happen and how violence may arise.

DEALING WITH INCIDENTS

If there is a violent incident in the workplace it will be necessary to consider the following:

- Debriefing - victims might need to talk through their experience as soon as possible.
- Time off work - individuals may need differing times to recover.
- Support - in some cases victims might need counselling. Consider a phased return to work.
- Legal help - legal assistance may be appropriate in serious cases.
- Other workers - may need guidance or counselling to help them react appropriately.

2.5 - Substance misuse at work

Hazards of alcohol and drugs at work

The regular use of alcohol and drugs is becoming increasingly common in society. People who start consuming alcohol or drugs usually have a nil or low dependency and do so for recreational reasons. However, this can quickly escalate into abuse when larger quantities of alcohol or drugs are consumed more frequently and consumption becomes habitual. Drugs may be prescribed for treatment of a medical condition or of the controlled type, whose general use is illegal, such as cocaine and heroin. The effects of alcohol or drugs can vary dependent upon the individual's state of health and fitness, and resilience to the chemicals. Alcohol and drugs can remain in the body for a considerable time after consumption and its effects still be present the next day when at work. Effects on health and safety include:

- Poor co-ordination and balance.
- Perception ability reduced.
- Overall state of poor health including fatigue, poor concentration and stress.

- Poor attitude, lack of adherence to rules.
- Increased risk of violence.
- Increased likelihood of transport incidents.

Specific legislation such as the Transport and Works Act (TWA) 1992 and the Road Traffic Act (RTA) 1988 (as amended) specifically prohibit being unfit in specified circumstances through the use of alcohol and drugs. The TWA 1992 prohibits conducting safety critical work and RTA 1988 prohibits driving whilst unfit due to alcohol or drugs.

Control measures for the misuse of alcohol and drugs at work

The private use of alcohol and drugs is a personal choice over which employers usually have little or no control when it is conducted in the worker's own time. However, employers should have a policy to deal with the issue, should it start to impact on the worker's performance at work.

Control strategies often start with the identification of safety critical work, where the influence of drugs and alcohol would have a significant effect. It is usual that workplace control strategies do not presume use or non-use of alcohol/drugs by those that conduct safety critical work, treating them all equally. In a simple approach, all workers that come on to a construction site might be considered to be in safety critical work and all workers would work to the same rules. This could include prohibiting workers being under the influence of alcohol and drugs while at work, offering them opportunities to talk to someone about how this affects them and carrying out random drugs and alcohol tests. When accidents occur, it is common to consider alcohol and drugs as potential causative factors. It may not always be possible to test an injured party to identify if they caused their own accident by being under the influence of alcohol or drugs, but, for example, it may be possible to test a driver of mobile equipment that ran into someone on site.

2.6 - Safe movement of people on construction sites

Hazards to pedestrians

SLIPS, TRIPS AND FALLS ON THE SAME LEVEL

Slips, trips and falls on the same level are the most common causes of major injuries reported to the Health and Safety Executive (HSE) under the Reporting of Injuries, Diseases and Dangerous Occurrences Regulations (RIDDOR) 2013. Broken bones are the usual result when the following conditions are present:

- Poorly maintained surfaces - for example holes in roads, site debris, excavations, insecure ducting or grates, poor re-instatements of roads or walk ways.

- Changes in level caused by temporary road surfaces or reinstatements, excavation covers, heavy plant tracks, ramps, slopes, kerbs, chamber lids or steps not clearly marked.
- Slippery surfaces caused by water, oils, fuels, silt, mud, or mixed compounds, for example mortar, plaster and render.
- Inappropriate footwear.
- Site rules not followed - for example running or not taking care when walking on site.
- General obstructions in walkways such as trailing cables, pipes and air hoses.
- Poor standards of housekeeping in the workplace - allowing rubbish to accumulate.
- Adverse weather conditions - for example high winds, rain, and snow.

Figure 2-34: Slips and trips.   *Source: Lincsafe.*

Figure 2-35: Trip hazards.   *Source: Lincsafe.*

FALLS FROM HEIGHT

Situations that increase the likelihood of this hazard are:

- Inadequate access to and from the workplace, for example, a flat roof.
- Fragile roofs, for example, asbestos cement composite roof panels (particularly if obscured by moss or covered by roofing felt).
- Failure to use roof ladders for sloping roof work.
- Inadequate maintenance of access equipment, for example, worn or damaged ladders.
- Inadequate barriers, for example, no hand rails or edge protection.
- Unprotected trenches, for example, no barriers/fences or designated cross over points.

Stairways represent situations where falls from height, related to movement of people, are more likely. Reasons why this is include:

- Poor design of the staircase.
- Not using handrail, for example, when carrying.
- Slippery condition of the stairs, for example, dust or water.
- Poor maintenance of treads and handrails.
- Obstructions on the stairs, for example, tools or materials.
- Too narrow for volume of people using it or the work to be carried out.
- Inadequate standards of lighting.

COLLISIONS WITH MOVING VEHICLES

Situations that increase the likelihood of this hazard are:

- Restricted space to allow for manoeuvring and passing, for example, where there is a high volume movement of mobile plant and materials.
- Undefined routes to segregate site traffic, for example, people with heavy goods vehicles, excavators, dump trucks or rough terrain vehicles.
- Disregard for site rules concerning site vehicles, for example, speed restrictions, competent operators.
- No or insufficient pedestrian warning devices fitted to vehicles and a general lack of maintenance.
- Poor or unstable ground conditions causing pedestrian to unexpectedly move into the path of the vehicle, for example, loose surface, slippery or sloping ground.

STRIKING BY MOVING, FLYING OR FALLING OBJECTS

When working above ground such as on a scaffold, it is easy to concentrate on protecting people from falling. It is also important to consider precautions to prevent people being struck by moving, flying or falling objects. Situations that increase the likelihood of this hazard are:

- Stacking materials too high and/or in an unstable state.
- Overloading of materials on scaffolds, roofs or mobile elevated work platforms.
- Lack of use of barriers or mesh screens to prevent materials falling from height or being blown off.
- Unstable workplace structure, for example, insufficient number of scaffold tie points or uneven ground.

- Use of damaged or unsuitable pallets.
- Loose materials stacked at too steep an angle, for example, soil.
- Insecure components or workpiece in moving machinery.
- Products of machining processes not contained, for example, swarf or waste material ejected.
- Free dust from work processes or outside areas blown into the eyes of workers.
- Faulty or inappropriate means of lifting or lowering materials to the workplace.
- Insufficient clearance between people and load when materials are being moved by lift trucks and cranes.
- Unstable loads on vehicles, for example, not correctly supported, tied, secured or shrink wrapped.

Figure 2-36: Collision with moving vehicles.   *Source: RMS.*

Figure 2-37: Falling materials.   *Source: Lincsafe.*

STRIKING AGAINST FIXED OR STATIONARY OBJECTS

Whilst bumps and bruises are considered by many as "minor" injuries, they are painful and can be distressing for the sufferer. The following situations could give rise to increased risk.

- Low level or protruding scaffold tubing not correctly protected or highlighted with hi-visibility warning tape.
- Poorly sited machinery and materials.
- Insufficient space for storing tools and materials when working causing poor access and egress.
- Poor lighting.
- Work in enclosed areas.
- Cranes or other lifting devices left with hanging hooks/slings or raised forks.

Treading on sharp items

Sharp objects represent a foot hazard to pedestrians. Construction sites have a large amount of materials moved onto and around them. Sometimes materials, such as sections of trunking (such as may be used to carry electrical wiring) and copper pipe are cut to length and sharp edged off cuts may fall to the ground and be left there. Material can often arrive on site secured by wire binding and when the binding is removed it is often left on the ground, presenting a sharp trip hazard.

In addition, nailed together timber is sometimes used for improvised tasks, and when it is finished with it may be broken apart and discarded, leaving nails protruding. Abandoned broken pallets will present a similar sharps hazard.

HAZARDS TO THE GENERAL PUBLIC CAUSED BY CONSTRUCTION ACTIVITIES

The majority of the general public are attracted to construction activities, including construction activities on public highways, usually out of curiosity for the project underway.

Figure 2-38: Obstructions.   *Source: Lincsafe.*

Figure 2-39: Public highway works.   *Source: RMS.*

The hazards and dangers present at the site are often significantly magnified due to the public's lack of knowledge or awareness of site issues of health and safety. Construction activities on public highways may pose a higher risk due to activities being carried out within the public area resulting in an increased level of public curiosity.

Due to the temporary nature of the majority of construction activities on public highways the working area is often within less secure barrier systems and security is reduced to the vigilance of staff working in the area providing enforcement of site access rules. Items of heavy plant or material deliveries often operate outside the barrier systems that are set up, thus creating increased risk to the public. Works involving scaffold structures on the highway pose an obstruction to members of the public. The risk of impact with scaffold tubes may be a result of not installing ledgers high enough to avoid head injury and the failure to cladding them with foam and high-visibility tape, where pedestrians may be at risk. Unauthorised access to work areas, outside the core working hours, may result in injuries if the site has inadequate access security. Injuries may result from the failure to leave the site safe after work, for example, excavations left unguarded, uncovered and not lit; ladders not removed or secured and mobile equipment not locked or disabled from use.

Control measures for pedestrian hazards

RISK ASSESSMENT

Some or all of the following issues might affect the hazards faced by pedestrians and should be considered when carrying out a risk assessment:

- Weather conditions - particularly snow and ice.
- Lighting - especially at night.
- Surfaces - the presence of holes in the floor or mud.
- Locations where workers need to go that are exposed to surfaces that become covered in environmental grime or slippery growth.
- Drainage.
- Unusually high numbers of people, for example, fitting out and multi-disciplines may be present, for example, plasterers, electricians, plumbers, and carpenters.
- The effectiveness of existing controls - such as barriers.
- Unexpected movements of people - such as shortcuts, entry into restricted areas, emergency evacuation.

SLIP RESISTANT SURFACES

In order to ensure the safe movement of people slip resistant surfaces should be provided:

- On designated walkways.
- On changes of level, such as stairs, steps, ladders, footholds to vehicles.
- On ramps or slopes.
- Where walkways intersect with mobile equipment routes and people may need to stop suddenly.
- In work areas where spills of dry powders are likely.
- Where liquids are decanted or containers filled or stored.
- On access areas used for inspection or maintenance.

Figure 2-40: Slip resistance surface on steps.   *Source: RMS.*

SPILLAGE CONTROL AND DRAINAGE

Many hazards of movement of people relate to slips, some of which are caused by materials and spilt liquids. It is important to establish good spillage control and, where necessary, drainage.

This can involve the use of spill resistant containers for storing substances in, instead of open cans, and provision of drip trays where substances are decanted. Spillage control may involve a change of process in order to avoid spills, for example, using pre-treated materials or enclosed spray containers instead of open pots and brushes.

Spillage controls should include means to control spread and removal of the spill; therefore spill absorbent materials and disposal points need to be provided where they can be readily accessed. This will include storage areas and locations where the substance is used in construction activities.

Some construction processes may use large amounts of water that can build-up and present slip hazards. These should be identified and arrangements made to drain the water to suitable points for collection/containment. This may require the provision of planned drainage on a temporary basis. As some substances may be harmful to the environment drainage may have to be controlled by the use of interceptor pits. A procedure for spillage response for hazardous liquids should include:

- Raise the alarm and inform emergency services and relevant authorities (for example, Fire Service, Water Company).
- Evacuate all personnel, seal off access from danger area.
- Quickly assess the nature and extent (if possible) of the incident.

- Do not approach the liquid if you do not know what it is.
- Raise first-aid treatment for those who might have been affected.
- Provide bunding or some other form of spillage containment such as sand or special granules to contain the spillage.
- Isolate any ignition sources.
- Keep people away.
- For internal spills with no fire risk, ventilate the area by opening windows and isolate the material by closing doors.
- For external spills, cover drains to prevent the material going into drains and watercourses. Do not wash spillage into drains.
- Issue appropriate personal protective equipment to those involved and competent in carrying out the procedure.
- Ensure safe disposal of the spilled substance and any absorbent material used.

DESIGNATED WALKWAYS

Regulation 26 of CDM 2007, "Safe places of work", requires:

"(1) There shall, so far as is reasonably practicable, be suitable and sufficient safe access to and egress from every place of work and to and from every other place provided for the use of any person while at work, which access and egress shall be properly maintained.

(2) Every place of work shall, so far as is reasonably practicable, be made and kept safe for, and without risks to health to, any person at work there".

Figure 2-41: Regulation 26 of CDM 2007. *Source: Construction (Design and Management) Regulations (CDM) 2007.*

The duty to provide a safe place of work relates to such matters as clearly designated and marked walkways that are free of obstruction, the maintenance of floors and staircases, a safe working environment and safe means of access and egress together with the organisation of traffic routes (including pedestrian traffic). The workplace of a construction worker may be some distance from the ground or some distance from the site entrance. Therefore, such things as approach roads, access platforms, and routes through work areas must be considered. Particular thought should also be given to designated walkways for emergency use.

Good site planning should ensure the provision of designated walkways as part of the site layout. For sites that will be used by a significant number of people over a period of time consideration should be made to laying formal concrete walkways for workers, particularly at parts of the site where there will be a high amount of pedestrian traffic - such as entrances, rest facilities and routes through the site. Effort should be made to segregate pedestrians from site traffic, particularly on approach roads and where vehicles manoeuvre. When arrangements are being made for designated walkways the need for emergency routes and exits need to be considered also. Routes must be clearly indicated and be adequate for the people and hazards present on site.

An important consideration when considering traffic systems for construction sites is the safety interface between pedestrians and traffic.

The routes that people use should be clearly designated and marked via fencing, barriers, crossing points and in the paper format via traffic management plans that are posted in relevant areas and signing in points.

It is a requirement of CDM 2007, Regulation 36, that every construction site be organised in such a way that pedestrians and vehicles can move safely and without risks to health, and that traffic routes are suitable for the persons or vehicles using them, sufficient in number, in suitable positions and of sufficient size.

Figure 2-42: Pedestrian vehicle segregation. *Source: HSE, HSG150.*

Regulation 26 of CDM 2007 requires that access and egress must, so far as is reasonably practicable, be constructed so that it is suitable for the purpose for which they are used and maintained. This means such things as designated walkways having no holes or being slippery or uneven. Measures to control hazards related to designated walkways may include:

- Being kept clean and free from obstructions that may hinder passage.
- Good drainage in wet process areas or wet weather conditions.
- Ramps kept dry and with non-skid surfaces.
- Level, even ground without holes or broken boards.
- Salting/sanding and sweeping of outdoor routes during icy or frosty conditions.
- Steps, corners and fixed obstacles clearly marked.
- Excavations and chambers kept covered when not in use and the edges clearly marked.

FENCING AND GUARDING

Particular attention should be taken to control hazards through the use of fencing and guarding. Fencing of the outer area of a work site, at a suitable distance, will assist in the control of movement of people and vehicles. In addition, workers and vehicles in the site need protection and in this case inner guarding using barriers may be necessary, for example, to protect the edge of an excavation. It is essential that any fences or guarding (barriers) provided are stable to ensure proper protection is achieved.

Physical barriers should be erected to ensure that there is adequate protection for pedestrians who may be exposed to falls, falling objects and being struck by a moving object such as a vehicle. In addition, where pedestrians may walk into or strike an object, such as a protruding scaffold pole or a ladder the area around the objects should be guarded by means of a barrier.

> *"Every employer shall, where necessary to prevent injury to any person, take suitable and sufficient steps to prevent, so far as is reasonably practicable, the fall of any material or object".*

Figure 2-43: Prevention of falling objects.

Source: Regulation 10 of Work at Height Regulations (WAH) 2005.

Figure 2-44: Outer fencing and inner guarding.   *Source: RMS.*

Figure 2-45: Fencing and guarding at height.   *Source: RMS.*

USE OF SIGNS AND PERSONAL PROTECTIVE EQUIPMENT

Signs

Signs must conform to the standards specified in the Health and Safety (Safety Signs and Signals) Regulations (SSSR) 1996. They must be clearly visible and be easily understood. Safety signs should indicate the need to use personal protective equipment, such as hard hats, protective footwear or high-visibility clothing, when entering certain work areas even if people are just visiting or passing quickly through. Some sites may insist on all people who enter the site wearing this equipment, therefore signs are posted at the entrance.

Signs to indicate the presence of a temporary hazard should be used to warn people who might be affected to keep clear of that area. Hazard signs might be used where excavations are present, a change in height occurs or for the demarcation of a hazard area to assist with the provision of diversionary routes, for example, a vehicle unloading area where pedestrians are prohibited.

Figure 2-46: Clothing and footwear.   *Source: RMS.*

Edges of steps, overhead obstructions and cables or pipes laid temporarily across walkways should also be clearly identified with hazard markings.

Personal protective equipment

Head protection

The Personal Protective Equipment at Work Regulations (PPER) 1992 have been amended so that they cover the provision and use of head protection on construction sites thus maintaining the level of protection when the Construction (Head Protection) Regulations (CHPR) 1989 were revoked as part of The Health and Safety (Miscellaneous Repeals, Revocations and Amendments) Regulations 2013.

Employers must ensure that all employees are provided with, and wear, suitable head protection whenever there is a foreseeable risk of injury to the head other than by falling. Head protection provided must fit the person wearing it and be worn properly.

Where employers, self-employed or employees have control over others they must ensure they wear head protection.

Footwear

Risk assessment conducted by the employer or self-employed should consider the possibility of slips, trips and sharp material hazards, and where the decided control of this hazard includes the use of specific footwear this should be arranged. On most construction sites appropriate footwear is important to avoid slips or trips, puncture wounds or injuries from items that are dropped.

If footwear provided has particular properties to deal with hazards related to construction work, such as anti-slip soles or steel mid-plates, this would fall under the requirements of the Personal Protective Equipment Regulations (PPE) 1992 and the employer should provide them to employees without charge.

High-visibility

On sites where vehicles operate and for street works it is essential that workers are able to be seen, therefore it is essential that high-visibility clothing be used. Though this is not a substitute for the separation of vehicles from people, for the many situations where construction workers work in close proximity to vehicles it will provide valuable assistance in preventing contact.

INFORMATION, INSTRUCTION, TRAINING AND SUPERVISION

The employer, through management, should ensure that rules, policies and procedures are followed and that people do not act irresponsibly. Certain circumstances may require specific information, instruction and training; for example, procedures for use of access equipment or wearing appropriate clothing (for example, head protection or high-visibility jackets).

The Health and Safety at Work Act etc (HASAWA) 1974 requires employers to provide supervision as necessary. This means that the employer must actively supervise the workplace and the work conducted in it, for example, if high-visibility clothing is required or walkways are to be kept clear this must be supervised. The duty to supervise "as necessary" requires the supervisor to increase the level of supervision on a needs basis, for example, the higher the risk related to the work or workplace hazard or the more persistent the problem, the greater is the supervision necessary. If a large number of people are to use a route after it has been cleaned the supervisor should make special effort to ensure that it is safe after the cleaning and before use. If an obstruction of a walk route keeps returning, the supervisor will need to put in extra effort to bring it under control.

Maintenance of a safe workplace

CLEANING AND HOUSEKEEPING REQUIREMENTS

Maintenance of a safe workplace may be achieved through the development of a housekeeping procedure. Good housekeeping implies "a place for everything and everything in its place". Laid down procedures are necessary for preventing the spread of contamination, reducing the likelihood of accidents resulting in slips, trips, and falls and reducing the chances of unwanted fire caused by careless storage of flammable waste. Many sites with restricted space work on 'a just in time basis', i.e. materials are delivered as required by the build phase rather than purchased with a view to storage before the build commences.

"(2) Every place of work shall, so far as is reasonably practicable, be made and kept safe for, and without risks to health to, any person at work there".

Figure 2-47: Safe place of work.   *Source: CDM 2007 Regulation 26.*

ACCESS AND EGRESS

- Adequate space for easy movement, and safe plant or equipment use.
- No tripping hazards, for example, trailing cables or pipes.
- Guardrails and toe boards where people or materials might fall from floor edges.
- Neat and tidy storage of tools, plant and equipment so that they do not present a hazard to passers-by.
- Identify storage areas.
- Mark areas to be kept clear.
- Pay particular attention to emergency routes.
- Emergency provision, for example life belts/jackets for work near water.

Figure 2-48: Guard rails and toe boards.   *Source: RMS.*

> *"(1) There shall, so far as is reasonably practicable, be suitable and sufficient safe access to and egress from every place of work and to and from every other place provided for the use of any person while at work, which access and egress shall be properly maintained".*

Figure 2-49: Access and egress. Source: CDM 2007 Regulation 26.

ENVIRONMENTAL CONSIDERATIONS

Heating

> *"Suitable and sufficient steps shall be taken to ensure , so far as is reasonably practicable, that during working hours the temperature at any indoor place of work is reasonable having regard to the purpose to which the place is used".*

Figure 2-50: Temperature and weather protection. Source: CDM 2007 Regulation 43.

The principal legislation relating to temperature of workplaces on construction sites is Regulation 43 of Part 4 of CDM 2007; this requires a reasonable temperature in any indoor workplace. In addition, the approved code of practice (ACOP) which accompanies the Workplace (Health, Safety and Welfare) Regulations (WHSWR) 1992 states that a temperature of 16°C should be maintained for sedentary (low activity mainly sitting) work, for example in site offices, and a temperature of 13°C for work that requires physical effort.

Though the WHSWR 1992 do not apply to construction activates the figures used in the WHSWR 1992 ACOP are meaningful minimum standards that should be considered in a construction context. Construction workers can be exposed to a varying degree of conditions and resultant temperatures. The effects of excessive cold or heat can have harmful effects on their health and accidents can result due to fatigue or thermal stress. When work in hot environments is required it will be necessary for workers to be acclimatised gradually. Drinks and the provision of refuge from heat may be necessary to reduce body temperatures.

Where the temperatures cannot be maintained, for example, when working outside, areas should be provided to enable workers who work in cold environments to warm themselves. Practical measures and adequate protection must be provided against adverse conditions, for example, workers may be provided with a sheeted area to work in order to protect them from the rain and wind.

Lighting

Lighting plays an important part in health and safety. Factors to consider include:

- Good general illumination with no glare, especially where there are vehicle movements.
- Regular cleaning and maintenance of lights and windows.
- Local lighting for dangerous processes and to reduce eye strain and fatigue.
- No flickering from fluorescent tubes (it can be dangerous with some rotating machinery).
- Adequate emergency lighting that is regularly tested and maintained.
- Specially constructed fittings for flammable or explosive atmospheres, for example, where paint spraying is carried out.
- Outside areas satisfactorily lit for work and access during hours of darkness - for security as well as safety.
- Light coloured wall finishes improving brightness, or darker colours to reduce glare. For example, arc welding flash.

> *"(1) Every place of work and approach thereto and every traffic route shall be provided with suitable and sufficient lighting, which shall be, so far as is reasonably practicable, by natural light".*

Figure 2-51: Outdoor work and weather protection. Source: CDM 2007 Regulation 43.

Care should be taken, in particular where temporary lighting is rigged, to ensure that glare and shadows are minimised. Particular attention should be paid to changes in level, corners and where workers pass between the outside and inside of buildings when darkness occurs.

Noise

Noise can produce a number of types of damage to the ear. Noise levels should be assessed and appropriate controls established. Noise can cause an environmental nuisance to surrounding areas, and can have negative effects on communities in general and wildlife. Controls implemented may include barriers and screens around site boundaries to contain noise produced, the use of equipment that produces lower noise levels and restrictions on operating times to reduce the nuisance dependent upon the sensitivity of the area. ***See also - Element 9 - Physical and psychological health - hazards and risk control.***

Dust

General strategies for dust

Dust is a common hazard on construction sites and because it enters the atmosphere can easily escape past site boundaries and then have adverse effects on the environment. The health hazards associated with dusts can vary but usually result in an attack on the respiratory system on humans and other living creatures. Dust can also present significant risk of eye injury and general discomfort.

Other problems are layers of dust settling within the environment, causing damage to vegetation, wildlife habitats and private property. Activities creating dust include external cleaning of buildings, cutting and chasing of masonry and sanding operations.

The area where dust may be created can be watered down to minimise dust transfer into neighbouring premises. Stockpiles of material should be damped down or otherwise suitably treated to prevent the emission of dust from the site. Stockpiles should be planned and sited to minimise the potential for dust generation. The handling of material should be kept to a minimum and when deposited onto a stockpile it should be from the minimum possible height.

Dust pollution must be minimised during construction activities by:

- The complete screening, if practicable, of the building or structure to be demolished with debris screens or sheets.
- Control of cutting or grinding of materials on the site.
- Mixing of large quantities of concrete or bentonite slurries in enclosed/shielded areas.
- Skips and removal vehicles must be properly covered when leaving the site.
- Materials should be handled in such a way that they do not give rise to excessive dust.
- Watering of rubble chutes shall be undertaken where necessary to prevent dust emission.

It is important to ensure that the area around the site, including the public highway, is regularly and adequately swept to prevent any accumulation of dust and dirt. The use of wheel cleaning facilities and road sweeping equipment may be required.

Any plant used for the crushing of materials must be authorised by a local authority under the Environmental Protection Act Part 1 (Prescribed Processes). All work must be carried out in accordance with the conditions of such an authorisation. Where plant is used to recycle materials, the appropriate licence from the Environment Agency must be obtained. The process operator should notify the local authority prior to the movement of the plant on to the site.

Sandblasting

Dust hazards must be minimised during sandblasting by:

- Close-sheeted the work area to reduce dust nuisance from grit. Routine checking is required to ensure that the sheeting remains sound and sealed during sandblasting activities.
- Particular attention should also be given to the working platform to ensure that it is properly sheeted or sealed to contain dust.
- Non-siliceous grit should be used to avoid long term irreversible lung damage from silica dust.
- Proper protection should be provided for any structure painted with lead-based paint.
- In cases where water is used for large scale cleaning and blasting the requirements of the Environment Agency should be followed.
- All grit must be prevented from falling into water courses.

CONTROL MEASURES FOR MAINTENANCE WORK

Some maintenance activities may involve using large pieces of equipment that may compromise access and/or egress routes. It is important that this is taken into consideration during the planning phase of the activity and where required, temporary signage may be displayed. Barriers may also be required, if there is a need to protect other employees/contractors or the general public from other hazards, for example, noise, fumes, dusts or light (UV from welding).

Temporary lighting will often be required to ensure the work area where maintenance work is to be conducted is sufficiently well lit. This should be installed by a competent electrician, taking into account any risks relating to where it is to be used, such as the potential for flammable or explosive atmospheres.

Competent supervision of the activity is essential to monitor and control any changes to the work, making sure any additional housekeeping is conducted at regular intervals to prevent slips/trips or falls from debris created during the work.

Working on public highways

MEASURES NEEDED TO PROTECT SITE PERSONNEL AND MEMBERS OF THE PUBLIC

It is the responsibility of whoever is in control of construction activities on public highways to sign, light, guard and maintain the works safely. This will require a certain amount of planning to ascertain what procedures need to be implemented and what equipment is required to ensure safety.

Measures to be taken can be found in the document, "Safety at Street Works and Road Works" that has statutory backing as a code of practice for the New Roads and Street Works Act (NRSWA) 1991 and the Street Works (Northern Ireland) Order. This code of practice gives guidance on temporary signing, lighting and guarding of construction activities on public highways. Failure to comply with the code of practice may lead to criminal prosecution in addition to any civil proceedings. Further recommendations regarding safety measures at road works can be found in Chapter 8 of the "Traffic Signs Manual".

Prior to any works starting, and in order to ensure compliance with current health and safety legislation, an on-site risk assessment must be carried out to ensure a safe system of working is derived in respect of signing, lighting and guarding is in place at all times.

Any signs, lights or guarding equipment must be secured against being blown over or moved out of position by wind or passing traffic. This is usually done by the use of sand bags. Hard items should not be used as these can be hazardous if struck by traffic or pedestrians. Signs should be placed sufficiently far away from the works in order to provide drivers with adequate prior warning of the works. They should not present a hazard to pedestrians if placed in footpaths. Signs should also be of a reflective nature and be monitored to ensure they remain clean and visible. Any permanent signs or signals that become overridden by the temporary signing, lighting and guarding may require covering over. Consent for this will need to be received from the highway authority.

Figure 2-52: Public highway works safety measures. *Source: RMS.*

The placing of signs must consider traffic approaching from all directions, whether it is by two-way traffic or traffic at road junctions. The working area must also be demarcated with an allowance made for a safety zone (between 0.5m to 1.2m) surrounding the works, and also marked off with cones and lighting as necessary.

The safety zone must never be used as a work area or for storing plant, equipment or vehicles. When the site is not in use, but signing, lighting and guarding are in place, then arrangements must be in place to ensure regular inspections and any damaged or displaced equipment remedied immediately.

Site vehicles at the works should always operate roof mounted amber beacons if fitted to the vehicles. Hazard warning indicators should not be used at road works as these confuse other road users. Following completion of a project, all plant, equipment, materials, signs, lights and guarding should be removed immediately.

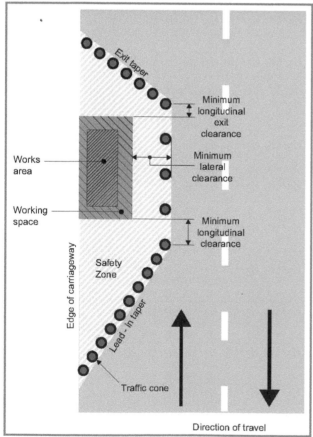

Figure 2-53: Typical work site layout.   *Source: TSO, Chapter 8.*   Figure 2-54: Lane widths and signs.   *Source: TSO, Chapter 8.*

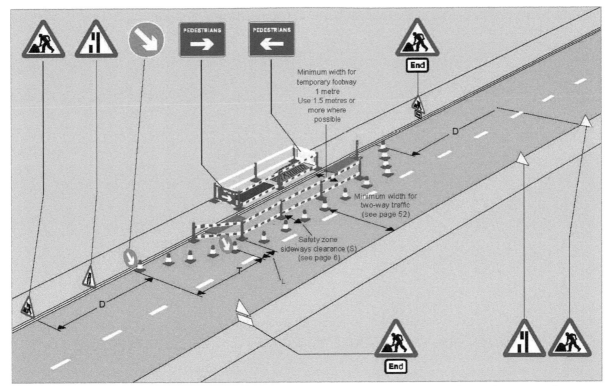

Figure 2-55: Arrangements for work on a footway.   *Source: Department of transport.*

Sample assessment questions

1. A project involves the construction of an in situ concrete structure, including the installation of drains, on a brownfield site. Up to 60 people are likely to be involved in the work at any one time.

    Identify the welfare facilities that should be provided for such work. (8)

2. **Identify** the factors to be considered when deciding upon adequate first-aid arrangements for a construction site. (8)

3. An initial site assessment should be completed before a construction project commences in order to determine possible hazards that could be present on or near a site.

    Outline factors that should be addressed when carrying out the initial site assessment. (8)

Please refer to back of assessment section for answers.

This page is intentionally blank

ELEMENT 2 - CONSTRUCTION SITE - HAZARDS AND RISK CONTROL

Vehicle and plant movement - hazards and risk control

Learning outcomes

On completion of this element, candidates should be able to demonstrate understanding of the content through the application of knowledge to familiar and unfamiliar situations. In particular they should be able to:

3.1 Explain the hazards and control measures for the safe movement of vehicles/plant within a construction environment, including when using public highways as a workplace.

3.2 Outline the factors associated with driving at work that increases the risk of an incident and the control measures to reduce work-related driving risks.

Content

Sources of reference

Driving at work, Managing work-related road safety, INDG382 ISBN 978-0-7176-2740-0

Essentials of health and safety at work, HSE Books ISBN 978-0-7176-6179-4

Lighting at work (HSG38), HSE Books ISBN 978-0-7176-1232-1

Safe use of vehicles on construction sites (HSG144), HSE Books, ISBN 978-0-7176-6291-3

Safety at street works and road works (Code of Practice), HMSO ISBN 978-0-1155-3145-3

Safe use of Work Equipment (ACOP) (L22), HSE Books ISBN 978-0-7176-6295-1

The Traffic Signs Manual (Chapter 8: The Traffic Safety Measures and Signs for Road Works and Temporary Situations) Department for Transport:

> Part 1: Design. The current edition is dated 2009 - ISBN 978-0-1155-3051-7
>
> Part 2: Operations. The current edition is dated 2009 - ISBN 978-0-1155-3052-4

Relevant statutory provisions

Construction (Design and Management) Regulations (CDM) 2007 - Part 4 in particular

Health and Safety (Safety Signs and Signals) Regulations (SSSR) 1996

New Roads and Street Works Act (NRSWA) 1991

Work at Height Regulations (WAH) 2005

Provision and Use of Work Equipment Regulations (PUWER) 1998 - Part III in particular Road Traffic Act 1988, 1991

3.1 - Safe movement of vehicles within a construction environment

Hazards from workplace vehicles and plant

There are five main kinds of accidents associated with vehicles; they form a significant part of the accidents that occur in workplace transport operations:

- Being struck by a moving vehicle.
- Injury caused by a vehicle collapse or overturn.
- Falling from a vehicle.
- Being hit by a load (materials) falling from a vehicle.
- Being hit against a vehicle whilst travelling in it.

Statistics provided by the Health and Safety Executive for 2010/11 show the following construction industry incidents:

		Fatal injury	*Major injury*	*Over 3 day injury*
1	Hit by a vehicle moving forward	5	41	27
2	Hit by a reversing vehicle	2	11	11
3	Vehicle overturning injury	2	4	2
4	Hit by runaway vehicle	-	6	2
5	Hit by vehicle cause unknown	-	5	1
	Total	9	67	43

Figure 3-1: Reported injuries to employees by kind of vehicle accident 2010/11, construction industry.   *Source: HSE.*

LOSS OF CONTROL

Hazards that can lead to loss of control of workplace vehicles include:

- Slippery surfaces due to contamination of the surface by materials such as oil and dusts, leading to poor traction when steering or braking. Weather conditions such as ice and water can also affect control of the vehicle.
- Potholes and other fracturing of the road surface, along with sudden changes of level, obstructions or kerbs. Contact with these may wrench the steering device from the hand of the driver or suddenly knock the steering in an unintended direction.
- Overloading of vehicles, which can influence their manoeuvrability and braking performance. A counterbalance vehicle, such as a rough terrain fork lift truck may be overloaded to such an extent that the steering wheels are not sufficiently in contact with the ground. The overloading of vehicles can cause the vehicle to require unusually long braking time or cause it to overbalance on cornering.
- Excessive speed will also affect the performance of brakes and the ability of the driver to manoeuvre the vehicle, leading to loss of control.
- Failure of one of the vehicle controls or critical items can lead to poor or loss of control of the vehicle. A sudden puncture in a pneumatic tyre could make the vehicle difficult to steer. If the conditions of brakes and steering deteriorate, they will perform badly and may cause the vehicle to move suddenly in an unintended direction.

OVERTURNING OF VEHICLES

Various circumstances may cause a construction vehicle to overturn including insecure and unstable loads, manoeuvring with the load elevated, colliding with kerbs and other obstructions, cornering at speed, braking harshly, driving on uneven or soft ground, driving across a slope, under inflated tyres, and mechanical failure.

Figure 3-2: Vehicle overturned.   *Source: Lincsafe.*

Causes of vehicles overturning

Possible causes include:

- Overloading/uneven loading of the bucket/forks.
- Driving with load elevated.
- Driving too fast, cornering at excessive speed.
- Sudden braking.
- Hitting obstructions, buildings, structures or other vehicle.
- Driving across slopes.
- Driving too close to the edges of embankments or excavations.
- Driving over debris, holes in the ground, such as drains.
- Mechanical defects that occur because of lack of maintenance.
- Inappropriate or unequal tyre pressures.

COLLISIONS WITH OTHER VEHICLES, PEDESTRIANS AND FIXED OBJECTS

Because construction work involves progressive change by building, altering or demolishing things there is an increased risk of vehicles colliding with other vehicles, pedestrians and fixed objects. A scaffolding or staging may be erected that a driver is not aware of or an excavation appear in a previously available route. The risk of collision is increased by the fact that scaffolds may overhang a vehicle route or power cables may run across the site. People may unexpectedly appear from a part built or demolished structure or workers intent on the work they are doing may step away from where they are working to collect materials or tools. Other factors are:

- Inadequate lighting.
- Inadequate direction signs.
- Inadequate signs or signals to identify the presence of vehicles.
- Drivers unfamiliar with site.
- Need to reverse.
- Poor visibility, for example, sharp bends, mirror/windscreen misted up.
- Poor identification of fixed objects, for example, scaffold, overhead pipes, doorways, storage materials, corners of buildings/structures.
- Lack of separation of pedestrians and vehicles.
- Lack of safe crossing points on roads and vehicle routes.
- Lack of separate entrance/exit for vehicles and pedestrians.

Figure 3-3: Potential collision with fixed objects.　　　*Source: RMS.*

- Pedestrians suddenly stepping from an exit/entrance into a vehicle's path.
- Poor maintenance of vehicles, for example, tyres or brakes.
- Excessive speed of vehicles.
- Lack of vehicle management, for example, use of traffic control, 'banksman'.
- Environmental conditions, for example, poor lighting, rain, snow or ice.

NON-MOVEMENT RELATED HAZARDS

Loading and un-loading

There is a risk of material falling on a vehicle driver where the vehicle is used to provide materials at a height or to remove materials from delivery vehicles. In addition, when vehicles are being unloaded by hand there is a possibility that the load has shifted and become unstable during transportation. This could mean that the load collapses onto the person unloading when a quantity of it is removed and this could lead to serious injury or death. Some loading and unloading tasks cause people to work at height, which creates the risk that people may fall from a vehicle. This may be more likely if the work is done in poor weather conditions, the load or vehicle surface is slippery or where there is no organised means of access to the vehicle. In addition, people loading or unloading may loose awareness of the edge of the load/vehicle when they are paying particular attention to the task they are doing.

"No person shall remain or be required or permitted to remain on any vehicle during the loading or unloading of any loose material unless a safe place of work is provided and maintained for such person".

Figure 3-4: Vehicles - loading and unloading.　　　*Source: CDM 2007 Regulation 37(5).*

Securing loads

The hazards relating to securing loads are work at height, slippery surfaces, weather conditions, and manual handling. There is the additional hazard of a badly secured load shifting at some stage in the transport operation. Tasks to secure loads may cause the person to go onto the vehicle in order to fix straps and tighten devices to hold the load. This will present them with the risk of falling from the vehicle or from the load onto the vehicle. The vehicle may be contaminated with dirt, dust, oil or materials spilt from previous loads, which presents a risk of slipping. Load securing equipment will usually have to be placed in position and tightened by the person securing the load; this could expose them to manual handling hazards related to moving things and over-exertion.

Sheeting

Sheeting is the covering of a load with a sheet or net to secure it; to prevent parts of it being disrupted by wind/air movement while being transported and to protect it from the weather. If this is not a mechanised process, it involves the manually unrolling of the sheet over the load and the sides of the vehicle, so that the hazards of height, slips and manual handling exist. Though it may be possible to sheet some vehicles from the ground it is not unusual for the person sheeting to have to gain access to the top of the vehicle and sometimes the top of the load. As with securing the load, this can present risks of falling or slipping. As sheets are designed to be robust they are also quite heavy and it takes a considerable amount of exertion to pull sheets over the load, leading to risk of strains and back injury.

Coupling

The task of coupling a tractor unit to a trailer requires that the tractor unit is reversed towards the front trailer. The '5th wheel' is the connection between the tractor and the trailer. If the 5th wheel jaws are not located properly, this can lead to unexpected movement of the trailer.

Though most accidents during coupling involve drivers or other people being run over, hit or crushed by moving vehicles, a number of non-movement based hazards exist. There is a significant risk of falling during coupling, especially in the dark, as the person coupling may be less able to see slippery surfaces, obstructions or steps.

A particular hazard is that the vehicle trailer could move or overturn. Though the ground may look flat it may be sufficient to cause the trailer to become unstable or move under its own weight. In addition, during uncoupling the trailer goes from being supported to bearing its own weight, and this can cause the trailer to sink into the ground and overturn.

Figure 3-5: Coupling. *Source: www.trucknetuk.com*

Vehicle maintenance work

There are hidden hazards and associated risks with maintenance work from open pits, access gantries, oils and greases and fitting of replacement parts. One of the particular hazards associated with large vehicle maintenance work is the hazard of being crushed by a falling cab that was tilted to gain access to parts of the vehicle for maintenance. Similar hazards exist at the rear of the vehicle where the vehicle has a tipping facility. Hydraulic ramps and hoists can create crush hazards as they are lowered to the ground or if there is a sudden failure of the hydraulic or mechanical system. There is an additional hazard that a vehicle or equipment could fall from a lift system, particularly if not located correctly or if the lift system is not raised uniformly.

There are many manual handling and posture hazards associated with vehicle maintenance work, from leaning over to reach parts to the movement of large vehicle wheels. The presence of flammable liquids, in the form of fuels, oils and paints present a hazard of fire and explosion.

Electrical hazards are present as portable electric equipment may be used, some operating at mains (230 volt) voltage. Where pneumatic equipment is used it presents the hazard of noise, flying particles and possible injection of air into the body.

It may be necessary to work on part of the vehicle at height, for example, to repair the top of a cement transporting and pumping vehicle. This work can present falling hazards that can lead to major injury or death. The hazards are accentuated when working on vehicles that come straight from use and are wet and slippery.

Figure 3-6: Tilted LGV cab and prop. *Source: HSE.*

Control measures to reduce risks from the movement of vehicles and plant

The employer, through its managers, needs to carry out an assessment of risk with regard to the safe movement of vehicles and their loads as part of the overall health and safety policy. This includes the use of vehicles such as dumper trucks, lift trucks, and those used for delivery. Consideration should be given to the following. Design features of the vehicle intended to minimise the consequences of an overturn include rollover protection and seat belts. In addition, features designed to prevent overturning include increasing the width of the wheelbase and lowering the position of the centre of gravity of the vehicles.

SUITABILITY AND SUFFICIENCY OF TRAFFIC ROUTES

The provision and use of safe traffic routes on site for pedestrians and vehicles is an essential component of managing access and egress to the site. Such factors to consider include the size of vehicles, including height, axel weight and the route to be taken should be considered before entry to the site is permitted. Where possible traffic routes should limit or eliminate the need for vehicles to reverse; establishing a one way system for the site would assist with this. In order for traffic routes to remain suitable for use they need to be maintained so that they are free of obstructions and sufficient clearance for vehicles is available. Traffic routes should be wide enough to allow manoeuvrability and passing. The proximity of pedestrians and other site traffic and their flow through the site is another important consideration when developing a site management plan.

> *(1) Every construction site shall be organised in such a way that, so far as is reasonably practicable, pedestrians and vehicles can move safely and without risks to health.*
>
> *(2) Traffic routes shall be suitable for the persons or vehicles using them, sufficient in number, in suitable positions and of sufficient size.*

Figure 3-7: Traffic routes.   *Source: CDM 2007 Regulation 36.*

In order to comply with Regulation 36 (2) of CDM 2007 and to establish good practice for traffic routes it is necessary to ensure that:

> *"(a) Pedestrians or vehicles may use it without causing danger to the health or safety of persons near it.*
>
> *(b) Any door or gate for pedestrians which leads onto a traffic route is sufficiently separated from that traffic route to enable pedestrians to see any approaching vehicle or plant from a place of safety.*
>
> *(c) There is sufficient separation between vehicles and pedestrians to ensure safety or, where this is not reasonably practicable:*
>
> > *(i)   There are provided other means for the protection of pedestrians.*
> >
> > *(ii) There are effective arrangements for warning any person liable to be crushed or trapped by any vehicle of its approach.*
>
> *(d) Any loading bay has at least one exit point for the exclusive use of pedestrians.*
>
> *(e) Where it is unsafe for pedestrians to use a gate intended primarily for vehicles, one or more doors for pedestrians is provided in the immediate vicinity of the gate, is clearly marked and is kept free from obstruction".*

Figure 3-8: Regulation 36 (2) of CDM 2007.   *Source: Construction (Design and Management) Regulations (CDM) 2007.*

MANAGEMENT OF VEHICLE MOVEMENTS

Many construction sites are complex in nature and require the careful management of vehicles in order to ensure that they are brought onto, move around and leave the site safely. This can start at the project planning stage as it can cause many problems when a vehicle is brought onto site too early when the site is at an earlier phase and is not ready for it. Conversely, if it is brought in part way through the project it may be difficult to get it to where it is needed and it may be better to get it to site early.

Where materials are brought to site it may be necessary to manage deliveries so that too many vehicles do not arrive at the site at the same time causing them to back up into the public highway. Site security arrangements play a significant part in the management of vehicles on site and will assist with controlling vehicles so that they are routed correctly and safely.

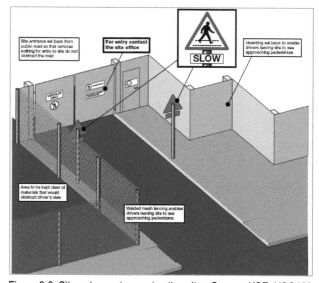

Figure 3-9: Site entrance to construction site. *Source: HSE, HSG150.*

It is not uncommon for vehicles to be sent to a site that are too big or too heavy to access the roadways. Site security staff should be trained to identify these to prevent them accessing the site and causing harm. Major vehicle movements, such as a heavy crane may be timed so that the minimum of workers are on site and that it can be conducted easily in a controlled manner.

Banksmen or signallers as they are also known are used to control vehicle movements i.e. reversing and lifting operations. Due to the amount of serious or fatal injuries every year, it is important that they are fully trained and competent. A safe system of work should be adopted with all drivers using standard signals that are easily understood. Drivers should know to stop their vehicle immediately if the banksman disappears from sight. The standard signals are given in the Health and Safety (Safety Signs and Signals) Regulations (SSSR) 1996. Additional points to consider include:

■ Drivers of vehicles that are visiting the premises should be made aware of any local rules and conditions.
■ Traffic routes should be clearly marked and signed. These should incorporate speed limits, one way systems, priorities and other factors normal to public roads.
■ Speed limits of 10 or 15 mph are usually considered appropriate, although 5 mph may be necessary in certain situations. It is important to have speed limits that are practicable and effective. Speed limit signs should be posted and traffic slowing measures, such as speed bumps and ramps, may be necessary in

certain situations. Monitoring speed limit compliance is necessary, along with some kind of action against persistent offenders.

■ Accidents can be caused where vehicles are unsafely parked as they can be an obstruction and restrict visibility. There should be clear entrance and exit routes in parking areas and designated parking areas to allow the loading and sheeting of outgoing transport to be checked safely before leaving the site.

■ As far as is practicable pedestrians should be kept clear of vehicle operating areas and/or a notice displayed warning pedestrians that they are entering an operating area.

■ Whenever possible separate routes should be provided for pedestrians with designated crossing places and suitable physical barriers at recognised danger spots.

■ Clear direction signs and marking of storage areas and buildings should be provided to avoid unnecessary movement, such as reversing.

■ Where reversing is required banksmen, also known as signallers, should be used to control vehicle movements.

"(4) Every traffic route shall be:

(a) Indicated by suitable signs where necessary for reasons of health or safety.

(b) Regularly checked.

(c) Properly maintained".

Figure 3-10: Traffic routes, supplementary requirements. *Source: CDM 2007 Regulation 36.*

ENVIRONMENTAL CONSIDERATIONS

Where vehicles operate, environmental conditions such as lighting and adverse weather will make a significant impact on their safe operation by affecting **visibility**. Where reasonably practicable a suitable standard of lighting must be maintained so that operators of vehicles can see to operate their vehicle and can be seen by others. When establishing suitable lighting, it is important to avoid areas of glare or shadow that could mask the presence of a person or vehicle. Similarly, if vehicles travel from within buildings to the outside it is important that the light level is maintained at a roughly even level in order to give the driver's eyes time to adjust to the change in light. Consideration should be given to adequate lighting on routes taken by vehicles, in loading/unloading/operating areas and where there is a change in level or camber to the road surface. Fixed structure hazards, such as overhead obstructions, edges, and pits should be made as visible as possible with additional lighting and/or reflective strips. If reasonably practicable barriers should be installed to make the hazard more visible and guide the vehicle operator around the hazard at a safe distance.

Roads, gangways and aisles should have sufficient width and overhead clearance for the largest vehicle. Attention should be paid to areas where they might meet other traffic, for example, the entrance to the site. If ramps (speed bumps) are used, a by-pass for trolleys and shallow draft vehicles should be provided. A one-way traffic system should be considered to reduce the risk of collision.

Gradients and changes in ground level, such as ramps and potholes, represent a specific hazard to plant and vehicle operation. Vehicles have a limit of stability dependent on loading and their wheelbase. These conditions could put them at risk of overturning or cause damage to articulated vehicle couplings. Any gradient in a vehicle operating area should be kept as gentle as possible.

Where **changes in level** are at an edge that a vehicle might approach, and there is risk of falling, it must be provided with a robust barrier or similar means to demarcate the edge. Particular care must be taken at points where loading and unloading are conducted.

"Suitable and sufficient measures shall be taken so as to prevent any vehicle from falling into any excavation or pit, or into water, or overrunning the edge of any embankment or earthwork".

Figure 3-11: Vehicles - falling into excavations etc. *Source: CDM 2007 Regulation 37(6).*

In some circumstances, materials from construction process and mud may contaminate the **surface condition** of the road making it difficult for vehicles to brake effectively. It is important to have a programme that anticipates this with regular cleaning or scarifying of the surface as well as means of dealing with spills. The road surface should be in good condition, free from potholes and obstructions.

Excessive ambient noise levels can mask the sound of vehicles working in the area; therefore additional visual warning should be used, for example, flashing lights. Sufficient and suitable parking areas should be provided away from the main work area and located where the risk of unauthorised use of the work vehicles will be reduced.

MAINTENANCE OF VEHICLES

All vehicles should be well maintained and 'roadworthy' with a formal system of checks and maintenance in place. All construction site vehicles should be maintained to the same good standard as those used on public roads for such critical items as tyres and brakes.

Vehicle maintenance should be planned for at regular intervals and vehicles taken out of use if critical items are not at an acceptable standard. In addition, it is important to conduct a pre-use check of the vehicle. This is usually done by the driver as part of their taking the vehicle over for a period of use, such as a work shift or day.

This would identify the condition of critical items and provide a formal system to identify and consider problems that may affect the safety of the vehicle.

Critical items would typically include the following health and safety items:

- Braking systems.
- Cab protection devices, for example, roll over protection structures (ROPS).
- Fire fighting equipment.
- Lights and indicators.
- Operational controls.
- Restraint systems, for example, seat belts.

- Safety devices, such as interlocks, guards and panels.
- Steering.
- Tyres, including condition and pressures.
- Vision aids, for example convex mirrors, CCTV.
- Warning devices and signals.
- Windscreen condition, washers and wipers.

If there is no nominated driver and the vehicle is for general use someone should be nominated to make these checks. A record book or card would usually be used to record the checks and the findings.

DRIVER PROTECTION AND RESTRAINT SYSTEMS

Roll over and restraint systems

In many work vehicle accidents the driver is injured because the vehicle does not offer protection when it rolls over or it does not restrain the driver to prevent them falling out of the vehicle and being injured by the fall or the vehicle falling on them.

Vehicles such as dumper trucks, road rollers and rough terrain forklift trucks (RTFLT) are examples of equipment that may present this risk. The Provision and Use of Work Equipment Regulations (PUWER) 1998, Part 3, Regulation 26, recognises the importance of this and now set out requirements for equipment to be adapted, where practicable, to provide this protection. New equipment must now be provided with roll over protection and restraint systems, for example, roll bars and seat/lap belts, where relevant. For some vehicles, the provision of a cab around the driver will provide protection in the event of a roll over and additional weather, dust and falling materials protection.

Figure 3-12: Roll bar and seat restraint.   *Source: RMS.*

Figure 3-13: Driver protection.   *Source: RMS.*

Protection from falling materials

There is a risk of material falling on a vehicle driver in situations where the vehicle is used to provide materials at a height or to remove materials from delivery vehicles. It is important that suitable protection of the driver be provided by the structure of the vehicle. Protection should also be provided where vehicles work in close proximity to areas where there is a risk from falling materials. This may be by the provision of a frame and mesh above the driver or by the provision of a totally enclosing cab. Safety helmets alone are unlikely to provide sufficient protection, but may be a useful addition where a mesh structure is provided.

Weather conditions

The protection of vehicle drivers from the weather is an important consideration. Protection may be achieved by the provision of a totally enclosing cab around the driver. This will provide protection from wind, rain and cold. However, it can lead to the driver being subject to increased temperatures as the glass in the cab causes heat to be retained. This can lead to discomfort and risk of thermal stress in summer months. The provision of a cab to protect a driver from weather has to be balanced with needs for visibility. There is a risk that when using a cab visibility may be impaired by the structure, windows may mist up or ice form on the window surfaces. The absence of a cab will improve visibility, but expose the driver to weather conditions.

SEGREGATING PEDESTRIANS AND VEHICLES

Means of segregation

"Every workplace shall be organised in such a way that pedestrians and vehicles can circulate in a safe manner".

Figure 3-14: Means of segregation.   *Source: Regulation 17(1) of WHSWR 1992.*

"Every construction site shall be organised in such a way that, so far as is reasonably practicable, pedestrians and vehicles can move safely and without risks to health".

"Traffic routes shall be suitable for the persons or vehicles using them, sufficient in number, in suitable positions and of sufficient size".

Figure 3-15: Traffic routes. *Source: CDM 2007 Regulation 36.*

Clearly defined and marked routes should be provided on construction sites for pedestrians and vehicles. These should be provided for access and egress points to work areas, car parks, and vehicle delivery routes. Safe crossing places should be provided where pedestrians have to cross main traffic routes. In buildings where vehicles operate, separate doors and walkways should be provided for pedestrians to get from building to building.

Meshed handrails can be used to channel people into the pedestrian route. Where it is not possible to have a pedestrian route entirely separate from vehicle movement, because of building and structure design, then a raised pedestrian walkway could be considered to help in segregation. Where segregation is by distance or delineation, any traffic route that is used by both pedestrians and vehicles should be wide enough to enable any vehicle likely to use the route to pass pedestrians safely.

Separate gates/doorways should be provided for vehicle entry and blind spots (where vision of the vehicle driver or pedestrian is restricted) should be dealt with by the careful positioning of mirrors on walls, plant, structures or storage materials.

Figure 3-16: Pedestrian crossing point. *Source: HSE, HSG150.*

Figure 3-17: Segregating pedestrians and vehicles. *Source: RMS.*

Measures to be taken when segregation is not practicable

Where pedestrians and vehicle routes cross, appropriate crossing points should be provided and used. Where necessary, barriers or rails should be provided to prevent pedestrians crossing at particularly dangerous points and to guide them to designated crossing places. At crossing places where volumes of traffic are particularly heavy, the provision of suitable bridges or subways should be considered. At crossing points there should be adequate visibility and open space for the pedestrian where the pedestrian route joins the vehicle route.

Where segregation is not practicable and vehicles share the same workplace as pedestrians it is important to mark the work areas as being separate from vehicle routes to warn drivers to adjust their approach and be more aware of pedestrians. This can be done by removable barriers or tape to indicate when the vehicle is being given access to a work area.

Figure 3-18: No segregation. *Source: RMS.*

Figure 3-19: Control of vehicle movement. *Source: RMS.*

Audible and visual warnings of the presence of the vehicle would also assist. Where vehicles are dominant, but pedestrians need to access the area in which they are working, similar means of warning may be used, but for the opposite reason.

The reversing of large vehicles that have a restricted view can be a particularly high risk to pedestrians sharing the same workplace and should be controlled by the use of a banksman to guide them.

Where segregation is not practicable the use of high visibility personal protective equipment by pedestrians increases the ability of the driver to see the pedestrian. High visibility clothing is mandatory on the majority of construction sites. Where it is unavoidable that pedestrians will come into proximity with vehicles, they should be reminded of the hazards by briefings, site induction and signs, so they are aware at all times.

PROTECTIVE MEASURES FOR PEOPLE AND STRUCTURES

It is important to anticipate that drivers of vehicles might misjudge a situation and collide with structures whilst operating vehicles. For this reason, people and vulnerable structures should be provided with barriers that continuously surround them; alternatively posts can be provided at key positions. Particular care should be taken of structures at a height as they may be less obvious to drivers, such as a scaffold spanning a traffic route, pipe bridges, roof trusses or door lintels.

Tall vehicles or those that have tipping mechanisms that can raise their effective height could damage these structures. Though it may not always be possible to protect all structures, such as a doorway, it is important to apply *markings* to make them more visible. In addition, *signs* warning of overhead structures or the presence of vehicles in the area will help increase awareness and avoid collisions. There is a need to alert people to the hazard when working in or near a vehicle operating area. Signs might help and these can be supplemented by *visual and audible warning systems* that confirm the presence of the vehicle. These may be operated by the driver, such as a horn on a dumper truck or automatically, such as an audible reversing signal on a large road vehicle. Visibility can be improved by mounting mirrors at strategic points. Consideration should be given to the provision of high visibility clothing to pedestrians working within areas where vehicles operate.

Barriers

Moving vehicles, and in particular large plant, have high impact energy when they are in contact with structures or people. It is essential that vehicles be separated from pedestrians and vulnerable structures. Because of the high energy involved the barrier used must reflect the type of vehicle in contact with it. If it is only pedestrians that might contact it a simple portable barrier may be adequate, but if it is heavy plant robust barriers including concrete structures may need to be considered. It is important to identify vulnerable locations that warrant protection, for example, steelwork, formwork, falsework and scaffolds. Barriers are also used to prevent vehicles falling into trenches and other areas below ground where people may be working.

Markings

Any structure that represents a height or width restriction should be readily identified for pedestrians and vehicle drivers. This will include low beams or doorways, pipe bridges, protruding scaffolds and edges where a risk of falling exists. These markings may be by means of attaching hazard tape, painting the structure to highlight the hazard or markings on barriers.

Signs

Signs should be used to provide information, such as height restrictions, and to warn of hazards on site. Signs may be used to direct vehicles around workers at a safe distance.

Figure 3-20: Fencing and barriers at a distance.   *Source: RMS.*

Figure 3-21: Visual warning on a dumper truck.   *Source: RMS.*

Warnings of vehicle approach and reversing

Warnings may be audible or visual or a combination of each. They are used to warn that the vehicle is operating in the area, such as a flashing light on the top of a dumper truck or to warn of a specific movement, such as an audible warning that a large vehicle is reversing.

These are designed to alert people in the area in order that they can place themselves in a position of safety. They do not provide the driver with authority to reverse the vehicle or to proceed in a work area without caution.

"(1) Suitable and sufficient steps shall be taken to prevent or control the unintended movement of any vehicle.

(2) Suitable and sufficient steps shall be taken to ensure that, where any person may be endangered by the movement of any vehicle, the person having effective control of the vehicle shall give warning to any person who is liable to be at risk from the movement of the vehicle.

(3) Any vehicle being used for the purposes of construction work shall when being driven, operated or towed:

(a) Be driven, operated or towed in such a manner as is safe in the circumstances.

(b) Be loaded in such a way that it can be driven, operated or towed safely.

(4) No person shall ride or be required or permitted to ride on any vehicle being used for the purposes of construction work otherwise than in a safe place thereon provided for that purpose".

Figure 3-22: Vehicles - safe operation and rules. *Source: CDM 2007 Regulation 37.*

SITE RULES

It is important to establish clear and well understood site rules regarding vehicle operations. These may have to be communicated to drivers by security staff at the time they visit the site. The rules often stipulate where the driver should be whilst vehicles are being loaded, where the keys to the vehicle should be, obligations not to reverse without permission and what access they have to areas of the site for such things as refreshment. Pedestrians should also know what the site rules are in order to keep themselves safe.

Site rules for pedestrians might include such things as using pedestrian exits/entrances or crossing points, not entering hazardous areas or the need to wear personal protective equipment in hazardous areas, and not walking behind a reversing vehicle.

Where construction sites are made up of or join a highway, such as carriageway repairs on a motorway, it is important to identify who has priority - the vehicle or the worker. Site rules may clarify that once the site boundary is crossed the worker has priority - this has to be clear. The site rules may be reinforced by the provision of additional signs to clarify a speed limit and the nature of the priority of workers.

SELECTION AND TRAINING OF DRIVERS

Only competent persons should be permitted to operate plant or vehicles after they have been selected, trained and authorised to do so, or are undergoing properly organised formal training under competent supervision.

Selection

The safe usage of plant and vehicles calls for a reasonable degree of both physical and mental fitness. The selection procedure should be devised to identify people who have been shown to be reliable and mature enough to perform their work responsibly and carefully. To avoid wasteful training for workers who lack co-ordination and ability to learn, selection tests should be used.

Consideration must be given to any legal age restrictions that apply to vehicles that operate on the public road. A similar approach may be adopted for similar vehicles used on site though the law is not specific on age limitations in such cases.

Potential operators should be medically examined prior to employment/training in order to assess the individual's physical ability to cope with this type of work.

They should also be examined every five years in middle age and after sickness or accident. Points to be considered are:

- General - normal agility, having full movement of trunk, neck and limbs.
- Vision - good eyesight in both eyes or corrected by spectacles, is important, as operators are required to have good judgement of space and distance.
- Hearing - the ability to hear instructions and warning signals with each ear is important.

Training

It is essential that immediate supervisors receive training in the safe operation of plant and vehicles and that senior management appreciates the risks resulting from the interaction of vehicles and the workplace.

For the operator/driver, safety must constitute an integral part of the skill training programme and not be treated as a separate subject. The operator/driver should be trained to a level consistent with efficient operation and care for the safety of themselves and other persons.

On completion of training they should be issued with a company authority to drive and a record of all basic training, refresher training and tests maintained in the individual's personal documents file. Certification of training by other organisations must be checked.

MANAGEMENT SYSTEMS FOR ASSURING DRIVER COMPETENCE

The trained operator/driver

It should not be assumed that employees who join as trained operators/drivers have received adequate training to operate safely in their new company. The management must ensure that they have the basic skills and receive training in company methods (local practices) and procedures for the type of work they are to undertake. They should be examined and tested before issue of a company driving authority. A copy of the site rules and any internal codes of practice must be given to all internal drivers and to external visitors such as delivery drivers preferably before they arrive at the site.

Testing

On completion of training, the operator/driver should be examined and tested to ensure that they have achieved the required standard. It is recommended that at set intervals or when there is indication of the operator/driver not working to required standards, or following an accident, formal check tests be introduced.

Refresher training

If high standards are to be maintained, periodic refresher training and testing should be considered. A vigorous management policy covering operator training, plant maintenance and sound systems of work, supported by good supervision will reduce personal injury and damage to equipment and materials. This in turn will lead to better vehicle utilisation and increased materials handling efficiency.

Operator/driver identification

Many organisations operate local codes of practice and take great care to confirm the authority they have given to operators/drivers by the provision of a licence for that vehicle and sometimes a visible badge to confirm this. Access to vehicles should be supervised and authority checked carefully to confirm that the actual class of vehicle is within the authority given. This is important with such things as rough terrain lift trucks that operate differently to a standard counterbalance truck. Where applicable, it is important to be able to confirm that the operator/driver has a suitable licence that allows them to take the plant/vehicle on the public highway.

It is essential that access to keys for vehicles is restricted to those that are competent to operate/drive them; this is not just a practical point but enables compliance with PUWER 1998.

3.2 - Driving at work

Extent of work-related road injuries

The true cost of accidents to any organisation is nearly always higher than just the costs of repairs and insurance claims. This can include personal costs such as ill-health, time in hospital, stress on family members and possible penalty points being imposed on the driver's licences following an incident. There is also the potential for the driver to lose their licence.

Therefore the benefits of managing driving activities through the introduction of policies, risk assessments and developing safe systems for work related driving is essential. This will ensure compliance with the Health and Safety at Work etc. Act (HASAWA) 1974 and the Management of Health and Safety at Work Regulations (MHSWR) 1999.

The Health and Safety Executive (HSE) provide guidance to assist management in managing driving risk, in the form of the document INDG382 "Health and Safety Driving at work - Managing work-related road safety". The HSE estimates that up to a third of all road traffic accidents involved somebody who was at work at the time. This may account for over 20 fatalities and 250 serious injuries per week.

Millions of vehicles - lorries, vans, taxis, buses, emergency service vehicles, company cars, motorcycles - are used for work purposes, and their drivers are 49% more likely to be involved in a road traffic collision. Indeed, very few organisations operate without using motor vehicles. About 30% of all miles driven on Britain's roads are by at-work vehicles.

In a recent survey, 75% of male employees and 49% of female employees in the manufacturing industry reported that they were required to use a vehicle (usually their own) in the course of their work (excluding commuting). Many people work on or by the road and are exposed to risks from traffic, including maintenance and construction workers.

Figure 3-23: Company driver road usage.   *Source: ORSA.*

"It has been estimated that between 800 and 1,000 road deaths a year are in some way work-related. Many bosses have ignored this problem in the past, but the Health and Safety Executive has now made it clear that employers have duties under health and safety law to manage the risks faced by their workers on the road".

Figure 3-24: Size of the road risk problem.   *Source: RoSPA.*

For the majority of people, the most dangerous thing they do while at work is drive on the public highway.

Figure 3-25: Road risk.   *Source: HSE 1996.*

Factors that increase risks of a road traffic incident

DISTANCE

Road conditions have improved over the years, which have allowed greater travel distances in shorter periods of time. However the fatigue encountered by drivers often increases due to other drivers' poor performance.

This can be associated with poor or inappropriate training or monitoring of the driver's competence. Large goods vehicle (LGV) drivers' travel distances are regulated by limitations on driving hours. However, there are no similar limits on drivers of smaller vehicles and private cars. When assessing risk of any kind, an important consideration is the frequency and duration of exposure to hazards. It is logical then that the greater the distance of the journey (i.e. the duration of exposure to the hazard) the greater the risk. It is possible that scheduling of routes may extend or reduce the distance that has to be travelled and therefore affect the level of risk significantly.

DRIVING HOURS

If driving hours related to construction activities are excessive the driver is likely to be come fatigued and their attention and reaction levels will fall, and this can lead to increased risk of making errors. The driving hours may be excessive because the driver has been driving too long without a break, their cumulative hours in a day have become too much or their rest period between work days has become too little.

Systems of work and appropriate training should be given to all drivers concerning the hazards and associated risks with excessive hours. It is important that cumulative hours are monitored and controlled and that breaks are taken at intervals on longer journeys.

The Highway Code recommends that drivers should take a 15 minute break every two hours. The responsibility for monitoring hours and taking breaks is a shared responsibility of both the driver and the employer. Driving hours of goods vehicles over 3.5 tonnes and some passenger vehicles are regulated by European Community rules. These set limits on driver's hours:

- Daily driving limit: 9 hours.
- Maximum driving limit: 4 ½ hours.
- Daily rest period: 11 hours.
- Weekly driving limit: 56 hours.
- Fortnightly driving limit: 90 hours.
- Weekly rest period: 45 consecutive hours.

WORK SCHEDULES

Work schedules that are badly organised can put increased pressure on drivers to be in a place by a given time. This can lead to them being tempted to increase speed and take abrupt action to change lanes to improve their progress. This risky action can lead to higher risk of collision and reduced stopping distances.

Work schedules should take account of periods when drivers are most likely to feel sleepy. The high risk times are 2am to 6am and 2pm to 4pm. Employers should provide drivers with the means to stop and take a break if they feel sleepy, without the fear of recrimination. Where possible, schedules should be organised so that breaks can naturally and easily be taken, with agreed break points if travel is going as planned or if not. Driving to and from the place of employment does not form part of the working day, but may be an accident causation factor if travelling home follows a long working day.

STRESS DUE TO TRAFFIC

Nearly one in three UK drivers report feeling stressed whilst behind the wheel. Driving-related stress is likely to be experienced when the demands of the road/traffic environment exceed the driver's ability to cope with or control that environment. Sometimes driving stress can show itself as a 'road rage'. That is an irrational human mechanism that is activated to protect the sufferer from what they perceive to be actual or potential danger. A person may often resort to irrational behaviour in order to avoid certain situations or events. Others may perceive the circumstances which aggravate the 'road rage' as being either insignificant or trivial, but to the individual concerned they are 'very real' and 'very relevant'.

WEATHER CONDITIONS

Weather conditions have a significant impact on the risks of driving. Sudden rainfall or snow and fog can lead to poor visibility and sudden breaking. Snow and surface water conditions can increase stopping distances. Even good weather can have a negative effect as glare from the sun can limit visibility. This is particularly the case in early morning or evening and is most significant during the winter when the sun is lower in the sky for longer.

Managing work-related road safety

POLICY

A road safety policy should be incorporated into the health and safety policy. Whether employers provide vehicles or expect employees to drive their own for work purposes, all employers should have a policy to address the issues.

As part of any driving at work policy, employers should include:

- A requirement that the employee must maintain their vehicle in a roadworthy condition if they are to use their own vehicle for work.
- A requirement that if the vehicle is over three years old, it has a valid MOT certificate.

- A requirement that the employee has a current driving licence.
- A requirement that the employee has appropriate insurance (the employee should present copies of certificates annually for inspection).
- A requirement that the employee informs their line manager of any changes in circumstances such as penalty points, changes in insurer or vehicle used or use of any prescription medication or changes to health that affect their ability to drive safely.
- Assessment of risks.
- The management strategy to plan, organise, control, monitor and review work-related road risk.
- Driver training and competence.
- Taking breaks.
- Breakdown of the vehicle.
- Reporting problems and delays.
- Weather conditions.

SYSTEMS TO MANAGE WORK-RELATED ROAD SAFETY

Competent staff should be trained to manage and implement the work-related road safety policy. These should be developed using the guidance provided by professional organisations that have many years of experience and expertise around this subject, for example, the Automobile Association (AA), the Occupational Road Safety Alliance (ORSA) the RAC or ROSPA.

Many employers carry out internal assessments of driving skills in addition to the minimum legal requirements. This can be done in-house or carried out by an external assessor. If drivers are being asked to drive minibuses, etc. then employers can require additional qualifications, as proof of abilities. Some employers offer specific training in safe driving techniques for their employees.

It is important that systems are put in place to ensure that driving distances are kept to a minimum, driving hours are controlled and work schedules are organised to reduce pressure on drivers to meet challenging times and in turn reduce undue road risk. Organisations should have systems in place to respond to inclement weather and enable drivers to take safe decisions about the effects of weather on their driving or journey.

MONITORING PERFORMANCE

It is a legal requirement to monitor health and safety systems to demonstrate compliance. Information which should be considered for effective monitoring includes:

- Legal responsibilities.
- Organisation and structure.
- Competence of drivers.
- Driving hours.
- Reporting of work-related road safety incidents.

Certain road traffic incidents are reportable under the Reporting of Injuries, Diseases and Dangerous Occurrences Regulations (RIDDOR) 2013. Employers should also monitor minor incidents to vehicles and premises.

ORGANISATION AND STRUCTURE

In a large organisation it is likely that various departments within the organisation will have different responsibilities for drivers at work. The despatch department will be responsible for planning journeys; the training department is responsible for driver competence; the human resources department could be responsible for driver selection and checking the validity of driving licences.

The maintenance department is responsible for the upkeep of vehicles and ensuring the roadworthiness of vehicles and the occupational health department is responsible for carrying routine health surveillance of large goods vehicle (LGV) drivers.

It is therefore essential that the structure of the organisation allows for the free and simple interchange of information regarding legal standards and any changes in legislation and/or good practice. Responsibilities of different parts of the organisation should be defined, including the responsibility to co-operate with each other.

LEGAL RESPONSIBILITIES OF INDIVIDUALS ON PUBLIC ROADS

Vehicle condition

Drivers must:

- Ensure the vehicle and any trailers comply with the full requirements of the Road Vehicles (Construction and Use) Regulations (RVCUR) 1986 and Road Vehicles Lighting Regulations (RVLR) 1989.

Fitness to drive

Drivers must:

- Report to the Driver and Vehicle Licensing Agency (DVLA) any health condition likely to affect their driving.
- Not begin a journey if tired.

Vision

Drivers must:

- Be able to read (with the aid of vision corrected lenses) a vehicle number plate, in good daylight, from a distance of 20 metres (or 20.5 metres where the old style number plate is used).
- Slow down, and if necessary stop, if dazzled by bright sunlight.
- At night or in poor visibility, not use tinted glasses, lenses or visors if they restrict vision.

Alcohol and drugs

Drivers must:

- Not drink and drive in excess of the legal limit for alcohol.
- Not drive under the influence of drugs or medicine.

General

Drivers must:

- Ensure they use all due care and attention for others when in charge of a vehicle.
- Not tow more than their licence permits. Those who passed a car test after 1 January 1997 are restricted on the weight of trailer they can tow.
- Not overload the vehicle or trailer.
- Secure the load and ensure it does not protrude out dangerously.
- Ensure they and other passengers wear a seat belt or suitable restraining device for babies or small children in cars, vans and other goods vehicles if one is fitted (exemptions are allowed for the holders of medical exemption certificates and those making deliveries or collections in goods vehicles when travelling less than 50 metres (approx 162 feet)).

For detailed information refer to the Road Traffic Act (RTA) 1991 and the 'new' Highway Code and related legislation refer to www.direct.gov.uk.

Risk assessments

RISK ASSESSMENT PROCESS APPLIED TO DRIVING

All work-related driving activity should follow the same principles as risk assessments for any other work activity. They should be carried out by a competent person with practical knowledge, qualifications and training relating to the work activity being assessed.

Step 1 - Identify the hazards

Hazards will fall into the following categories:

The Driver   Competence, training, qualifications, fitness and health, alcohol and drug use, etc.

The Vehicle   Suitability, condition, safety equipment, ergonomic considerations, the load, security, etc.

The Journey   Route planning, scheduling, time, distance, driving hours, weather conditions, stress, volume of traffic, weather conditions, passengers, etc.

Step 2 - Decide who might be harmed

Obviously the driver, but this might also include any passengers, other road users and/or pedestrians. Consideration should also be given to other groups who may be particularly at risk, such as young or newly qualified drivers and those driving long distances.

Step 3 - Evaluate the risk and decide on precautions

Risks may vary depending on whether driving is done at night or in the day, the type of vehicle or driving conditions. Decide the likelihood of the harm and severity (consequence) of any outcome. Consider risk factors such as distance travelled, driving hours, work schedules, traffic levels and weather conditions. Decide on appropriate precautions and once this has been established, decide whether the residual risk is acceptable.

Step 4 - Record the findings and implement them

Significant findings need to be recorded and risk assessments findings should be made available to all drivers.

Step 5 - Review the assessment and update it if necessary

Monitoring and reviewing the assessments to ensure these risks are suitability controlled. Systems should be put into place to gather, monitor, record and analyse about incidents which might effect these risk assessments. The vehicle and driver's history should also be recorded. Any changes in the route, new equipment and changes in the vehicle specifications should be reviewed and recorded. This will ensure the effectiveness of controlling the risks.

THE DRIVER

The level of risk is particularly affected by the driver's *competency*. If someone is new to driving their skill may be adequate to provide them with a national driving licence but their experience of driving will be low.

Drivers that only drive intermittently also present a high risk as any competence they may have may decay over the time between driving. The driver's competence has to be appropriate to the driving being expected of them; an inexperienced driver driving in heavy traffic in complicated driving settings at night in the winter will present a particularly high risk. Similarly a person that is reasonably experienced in driving their small car may have difficulty when first driving a larger or faster accelerating vehicle. Some drivers will need to adjust to driving slower vehicles and ones with a different centre of gravity.

Driver *fitness* may influence their ability to see well when driving at night, their ability to travel distances without breaks and may put them in a high risk category for heart attack or other type of seizure. Pre-existing *health* conditions such as back injuries and late term pregnancy could influence the driver's ability to concentrate on road conditions. The level of training that the driver has received may affect risk in that if no training is given a driver may have developed bad driving habits and not be aware of them. Refresher driver training may help to reduce risk.

THE VEHICLE

The size, weight, centre of gravity and power of a vehicle will all influence the functioning of the vehicle and therefore the risk that may arise from its use. It is important that the vehicle is *suitable* for the task and the driver. A large, powerful, fast acceleration car may be suitable for a specific task but very unsuitable for an inexperienced driver. The *condition* of the vehicle will have a significant effect on the level of risk. Vehicles that have poor brakes, lights, do not steer well and have poor suspension will represent a high risk in any driving situation. Vehicles with broken or missing mirrors will mean that the driver will not be able to see other road users adequately and will increase the risk when changing lanes.

Much of the *safety equipment* to prevent accidents, such as active braking systems (ABS) should be built into most modern vehicles. Other items may be optional, such as run-flat tyres: these may reduce certain road risks. Other safety equipment is designed to reduce the consequences of accidents and can therefore reduce risk, such as airbags, escape kits, warning triangles and high-visibility vests. The absence of safety critical information, like the height of the vehicle, can have an immediate and significant effect on the level of risk.

Consideration has to be made of the *safety critical information* related to the vehicle, including its height, width, length, weight and load carrying/towing capacity.

Ergonomic considerations have an effect on both comfort and ability to control the vehicle effectively. The comfort issues can increase fatigue, and ergonomic considerations like seat height adjustment can significantly affect the ability of the driver to see out of the vehicle properly.

THE JOURNEY

When evaluating the risk related to journeys it is important to take into account such factors as:

- The *route* being taken - motorways are safer than smaller roads; routes using motorways will be lower in risk.
- *Scheduling* - if the journey is to be made early in the morning there might be an increased level of risk due to tiredness but this may be offset by the reduced level of traffic.
- *Time* allowed for travel - if not enough time is allowed for the journey and normal delays the risk will be higher.
- *Weather conditions* - can rapidly increase risks, conditions such as ice and snow will have a significant effect.

Control measures to reduce work-related driving risks

THE DRIVER

It is the employer's duty to ensure that drivers are competent, fit and in good health and capable of doing their work in a way that is safe for them. Employers must insist that all drivers produce evidence that they have a current licence to drive their vehicle. Without a current licence and/or test certificate the driver's insurance will be invalid. Regular assessments of driver competence and monitoring the validity of documentation such as insurance and driving licence should be carried out. Large goods vehicle (LGV) drivers and passenger carrying vehicle (PCV) drivers have to maintain a certificate of professional competence by undertaking 35 hours of training every 5 years.

Measures should be put into place to ensure that all drivers' hours of work are controlled in order to avoid excessive working hours. In addition, it will be important to ensure that the duration of time driving is controlled to avoid fatigue. This may involve work rotation or planned breaks. Breaks and rotation should take account of additional fatigue factors like the circumstances the person is driving in or the terrain exposed to; bad weather or rough terrains will increase fatigue and the need for breaks.

THE VEHICLE

It is the employer's responsibility to ensure that the vehicle fits the purpose for which it is used. It is important that the vehicle is safe and in a fit condition and suitable for the task to be carried out this will include any safety equipment that is required being properly fitted and maintained. Any safety critical information should be displayed within the cab, for example, height or width of the vehicle.

Ergonomics, such as the driver's seat should also be considered; it may require additional support, for example, lumbar cushions. Full body vibration should be considered and air-suspension seats may be required as a precaution.

Ensure safety equipment is used, for example:

■ Seat belts, air bags are installed, maintained and used correctly.
■ Two-wheeled vehicle users should have appropriate safety helmets and protective clothing.
■ Ensure vehicles do not exceed speed limits by fitting trackers to monitor the speed limits.

THE JOURNEY

Journey planning and scheduling is essential in ensuring the safety of employees who drive for work. Investing time in ensuring that journey planning is implemented as a component of the policy, will ensure that where possible, routes are planned thoroughly, schedules are realistic, and sufficient time is allocated to complete journeys safely. It may be required to plan overnight stopovers (provide hotel accommodation) if the journey time extends due to bad weather or traffic conditions. Delivery schedules should be adjusted so that unrealistic targets are not set. This will reduce the stress to drivers and will not encourage them to drive too fast for the conditions, or exceed speed limits. Take into account total driving time, both off site and on site, when assessing the maximum hours which should be worked and the frequency of breaks which will be required.

INCIDENT REPORTING

Drivers must be required to record information about all incidents, whether minor or serious, for all journeys. A similar reporting procedure should be in place for reporting significant "near misses" with emphasis in training on how to recognise, analyse and learn from such events. The data provided should be analysed and any changes or improvements noted. These should be agreed, fed back to those concerned and the policy procedures updated.

Sample assessment questions

1. Approximately one quarter of all accidents on construction sites are associated with plant, machinery and vehicles.

   Outline possible control measures which may prevent such accidents. (8)

2. A dumper truck overturned whilst being driven across a construction site.

   (a) **Identify FOUR** reasons why the dumper truck may have overturned. (4)

   (b) **Outline** practical measures that could be taken to minimise the risk of a dumper truck overturn. (4)

3. **Outline** features of pedestrian routes on a construction site that will help to minimise the risk of accidents to workers. (8)

Please refer to back of assessment section for answers.

This page is intentionally blank

© RMS

This page is intentionally blank

Musculoskeletal hazards and risk control

Learning outcomes

On completion of this element, candidates should be able to demonstrate understanding of the content through the application of knowledge to familiar and unfamiliar situations. In particular they should be able to:

4.1 Explain work processes and practices that may contribute to musculoskeletal disorders, work-related upper limb disorders and the appropriate control measures.

4.2 Explain the hazards and control measures which should be considered when assessing risks from manual handling activities.

4.3 Explain the hazards and control measures to reduce the risk in the use of lifting and moving equipment with specific reference to manual and mechanically operated load moving equipment.

Content

Sources of reference

Getting to grips with manual handling (INDG143 rev2)

Manual Handling Operations Regulations 1992 (as amended), Guidance on Regulations, L23, third edition 2004, HSE Books, ISBN 978-0-7176-2823-0

Rider-operated lift trucks. Operator training and safe use, ACOP and Guidance, L117, HSE Books, ISBN 978-0-7176-6441-2

Safety in working with lift trucks, HSG6, third edition 2000, HSE Books, ISBN 978-0-7176-1781-4

Safe use of lifting equipment, Lifting Operations and Lifting Equipment Regulations Regulations 1998, ACoP and Guidance, L113, HSE Books, ISBN 978-0-7176-1628-2

Safe use of work equipment, Provision and Use of Work Equipment Regulations, ACOP and Guidance, L22, third edition 2008, HSE Books, ISBN 978-0-7176-6295-1

The law on VDUs – An Easy Guide, HSG90, second edition 2003, HSE Books, ISBN 978-0-7176-2602-1

Understanding ergonomics at work, INDG90(rev2), HSE Books

Work Related Upper Limb Disorders – A Guide, HSG60, second edition 2002, HSE Books, ISBN 978-0-7176-1978-8

Work with display screen equipment: Health and Safety (Display Screen Equipment) Regulations 1992 as amended by the Health and Safety (Miscellaneous Amendments) Regulations 2002, (L26) Guidance on Regulations HSE Books ISBN: 978-0-7176-2582-6

Relevant statutory provisions

Health and Safety (Display Screen Equipment) Regulations (DSE) 1992 (as amended)

Lifting Operations and Lifting Equipment Regulations (LOLER) 1998

Manual Handling Operations Regulations (MHOR) 1992

Provision and Use of Work Equipment Regulations (PUWER) 1998

4.1 - Musculoskeletal and work-related upper limb disorders

Meaning of musculoskeletal and work related upper limb disorders

Work-related musculoskeletal disorders (MSD's) are disorders of parts of the body such as muscles, joints, tendons, ligaments, nerves, bones and the localised blood circulation system, that are caused by work and working conditions. Most work-related MSDs are cumulative disorders, resulting from repeated exposure to high or low intensity loads over a long period of time. These disorders mainly affect the back, neck, shoulders and upper limbs, but can also affect the lower limbs. Some MSDs, such as carpal tunnel syndrome in the wrist, are specific because of their well-defined signs and symptoms. Others are non-specific because only pain or discomfort exists without evidence of a clear specific disorder.

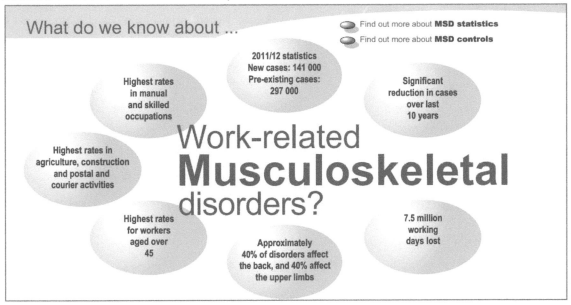

Figure 4-1: Work related musculoskeletal disorder statistics. *Source: HSE.*

Work-related upper limb disorders (WRULD's) are that group of MSDs that affect any part of the arm from the fingers to shoulders, or the neck. They can affect soft tissues, muscles, tendons, ligaments as well as the circulatory and nerve systems. Symptoms include aches, pains, tenderness, tingling, numbness, weakness, swelling, stiffness and cramp. Recognised WRULD conditions include carpel tunnel syndrome and tenosynovitis. Carpal tunnel syndrome is the painful inflammation of the nerves and tendons passing through the carpal bone in the wrist area and affects the whole hand. Tenosynovitis is inflammation of the synovial lining of the tendon sheath.

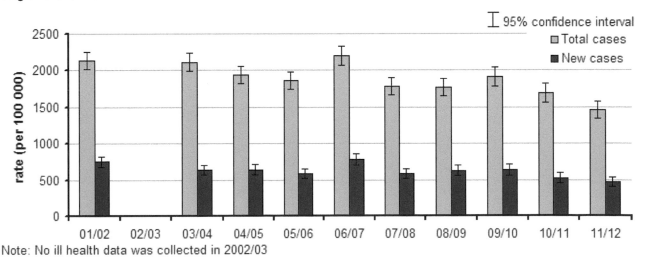

Figure 4-2: Total cases (prevalence) and new cases (incidence) of MSDs. *Source: HSE.*

Musculoskeletal disorders have consistently been the most commonly reported type of work-related illness in the Self-reported Work-related Illness (SWI) questionnaire module included annually in the National Labour Force Survey (LFS). Results of the 2011/12 survey indicate that an estimated prevalence of 439,000 (508,000 in 2010/11) people in Great Britain, who worked in the last year, suffered from a musculoskeletal disorder caused or made worse by their current or past work. Of these, an estimated 51,000 suffered from a disorder mainly affecting their back, 60,000 from a disorder mainly affecting their upper limbs or neck, and 29,000 mainly affecting their lower limbs.

About one third, 141,000 (158,000 in 2010/11) of the estimated prevalence of work-related musculoskeletal disorders were new (incidence) cases.

Examples of repetitive construction activities

Anyone who over-uses their back, arms and hands repeatedly may develop a musculoskeletal disorder. Keyboard operators, workers on factory assembly lines, musicians, dressmakers, bricklaying, check out operators and cleaners are examples of workers at particular risk. Those that are involved in repetitive construction activities are particularly at risk of experiencing MSDs and WRULDs. There are a great deal of construction activities that involve repetitive actions, some of these are considered in the following outlines of how the risk presents itself.

DIGGING

Hand digging becomes progressively more difficult and potentially more injurious the deeper below foot level the work is carried out. This is particularly the case if the spoil being removed has to be lifted above waist height for disposal. The use of narrow trenching techniques that can restrict posture significantly will also increase risk of musculoskeletal injuries, fatigue and strain on the limbs.

KERB LAYING

Traditionally, kerbs (in one form or another) have been specified on the majority of roads. The standard components used are principally pre-cast concrete and weigh approximately 67 kg. Feature kerbs, stone kerbs or other associated products may be considerably heavier. More recently a number of manufacturers have developed lighter kerbs.

The main hazards associated with the manual handling of kerbs are the weight of the kerb, the repetitive nature of the work and poor posture during the work. These hazards create excessive stress and strain on the body, which can cause damage to muscles and tendons, and in the longer term may lead progressively to more serious musculoskeletal injury.

MOVEMENT AND FIXING OF PLASTERBOARD

Plasterboard is widely used in construction to line internal walls and ceilings. Workers often have to handle the sheets manually and may need to do so in a restricted space, for example, a stairwell. The sheets, which are typically 2.5 metres x 1.25 metres and weigh 32.5kg, are difficult to grip and unwieldy.

The work is physically demanding and the main hazards involve extended reach, and posture flexibility to enable work in a variety of awkward postures, including on raised platforms.

PLACEMENT AND FINISHING OF CONCRETE SLABS

The placement and finishing of concrete slabs will often involve heavy repetitive work and poor posture due to having to work at the level of the worker's feet. The placement and levelling of concrete labs, may involve lifting and repositioning of each slab more than once, putting stain on the fingers, hands and lower back.

BRICKLAYING

Bricklayers are often self-employed and therefore cannot afford to lose time from work. They will carry on working and ignore the warning signs, such as aches and fatigue, which are often a precursor to more serious musculoskeletal injuries. The size of the bricks being laid, the number of bricks they are expected to lay (often several hundred per day) and the relative position of a wall or structure are significant risk factors.

ERECTING/DISMANTLING SCAFFOLDS

The erecting and dismantling of scaffold, by the nature of the work, will involve lifting and placing of materials progressively higher (when erecting) or lower (dismantling). The work involves the need to maintain balance whilst carrying or placing materials, often involving long reaching to position and secure components. The risk of overreach related injuries to the hands, arms and spine is high when working with materials of extended length that are held at one end, such as scaffold boards and poles.

USE OF DISPLAY SCREEN EQUIPMENT

Traditional drafting of drawings and plans has now been replaced by computer aided design programmes (CAD). CAD systems enable architects to modify and amend drawings as often as is necessary. The designs can be manipulated from any number of elevations and many systems allow the construction of three dimensional models (3D). The designs can be sent electronically to the client for approval, speedily enabling early completion of the work.

Display screen equipment (DSE) users working in design and other similar roles may make many thousands of movements an hour, which will create repeated movement of the fingers. Where the DSE user is not fully proficient in using all fingers to operate the keyboard, many of the movements are centred on a small number of fingers. Where the use of the display screen equipment requires the use of a mouse this can also accentuate the use of a small number of fingers centred on the user's dominant hand. Because of the amount of repeated movements, sometimes without taking breaks, the risks of WRULD are high and the effects are cumulative.

The ill-health effects of poorly designed tasks and workstations

There are a number of types of injury and ill-health conditions that result from poorly designed tasks and workstations, particularly where they involve repetitive physical activities, manual handling or poor posture.

The human body will be affected to a varying degree by tasks that involve bending, reaching, twisting, repetitive movements and poor posture. This could result in a range of musculoskeletal problems, such as pain in parts of the spine, joint injuries, muscle strain and pain.

ILL-HEALTH EFFECTS OF POOR POSTURE

Some construction related work activities may cause a worker to develop poor posture, such as movement and fixing of plasterboard or placement and finishing concrete slabs or operating display screen equipment that has a poor layout. Some general musculoskeletal risks can also cause muscle tension and fatigue that, ultimately, lead to poor posture. The effects of working with a poor posture include:

- Rounded shoulders.
- Potbelly.
- Bent knees when standing or walking.
- Head that either leans forward or backward.

- Back pain.
- Body aches and pains.
- Muscle fatigue.
- Headache.

BACK PAIN

Back pain usually affects the lower back. It can be a short-term problem, lasting a few days or weeks, or continue for many months or even years. Eight out of ten adults will have some form of back pain at some stage in their life.

In many cases there is not a specific, underlying problem or condition that can be identified as the cause of the pain.

However, there are a number of factors that can increase the risk of developing back pain, or aggravate it once it starts. These include:

- Standing, sitting or bending down for long periods.
- Lifting, carrying, pushing or pulling loads that are too heavy, or going about these tasks in the wrong way.
- Operating equipment that subjects the person to whole body vibration.
- Having a trip or a fall.
- Being stressed or anxious.
- Being overweight.
- Having poor posture.

One of the causes of lower back pain is the strain of back muscles or other soft tissue (ligaments or tendons) connected to the vertebrae. Sometimes it is the intervertebral disc that is strained.

Lumbar spine illustration

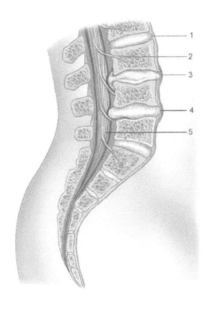

1. Healthy disc
2. Nerve
3. Slipped disc
4. Damaged disc
5. Spinal cord

Figure 4-3: Lumber and slipped disc. *Source: NHS.*

The discs are made from a tough, fibrous case, which contains a softer, gel-like core. The strain on the disc can cause it to bulge and protrude out between the vertebrae (called slipped, prolapsed or herniated) and press on nearby nerves or spinal cord.

This can cause pain and inflammation in the area of the spinal cord contacted. Pain may also be felt in the area of the body that the part of the spinal cord affected relates to, as in sciatica. If the sciatic nerve is contacted by the damaged disc pain will be felt in the leg, which is the part of the body that the sciatic nerve controls; this is called a referred pain.

The damage to the disc is usually caused by too much pressure being applied to it during lifting and handling operations that involve 'top-heavy' bending. This is where the knees are not bent sufficiently and the head and upper body are bent over, causing the spine to bend in a curved manner (sometimes called stooping).

This bending creates a high degree of leverage force on the base of the spine, which leads to the extreme pressure exerted on the disc. The force and therefore pressure on the disc is accentuated by the carrying of heavy loads. Though top-heavy bending is a particular cause of this damage, poor posture due to leaning over for a sustained period could lead to similar damage.

SPRAINS/STRAINS, FRACTURES AND LACERATIONS

Around 25% of all injuries reported to the appropriate enforcing authority have been attributed to the manual lifting and handling of loads. The most common injuries are sprains, strains, fractures and lacerations.

Sprains and strains

Sprains and strains often occur in the back or in the arm and wrists. Though injuries in the legs can also occur where the leg has been hyperflexed and where the soft tissues (ligament, tendons and muscles) are overstretched, through kneeling or handling loads beyond the worker's limit.

- A *sprain* is an injury to a ligament, the tough fibrous tissue that connects a bone to another bone. Ligament injuries involve a stretching or a tearing of this tissue.
- A *strain* is an injury to either a muscle or a tendon, the tissue that connects muscles to bones. Depending on the severity of the injury, a strain may be a simple overstretch of the muscle or tendon or it can result in a partial or complete tear. Rupture of the muscles in a section of the abdominal wall can cause a hernia.

These types of injuries tend to occur where a person's body has been over loaded due to a large steady load being applied, a sudden smaller load being applied without the opportunity of the ligament or tendon to stretch or a part of the body being forced to move in an unusual way. This can be because a person is reaching over to an extreme level (sometimes without picking up a load as their own body weight may be sufficient to cause damage), two people picking up a load together in an unco-ordinated way or a load may slip and someone move into an awkward position to prevent it falling completely.

Fractures and lacerations

A fracture is a break in a bone, which is usually the result of trauma where the physical force exerted on the bone is stronger than the bone itself. Fractures of the hands and feet are the most likely type of fractures to arise from manual handling work and may be due to the load that is being lifted inadvertently being dropped.

Lacerations are often caused by the unprotected handling of loads with sharp corners or edges, or slippage of grip when trying to prevent a dropped load.

WORK RELATED UPPER LIMB DISORDERS

Work related upper limb disorders (WRULD) were first defined in medical literature as long ago as the 19th century as a condition caused by forceful, frequent, twisting and repetitive movements. The body will be affected to a varying degree by tasks which involve bending, reaching, twisting, repetitive movements and poor posture. WRULD covers well-known conditions such as tennis elbow, flexor tenosynovitis and carpal tunnel syndrome. It is usually caused by repetitive tasks and movements and aggravated by excessive workloads, inadequate rest periods and sustained or constrained postures.

This can result in pain, soreness or inflammatory conditions of muscles and the synovial lining of the tendon sheath. Present approaches to treatment are largely effective, provided the condition is treated in its early stages. Clinical signs and symptoms are local aching, pain, tenderness, swelling, crepitus (a grating sensation in the joint). Some common WRULDs are:

Carpal Tunnel Syndrome (CTS)	CTS occurs when tendons or ligaments in the wrist become enlarged, often from inflammation, after being aggravated. The narrowed tunnel of bones and ligaments in the wrist pinches the nerves that reach the fingers and the muscles at the base of the thumb. The first symptoms usually appear at night. Symptoms range from a burning, tingling numbness in the fingers, especially the thumb and the index and middle fingers, to difficulty gripping or making a fist, to dropping things.
Tenosynovitis	An irritation of the tendon sheath. It occurs when the repetitive activity becomes excessive and the tendon sheath can no longer lubricate the tendon. As a result, the tendon sheath thickens and becomes aggravated.
Tendinitis	Tendinitis involves inflammation of a tendon, the fibrous cord that attaches muscle to bone. It usually affects only one part of the body at a time, and usually lasts a short time, unless involved tissues are continuously irritated. It can result from an injury, activity or exercise that repeats the same movement.
Peritendinitis	Inflammation of the area where the tendon joins the muscle.
Epicondylitis	Tennis Elbow or Lateral Epicondylitis is a condition when the outer part of the elbow becomes painful and tender, usually because of a specific strain, overuse, or a direct bang. Sometimes no specific cause is found. Tennis Elbow is similar to Golfer's Elbow (Medial Epicondolytis) which affects the other side of the elbow.

The aches, pains and fatigue suffered doing certain tasks will eventually impair the operator's ability and lead to degradation in performance. It is therefore essential to consider the task in order to match it to the individual so the level of general comfort is maximised. For example, when carrying out manual handling assessments it is important to look at the relationship between the individual, the task, the load and the environment.

Factors giving rise to ill-health conditions

TASKS

Tasks should be assessed to determine the musculoskeletal health risk factors that arise from them.

If the task is *repetitive* in nature, i.e. the same series of operations are repeated in a short period of time, such as ten or more times per minute, then injury may occur to the muscles and ligaments affected. Similarly, work of a *strenuous* nature, such as moving heavy or difficult shaped objects, perhaps in limited space or hot environments, will cause fatigue, strains and sprains.

Whether the worker is able to take appropriate breaks from the task is an important factor. If this is not possible due to technical factors driving completion of an activity, for example, when dealing with continuous pouring of concrete, then this can be a significant factor influencing musculoskeletal ill-health conditions unless the work is designed to provide facilities for work rotation to reduce these effects.

ENVIRONMENT

Poor working environments. Working in *extremes of temperature* or handling hot or cold items will make simple work more strenuous. Long hours of work in cold conditions causes problems with blood circulation which, in turn, may increase the likelihood of hand arm vibration syndrome. Fatigue will also occur to the eyes if the *lighting* levels are low, typically below 100-200 lux or bright, typically greater than 800 lux. *Glare* can be a significant factor, causing discomfort to the eyes and leading to a person taking up awkward postures to avoid the glare. Other lighting factors may need to be considered such as the stroboscopic effects associated with moving machinery, which may appear to be stationary when viewed under fluorescent light powered by alternating current.

The risk of injury increases with the *length of time* that a task is carried out. However, injury may occur over a short period if the work requires a lot of effort.

Working in *uncomfortable positions* such as working above head height or holding something in the same place for a long period of time increases the risk of injury. These factors will often be reduced if the worker is able to adjust the conditions to their personal needs.

Poor posture. The position of the body and the way it has to move to carry out a particular function. This can be affected by such things as:

- Badly designed work methods (for example, the need for regular bending or twisting and the need to hold a position for a long period while material is being fixed in position).
- Poor layout of the workplace (for example, having to kneel or stretch to put articles in position).

Figure 4-4: Poor posture.   *Source: Speedy Hire Plc.*

EQUIPMENT

Equipment design should take into account the ergonomic *requirements of the user* and, where possible, allow the user to *adjust* any settings to suit their needs. Such things as workbench height and positioning of switches and buttons should be in the operator's easy control. The weight of the equipment should be considered, because excessive weight may put strain on the upper body when it is in use. Equipment should be kept in good working condition so that it is effective with the minimum of effort of the operator, thus reducing the need for extra grip and force.

Appropriate control measures

A number of changes may need to be made and ergonomic solutions should be given first consideration. This means making the workplace and the work fit the person, rather than making the person adapt to fit the workplace and work. The study of ergonomics is essential to good job design. It is the applied science of equipment design intended to maximise effectiveness by reducing worker fatigue and discomfort. It can be defined as "the study of the relationship between human beings, the equipment with which they work and the physical environment in which this human-machine system operates".

It is a broad area of study that includes the disciplines of psychology, physiology, anatomy and design engineering. Ergonomics has the human being at the centre of the study where individual capabilities and fallibilities are considered in order to, ultimately, eliminate the potential for human error and harm to effectiveness and efficiency. This includes the minimisation of such things as work-related musculoskeletal disorders that are caused by poorly designed machines, tools, task and workplace.

The aims of ergonomics, therefore, are to design the equipment and the working environment to fit the needs and capabilities of the individual, i.e. fitting the task to the individual, and to ensure that the physical and mental well-being of the individual is being met. This involves the consideration of psychological and physical factors, including the work system, body dimensions, capability, competence and the work environment (layout, noise, temperature and lighting). Individuals, have different physical capabilities due to height, weight, age and levels of fitness. They also have different mental capabilities, memory retention and personalities. All these factors can influence ergonomic choices and the successful matching of the workplace to the individual.

Workstation

- Ensuring that working heights are appropriate for the full range of workers.
- Relocating equipment to provide more space.
- Relocating items that workers have to see clearly within their comfortable range of vision.
- Providing adjustable workstations that allow postures to be varied between standing and sitting.

Temperature

- Avoiding handling or insulating cold items or equipment.
- Directing warm/cool air flow (as appropriate) to the worker to increase thermal comfort.

Hand tools

- Providing tools with ergonomically designed handles.
- Using lighter tools, or providing supports or counterbalances.
- Ensuring tools are regularly maintained.

Vibration

- Using vibration-damped equipment.
- Ensuring tools are regularly maintained.
- Limiting exposure to agreed safe limits.

Use of muscular force

- Reducing the weight of items.
- Using jigs or counterbalances to hold items.
- Using stronger muscle groups to perform the task.
- Using foot pedals as opposed to hand controls.
- Using more effective tools that need less muscular power; for example, tools with engines or other mechanical advantage.

Repetitive movements

- Mechanising or automating repetitive processes.
- Rotation of workers between tasks with high and low exposures.
- Allowing adequate rest pauses.

Postures

- Relocating equipment or items that must be held to within easy reach.
- Ensuring working heights are at or around waist level.
- Ensuring workplaces and equipment are suitable for the full range of workers' sizes and strengths.
- Providing jigs for re-positioning work pieces.
- Ensuring that items that must be viewed clearly are within the normal visual range.

Gloves

- Providing gloves in a wide range of sizes to fit workers' hands.
- Providing gloves made from flexible materials.

Mechanical pressure

- Providing suitable hand tools as effective substitutes for the use of inappropriate parts of the body.
- Ensuring that edges on work pieces and equipment items are rounded to distribute pressure during contact with parts of the body.

Organisation of work

- Improving work flow to avoid production peaks and troughs through better planning and scheduling.
- Encouraging better communication and team work.
- Providing appropriate training.

Figure 4-5: Actions to be taken to control WRULD risks.

Source: European Agency for Safety and Health at Work.

4.2 - Manual handling hazards and control measures

Common types of manual handling injury

Around 25% of all injuries reported to the appropriate enforcing authority have been attributed to the manual lifting and handling of loads. The injuries arise from such *hazards* as stooping while lifting, holding the load away from the body, twisting movements, frequent or prolonged effort, heavy/bulky/unwieldy/unstable loads, sharp/hot/slippery surfaces of loads, space constraints, and lack of capability of the individual.

Manual handling operations can cause many types of *injury*. The most common injuries are:

- Rupture of intervertebral discs ('slipped disc') in the lower spine.
- Muscle strain and sprain.
- Tendons and ligaments can also be over-stretched and torn.
- Rupture of a section of the abdominal wall can cause a hernia.
- Loads with sharp edges can cause cuts.
- Dropped loads can result in bruises, fractures and crushing injuries.

Assessment of manual handling risks

Musculoskeletal injuries are common in the construction industry. The HSE reports that they typically arise from work that involves:

- Awkward working positions (for example, bending or crouching) or restricted space (for example working in a roof void).
- Bending and twisting (for example, plastering).
- High job demands or time pressure, which may mean that workers resort to brute force rather than using a mechanical handling solution.
- Lifting, lowering and carrying heavy materials (for example, roof tiles).
- Pushing and pulling objects and equipment (for example, barrows).

- Repetitive movements (for example, tying rebar).
- Working too long without breaks.

The HSE identify that the kinds of activity that are likely to require a manual handling assessment include:

- Asbestos removal.
- Block laying.
- Ceiling fixing.
- Cladding/sheeting.
- Curtain wall installation.
- Diamond drilling/sawing.
- Dry lining.

- Ductwork installation.
- Ground works.
- Mechanical and electrical work.
- Piling operations.
- Plant operation.
- Plastering.
- Pre-cast concrete installation.

- Roads and paving.
- Scaffolding.
- Structural steel work.
- Tunnelling.
- Window installation.

FACTORS TO CONSIDER

The Manual Handling Operations Regulations (MHOR) 1992 specify that the four factors to which the employer must have regard, and questions he must consider, when making an assessment of manual handling operations are:

- **L** oad.
- **I** ndividual capability.
- **T** ask.
- **E** nvironment.

Each factor in turn should be assessed to determine whether there is a risk of injury. When this has been completed the information can then be processed giving a *suitable and sufficient* risk assessment.

FACTORS	QUESTIONS	Level of Risk:		
		High	Med	Low
Load	Is it: - Heavy? - Bulky or unwieldy? - Difficult to grasp? - Unstable, or with contents likely to shift? - Sharp, hot or otherwise potentially damaging?			
Individual capability	Does the job: - Require unusual strength, height, etc.? - Create a hazard to those who have a health problem? - Require special knowledge or training for its safe performance? - Do clothing and footwear present an increased risk?			
Task	Does it involve: - Holding load at distance from trunk? - Unsatisfactory bodily movement or posture? • Twisting the trunk. • Stooping. - Excessive movement of load? • Excessive lifting or lowering distances. • Excessive pushing or pulling distances. • Risk of sudden movement of load. • Frequent or prolonged physical effort. • Insufficient rest or recovery periods.			
Working environment	Are there: - Space constraints preventing good posture? - Uneven, slippery or unstable floors? - Variations in level of floors or work surfaces? - Extremes of temperature, humidity or air movement? - Poor lighting conditions?			

Figure 4-6: Manual handling risk assessment.   Source: HSE Guidance L23.

The detailed consideration of each factor is necessary to achieve a suitable and sufficient risk assessment. The process of risk assessing includes observing the task as it is actually done; recording the factors that contribute to risk; assessing the level of risk that each factor represents (taking account of the circumstances and controls in place), considering if the risks are different at different times and for different people and determining the adequacy of current controls. The following should be considered when making a risk assessment.

The load

Consideration should be given to:

- The weight, although reducing it may mean increasing the frequency of handling.
- If there is a great variety of weight to be handled and whether loads are sorted into weight categories so that precautions can be applied selectively.
- The size, surface texture or nature of a load as it may make it difficult to grasp. Consideration should be given to whether handles, hand grips, indents etc. are provided to improve the grasp.
- Loads in packages and whether they can shift unexpectedly while being handled.
- Any loads to be handled that have sharp corners, jagged edges, rough surfaces and the like.

Figure 4-7: Manual handling.   *Source: RMS.*

Individual capability

Consideration should be given to:

- The individual's state of health, fitness and strength can significantly affect the ability to perform a task safely.
- An individual's physical capacity can also be age-related, typically climbing until the early 20's and declining gradually from the mid 40's.

It is clear then that an individual's condition and age could significantly affect the ability to perform a task safely.

The task

Consideration should be given to whether:

- Work and components in regular use are stored at waist height. Storage above or below this height should be used for lighter or less frequently used items.
- Layout changes avoid the necessity for frequent bending, twisting, reaching, etc. and the lessening of any travel distances.
- The work routine creates an increased risk i.e. fixed postures dictated by sustained holding or supporting loads, frequency of handling loads, with particular emphasis on heavy and awkward loads.
- Fixed breaks are dictated, they are generally less effective than those taken voluntary within the constraints of the work organisation.
- Handling while seated takes place. Use of the powerful leg muscles is precluded and the weight of the handler's body cannot be used as a counterbalance. For these reasons, the loads that can be handled in safety by a person who is seated are substantially less than can be dealt with while standing.
- Team handling is used for tasks that are beyond the capability of one person. Team handling can create additional problems. The proportion of the load carried by each member of the team will vary; therefore, the load that can be handled in safety will be less than the sum of the loads with which each individual could cope.

The working environment

Consideration should be given to:

- Whether gangways, space and working areas are adequate to allow room to manoeuvre during handling.
- Lack of headroom, which could cause stooping and constrictions and may be caused by such things as a poor workstation or adjacent machinery.
- Poor housekeeping, which can lead to an unstable footing for the person carrying the load and may cause them to stretch their leg out to step over something.
- If manual handling tasks are carried out on more than one level as this can increase risk, this may involve stairs, steps, ladders or ramps.
- Whether workbenches are of a uniform height, thus reducing the need for raising or lowering loads.
- The general working environment. A comfortable working environment (for example, heating, ventilation and lighting) will help to reduce the risk of injury. Risks can be increased if the manual handling work is to be done in windy or cold conditions, such as on the roof of an exposed building.

GUIDELINES FOR ASSESSMENT OF MANUAL HANDLING OPERATIONS

Lifting

The Manual Handling Operations Regulations (MHOR) 1992 set no specific requirements such as weight limits. The following guidelines set out an approximate boundary within which manual handling operations are unlikely to create a risk of injury sufficient to warrant assessment that is more detailed.

This should enable assessment work to be concentrated where it is most needed. The guideline figures are not weight or force limits. They may be exceeded where a more detailed assessment shows it is safe to do so.

However, the guideline figures should not normally be exceeded by more than a factor of about two. The guideline figures for weight and force will give reasonable protection to nearly all men and between one half and two thirds of women.

Carrying

The guideline figures for manual handling operations involving carrying are similar to those given for lifting and lowering. It is assumed that the load is held against the body and is carried no further than about 10 metres without resting.

If the load is carried over a longer distance without resting, the guideline figures may need to be reduced. Where the load can be carried securely on the shoulder without attendant lifting (for example, unloading sacks from a lorry) a more detailed assessment may show that it is safe to exceed the guideline figure.

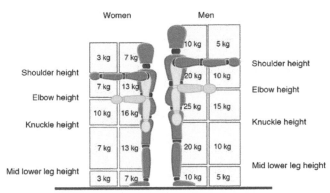

Figure 4-8: Lifting and lowering. *Source: HSE Guidance L23.*

Pushing and pulling

Guideline figures for manual handling operations involving pushing and pulling, whether the load is slid, rolled or supported on wheels, are as follows:

■ The guideline figure for starting or stopping the load is a force of about 250 newtons (i.e. a force of about 25 Kg as measured on a spring balance).

■ The guideline figure for keeping the load in motion is a force of about 100 newtons.

■ No specific limit is intended as to the distances over which the load is pushed or pulled provided there are adequate opportunities for rest or recovery.

Handling while seated

The guideline figure for handling operations carried out while seated is given below and applies only when the hands are within the box zone indicated.

If handling beyond the box zone is unavoidable, a more detailed assessment should be made.

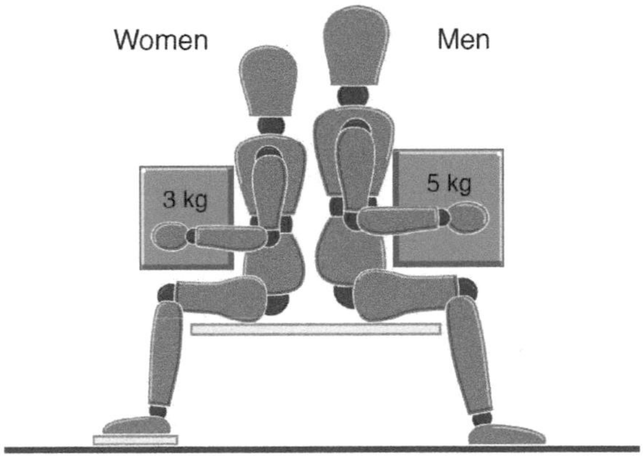

Twisting

The basic guideline figures for lifting and lowering should be reduced if the handler twists to the side during the operation.

As a rough guide, the figures should be reduced by about 10% where the handler twists through 45° and by about 20% where the handler twists through 90°.

Assumptions

The guideline figures should not be regarded as precise recommendations and should be applied with caution, noting particularly that they are based on the following assumptions:

■ The handler is standing or crouching in a stable body position with the back substantially upright.

■ The trunk is not twisted during the operation.

■ Both hands are used to grasp the load.

■ The hands are not more than shoulder width apart.

■ The load is positioned centrally in front of the body and is itself reasonably symmetrical.

■ The load is stable and readily grasped.

■ The work area does not restrict the handler's posture.

■ The working environment (heat, cold, wet, condition of floor) and any personal protective equipment used do not interfere with performance of the task.

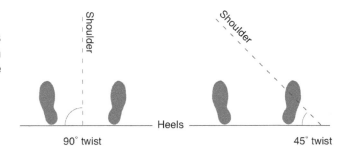

Figure 4-9: Handling while seated. *Source: HSE Guidance L23.*

Figure 4-10: Twisting. *Source: HSE Guidance L23.*

REVIEWING ASSESSMENTS

The assessment should be kept up to date. It should be reviewed whenever there is a reason to suppose that it is no longer valid, for example, because the working conditions or the personnel carrying out the operations have changed.

It should also be reviewed whenever there has been a significant change in the manual handling operations, for example, affecting the nature of the task or load.

Avoiding or minimising manual handling risks in construction activities

Each manual handling operation should be examined and appropriate steps taken to minimise the risk of injury to the lowest level reasonably practicable in order to eliminate the potential for the creation or further degeneration of musculoskeletal disorders (MSDs) i.e. problems to the back, bone, muscle and tissue injury.

Wherever reasonably practicable, manual handling should be avoided or reduced by using mechanical handling aids, examples of which are shown below. Practical measures that may be taken to reduce the risk of injury can also be based on *LITE*.

For example:

L OAD

By changing the load by lightening, reducing in size, provision of handles, elimination of sharp edges etc. Find ways of either avoiding the operation altogether; or using lightweight materials, for example, replacing pre cast concrete kerbs and drainage blocks with plastic equivalents. Alternatively where heavy blocks need to be used provide mechanical aids, such as vacuum lifters or grabs for concrete kerbs and paving.

Figure 4-11: Light weight plastic kerbs. Source: HSE, COH14.

Figure 4-12: Vacuum lift for heavy concrete kerbs.
Source: www.vacuumliftinguk.co.uk

I NDIVIDUAL

Address the individual factors such as selection, provision of information and training, provision of appropriate protective equipment and clothing. Individuals should be selected according to their capability. Personal factors such as height, build, physical condition, and pre-existing health conditions such as pregnancy must be considered.

T ASK

Consider redesigning the task so that manual handling is eliminated or reduced by mechanisation, reducing carrying distances, team lifting, job rotation and improved technique. On most sites brick and block laying at ground level involves bending down repeatedly to the stack and mortar spot board as well as to the wall that is being built. The combination of awkward postures and continuous handling can contribute to discomfort and a risk of injury. Excessive bending to trowel mortar and lay bricks at ground level can be avoided by raising the height of the spot board as the work proceeds.

Figure 4-13: Excessive bending to trowel mortar.
Source: HSE, COH01.

Figure 4-14: Raised spot board avoids excessive bending.
Source: HSE, COH01.

ENVIRONMENT

Risks can be minimised by improving the working environment, for example optimum heights of surfaces, improving floor conditions, increasing workspace, improving lighting, avoidance of changes in floor level.

DESIGN

The risks from manual handling may be minimised by the use of good design of the workplace. This can involve placing items where they can be conveniently handled, improving work layouts so that travel distances are minimised and arranging that items can be picked up or put down at a suitable height. The design of loads can also minimise risks. This can include designing the load to be smaller through concentration of substances contained in it or breaking the load up into suitable sized containers.

The HSE explain the benefits of good design in their case study related to trench blocks used for straight runs of foundations. Large heavy trench blocks were used to build foundations.

The combination of block weight and poor posture when working in a restricted space exposed workers to manual handling risks and finger trapping. Lighter trench blocks (weighing less than 20 kg) with handholds were designed and made available in place of the traditional heavier units.

Figure 4-15: Trench block with 'handholds'. *Source: HSE, COH04.*

The benefits included:

■ Lighter blocks help to reduce manual handling risks.
■ Handholds make the blocks easier to lift and reduce the risk of finger trapping when lowered into position.
■ Blocks had a tongue and groove system, which makes them easier and quicker to install.

AUTOMATION

The opportunities for automation in the construction industry are limited; however automation can include work done away from the site in order to prepare materials. When materials are manufactured with features included, pre-assembled or pre-prepared for fixing, it can greatly limit risks from manual handling tasks.

MECHANISATION

This involves the use of handling aids. Although this may retain some elements of manual handling, bodily forces are applied more efficiently.

Examples are:

Levers	Reduces bodily force to move a load. Can avoid trapping fingers.
Hoists	Can support weights, allowing handler to position load.
Trolley, sack truck, truck roller or hoist	Reduces effort to move loads horizontally.
Chutes	A way of using gravity to move loads from one place to another.
Handling devices	Hand-held hooks or suction pads can help when handling a load that is difficult to grasp.

Figure 4-16: Mechanical assistance. *Source: RMS.*

OTHER CONSIDERATIONS

Involving the workforce

Effort should be made to seek contributions from employees and, where applicable, safety representatives or representatives of employee safety.

Training

Employers should ensure that all employees who carry out manual handling operations receive the necessary training to enable them to carry out the task in a safe manner.

■ A training programme should include:
■ How potentially hazardous loads may be recognised.
■ How to deal with unfamiliar loads.
■ The proper use of handling aids.
■ The proper use of personal protective equipment.

- Features of the working environments that contribute to safety.
- The importance of good housekeeping.
- Factors affecting individual capability.
- Good handling techniques.

It should always be remembered that training should be kept under review. For training to be effective it should be on-going to reflect improved techniques developed by experienced workers and be supported by periodic refresher training and supervision.

Efficient movement principles for manually lifting loads

LIFTING TECHNIQUES USING KINETIC HANDLING PRINCIPLES

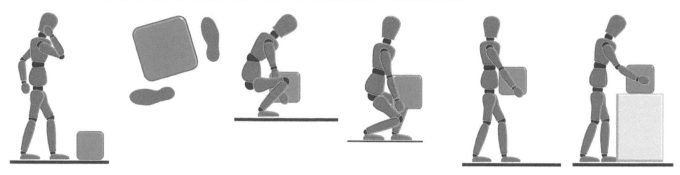

Figure 4-17: Basic lifting techniques.   *Source: HSE Guidance L23.*

The foundations of good lifting and moving techniques have been established for some considerable time. The basic principles are:

- ***Think before lifting/handling.*** Plan the lift. Can handling aids be used? Where is the load going to be placed? Will help be needed with the load? Remove obstructions such as discarded wrapping materials. For a long lift, consider resting the load midway on a table or bench to change grip.
- ***Keep the load close to the waist.*** Keep the load close to the body for as long as possible while lifting. Keep the heaviest side of the load next to the body. If a close approach to the load is not possible, try to slide it towards the body before attempting to lift it.
- ***Adopt a stable position.*** The feet should be apart with one leg slightly forward to maintain balance (alongside the load, if it is on the ground). The worker should be prepared to move their feet during the lift to maintain their stability. Avoid tight clothing or unsuitable footwear, which may make this difficult.
- ***Get a good hold.*** Where possible the load should be hugged as close as possible to the body. This may be better than gripping it tightly with hands only.
- ***Start in a good posture. At*** the start of the lift, slight bending of the back, hips and knees is preferable to fully flexing the back (stooping) or fully flexing the hips and knees (squatting).
- ***Don't flex the back any further while lifting.*** This can happen if the legs begin to straighten before starting to raise the load.
- ***Avoid twisting the back or leaning sideways,*** especially while the back is bent. Shoulders should be kept level and facing in the same direction as the hips. Turning by moving the feet is better than twisting and lifting at the same time.
- ***Keep the head up when handling.*** Look ahead, not down at the load, once it has been held securely.
- ***Move smoothly.*** The load should not be jerked or snatched as this can make it harder to keep control and can increase the risk of injury.
- ***Don't lift or handle more than can be easily managed.*** There is a difference between what people can lift and what they can safely lift. If in doubt, seek advice or get help.
- ***Put down, then adjust.*** If precise positioning of the load is necessary, put it down first, then slide it into the desired position.

POOR POSTURE

Injuries that are received as a result of carrying out activities that include manual handling operations need not necessarily arise solely from lifting large, awkward or heavy items. Poor posture can greatly increase the likelihood of suffering manual handling injuries.

Examples of poor posture can include over-stretching, twisting, lifting with the spine (in bending position) or lifting whilst seated. Many construction and maintenance tasks can encourage the worker to take up a poor posture so they are bent over for a period of time, for example, laying a floor.

Training should be given in correct manual handling techniques, adoption of the correct posture and ensuring that the 'kinetic' lifting method is used (feet slightly apart, straight back and use of the leg muscles to lift).

Guidance published by the Health and Safety Executive (HSE), indicates values of weights and ideal positions for these given weight values that should be adopted when manually handling *(see figure ref 4-8 earlier in this element)*. It can be seen from the guidance that the ideal position for manually handling is waist height whilst standing; also to be noted are the different values given for the male and female gender. These figures are not strict and are quoted as maximum under guidance only and allowances must be made for individual differences in capability.

Whilst standing is seen to give the more suitable posture for lifting, it should also be noted that movements made in the standing or seating position can also reduce individual weight values and lifting zones significantly, as discussed earlier.

REPETITIVE MOVEMENTS

The aim of the Manual Handling Operation Regulations (MHOR) 1992 is to reduce the risk of injury from manual handling operations. One of the main methods used to reduce the load being manually lifted is to package smaller weights or break the bulk load down into smaller batches. This solution avoids the need to lift heavy items; however it will introduce increased frequency.

Injuries received from manual handling operations can either be immediate, resulting from over exertion and poor posture or also occur over time as a result of performing the manual handling task repeatedly, for example digging an excavation or laying bricks. Whilst acute, painful injuries are typically more immediately noticeable, long-term effects from cumulative muscle strain can prove equally detrimental to individual health.

Where frequency is increased, in addition to training in the correct lifting method, regular breaks or job rotation must be introduced in order to share the workload suitably throughout the workforce. Mechanical assistance may also be introduced to prevent twisting or bending under strain (rollers, conveyors, air suction devices, and waist height benches).

AWKWARD MOVEMENTS

Training should be given in the correct lifting method (the kinetic method), that if used correctly, should eliminate incorrect posture and provide a means for lifting safely in most positions (floor level, waist height, not stretching). Awkward movements that should be avoided include stretching, bending at the waist using the spine, twisting, lifting whilst seated, sudden movements, jerky movements, over exertion whilst pushing or pulling.

It should be remembered that many construction and maintenance tasks require a person to hold awkward positions for a period of time, for example the fitting of overhead lights or tiles. These awkward movements can lead to cumulative strain and it is important that there are sufficient rest periods or work rotation built into the work activity to allow relief of the muscles likely to be affected.

4.3 - Lifting and moving equipment

Hazards and controls for mechanically operated load handling equipment

FORK-LIFT TRUCKS (FLT)

Hazards

Many of the hazards set out for fork-lift trucks, including rough terrain for lift trucks, would be equally applicable to other mobile work equipment used for load handling and may be seen as generic hazards of mechanically operated load handling equipment.

- Overturning:
  - Driving too fast.
  - Sudden braking.
  - Driving on slopes.
  - Driving with load elevated.
  - Driving with the load incorrectly positioned on the forks.
  - Driving over debris.
  - Under-inflated tyres.
  - Driving over holes, such as drains or potholes.
  - Overloading - exceeding maximum rated capacity.
  - Collisions with buildings or other vehicles.

- Overloading:
  - Exceeding maximum rated capacity.
- Collisions:
  - With buildings.
  - With pedestrians.
  - With other vehicles.
- Failure:
  - Load bearing part (for example, chain).
- Loss of load:
  - Insecure load.
  - Poor floor surface.
  - Passengers should not be carried.

Overturning

The stability of fork-lift trucks is particularly affected by the forces generated when turning, especially at speed, or if the equipment is tilted sideways, for example, by travelling across an incline or by the wheels running into a pothole or over an obstruction. The danger of a fork-lift truck being turned on its side is greater with the load in the raised position *(see figure ref 4-18a)*, than in the lowered position *(see figure ref 4-18b)*.

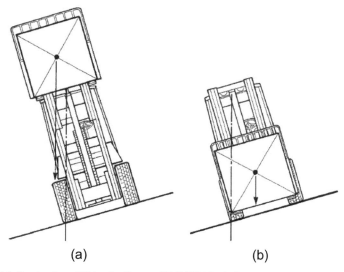

Figure 4-18: Overturning of lift truck. *Source: HSE, HSG6 - Safety in working with lift trucks.*

Over balancing

The mass of a counterbalance fork-lift truck acts as a counterweight so that the load can be lifted and moved without the lift truck overbalancing and tipping forwards *(see figure ref 4-19a)*. However, the lift truck can be tipped forward if the load is too heavy *(see figure ref 4-19b)*, if the load is incorrectly placed on the forks *(see figure ref 4-19c)*, or if the lift truck accelerates or brakes harshly while carrying a heavy load.

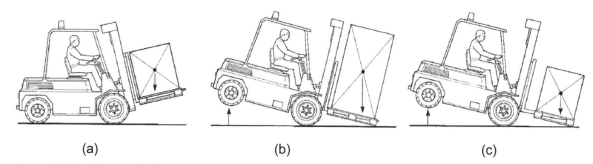

Figure 4-19: Overbalancing of lift truck.   *Source: HSE, HSG6 - Safety in working with lift trucks.*

This may not cause the equipment to overturn, but the overbalancing can injure the operator and lead to loss of control of steering. The lift trucks are usually provided with rear wheel steering, the overbalancing lifts the equipment from the ground preventing the steering wheels from contacting the ground properly.

Collisions with other vehicles, pedestrians or fixed objects

People may unexpectedly appear from a part of a building structure or workers intent on the work they are doing may step away from where they are working to collect materials or tools. Often the space in workplaces, such as construction sites, is restricted. Material may be stored to a height because it is large or to maximise the available space. This in turn leads to restricted visibility especially at busy junctions where vehicles come together. This may lead to collisions with other vehicles and pedestrians or, in the avoidance of these, fixed objects.

Control measures

Many of the control measures set out for fork-lift trucks would be equally applicable to other mobile work equipment used for load handling and may be seen as generic control measures for mechanically operated load handling equipment.

Traffic routes

- Separate routes, designated crossing places and suitable barriers at recognised danger spots.
- Roads, gangways and aisles should have sufficient width and overhead clearance for the largest fork-lift truck.
- Clear direction signs.
- Sharp bends and overhead obstructions should be avoided.
- The ground surface should be in good condition, taking into account a rough terrain fork-lift truck's ability.
- Any gradient in a fork-lift truck operating area should be kept as gentle as possible.

Parking areas

Sufficient and suitable parking areas should be provided away from the main work area.

Protection of personnel

There is a need to alert people to the hazard when working in or near a fork-lift truck operating area. This is achieved by putting up signs and/or fitting visual/audible warnings to vehicles.

Procedures

Selection of equipment

There are many types of truck available for a range of activities. There are many situations when specialist trucks, such as, overhead telescopic or rough terrain trucks, are required. Many accidents happen due to the incorrect selection and/or use of fork-lift trucks. When choosing the right truck for the job the following factors should be taken into account:

- Power source - the choice of battery or diesel will depend on whether the truck is to be used indoors or outdoors. Where lift trucks are used indoors, for example, inside large buildings under construction it is preferable to use battery operated lift trucks to avoid the hazard of exhaust gases from diesel trucks.
- Tyres - solid or pneumatic depending on the terrain.
- Size and capacity - dependent on the size and nature of loads to be moved.
- Height of the mast: a large mast may be an advantage with a rough terrain lift truck used outside but may be a disadvantage when used indoors to move materials.

Figure 4-20: Rough terrain fork-lift truck. *Source: RMS.*

- Audible and/or visual warning systems fitted according to the proximity of pedestrians.
- Protection provided for the operator for overturning or the possibility of falling objects.
- Training given to operators must be related specifically to the type of truck.
- Provision of a suitable mechanism to prevent unauthorised use, for example, key or electronic pad.

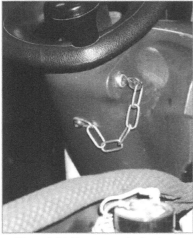

Figure 4-21: Keys - unauthorised use not controlled. *Source: RMS.*

Figure 4-22: Pin pad to prevent unauthorised use. *Source: RMS.*

Provision of information

Operators and supervisors should be familiar with the following information which should be shown on the lift truck:

- Name of the manufacturer (or authorised supplier) of the lift truck.
- Model designation.
- Serial number.
- Unladen weight.
- Rated weight carrying capacity.
- Load centre distance.
- Maximum lift height.
- Inflation pressures of pneumatic tyres.

In addition, the functions of all the controls should be clearly marked so that they can be seen from the operator's position.

Operators

Selection of personnel

The safe use of fork-lift trucks calls for a reasonable degree of both physical and mental fitness and of intelligence. The selection procedure should be devised to identify people who have shown themselves reliable and mature during their early years at work.

Training

Training should consist of three stages, the last being the one in which the operator is introduced to his future work environment. This is illustrated by the stages of training of a fork-lift truck operator.

Stage one - should contain the basic skills and knowledge required to operate the fork-lift truck safely, to understand the basic mechanics and balance of the machine, and to carry out routine daily checks.

Stage two - under strict training conditions closed to other personnel. This stage should include:

- Knowledge of the operating principles and controls.
- Use of the fork-lift truck in gangways, slopes, cold-stores, confined spaces and bad weather conditions as appropriate.
- The work to be undertaken, for example, loading and unloading vehicles or lifting to materials platforms at height.

Stage three - after successfully completing the first two stages, the operator should be given further instruction in the place of work.

Testing - on completion of training, the operator should be examined and tested to ensure that he/she has achieved the required standard.

Refresher training - if high standards are to be maintained, periodic refresher training and testing is essential good practice.

Summary of controls measures for fork-lift trucks

- Make someone responsible for transport.
- Select and train drivers thoroughly.
- Daily vehicle checks.

- Keep keys secure. **Do not leave in the ignition.**
- Maintain and light traffic routes.
- Separate vehicles and pedestrians.

A vigorous management policy covering operator training, vehicle maintenance and sound systems of work, supported by good supervision will reduce personal injury and damage to equipment and materials. This in turn will lead to better utilisation of plant and increased materials handling efficiency.

TELEHANDLERS

Hazards

Telehandlers are all-purpose machines that can be used for construction site preparation, material handling, scaffold erection, elevated work platforms and for final site cleanup. A telehandler consists of a heavy duty chassis, body and lifting gear on large diameter wheels and deep tread pneumatic traction tyres. Increased power required to cope with the demands of construction sites is transferred through larger drive shafts/wheels and generally larger and heavier duty mechanical ancillary items. In the case of a telehandler, hazards include moving large hydraulic rams that actuate the front forks or bucket with hydraulic hoses attached that are under high pressure. Materials handling is through various attachments fixed to a boom that enables vertical, horizontal and diagonal reach. Construction sites are finding various uses for telehandlers and, with the different attachments available, greater flexibility is provided for the variety of jobs that may be encountered.

Hazards include the generic hazards of mobile load handling equipment and are similar to that of a rough terrain fork-lift truck. There are various mechanical hazards involved, such as impact, crush, trap, and shear. In addition to these there are non-mechanical hazards such as heat, fumes, chemicals and noise.

Control measures

Control measures should include: use only by competent operators, barriers to segregate pedestrians from machinery to a safe distance, good visibility with the assistance of mirrors, high visibility clothing for those working nearby, and seat restraints for the operator who should be enclosed in a protective cage that can also act as a guard against contact with moving machinery and the effects of overturning.

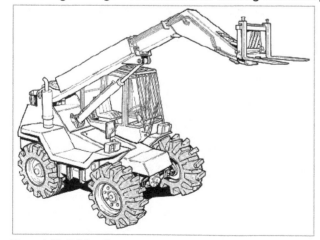

Figure 4-23: Telehandler.   *Source: HSE, HSG6.*

Figure 4-24: Dumper truck.   *Source: RMS.*

DUMPER TRUCKS

Hazards

A dumper truck is a general piece of plant consisting of a heavy-duty chassis, body and tipping bucket on large diameter wheels and deep tread, traction tyres, used for transporting materials around a construction site or street works. The equipment is generally used as a large mechanised wheelbarrow.

Hazards include the generic hazards associated with mobile load handling equipment. Specific hazards associated with dumper trucks are the risk of complete 360° rollover, impact with pedestrians or vehicles, trap and crush beneath the tipping bucket as it discharges its contents, falling items or objects from the bucket, high pressure hydraulic lines and tipping over on unstable ground or into excavations. Other hazards include noise, chemicals and fumes emitted from the exhaust of the dumper truck.

Possible causes of a dumper truck overturning include:

- Overloading or uneven loading of the bucket.
- Cornering at excessive speed.
- Hitting obstructions.
- Driving too close to the edges of embankments or excavations.

- Mechanical defects that occur because of lack of maintenance.
- Inappropriate or unequal tyre pressures.
- Driving across slopes.

Control measures

Control measures should include trained, authorised, operatives; maintenance and inspection; segregation of pedestrians to a safe distance by the provision of suitable barriers and signs advising of the dangers of operating plant; stop blocks for tipping into excavations; seat restraints and rollover protection for the operator.

EXCAVATORS

Hazards

Consisting of a heavy duty chassis, fixed or rotating body and digging gear (jib arms and bucket) on large diameter wheels and deep tread, pneumatic traction tyres or caterpillar track system.

Figure 4-25: Excavator hazards.   *Source: RMS.*

Figure 4-26: Excavator.   *Source: RMS.*

Specific hazards associated with excavators are impact with pedestrians or vehicles by swinging jibs and booms, trap and crush beneath the excavator bucket as it digs into the ground or discharges its contents, falling items or objects from the bucket, high pressure hydraulic lines and tipping over on unstable ground or into excavations.

Other hazards include noise, chemicals and exhaust fumes. The exhaust fumes may find their way into excavations while digging the trench. Excavation equipment is generally adapted and used for a variety of different purposes that it may not specifically be designed for, including towing/shunting, lifting, loading/unloading transport of articles and equipment. The fact that these are improvised activities increases the risk of injury.

Control measures

Control measures should include trained and authorised operatives; not overloading the bucket; maintenance and inspection; segregation of pedestrians to a safe distance by the provision of suitable barriers and signs advising of the dangers of operating plant; good visibility with the assistance of mirrors where necessary, high visibility clothing for those working nearby, seat restraints for the operator who should be enclosed in a protective cage that can also act as a guard against contact with moving machinery and the effects of overturning.

LIFTS AND HOISTS

Lifts are generally lifting equipment that raises the item to be moved from below, often using some form of mechanical or hydraulic mechanism. These include passenger and goods lifts, scissor lifts, vehicle inspection lifts and mobile elevating work platforms (MEWPs). The term 'lift' is often used in common language to describe lifting equipment used to move people in a building, even though the lifting equipment often uses a hoist mechanism.

Hoists are generally lifting equipment that raises the item to be moved from above, often using some form of rope (for example, man made, artificial fibre or wire rope). These include platform hoists and hand operated gin wheels.

Hazards

In general, the hazards associated with lifts and hoists are the same as with any other lifting equipment.

■ The lift/hoist may overturn or collapse.
■ The lift/hoist can strike persons, during normal operations, who may be near or under the platform or cage.
■ The supporting ropes may fail and the platform/cage falls to the ground.
■ The load or part of the load may fall.
■ The lift/hoist may fail in a high position.
■ Persons being lifted may become stranded if the lift or hoist fails.

Control measures

Lifts and hoists for movement of goods require:

■ Adequate design.
■ Sound construction.
■ Correct selection and installation.
■ Competent operation.
■ Regular inspection.
■ Adequate maintenance.
■ Statutory safety devices.
■ Holdback equipment (for rope or lifting mechanism failure).
■ Overrun tip systems.
■ Guards on hoist/lift machinery.
■ Landing gates (securely closed down during operation).
■ Adequate lighting at landings.

In addition, passenger hoists/lifts require more sophisticated controls:

■ Operating controls inside the cage.
■ Electromagnetic interlocks on the cage doors.
■ The enclosing shaft must be of fire-proof construction, if within a building.

The lift/hoist should be protected by a substantial enclosure to prevent anyone from being struck by any moving part of the hoist or material falling down the hoist way.

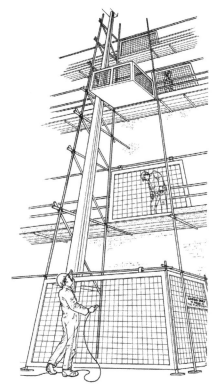

Figure 4-27: Construction platform hoist. *Source: HSE, HSG150.*

Gates must be provided at all access landings, including at ground level. The gates must be kept shut, except when the platform is at the landing. The controls should be arranged so that the lift/hoist can be operated from one position only, which may be from within the lift/hoist. If an operator is provided they must be trained and competent. The safe working load of the lift/hoist must be clearly marked and visible to the operator. If the lift/hoist is for materials only there should be a prominent warning notice on the platform or cage to stop people riding on it.

The lift/hoist should be inspected weekly. Passenger lifts are required to be examined every six months and goods lifts every twelve months or alternatively at intervals detailed in an examination scheme drawn up by a competent person based on an assessment of risks. The results of inspection/examination must be recorded. The lift/hoist should be regularly serviced by a reputable maintenance company (approximately every three months).

Figure 4-28: Material hoist. *Source: HSS.*

The service report provided should relate to the efficient working of the lift/hoist and is not a substitute for the thorough examination mentioned above. Any remedial work identified should receive prompt attention. A system should be developed for rescuing people trapped in the lift car of passenger lifts and where this is to be carried out by workers, provide adequate training on this procedure. Written rescue procedures should be displayed at appropriate locations and it should be ensured that the alarm bell can be activated.

SCISSOR LIFTS

Scissor lifts can provide excellent movement of goods to the desired level. They are therefore particularly useful for loading or unloading goods from vehicles and to storage levels in warehouses.

Hazards

- Crush injuries may occur as the platform is raised to or past a fixed part of a structure.
- People, equipment or materials falling from the platform.
- Overload.
- The scissor lift may overturn or collapse.
- The sheer effect of the scissor mechanism as it closes.

Controls measures

Before using the scissor lift ensure:
- Whoever is operating it is fully trained and competent.
- The scissor lift is fitted with a guard covering the scissor mechanism to a height that is reasonably practicable.

Figure 4-29: Scissor lift.   *Source: HSE, HSG150.*

- Anyone in the area is kept clear of the work area.
- That it is not possible to insert a foot or similar part of the body underneath the lifting platform when it is being lowered.
- That there is a safe system of work for the retrieval of items dropped down near the scissor mechanism and for maintenance underneath it.

MOBILE AND TOWER CRANES

Hazards

The principal hazards associated with any lifting operation are:

- ***Overturning,*** which can be caused by weak support, operating outside the capabilities of the machine, uneven or weak ground (cellars or drains), outriggers not extended, insufficient counter weight, adverse weather and by striking obstructions.
- ***Overloading,*** by exceeding the operating capacity or operating radii, or by failure of safety devices.
- ***Collision,*** with other cranes, overhead cables, structures or people.
- ***Failure of load bearing part,*** from structural components of the crane itself or an accessory fitted to it. This may be due to overloading or degradation of the load bearing part due to damage, use (wear) or faults (corrosion).
- ***Loss of load,*** from failure of lifting tackle, incorrect hook fittings or poor slinging procedure.

Control measures

General requirements for cranes

The main control measures associated with any crane and lifting operation are to ensure:

- Lifting operations are properly planned by a competent person, appropriately supervised and carried out in a safe manner.
- The ground the crane stands on is it capable of bearing the load; check for underground services and cellars.
- The ground is level, if not select a crane, with hydraulic level adjustment stabilisers.

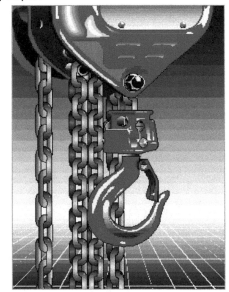

Figure 4-30: Safety latch on hook. *Source: Corel Clipart.*

- The load bearing capacity of the crane is sufficient of for the task.

- The correct procedure is followed when erecting or dismantling any crane.
- The crane is positioned so that there is enough room for the lift and to avoid collision hazards.
- Non-essential people are kept clear of the work area.
- The crane is not operated in adverse weather conditions.
- The structural integrity of the crane is maintained; check for any signs of corrosion.
- The correct procedure is followed when erecting or dismantling any crane.
- Pre-use check by operator is carried out.
- Lifting equipment is of adequate strength and stability for the load. Stresses induced at mounting or fixing points must be taken into account. Similarly, every part of a load, anything attached to it and used in lifting must be of adequate strength.
- The safe working load (SWL) is clearly marked on lifting machinery, equipment and accessories in order to ensure safe use. Where the SWL depends on the configuration of the machinery, it must be clearly marked for each configuration used and kept with the machinery.
- Equipment that is not designed for lifting persons, but which might be used as such, must have appropriate markings to the effect that it is not to be used for passengers.
- Load indicators are fitted. It is preferable that there are two types, a requirement with jib cranes, but beneficial if fitted to all cranes.
- Load/radius indicator is fitted. This shows the radius the crane is working at and the safe load for that radius. It must be visible to the operator.
- Automatic safe load indicator is fitted. This provides a visible warning when the SWL is approached and audible warning when the SWL is exceeded.
- Controls are clearly identified and of the "hold to run" type.
- Over travel switches are fitted. These are limit switches to prevent the hook or sheave block being wound up to the cable drum.
- Access is provided. Safe access should be provided for the operator and for use during inspection and maintenance/emergency.
- Operating position provides clear visibility of hook and load, with the controls easily reached.
- Passengers are not carried without authorisation, and never on lifting tackle.
- Lifting tackle - chains, slings, wire ropes, eyebolts and shackles - should be tested/examined.

Figure 4-31: Lifting operation.   *Source: RMS.*

Figure 4-32: Lifting points on load.   *Source: RMS.*

See also - 'Requirements for lifting operations' later in this section for more information.

Figure 4-33: Safety latch on hook.   *Source: RMS.*

Figure 4-34: Accessories.   *Source: RMS.*

Accessories

Lifting accessories include slings, hooks, chains eyes and cradles. This equipment is designed with the aim of assisting in lifting items without the need for manual force. Because these accessories are in a constantly changing environment and are in and out of use they need to be protected from damage; a failure of any one item could result in a fatality. For example, lifting eyes need to be correctly fitted, slings have to be used with the correct technique and all equipment must be stored when not in use to prevent damage. Accessories must be attached correctly and safely to the load by a competent person, and then the lifting equipment takes over the task of providing the necessary required power to perform the lift. As with all lifting equipment, accessories must be regularly inspected and certificated and only used by trained authorised persons.

Manually operated load handling aids

WHEELBARROWS

A wheelbarrow is a low-tech fabrication, generally consisting of a shallow hopper style bucket supported on a single wheel at the front and two legs at the rear with handle bars for grip and use when moving. In use, the load being carried is pivoted and supported over the front wheel. There is still a need to manually handle materials when loading and unloading the wheel barrow, with speed of operation and the capacity of the truck governed by the individual that uses the equipment.

Hazards and control measures

Wheel barrows are typically manually driven pieces of equipment and the hazards arising from their use are generally of an ergonomic nature relating to posture and over exertion. Mechanical hazards are restricted to the single wheel of the barrow that only moves when moved by the operator. Other associated hazards are tripping and falling whilst using the equipment or ejecting the contents of the barrow. Control measures include indicating a safe working load for the equipment and the provision of information/instruction in the safe loading and use of the equipment for the operator.

Figure 4-35: Wheelbarrow.   *Source: RMS.*

Figure 4-36: Sack truck.   *Source: RMS.*

SACK TRUCK

A sack truck is a simple fabrication fitted with two wheels on which the load is pivoted and supported when the truck is tilted back and pushed manually. A risk assessment must be made of manual handling operations associated with using equipment of this type. As with the wheelbarrow there is still a need to manually handle materials when using a sack truck.

Hazards and control measures

Sack trucks are typically manually powered and as with the wheelbarrow the hazards arising from their use are generally of an ergonomic nature relating to posture and over exertion through manual handling. Mechanical hazards are restricted to the wheels of the truck that only move when moved by the operator. Other associated hazards are tripping and falling whilst using the equipment and manual handling back and strain injuries.

Control measures include indicating a safe working load for the equipment and the provision of information/instruction in the safe loading and use of the equipment for the operator. A manual handling assessment may be required when using this equipment.

THE PALLET TRUCK

This truck has two elevating forks for insertion below the top deck of a pallet. When the forks are raised the load is moved clear of the ground to allow movement. This truck may be designed for pedestrian or rider control. It has no mast and cannot be used for stacking. Pallet trucks may be powered or non-powered.

Hazards and control measures

Pallet trucks can be driven both manually or by quiet running electric motor. Hazards include crush from moving loads or momentum of the equipment when stopping, crush and trap in the forks of the equipment, manual handling strain injuries and electricity hazards from battery power points.

In addition, some pallet trucks have a lifting mechanism to raise and lower the load. Control measures should include trained and authorised operatives; identification of safe working loads; inspection and maintenance; and designated areas for parking the equipment.

Figure 4-37: Battery powered pallet truck. *Source: RMS.*

Figure 4-38: Manually operated pallet truck. *Source: RMS.*

MANUALLY OPERATED HOISTS - GIN WHEEL

Gin wheel hoists provide a very convenient way of raising loads. They comprise a pulley wheel and rope suspended from a fixed point, for example, a scaffold. The material to be moved is attached to one end of the rope and is raised by pulling the other end. Though they are simple pieces of equipment, care is required when assembling and using them.

Gin wheels are in wide use on small construction sites, but are being replaced by small electric hoists that use a single wire rope to raise materials.

Hazards

The main hazards are:

- The loss of the gin wheel and or any load from its fixing point.
- The loss of load from the hook.

Controls measures

Ensure that the:

- The gin wheel is securely fixed to the anchorage.
- A proper hook is being used with a safety catch to secure the load.
- A safe working platform exists from which the hook can be loaded or unloaded.

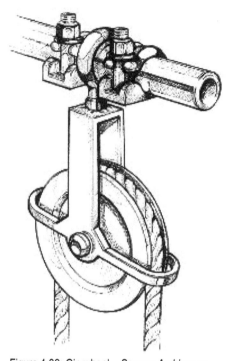

Figure 4-39: Gin wheel. *Source: Ambiguous.*

Requirements for lifting operations

CONTROL OF LIFTING OPERATIONS

Under regulation 8 of the Lifting Operations and Lifting Equipment Regulation (LOLER) 1998 employers have a duty to ensure that every lifting operation involving lifting equipment for the purposes of lifting or lowering of a load is organised safely. This will include ensuring the following:

- Lifting operations to be properly planned by a competent person.
- Provision of appropriate supervision.
- Work is to be carried out in a safe manner.

STRONG, STABLE AND SUITABLE EQUIPMENT

Strength

Regulation 4 of LOLER 1998 requires every employer shall ensure that:

- Lifting equipment is of adequate strength and stability for each load, having regard in particular to the stress induced at its mounting or fixing point.
- Every part of a load and anything attached to it and used in lifting it is of adequate strength.

When assessing whether lifting equipment has adequate strength for the proposed use, the combined weight of the load and lifting accessories should be taken into account. It is important to consider the load, task and environment in order to match the strength of the lifting equipment to the circumstances of use. For example, if the environment is hot or cold this can affect the lifting capacity of the lifting equipment. In order to counteract this effect equipment with a higher rated safe working load may be needed.

Figure 4-40: Lifting operations.   *Source: RMS.*

Figure 4-41: Lifting operations.   *Source: RMS.*

If the load to be lifted is a person, equipment with a generous capacity above the person's weight should be selected in order to provide an increased factor for safety. If the load is likely to move unexpectedly, because of the movement of an animal or liquids in a container, this sudden movement can put additional forces on the equipment and may necessitate equipment with higher strength to be selected. When lifting a load that is submerged in water, the initial lifting weight will be misleading because the load will be supported by the water. When the load emerges from the water the support will no longer be available and this sudden increase in weight can put additional stress on the crane and its lifting accessories.

When conducting the lifting task the lifting accessories may be used in such a way that may reduce its lifting capacity below its stated safe working load; sharp corners on a load and 'back hooking' can have this effect. In these circumstances accessories with a higher rated safe working load may be required.

It is essential to remember that in a lifting operation the equipment only has an overall lifting capacity equivalent to the item with the lowest strength. For example, in a situation where a crane with a lifting capacity of 50 tonnes is used with a hook of 10 tonnes capacity and a wire rope sling of 5 tonnes capacity this would give an overall maximum lifting strength/capacity of 5 tonnes.

Stability

A number of factors can affect the stability of lifting equipment, for example wind conditions, slopes/cambers, stability of ground conditions and how the load is to be lifted.

Lifting equipment must be positioned and installed so that it does not tip over when in use. Anchoring can be achieved by securing with guy ropes, bolting the structure to a foundation, using ballast as counterweights or using outriggers to bring the centre of gravity down to the base area.

Mobile lifting equipment should be sited on firm ground with the wheels or outrigger feet having their weight distributed over a large surface area. Care should be taken that the equipment is not positioned over cellars, drains or underground cavities, or positioned near excavations.

Sloping ground should be avoided as this can shift the load radius out or in, away from the safe working position. In the uphill position, the greatest danger occurs when the load is set down. This can cause the mobile lifting equipment to tip over. In the downhill position, the load moves out of the radius and may cause the equipment to tip forwards.

Suitability

Lifting equipment, and any accessories used for lifting, are pieces of work equipment under the Provision and Use of Work Equipment Regulations (PUWER) 1998.

Regulation 4 of PUWER 1998 states:

> *"Every employer shall ensure that work equipment is used only for operations for which, and under conditions for which, it is suitable in order to avoid any reasonably foreseeable risk to the health and safety of any person".*

Figure 4-42: Regulation 4 of PUWER 1998.   *Source: The Provision and Use of Work Equipment Regulations (PUWER) 1998.*

In order for lifting equipment to be suitable it must be of the correct type for the task, have a safe working load limit in excess of the load being lifted, and have the correct type and combination of lifting accessories attached.

Lifting equipment used within industry varies and includes mobile cranes, static tower cranes and overhead travelling cranes. The type of lifting equipment selected will depend on a number of factors including the weight of the load to be lifted, the radius of operation, the height of the lift, the time available, and the frequency of the lifting activities. This equipment is often very heavy, which means its weight can cause the ground underneath the equipment to sink or collapse. Other factors like height and size may have to be considered as there may be limitations in site roads that are located between structures or where overhead restrictions exist. Careful consideration of these factors must be made when selecting the correct crane. Selecting lifting equipment to carry out a lifting activity should be done at the planning stage, where the most suitable equipment can be identified that is able to meet all of the lifting requirements and the limitations of the location.

POSITIONED AND INSTALLED CORRECTLY

Lifting equipment must be positioned or installed so that the risk of the equipment striking a person is as low as is reasonably practicable. Similarly, the risk of a load drifting, falling freely or being unintentionally released must also be considered and equipment positioned to take account of this.

All nearby hazards, including overhead cables and uninsulated power supply conductors, should be identified and removed or covered by safe working procedures such as locking-off and permit systems. The possibility of striking other lifting equipment or structures should also be examined.

Detailed consideration must be given to the location of any heavy piece of lifting equipment due to the fact that additional weight is distributed to the ground through the loading of the equipment when performing a lift. Surveys must be carried out to determine the nature of the ground, whether soft or firm, and what underground hazards are present such as buried services or hollow voids.

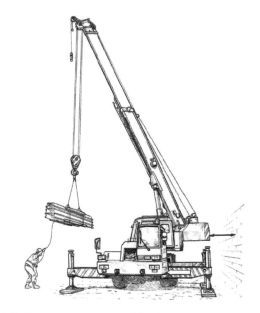

Figure 4-43: Danger zone - crane and fixed item. *Source: HSE, HSG150.*

If the ground proves to be soft, then this can be covered using timber, digger mats or hard core to prevent the equipment or its outriggers sinking when under load. The surrounding environment must also be taken into consideration and factors may include highways, railways, electricity cables, areas of public interest. The area around where lifting equipment is sited should be securely fenced, including the extremes of the lift radius, with an additional factor of safety to allow for emergency arrangements such as emergency vehicle access or safety in the event of a collapse or fall.

Where practicable, lifting equipment should be positioned and installed such that loads are not carried or suspended over areas occupied by people. Where this is necessary appropriate systems of work should be used to ensure it is done safely.

If the operator cannot observe the full path of the load an appointed person (and assistants as appropriate) should be used to communicate the position of the load and provide directions to avoid striking anything or anyone.

VISIBLY MARKED (SWL)

The safe working load (SWL) must be clearly marked on lifting machinery, equipment and accessories in order to ensure safe use. Where the SWL depends on the configuration of the machinery, it must be clearly marked for each configuration used and kept with the machinery. Accessories must be marked with supplementary information that indicates the characteristics for its safe use, for example safe angles of lift. Equipment designed for lifting people must be clearly marked as such and equipment which is not designed for lifting persons, but which might be used as such, must have appropriate markings to the effect that it is not to be used for lifting people.

Figure 4-44: Marking of accessories. *Source: RMS.*

PLANNED, SUPERVISED AND CARRIED OUT IN SAFE MANNER BY COMPETENT PEOPLE

Regulation 8 of LOLER 1998 requires that every employer shall ensure that every lifting operation involving lifting equipment is:

- Properly planned by a competent person.
- Appropriately supervised.
- Carried out in a safe manner.

The type of lifting equipment that is to be used and the complexity of the lifting operations will dictate the degree of planning required for the lifting operation.

Planned

Planning combines two parts: initial planning to ensure that lifting equipment is provided which is suitable for the range of tasks that it will have to carry out.

■ Planning of individual lifting operations so that they can be carried out safely with the lifting equipment provided.

Factors that should be considered when formulating a plan include:

■ The load that is being lifted - weight, shape, centers of gravity, surface condition, lifting points.
■ The equipment and accessories being used for the operation and suitability - certification validity.
■ The proposed route that the load will take including the destination and checks for obstructions.
■ The team required to carry out the lift - competencies and numbers required.
■ Production of a safe system of work, risk assessments, permits to work.
■ The environment in which the lift will take place - ground conditions, weather, local population.
■ Securing areas below the lift - information, restrictions, demarcation and barriers.
■ A suitable trial to determine the reaction of the lifting equipment prior to full lift.
■ Completion of the operation and any dismantling required.

Supervised

It is important that someone takes supervisory control of lifting operations at the time they are being conducted. Though the operator may be skilled in lifting techniques this may not be enough to ensure safety as other factors may influence whether the overall operation is conducted safely, for example, people may stray into the area.

Figure 4-45: Siting and stability.　　　Source: RMS.

The supervisor of the lifting operation must remain in control and stop the operation if it is not carried out satisfactorily.

Carried out in a safe manner

Lifting equipment and accessories should be subject to a pre-use check in order to determine their condition and suitability. In addition, care should be taken to ensure the lifting accessories used are compatible with the task and that the load is protected or supported such that it does not disintegrate when lifted.

Lifting operations should not be carried on where adverse weather conditions occur, such as fog, poor lightning, strong wind or where heavy rainfall makes ground conditions unstable. It is important that measures be used to prevent lifting equipment overturning and that there is sufficient room for it to operate without contacting other objects. Lifting equipment should not be used to drag loads and should not be overloaded. Special arrangements need to be in place when lifting equipment not normally used for lifting people is used for that purpose, for example, de-rating the working load limit, ensuring communication is in place between the people being lifted and the operator, and ensuring the operation controls are manned at all times.

The driver of a *mobile crane* should carry out the following:

■ Before travelling unladen, lower jib onto its rest (if fitted) or to the lowest operating position and point in the direction of travel, but beware of steep hills.
■ Understand the signalling system and observe the signals of the appointed banksman.
■ Do not permit unauthorised persons to travel on the crane.
■ Do not use the crane to replace normal means of transport, or as a towing tractor.
■ Before lifting, check that the crane is on firm and level ground, and that spring locks and out-riggers are properly in position.
■ Keep a constant watch on the load radius indicator. Do not lift any suspected overload. Overloads are forbidden.
■ Ensure movements are made with caution. Violent handling produces excess loading on the crane structure and machinery.
■ Make allowances for adverse weather conditions.
■ Do not attempt to drag loads or cause loads to swing. Always position the crane so that the pull on the hoist rope is vertical.
■ Ensure that the load is properly slung. A load considered unsafe should not be lifted.
■ Ensure that all persons are in a safe position before any movement is carried out.
■ Make certain before hoisting that the hook is not attached to any anchored load or fixed object.
■ Do not drag slings when travelling.
■ If the crane is slewing (swinging in a sideways or circular motion), the jib, hook or load must be in a position to clear any obstruction, but the load must not be lifted unnecessarily high.
■ Be on a constant lookout for overhead obstructions, particularly electric cables.
■ Never tamper with or disconnect safe load indicators.
■ If the hoist or jib ropes become slack or out of their grooves, stop the crane and report the condition.

- Report all defects to the supervisor and never attempt to use a crane with a suspected serious defect until rectified and certified by a competent person that it is not dangerous.
- When leaving a crane unattended, ensure that the power is off, the engine stopped, the load unhooked, and the hook is raised up to a safe position.
- Where using special devices; for example, magnets, grabs, etc. ensure they are used only for the purpose intended and in accordance with the instruction given.
- Keep the crane clean and tidy.
- When parking a crane after use, remember to apply all brakes, slew locks, and secure rail clamps when fitted. Some cranes, however, particularly tower cranes, must be left to weather vane and the manufacturers instructions must be clearly adhered to. Park the crane where the weather vaning jib will not strike any object. Lock the cabin before leaving the crane.
- When it is necessary to make a report this must be done promptly through supervision.
- Drive smoothly - drive safely. Remember that cranes are safe only when they are used as recommended by the makers. This applies in particular to speciality cranes.

Rules for safe operation of a crane

Always	Ensure operators/slingers are trained and competent.
Always	Select the right appliance and tackle for the job.
Always	Ensure the appliance is stable when lifting - for example, not outside lifting radius, firm, level ground, outriggers.
Always	Use correct slinging methods.
Always	Protect sling from sharp edges - pack out and lower onto spacers.
Always	Ensure the sling is securely attached to the hook.
Always	Ensure load is lifted to correct height and moved at an appropriate speed.

Figure 4-46: Crane operation.   *Source: RMS.*

Always	Use standard signals - refer to the Health and Safety (Safety Signs and Signals) Regulations (SSSR) 1996.
Never	Use equipment if damaged (check before use) - for example stretched or not free movement, worn or corroded, outside inspection date.
Never	Exceed the safe working load.
Never	Lift with sling angles greater than 120 degrees.
Never	Lift a load over people.
Never	Drag a load or allow sudden shock loading.

Competent people

The Health and Safety at Work etc Act (HASAWA) 1974 places a duty on employers to their employees for the provision of information, instruction, training and supervision as is necessary to ensure, so far as is reasonably practicable, the health and safety at work of the employees. In addition to this general duty, a further duty exists under the Provision and Use of Work Equipment Regulations (PUWER) 1998. Employers must ensure that any person who uses a piece of work equipment has received adequate training for purposes of health and safety, including training in the methods which may be adopted when using work equipment, and any risks which such use may entail and precautions to be taken.

Drivers/operators of cranes and other lifting appliances, including others involved in lifting operations (for example those that direct the movement of the load), must be adequately trained, experienced and aged 18 years or over. The only exception is when under the direct supervision of a competent person for training requirements.

There are various appointments with specified responsibilities in order to ensure the safety of lifting operations on site.

These are as follows:

■ Competent person	-	Appointed to plan the operation.
■ Load handler	-	Attaches and detaches the load.
■ Authorised person	-	Ensures the load safely attached.
■ Operator	-	Appointed to operate the equipment.
■ Responsible person	-	Appointed to communicate the position of the load (banksman).
■ Assistants	-	Appointed to relay communications.

SPECIAL REQUIREMENTS FOR LIFTING EQUIPMENT FOR LIFTING PERSONS

Regulation 5 of PUWER 1998 requires every employer to ensure that lifting equipment for lifting persons:

- Is such as to prevent a person using it being crushed, trapped or struck or falling from the carrier.
- Is such as to prevent so far as is reasonably practicable a person using it, while carrying out activities from the carrier, being crushed, trapped or struck or falling from the carrier.
- Has suitable devices to prevent the risk of a carrier falling.
- Is such that a person trapped in any carrier is not thereby exposed to danger and can be freed.

In addition, every employer shall ensure that if the risk described above cannot be prevented for reasons inherent in the site and height differences:

- The carrier has an enhanced safety coefficient suspension rope or chain.
- The rope or chain is inspected by a competent person every working day.

Special arrangements need to be in place when lifting equipment not normally used for people is used for that purpose, for example de-rating the working load limit, ensuring communication is in place between the people and operator, and ensuring the operation controls are manned at all times. Lifting equipment for lifting people is subject to specific requirements for statutory examination.

Visual inspection and statutory thorough examination and inspection

Statutory requirements to conduct examinations and inspections of lifting equipment are set out in Regulation 9 of the LOLER 1998. Used lifting equipment must be thoroughly examined before being put into service for the first time by a new user. This does not apply to new lifting equipment (unless its safety depends on installation conditions) or equipment that conforms to European Community requirements and has been certified as being examined within the previous 12 months. Suppliers of used lifting equipment are obliged to certify that a thorough examination has been carried out. Where the safety of lifting equipment depends on the installation conditions, for example a tower crane, it must be thoroughly examined prior to first use, after assembly and on change of location in order to ensure that it has been installed correctly and is safe to operate. Lifting equipment exposed to conditions causing deterioration that is liable to result in dangerous situations is to be thoroughly examined by a competent person:

- At least every 6 months - lifting equipment for lifting persons and lifting accessories.
- At least every 12 months - other lifting equipment.
- In either case, in accordance with an examination scheme.
- On each occurrence of exceptional circumstances liable to jeopardise the safety of the lifting equipment.

Regulation 10 of LOLER 1998 requires that where a defect is discovered that represents a danger to people it must be notified immediately to the employer responsible for conforming to LOLER 1998. In addition, a written report containing information specified in Schedule 1 of LOLER 1998 must be produced and provided as soon as is practicable. The report is to be signed by the competent person carrying out the thorough examination. Where defects are notified, the employer must ensure the equipment is not used until the defect is rectified.

Regulation 11 of LOLER 1998 concerns the keeping of information in relation to examinations and specifies that any report written by a competent person, following an examination, must be kept available for inspection for the period of validity of the report.

Regulation 9 of LOLER 1998 requires that where appropriate to ensure health and safety, inspections must be carried out at suitable intervals between thorough examinations. Similar to thorough examinations, Regulation 10 of LOLER 1998 requires that the person carrying out the inspection must notify the employer if defects that represent a danger to people are discovered and, in any case, as soon as practicable make a record of the inspection in writing. Examinations and inspections must ensure that the good condition of equipment is maintained and that any deterioration can be detected and remedied in good time.

Sample assessment questions

1. A lifting operation is to be carried out with the use of a crane hired for the purpose.

   Outline the main items to be checked by the person appointed to have overall control of this operation. (8)

2. An audit by Senior Management on lifting operations identified that lifts were not planned, defective accessories were being used during lifting and the statutory testing of lifting equipment had not been carried out.

   (a) **Outline** the issues that could be included in a lifting plan. (8)

   (b) **Identify** factors relating to the condition of lifting accessories that could form part of a pre-use checklist. (8)

   (c) **Identify** the frequency of thorough examinations and inspections of lifting equipment required by the Lifting Operations and Lifting Equipment Regulations (LOLER). (4)

3. Manual handling operations can cause injuries.

   (a) **Identify THREE** types of injury that may be caused by the incorrect manual handling of loads. (3)

   (b) With reference to the task, **identify** means of reducing the risk of injury during manual handling operations. (5)

Please refer to back of assessment section for answers.

Work equipment - hazards and risk control

Sources of reference

Buying new machinery, INDG271 (rev1), HSE

BS EN ISO 12100 (formerly BS EN 292), British Standards Institution ISBN 978-0-5806-8672-6

Chainsaws at work, INDG317, HSE Books ISBN 978-0-7176-6187-9

Personal Protective Equipment at Work Regulations 1992 (as amended). Guidance on Regulations, (L25), HSE Books ISBN 978-0-7176-6139-8

Safe use of woodworking machinery (L114), HSE Books ISBN 978-0-7176-1630-5

Safe Use of Work Equipment, ACoP and guidance (part II in particular), L22, third edition 2008, HSE Books ISBN 978-0-7176-6295-1

Supplying new machinery, INDG270 (rev1), HSE

The Health and Safety (Safety Signs and Signals) Regulations 1996, Guidance on regulations, second edition 2009, L64, HSE Books ISBN 978-0-7176-6359-0

Relevant statutory provisions

Health and Safety (Safety Signs and Signals) Regulations 1996

Personal Protective Equipment at Work Regulations (PPER) 1992

Provision and Use of Work Equipment Regulations (PUWER) 1998

Supply of Machinery (Safety) Regulations (SMSR) 2008

5.1 - General requirements for work equipment

Scope of work equipment

The Provision and Use of Work Equipment Regulations (PUWER) 1998 are concerned with most aspects relating to work equipment. The Regulations define work equipment as any machinery, appliance, apparatus, tool or assembly of components that are arranged so that they function as a whole. The term embraces many types of hand tool, power tool and machinery. It also extends to lifting accessories, such as a chain sling.

HAND TOOLS

Common hand tools include trowels, spades, hammers, chisels, planes, screwdrivers.

POWER TOOLS

Common power tools use electric power (battery or 110 volts), diesel or petrol and include various drills, and piling hammers, road breakers, chain and circular saws, bench saws, floor saws, cartridge nail guns.

MACHINERY

In common with power tools, machinery is usually powered by diesel, petrol fuel or compressed air. Examples include:

- Air compressor.
- Scabblers.
- Mobile elevating work platforms (MEWP's).

- Cranes.
- Excavator.
- Rough terrain fork-lift truck (RTFLT).

Not work equipment:

- Livestock.
- Substances.

- Structural items (buildings).
- Private car.

Figure 5-1: Air road breakers.   *Source: Speedy Hire plc.*

Figure 5-2: Floor scabbler.   *Source: Speedy Hire plc.*

Figure 5-3: Hand held scabbler.   *Source: Speedy Hire plc.*

Figure 5-4: Lifting sling.   *Source: RMS.*

Suitability as it relates to provision of equipment

PROVISION OF WORK EQUIPMENT REGULATIONS [PUWER] 1998

PUWER Regulation 4 - Suitability of work equipment

Every employer shall ensure that work equipment is so constructed or adapted as to be suitable for the purpose for which it is used or provided. In selecting work equipment, every employer shall have regard to the working conditions and to the risks to the health and safety of persons which exist in the premises or undertaking in which that work equipment is to be used and any additional risk posed by the use of that work equipment.

Every employer shall ensure that work equipment is used only for operations for which, and under conditions for which, it is suitable. In this regulation "suitable" means suitable in any respect which it is reasonably foreseeable will affect the health or safety of any person.

Suitability should consider:

- Its initial integrity.
- The place where it will be used.
- The purpose for which it will be used.

Integrity - is equipment safe through its design, construction or adaptation - Sharp edges removed from the pen tray of a flip chart stand; 'home made' tools; equipment adapted to do a specific task.

Place - is equipment suitable for different environments (risks) - Wet or explosive. Account must be taken of the equipment causing a problem - a petrol generator used in a confined space; a hydraulic access platform used in a location with a low roof.

Use - is equipment suitable for the specific task - A hacksaw being used to cut metal straps used to secure goods to a pallet (instead of a purpose designed tool); the use of a ladder to do work at a height (instead of a scaffold or other access platform); exceeding the safe working load of a crane or fork-lift truck, a swivel chair used as a means of access to a shelf.

CONFORMITY WITH RELEVANT STANDARDS, CE MARKING

Section 6 of The Health and Safety at Work Act (HASAWA) 1974 requires those involved in the supply (including design and manufacture) of equipment to ensure that it is safe and healthy, so far as is reasonably practicable. This will require them to take account of all relevant standards.

PUWER Regulation 10 - Conformity with community requirements

Every employer shall ensure that an item of work equipment has been designed and constructed in compliance with any essential requirements, that is to say, requirements relating to its design or construction in any of the instruments listed in Schedule 1 (being instruments which give effect to Community directives concerning the safety of products).

Where an essential requirement is applied to the design or construction of an item of work equipment, the requirements of regulations 11 to 19 and 22 to 29 shall apply in respect of that item only to the extent that the essential requirement did not apply to it.

This regulation applies to items of work equipment provided for use in the premises or undertaking of the employer for the first time after 31st December 1992.

Work equipment provided for use after 31 December 1992 must conform with legislation made in the UK in response to EC directives relating to work equipment. Only those directives listed in schedule 1 of PUWER 1998 are to be considered and then only those that have been translated to UK law. Examples relate to:

- The amount of noise emitted from a variety of equipment (for example, construction equipment or lawn mowers).
- Electro-medical equipment.
- Simple pressure vessels.
- Machinery safety. *See also - Supply of Machinery (Safety) Regulations (SMSR) 2008 - Relevant statutory provisions section.*
- Personal protective equipment.

Directives, and in turn UK Regulations, tend to contain details of 'essential health and safety requirements' and a system whereby compliance may be demonstrated. Compliance is usually demonstrated by the attachment of a CE (Conformité Européene) mark and the manufacturer/supplier holding an EC declaration of conformity.

FIT FOR PURPOSE

Equipment used for any activity must be suitable to fulfil the exact requirements of the task. This means considering the ergonomic requirements *(see following paragraph)*, strength, durability, power source, portability, and protection against the environment, range of tasks to be carried out and the frequency and duration of use.

Equipment that is designed to perform a specific task must only be used for that task and not adapted for other tasks not considered in the manufacturer's design and instructions. An example of this is where a portable battery operated drill is rotated by hand or the back/butt of the drill is used as a hammer, clearly a task not meant for this equipment. Equipment used in these types of situation identifies a lack of forethought in the planning stage of a project when the correct equipment should have been sought and used.

The equipment may be used indoors or outdoors where consideration must be given to the dangers of damp, water and electricity or explosive atmospheres within confined spaces. The grade of equipment should be industrial or commercial type for work activities and not the type of equipment designed for personal use at home.

Whenever equipment is required, the full capacity and limitation requirements should be identified and it should be confirmed that the equipment provided can cope with the demands/limitations placed upon it. For example, construction sites use 110 volt supply and it is important that workers only use equipment that suits this power supply.

ERGONOMIC CONSIDERATIONS

Ergonomic considerations involve the study of person-equipment interface, with an emphasis on adjustability of the machinery and equipment. The aim is to suit a variety of individual sizes and positions in order to provide the most comfortable position possible. In considering the ergonomic factors of a task that requires equipment to be used, it is essential to include the operator's individual attributes, and how they affect and may be affected by the process. Factors might include posture when seated or standing, height of the work station, how the equipment may be adjusted and frequency of the task being performed. It is essential that ergonomic considerations form an active part at the planning stage of a process to ensure the correct equipment is obtained and the reactive effects of poor ergonomics eliminated.

Requirement to restrict the use and maintenance of equipment

PUWER 1998, Regulation 7, sets out the following requirements to control specific risks related to work equipment:

"(1) Where the use of work equipment is likely to involve a specific risk to health or safety, every employer shall ensure that:

(a) *The use of that work equipment is restricted to those persons given the task of using it.*

(b) *Repairs, modifications, maintenance or servicing of that work equipment is restricted to those persons who have been specifically designated to perform operations of that description (whether or not also authorised to perform other operations).*

(2) *The employer shall ensure that the persons designated for the purposes of sub-paragraph (b) of paragraph (1) have received adequate training related to any operations in respect of which they have been so designated."*

For example, in view of the specific risks, it would be appropriate to restrict the use of a nail gun, circular saw or mobile elevated work platform to those competent and authorised to use it. In the same way, maintenance of an abrasive wheel (replacement of a grinding wheel) or a rough terrain fork-lift truck (replacement of load bearing components) should be restricted.

Information, instruction and training

INFORMATION AND INSTRUCTION

Whenever equipment is provided and used in the workplace there is a requirement to ensure that all operators are given adequate information and instruction in order that they can use the equipment safely. The issues covered should include the safe operation of the equipment and also the capacities and limitations of the equipment. Specific information must be given on the particular hazards of equipment, and instruction and training given on how to implement, use and maintain control measures correctly.

PUWER Regulation 8 - Information and instruction

PUWER 1998, Regulation 8, sets out the following requirements with regard to information and instruction:

"Every employer shall ensure that all persons who use work equipment have available to them adequate health and safety information and, where appropriate, written instructions pertaining to the use of the work equipment.

Every employer shall ensure that any of his employees who supervises or manages the use of work equipment has available to him adequate health and safety information and, where appropriate, written instructions pertaining to the use of the work equipment, information and, where appropriate, written instructions on:

(a) *The conditions in which and the methods by which the work equipment may be used.*

(b) *Foreseeable abnormal situations and the action to be taken if such a situation were to occur.*

(c) *Any conclusions to be drawn from experience in using the work equipment".*

TRAINING

PUWER Regulation 9 - Training

PUWER 1998, Regulation 9, sets out the following requirements with regard to training:

"Every employer shall ensure that all persons who use work equipment have received adequate training for purposes of health and safety, including training in the methods which may be adopted when using the work equipment, any risks which such use may entail and precautions to be taken.

Every employer shall ensure that any of his employees who supervises or manages the use of work equipment has received adequate training for purposes of health and safety, including training in the methods which may be adopted when using the work equipment, any risks which such use may entail and precautions to be taken".

Training may be needed for existing staff as well as inexperienced staff or new starters (including temporary staff), particularly if they have to use powered machinery. The greater the danger, the better the training needs to be. For some high risk work such as driving fork-lift trucks, using a chainsaw and operating a crane, training should be carried out by specialist instructors. Remember that younger people can be quite skilful when moving and handling powered equipment, but they may lack experience and judgment and may require closer supervision to begin with.

Examples:

- *Users* - how to carry out pre-use checks, report defects, only to use equipment for the purpose designed.
- *Maintenance* - safe isolation, acceptable replacement parts and adjustments in accordance with manufacturer's manuals.
- *Managers* - be aware of the hazards and controls and maintain effective supervision.

In addition, where the use of work equipment is likely to involve a specific risk to health and safety the employer must provide those restricted to repair, modify, maintain or service the equipment with adequate training.

Equipment to be maintained and maintenance conducted safely

EQUIPMENT TO BE MAINTAINED

Procedures for defective equipment

Under section 7 of the HASAWA 1974 and Regulation 14 of the Management of Health and Safety at Work Regulations (MHSWR) 1999, employees have a duty to and should notify any shortcomings in the health and safety arrangements, even when no immediate danger exists, so that employers can take remedial action if needed. The duties placed on employees do not reduce the responsibility of the employer to comply with his own duties. Regulation 5 of PUWER 1998 requires equipment to be maintained. With duties being placed upon both the employer and the employee to ensure the use of safe equipment, when identified in the workplace, faulty equipment should be isolated until such a time it can be repaired by a competent party.

PUWER Regulation 5 - Maintenance

PUWER 1998, Regulation 5, sets out the following requirements with regard to the maintenance of work equipment:

"Every employer shall ensure that work equipment is maintained in an efficient state, in efficient working order and in good repair".

In order to achieve this, a system of maintenance should be in place that includes regular adjustment, replacement of parts and testing. Maintenance logs, where they exist, must be kept up to date.

MAINTENANCE TO BE CONDUCTED SAFELY

PUWER Regulation 22 - Maintenance

No one should be exposed to undue risk during maintenance operations. In order to achieve this equipment should be stopped and isolated as appropriate before work starts. If it is necessary to keep equipment running then the risks must be adequately controlled. This may take the form of controlling running speed, range of movement or providing temporary guards. Consideration must be given to other legislation, such as Electricity at Work Regulations (EWR) 1989, during the assessment of risks involved in maintenance work.

Maintenance hazards

The principal sources of hazards are associated with maintenance work on:

- Heavy plant.
- Crushers.
- Cranes.
- Concrete pumps.
- Storage tanks.
- Large hoists and lifts.

Typical hazards associated with maintenance operations

Mechanical	Entanglements, machinery traps, contact; shearing traps, in-running nips, ejection, unexpected start up.
Electrical	Electrocution, shock, burns.
Pressure	Unexpected pressure releases, explosion.
Physical	Extremes of temperature, noise, vibration, dust.
Chemical	Gases, vapours, mists, fumes, etc.
Structural	Obstructions and floor openings.
Access	Work at heights, confined spaces.

Typical accidents

- Crushing by moving machinery.
- Falls.
- Asphyxiation.
- Electrocution.
- Explosions.
- Burns.

One or more of the following factors causes maintenance accidents:

- Lack of perception of risk by managers/supervisors, often because of lack of necessary training.

- Unsafe or no system of work devised, for example, no permit-to-work system in operation, no facility to lock off machinery and electricity supply before work starts and until work has finished.
- No coordination between workers, and communication with other supervisors or managers.
- Lack of perception of risk by workers, including failure to wear protective clothing or equipment.
- Inadequacy of design, installation, siting of plant and equipment.
- Use of contractors with no health and safety systems or who are inadequately briefed on health and safety aspects.

Maintenance to be conducted safely

Isolation

This does not simply mean switching off the equipment using the stop button. It includes switching the equipment off at the start button and switching off the isolator for the equipment. In new workplaces, individual equipment isolators should be provided; i.e. each piece of equipment has its own isolator near to it. One isolator should not control several items of equipment as it is then impossible to isolate a single piece of equipment on its own.

Figure 5-5: Conveyor.   Source: RMS.

Figure 5-6: Electrical isolator with hole for padlock. *Source: RMS.*

Lock out and tag out

Isolation alone does not afford adequate protection, because there is nothing to prevent the isolator being switched back on, or removed fuses being replaced inadvertently while the person who isolated the item in the first place is still working on the equipment. To ensure that this does not happen, the isolator needs to be physically locked in the off position (typically using a padlock, the key to be held by the person in danger). Multiple lock out devices are often used where multiple trades are carrying out work on the same equipment or plant; they are designed to carry a number of isolation padlocks for the different people working on the equipment; the equipment cannot be energised until all the padlocks are removed, thereby protecting the last worker on the job. It is also a good idea to sign *"Do not switch on..."* or tag on the equipment at the point of isolation.

Figure 5-7: Physical isolation of valve.   *Source: RMS.*

Figure 5-8: Multiple (padlock) lock off device.   *Source: RMS.*

Summary of control measures

- Plan work in advance - provide safe access, support parts of equipment which could fail.
- Use written safe systems of work, method statements or permit to work systems as appropriate.
- Plan specific operations using method statements.
- Use physical means of isolating or locking off plant.
- Systems of working should incorporate two-man working for high risk operations.
- Integrate safety requirements in the planning of specific high risk tasks.
- Prevent unauthorised access to the work area by using barriers and signs.
- Ensure the competence of those carrying out the work.

- Ensure the availability and use of appropriate personal protective equipment (PPE) - gloves, eye protection.
- Prevent fire or explosion - thoroughly clean vessels that have contained flammable solids or liquids, gases or dusts and check them thoroughly before hot work is carried out.

Visual inspection and statutory thorough examination and inspection

INSPECTION

PUWER Regulation 6 - inspection

"Every employer shall ensure that work equipment exposed to conditions causing deterioration which is liable to result in dangerous situations is inspected:

(a) At suitable intervals.

(b) Each time that exceptional circumstances which are liable to jeopardise the safety of the work equipment have occurred, to ensure that health and safety conditions are maintained and that any deterioration can be detected and remedied in good time.

Every employer shall ensure that the result of an inspection made under this regulation is recorded and kept until the next inspection under this regulation is recorded".

Figure 5-9: Inspection and examination.   *Source: RMS.*

Equipment must be inspected on a regular basis in order to confirm the condition that it is in. The inspection required may be a regular visual inspection or daily pre-use check carried out by the operator. The person using equipment, who should be confirmed as competent, should carry out operator checks prior to the use of any equipment. Operator checks should include guards, cables, casing integrity, cutting or machine parts and safety devices such as cut-outs.

The requirements of Regulation 6 of PUWER 1998 extend to inspections that are more significant and address a list of identifiable health and safety critical parts. For example, the main items on a *dumper truck* that should be the subject to periodic inspection include: the provision and condition of roll over protection and driver restraints (for example, seat belts); the condition of the bodywork and seats; the condition of the tyres; the effectiveness of the braking system, steering and warning devices; the performance of the bucket release and tilt mechanisms; the integrity of fuel, oil and hydraulic systems and the legibility of labels and signs.

Similarly, the main items for regular (for example, weekly) inspection of a 360° wheeled *excavator* include: hydraulic systems; wheels and tyres; windscreens and other windows; brakes and steering; the condition of bodywork and seats (including any seat belts); lights and visual warning devices; the condition of mirrors and other rear view equipment and the proper functioning of the controls. An inspection sheet should be used to control the inspection process. The purpose of an inspection sheet is to record deterioration of specific parts, abuse and misuse, also to ensure that all items are considered at the time of inspection, by serving as an aide memoir. The results of the inspection will confirm whether or not a piece of equipment is in a safe enough condition to use. Other regulations, such as the Lifting Operations and Lifting Equipment Regulations (LOLER) 1998 require and set certain statutory inspection requirements. Note also that Regulation 6(5) of PUWER 1998 has been amended by the Work at Height Regulations (WAH) 2005 to include 'work equipment to which Regulation 12 of the WAH 2005 applies'. *See also - Work at Height Regulations (WAH) 2005 - Relevant statutory provisions section.*

THOROUGH EXAMINATION

PUWER 1998 does not contain a general requirement for the thorough examination of all work equipment. However, specific requirements exist in the Lifting Operations and Lifting Equipment Regulations (LOLER) 1998 regarding such equipment as MEWPs, cranes and accessories. LOLER 1998 essentially sets out requirements for thorough examination under four situations:

- When lifting equipment is first 'supplied', i.e. used for the first time by that employer.
- When certain equipment is 'installed' and its safety is dependent on installation conditions, for example, a tower crane.
- Periodically, during the lifetime of the equipment.
- Following exceptional circumstances.

The periodic thorough examination must be:

- In the case of lifting equipment for lifting persons or an accessory for lifting, at least every 6 months.
- In the case of other lifting equipment, at least every 12 months.
- In either case, in accordance with an examination scheme determined by a competent person.

Where a defect is discovered that represents a danger to people it must be notified immediately to the employer responsible for compliance with LOLER 1998. In addition, a written report containing information specified in

Schedule 1 of LOLER 1998 must be produced and provided. Where defects are notified, the employer must ensure the equipment is not used until the defect is rectified.

See also – Element 4 - "Requirements for regular visual inspection and statutory requirements for the thorough examination and inspection of lifting equipment" - for further information.

There is also a legislative requirement for the thorough examination of pressure systems under the Pressure Systems Safety Regulations (PSSR) 2000.

A pressure system is, as defined in the Pressure Systems Safety Regulations (PSSR) 2000, as follows:

- A system comprising one or more pressure vessels of rigid construction, and any associated pipework and protective devices.
- The pipework with its protective devices to which a transportable gas container is or is intended to be connected.
- A pipeline and its protective devices.

A pressure vessel is generally considered to be one that operates at a pressure greater than atmospheric pressure, for example, steam boilers and air receivers. PSSR 2000 requires that a competent person draw up a written scheme of examination for the pressure system and that thorough examinations are carried out in accordance with the written scheme.

Adequate records of thorough examinations, repairs, modifications etc., should be kept at the premises where the equipment is used.

Figure 5-10: Air compressor. *Source: Speedy Hire plc.*

Importance of operation and emergency controls, etc.

OPERATION AND EMERGENCY CONTROLS

PUWER Regulation 14 - Controls for starting or making a significant change in operating conditions

PUWER 1998, Regulation 14, sets out the following requirements with regard to operating controls for work equipment:

"(1) Every employer shall ensure that, where appropriate, work equipment is provided with one or more controls for the purposes of:

(a) Starting the work equipment (including re-starting after a stoppage for any reason).

(b) Controlling any change in the speed, pressure or other operating conditions of the work equipment where such conditions after the change result in risk to health and safety which is greater than or of a different nature from such risks before the change.

(2) Subject to paragraph (3), every employer shall ensure that where a control is required by paragraph (1), it shall not be possible to perform any operation mentioned in sub-paragraph (a) or (b) of that paragraph except by a deliberate action on such control."

Paragraph (1) does not apply to re-starting or changing operating conditions as a result of the normal operating cycle of an automatic device.

Any change in the operating conditions should only be possible by the use of a control, except if the change does not increase risk to health or safety. Examples of operating conditions include speed, distance, height, angle, pressure, temperature and power. The controls provided should be designed and positioned so as to prevent, so far as possible, inadvertent or accidental operation. Buttons and levers should be of appropriate design, for example, including a shroud or locking facility. It should not be possible for the control to 'operate itself' because of the effects of gravity, vibration, or failure of a spring mechanism.

For most equipment used in construction activities, the controls should be of the 'hold to run' type, as it is not generally appropriate to leave it in an active condition without operator attention. This will also provide a higher standard of safety, ensuring that the operator is in immediate control of such equipment as MEWPs, cranes, excavators and other high hazard equipment.

PUWER Regulation 15 - Stop controls

PUWER 1998, Regulation 15, sets out the following requirements with regard to stop controls for work equipment:

"(1) Every employer shall ensure that, where appropriate, work equipment is provided with one or more readily accessible controls the operation of which will bring the work equipment to a safe condition in a safe manner.

(2) Any control required by paragraph (1) shall bring the work equipment to a complete stop where necessary for reasons of health and safety.

(3) Any control required by paragraph (1) shall, if necessary for reasons of health and safety, switch off all sources of energy after stopping the functioning of the work equipment.

(4) Any control required by paragraph (1) shall operate in priority to any control, which starts or changes the operating conditions of the work equipment."

The primary requirement of this Regulation is that the action of the control should bring the equipment to a safe condition in a safe manner. This acknowledges that it is not always desirable to bring all items of work equipment immediately to a complete or instantaneous stop, for example, to prevent the unsafe build-up of heat or pressure or to allow a controlled run-down of large rotating parts. Similarly, stopping the mixing mechanism of a reactor during certain chemical reactions could lead to a dangerous exothermic reaction.

The Regulation is qualified by 'where necessary for reasons of health and safety'. Therefore, accessible dangerous parts must be rendered stationary. However, parts of equipment which do not present a risk, such as suitably guarded cooling fans, do not need to be positively stopped and may be allowed to idle.

PUWER Regulation 16 - Emergency stop controls

The function of an emergency stop control device is to provide a means to bring a machine to a rapid halt. It is provided in such circumstances where it would be of benefit and should be readily available to the operator and/or others. It should be easy to operate and clearly discernible from other controls. PUWER 1998, Regulation 16, sets out the following requirements with regard to emergency stop controls for work equipment:

"(1) Every employer shall ensure that, where appropriate, work equipment is provided with one or more readily accessible emergency stop controls unless it is not necessary by reason of the nature of the hazards and the time taken for the work equipment to come to a complete stop as a result of the action of any control provided by virtue of regulation 15(1).

(2) Any control required by paragraph (1) shall operate in priority to any control required by regulation 15(1)."

Emergency stops are intended to affect a rapid response to potentially dangerous situations and they should not be used as functional stops during normal operation. Emergency stop controls should be easily reached and actuated. Common types are mushroom-headed buttons, bars, levers, kick plates, or pressure-sensitive cables.

Figure 5-11: Controls and emergency stop.   Source: RMS.

Figure 5-12: Controls.   Source: RMS.

PUWER Regulation 17 - Controls

PUWER 1998, Regulation 17, sets out the following general requirements for controls fitted to work equipment:

"(1) Every employer shall ensure that all controls for work equipment shall be clearly visible and identifiable, including by appropriate marking where necessary.

It should be possible to identify easily what each control does and on which equipment it takes effect. Both the controls and their markings should be clearly visible. As well as having legible wording or symbols, factors such as the colour, shape and position of controls are important.

(2) Except where necessary, the employer shall ensure that no control for work equipment is in a position where any person operating the control is exposed to a risk to his health or safety.

(3) Every employer shall ensure where appropriate:

(a) That, so far as is reasonably practicable, the operator of any control is able to ensure from the position of that control that no person is in a place where he would be exposed to any risk to his health or safety as a result of the operation of that control, but where or to the extent that it is not reasonably practicable.

(b) That, so far as is reasonably practicable, systems of work are effective to ensure that, when work equipment is about to start, no person is in a place where he would be exposed to a risk to his health or safety as a result of the work equipment starting, but where neither of these is reasonably practicable.

(c) That an audible, visible or other suitable warning is given by virtue of regulation 24 whenever work equipment is about to start.

(4) Every employer shall take appropriate measures to ensure that any person who is in a place where he would be exposed to a risk to his health or safety as a result of the starting or stopping of work equipment has sufficient time and suitable means to avoid that risk."

Warnings given in accordance with regulation 17(3)(c) should be given sufficiently in advance of the equipment actually starting to give those at risk time to get clear. As well as time, suitable means of avoiding the risk should be provided. This may take the form of a device by means of which the person at risk can prevent start-up or warn the operator of his/her presence.

Figure 5-13: Controls.   Source: RMS.

Otherwise, there must be adequate provision to enable people at risk to withdraw, for example, sufficient space or exits. Circumstances will affect the type of warning chosen.

PUWER Regulation 18 - Control systems

PUWER 1998, Regulation 18, sets out the following requirements with regard to control systems for work equipment:

"(1) Every employer shall:

(a) Ensure, so far as is reasonably practicable, that all control systems of work equipment are safe.

(b) Are chosen making due allowance for the failures, faults and constraints to be expected in the planned circumstances of use.

(2) Without prejudice to the generality of paragraph (1), a control system shall not be safe unless:

(a) Its operation does not create any increased risk to health or safety.

(b) It ensures, so far as is reasonably practicable, that any fault in or damage to any part of the control system or the loss of supply of any source of energy used by the work equipment cannot result in additional or increased risk to health or safety.

(c) It does not impede the operation of any control required by regulation 15 or 16."

Failure of any part of the control system or its power supply should lead to a 'fail-safe' condition (more correctly and realistically called 'minimised failure to danger'), and not impede the operation of the 'stop' or 'emergency stop' controls. The measures, which should be taken in the design and application of a control system to mitigate against the effects of failure, will need to be balanced against the consequences of any failure, and the greater the risk, the more resistant the control system should be to the effects of failure.

STABILITY

PUWER Regulation 20 - Stability

PUWER 1998, Regulation 20, sets out the following requirements with regard to stability of work equipment:

"Every employer shall ensure that work equipment or any part of work equipment is stabilised by clamping or otherwise where necessary for purposes of health or safety."

Most machines used in a fixed position should be bolted or otherwise fastened down so that they do not move or rock during use. This is particularly important where the equipment is tall relative to its base or has a high centre of gravity, for example, a pedestal mounted abrasive wheel, platform hoists and tower cranes.

LIGHTING

PUWER Regulation 21 - Lighting

PUWER 1998, Regulation 21, sets out the following requirements with regard to lighting for work equipment:

"Every employer shall ensure that suitable and sufficient lighting, which takes account of the operations to be carried out, is provided at any place where a person uses work equipment."

Local lighting may be needed to give sufficient view of a dangerous process or to reduce visual fatigue.

MARKINGS AND WARNINGS

PUWER Regulation 23 - Markings

PUWER 1998, Regulation 23, sets out the following requirements with regard to markings on work equipment:

"Every employer shall ensure that work equipment is marked in a clearly visible manner with any marking appropriate for reasons of health and safety."

There are similarities between regulation 23 and 24 covering markings and warnings. Certain markings may also serve as a warning, for example, the maximum working speed, maximum working load or maximum reach.

PUWER Regulation 24 - Warnings

PUWER 1998, Regulation 24, sets out the following requirements with regard to warnings on work equipment:

"Every employer shall ensure that work equipment incorporates any warnings or warning devices which are appropriate for reasons of health and safety."

Warnings given by warning devices on work equipment shall not be appropriate unless they are unambiguous, easily perceived and easily understood.

Warnings and warning devices are introduced following the implementation of markings and other physical measures, where appropriate risks to health and safety remain. Warnings are usually in the form of a notice, sign or similar. Examples of warnings are positive instructions (hard hats must be worn); prohibitions (no naked flames) and restrictions (do not heat above 60°C). Warning devices are active units that give out either an audible or visual signal, usually connected to the equipment in order that the warning operates only when a hazard exists. Warning devices are also used where the equipment is mobile; such things as a flashing light can warn of the presence of a dumper truck and an audible device may warn of a vehicle reversing or a concrete pump about to start.

CLEAR UNOBSTRUCTED WORKSPACE

Construction (Design and Management) Regulations (CDM) 2007

Regulation 26 - Safe place of work

CDM 2007, Regulation 26, sets out the following requirements with regard to a safe place of work, including when using work equipment:

"(1) There shall, so far as is reasonably practicable, be suitable and sufficient safe access to and egress from every place of work and to and from every other place provided for the use of any person while at work, which access and egress shall be properly maintained.

(2) Every place of work shall, so far as is reasonably practicable, be made and kept safe for, and without risks to health to, any person at work there.

(3) Suitable and sufficient steps shall be taken to ensure, so far as is reasonably practicable, that no person uses access or egress, or gains access to any place, which does not comply with the requirements of paragraph (1) or (2) respectively.

(4) Every place of work shall, so far as is reasonably practicable, have sufficient working space and be so arranged that it is suitable for any person who is working or who is likely to work there, taking account of any necessary work equipment present."

Workrooms should have enough free space to allow people to get to and from workstations and to move within the room with ease. Where work equipment, such as a circular saw, is used in a workplace care should be taken to ensure that adequate space exists around the equipment to ensure it is not overcrowded and does not cause risk to operators and those passing by the equipment when it is operating.

It is important that the workspace allocated for users of work equipment is maintained clear and unobstructed. Obstructions could lead to slips, trips and falls, which could also involve contact with the equipment or moving parts of the equipment. Material being readied to be worked on, material worked on and any scrap material should not be allowed to build-up in the workspace. Material such as dust, scraps of wood or metal can quickly build-up as the equipment is used. Scrap material must be removed from the workspace at suitable intervals, so that it does not build-up and obstruct the workspace. Good control of the input, output and processing of material is essential.

Responsibilities of users

Management of Health and Safety at Work (MHSWR) Regulation 1999, Regulation 14 - Employees' duties

MHSWR 1999, Regulation 14, sets out the following requirements with regard to employees' duties, including use of work equipment:

"Every employee shall use any machinery, equipment, dangerous substance, transport equipment, means of production or safety device provided to him by his employer in accordance both with any training in the use of the equipment concerned which has been received by him and the instructions respecting that use which have

been provided to him by the said employer in compliance with the requirements and prohibitions imposed upon that employer by or under the relevant statutory provisions".

Employees have a duty under Section 7 of the HASAWA 1974 to take reasonable care for their own health and safety and for that of others who may be affected by their acts or omissions and to co-operate with the employer to enable him to comply with statutory duties for health and safety. This includes the appropriate use of work equipment. The duty under Section 7 is further accentuated by the duties expressed in Regulation 14 of MHSWR 1999 to use equipment in accordance with training and instructions.

Supporting the Section 7 of HASAWA 1974 duty to co-operate with the employer employees have a duty under Regulation 14 of MHSWR 1999 to:

"Inform his employer or any other employee of that employer with specific responsibility for the health and safety of his fellow employees:

(a) Of any work situation which a person with the first-mentioned employee's training and instruction would reasonably consider represented a serious and immediate danger to health and safety.

(b) Of any matter which a person with the first-mentioned employee's training and instruction would reasonably consider represented a shortcoming in the employer's protection arrangements for health and safety, in so far as that situation or matter either affects the health and safety of that first mentioned employee or arises out of or in connection with his own activities at work, and has not previously been reported to his employer or to any other employee of that employer in accordance with this paragraph".

This would mean that if a user of work equipment, for example, a crane operator, found that the equipment was not working safely or had missed a scheduled thorough examination that they were aware it required they must report this to their employer. The duties placed on employees do not reduce the responsibility of employers to comply with their own duties.

5.2 - Hand-held tools

Hand tools

HAZARDS AND MISUSE OF HAND TOOLS (NON-POWERED)

Anyone who uses a non-powered hand-held tool (hand tool) may be at risk of injury, either accidentally, through misuse or equipment failure. There is a range of risks from using hand tools, many of the hazards can affect the user of the hand tools and those passing or working nearby. For example:

- Noise induced hearing loss from cutting or impact tools.
- Respiratory disease from inhalation of dust from sanding.
- Eye injury from material thrown off from chiselling.
- Punctures and cuts caused by sharp equipment such as knives, chisels, saws, planes and screwdrivers.
- Heat-producing equipment, such as blowtorches, can cause burns and permanent scarring.
- Hammers are basic tools, but they are also notorious for causing thumb and finger injuries.

Misuse includes using the wrong tool for the job, for example, a hammer to drive home a screw, rather than a screwdriver, or a file, which is brittle, as a lever.

CONTROL MEASURES FOR HAND TOOLS

Hammers

The following checklist will help to avoid incidents with hammers:

- Check the condition of the hammer - avoid split, broken or loose handles and worn or chipped heads. Heads should be properly secured to the handles.
- Grip the handle firmly.
- Hold the hammer at the end of the handle.
- Hit the surface squarely with the hammer.
- Use the whole arm and elbow.
- Place the work against a hard surface.
- Work in a natural position.
- Check area is clear around you before swinging the hammer.
- Practice good hammering technique.

Files

These should have a proper, well designed handle. The file should be held firmly in one hand with the fingers of the other hand used only to guide the file. The material being filed should be firmly held in clamps or a vice. File strokes should be made away from the user. Take care to avoid the file slipping on the surface of the material causing sudden forward movement of the user. Files must never be used as a lever - they are very brittle and will shatter easily. They should only be cleaned by using a cleaning card and not by striking them against a solid object as this can also cause the file to shatter.

Chisels

Choose a chisel large enough for the job, so the blade is used rather than only the point or corner. Never use chisels with dull blades - the sharper the tool, the better the performance. Chisels that are bent, cracked, or chipped should be discarded. The cutting edge should be sharpened to the correct angle. Do not allow the head of cold chisels to spread to a mushroom shape - grind off the sides regularly. Use a hand guard on the chisel and hit the chisel squarely. Chisels should not be used as a lever as they may break suddenly.

Screwdrivers

A screwdriver is one of the most commonly used and abused tools. The practice of using screwdrivers as punches, wedges, or levers should be discouraged as this practice dulls blades and may cause injury if the blade fractures or slips in use. Screwdrivers should be selected so the tip fits the screw. When working on electrical equipment screwdrivers must be equipped with insulated handles and blades. Screwdrivers with split handles or damaged tips should be taken out of use and discarded safely.

Spanners

Avoid spanners with splayed or damaged jaws. Use ring spanners or sockets where possible, as these are less likely to slip. Discard safely any spanners that show signs of slipping. Ensure enough spanners of the correct size are available. Do not improvise by using pipes, etc., as extensions to the handle. Where necessary use penetrating oil to loosen tight nuts. Where there is a potential for a flammable atmosphere to be present use alloy or bronze tools to prevent sparks.

Common portable power tools used in construction

PNEUMATIC DRILL/CHISEL

Pneumatic drills or chisels are used commonly where heavy duty tasks are performed such as penetrating tarmac or concrete surfaces. This equipment is usually very heavy and labour intensive, resulting in manual handling hazards and risks. The pneumatic energy is usually delivered through mobile industrial compressors that are capable of supplying adequate power.

Hazards

The compressor is a separate piece of equipment that introduces its own specific hazards. Perhaps the most obvious hazard is the drill or chisel piece which, when operating, presents a risk of impact injury to the feet of users, and others nearby. During normal operation, the drill or chisel tool produces high intensity noise from contact with the surface. Other noise includes the exhausting of the pneumatic pressure from the internal drive of the equipment as the tool operates. The noise sources are located very close to the user's ears, are at a level that is damaging to the ear and require the user to wear hearing protection. The operation of the chisel produces the hazard of flying debris in the form of dust and fragments that pose the risk of abrasion, cuts or eye damage.

Control measures

In order to control this risk the surface may be damped down and protective goggles worn by the user. The energy produced by the compressor is converted into vibration. Vibration introduces the risk of injuries, such as hand arm vibration syndrome (HAVS), with possible long term effects, including damage to the nervous system beginning at the fingertips. Precautions for vibration include using well maintained equipment, using equipment with lower vibration levels, taking frequent breaks or job rotation, exercise to improve circulation and warm the hands and seeking suitable personal protective gloves. There are risks associated with high pressure air lines becoming broken or damaged resulting in pipes lashing freely. Equipment should always be inspected as safe to use with certification for pressure lines. Screens can be used as a final measure to protect others at the location where the equipment is used.

ELECTRIC DRILL

Electric drills are used for penetrating various materials and in construction are usually of a medium to heavy-duty nature. This equipment involves rotating shafts and tool bits, sharp tools, electricity and flying debris.

Hazards

Hazards include shock and electrocution leading to possible fatalities; however this potential is reduced by using 110 volt or battery operated equipment. Other hazards include puncture, entanglement, ejection of materials and parts of the drill, noise and dust.

Control measures

Control measures include using only equipment that is suitable for the task, ensuring equipment is tested and inspected as safe to use, suitable shut off and isolation measures, goggles, hearing protection. It is important to check that drill bits are securely and centrally held in the drill chuck. Care should be taken to ensure the drill bits are kept sharp as injuries can occur when the rotating drill bit gets stuck in the material being drilled and the drill is caused to kick and rotate in the user's hands.

DISC CUTTER/CUT OFF SAW

Disc cutters/cut off saws consists of a motor providing power to a circular cutting disc, usually made of steel with diamond cutter sections. Power is provided by petrol, diesel, electricity or pneumatic energy. This equipment is used for slicing materials into sections or cutting grooves into surfaces.

Control measures

Goggles must be worn when operating this equipment. Due to the velocity of the flying debris they must be grade 1 impact resistant and totally enclose the eye region of the face. Dust masks must also be worn when using this equipment; however the area being cut into may be damped down to minimise the production of dust clouds into the atmosphere. Vacuum attachments are available that make these operation almost dust-less when working correctly. Sparks arising from cutting operations can result in a fire and in order to control this risk, good housekeeping practice is essential; sources of fuel must be removed from the work area.

Figure 5-14: Cut off saw.   *Source: STIHL.*

Misuse of this equipment must be prevented through training and supervision, including using the side of the cutting disc, using over worn discs, using the incorrect disc for the material being cut, leaving the cutter with the disc still spinning and not wearing the appropriate personal protective equipment (PPE). The disc, when spinning, may lead to cuts of cables, hands and legs; entanglement with rotating parts; noise and hearing damage.

CHOP SAW

These saws are normally powered by electricity, however petrol motors are available. They consist of a motorised disc or saw blade, which has an enclosed guard. This is mounted on a counter sprung or a pneumatic arm which is operated by pulling down onto the materials to be cut. These are usually used to cut brick, stone, timber, steel, aluminium and plastic into manageable lengths.

Hazards

Hazards associated with these saws are cuts, entanglement, electric shock, fire, inhalation of fumes, dusts, ejection of material, such as metal shavings or small off-cuts.

Figure 5-15: Chop saw. *Source: Draper Tools.*

Control measures

Only trained and competent workers should use this equipment due to the hazards; the saw should be fitted with a method of locking-off the equipment to prevent unauthorised use. The saw should be fitted with an adjustable fixed or self-adjusting guard to enclose the blade. Goggles and protective clothing must be worn to prevent injuries from flying debris or dusts/fumes from harming the human body. The equipment should be isolated from the mains supply prior to changing any cutting discs or replacing saw blades.

SANDER

Hazards

Sanding equipment is available in a variety of sizes from hand held equipment to large industrial machines. Sanders are used to provide a smooth finished surface, using a mechanical abrasive action.

Sanding operations are carried out on a wide variety of materials including wood, minerals such as marble and man-made fibres. The main hazards associated with the sanding process are vibration and noise. Also, harm can be caused by the inhalation of respirable particles from dust. Where organic materials such as wood are being processed, fire may result from overheated surfaces or explosion from dust by-products. Associated hazards may include electrocution if supply cables are damaged by hand held sanders, particularly if the sander is placed on the ground whilst still rotating.

Figure 5-16: Belt sander. *Source: Clarke International.*

Other risks include trips from trailing leads, cuts from sharp surfaces and strains or sprains from manual handling of process materials.

Control measures

When using sanding equipment, suitable personal respiratory protective equipment (RPE) is required to protect the user from dust exposure. Where possible, local exhaust ventilation equipment should be used to minimise dust in the atmosphere. In order to protect against vibration injuries, the operator should be given regular breaks and the equipment maintained at intervals, including the renewal of sanding media to prevent the need for over exertion by the operator.

Where tools like sanders are held in the hand, suitable hand protection will also reduce injuries from vibration, cuts and manual handling. Pre-use inspections by the operator and regular thorough examinations should be carried out to identify potential electrical problems. Care should be taken to ensure that power leads do not create tripping hazards and they are positioned so that the likelihood of mechanical damage is minimised.

CARTRIDGE AND PNEUMATIC NAIL GUNS

Guns for nails and other fixings are used in many activities in construction including carpentry, steelwork, plastering and surveying. Power sources range from battery power, electrical low voltage, pneumatic and explosive cartridge. They are used for shooting nails or pins into materials in order to secure a section.

Figure 5-17: Cartridge fixing gun. *Source: ITW.*

Pneumatic guns may be operated by a pressurised changeable cylinder or compressor fed supply. Pneumatic guns usually provide a continuous supply of fixings from a belt or other type of magazine. Explosive cartridge guns are available in single cartridge manual change or fast loading format, the latter often being used to fix roofing and decking to steelwork. Some fixing guns operate using a fuel cell and small linear combustion engine, the controlled combustion/explosion providing the energy to drive the fixing into the material.

Hazards

The puncture hazard of fixings fired from the gun is the main hazard and can affect the user and people in the area where the gun is used.

Figure 5-18: Pneumatic nail gun. *Source: Bostitch.*

There is a significant risk of flying debris from fixing operations and impact/puncture injuries to eyes or hands are likely from the flying debris and fixings released incorrectly from the gun. The noise produced is high intensity impact noise and represents a significant hazard; it may also be amplified by the material it is vibrating through.

Vibrations produced by the use of this equipment, which is grasped in the hand, may present a risk of causing HAVS in sustained use. The high pressure air used with some fixing guns creates a hazard of injection of air into the body. The explosive cartridges used with some fixing guns can present an explosive hazard coupled with the hazard of ejection of cartridge materials.

Figure 5-19: Pneumatic nail gun. *Source: Bostitch.*

Control measures

It is important users of these guns are trained to keep their hands away from the firing zone. This may be assisted by using clamps and other devices instead of the user's hand to hold materials in position prior to fixing. Impact resistant goggles or face protection must be worn when using the gun.

Personal hearing protection must be worn at all times due to the risk of hearing damage from the high intensity impact noise. Equipment must be maintained to reduce vibration levels and operators instructed to take regular rest breaks and report any prolonged numbness to fingers or hands to their supervisor.

Procedures should be in place to ensure there is a safe zone around and behind the fixing area. The lowest power explosive cartridge or air pressure capable of making the fixing should be used, to avoid fixings passing through material being fixed. Arrangements should be in place to deal with 'miss-fires" and jams of fixings within the gun. Where explosive cartridges are used, strict control must be placed over the storage and issue of the cartridges.

CHAINSAW

Chainsaws are predominately used in arboreal work, for tree felling, logging and pruning. In construction activities this may be part of remediation/site preparation work or final ground works before handover to users of a building or structure.

Hazards

Chainsaws are potentially dangerous pieces of equipment that can cause major injuries and even death if not used correctly. Injuries can occur to the head from kick back of the blade and injuries to the legs from inadvertent follow through when cutting horizontally. The potential for eye injuries from wood chipping is also high. Other hazards include falls from a height, falling branches, sawdust and exhaust gas inhalation. As the equipment used is often powered by a petrol engine there is a risk of fire. Health hazards include potential back problems from poor posture whilst working with extended reach.

Figure 5-20: Petrol chainsaw. *Source: Mowdirect Garden Machinery.*

Chainsaws also expose users to high levels of noise and hand-arm vibration, which can lead to hearing loss and conditions such as vibration white finger.

Control measures

The Approved Code of Practice supporting Regulation 9 of the Provision and Use of Work Equipment Regulations (PUWER) 1998, regarding training, sets a minimum standard for competence of people using chainsaws in tree work. All employees using chain saws should receive adequate and appropriate training and have obtained a relevant certificate of competence or a national competence award. The Health and Safety Executive (HSE) information leaflet INDG317 and Arboriculture and Forestry Advisory Group (AFAG) leaflet AFAG805 advises that chainsaw users should have regular refresher/update training to ensure they work to industry best practice and maintain their levels of competence. The suggested intervals for such training are: occasional users - every two to three years; full-time users - every five years.

Maintenance schedules are essential for safe use and protection against ill-health from excessive noise and vibration. The saw must be maintained in its manufactured condition with all the safety devices in efficient working order and all guards in place. It should be regularly serviced by someone who is competent to do the job. Chainsaw users should report any damage or excessive wear from daily checks. Suitable PPE is essential to protect the user from hazards; this must comply with European standards for suitability of use with chainsaws ("Protective clothing for users of hand-held chain saws" - BS EN 381). PPE selected should be suitable for chainsaw work and whenever possible hand, arm and legs should be protected by PPE lined with cut prevention webbing that jams and stops the chain on contact. Head and face protection should also be of a suitable quality for protection against chainsaw contact. Equipment must be maintained to reduce vibration levels and operators instructed to take regular rest breaks and report any prolonged numbness to fingers or hands to their supervisor.

Suitability for location

In explosive or flammable atmospheres only correctly rated anti-spark hand-held tools should be used. Electrical tools for example, drills should be totally enclosed to prevent sparks from the motor igniting and causing explosions in flammable atmospheres. These tools are made from an alloy metal know commonly as 'gun metal' which do not cause sparks when in contact with other metals. A good example of this is fuel tanks on cars and petrol pumps.

It should be remembered that petrol driven portable power tools are popular in construction activities as they can be used where no electrical supply is available. This makes them useful for use on large open construction sites, particularly in the first phases of the construction activities, including site surveying, clearance and preparation. However, they will not be suitable for use in confined areas where the exhaust gases could build-up. The carbon monoxide created as a product of combustion would make them unsuitable in cellars, sewers and many indoor areas. Electrical equipment may be unsuitable for use in particularly adverse wet weather conditions, working in or near water or where water from processes may fall onto or be transferred by hand to the equipment.

Procedures for defective equipment

With duties being placed upon both the employer and the employee to ensure the use of safe equipment, when faulty equipment is identified in the workplace it should be isolated until such a time it can be repaired by a competent person.

Under section 7 of the HASAWA 1974 and Regulation 14 of MHSWR 1999 employees have a duty to notify any shortcomings in the health and safety arrangements where there is a danger, and should do this even when no immediate danger exists. This is to enable employers to take remedial action if needed. The duties placed on employees do not reduce the responsibility of employers to comply with their own duties. A formal procedure should be in place to anticipate this need for reporting shortcomings; it should particularly take account of the need to report defects in hand tools. Under Regulation 5 of the PUWER 1998, *"every employer shall ensure that work equipment is maintained in an efficient state, in efficient working order and in good repair"*. Regulation 6 of PUWER 1998 lays down requirements for inspecting work equipment to ensure that health and safety conditions are maintained and that any deterioration can be detected and remedied in good time.

5.3 - Machinery hazards

Main mechanical and non-mechanical hazards

Machinery hazards are discussed in this section and *"control of hazards"* is considered in 'Application of protection methods to a range of equipment' *see section 5.4 - Control measures for machinery hazards.* Mechanical and other hazards identified in BS EN ISO 12100 Part 1 are described as follows.

MECHANICAL HAZARDS

Entanglement

The mere fact that a machine part is revolving can constitute a very real hazard of entanglement. Loose clothing, jewellery, long hair, etc. increase the risk of entanglement. Examples of entanglement hazards include couplings, drill chucks/bits, flywheels, spindles, shafts (especially those with keys/bolts) and rotating tools like abrasive wheels.

Figure 5-21: Auger drill - entanglement. *Source: STIHL.*

Friction and abrasion

Friction burns and encountering rough surfaces moving at high speed, as found in a sanding machine, grinding wheel or conveyor belt, can cause abrasion injuries.

Figure 5-22: Chop saw - cutting.   *Source: Speedy Hire plc.*

Figure 5-23: Abrasive wheel - abrasion.   *Source: RMS.*

Cutting

Saw blades, knives and even rough edges, especially when moving at high speed, can result in serious cuts and even amputation injuries. The dangerous part can appear stationary due to the stroboscopic effect under certain lighting conditions. Examples of cutting action hazards include saws, slicing machines, abrasive cutting discs and chainsaws.

Shear

When two or more machine parts move towards/past one another a "trap" is created. This can result in a crush injury or even an amputation. Examples of shearing action hazards include scissor lifts, platform hoists passing a landing and guillotines.

Stabbing and puncture

The body may be penetrated by sharp pieces of equipment, or material contained in the equipment. Examples of stabbing and puncture hazards include fixing materials such as nails fired from a nail gun or a drill bit which could puncture the hand when operating the drill.

Impact

Impact is caused by objects that strike the body, but do not penetrate it. They may cause the person or part of the person to be moved, sometimes violently, resulting in injury. For example, a person could be struck by the jib of a crane/excavator or materials on a hoist.

Figure 5-24: Stabbing and puncture. *Source: Speedy Hire plc.*

Figure 5-25: Shear.   *Source: RMS.*

Crushing

Crushing is caused when part of the body is caught between either two moving parts of machinery or a moving part and a stationary object. Examples of crushing hazards include the platform of a hoist closing together with the ground or an overhead beam or the folding arms of a MEWP.

Figure 5-26: Crushing.   *Source: RMS.*

Figure 5-27: Impact.   *Source: RMS.*

Drawing-in

When a belt runs round a roller an 'in-running nip' is created between the moving parts, in the direction of travel of the belt. This inward movement draws in any part of the body presented to it. Examples of drawing-in hazards are the rollers of a surface roller, chain drives of a fork-lift truck lifting mast, V-belts on the drive from a motor to the drum of a cement mixer or the spindle of a drill.

Figure 5-28: Drawing-in.   *Source: RMS.*

Figure 5-29: Ejection.   *Source: RMS.*

Ejection

When pieces of the material being worked on or components of the machinery are thrown or fired out of the equipment during operation, they represent an ejection hazard. Ejection hazards include parts of a shattered grinding wheel, waste metal turnings, and dust from a grinder/disc saw or a nail from a nail gun.

Injury by compressed air or high pressure fluid injection

Injection of fluids through the skin may lead to soft tissue injuries similar to crushing. Air entering the blood stream through the skin may be fatal. Examples of high pressure fluid injection hazards include leaking hydraulic lift systems, diesel injectors, spray painting, compressed air jets for blast cleaning the outside of a building and a high pressure lance for cutting concrete.

Figure 5-30: Disc saw - ejection. *Source: Water Active, Nov 06.*

Figure 5-31: Fluid injection. *Source: RMS.*

OTHER (NON MECHANICAL) HAZARDS

Machinery may also present other hazards. The nature of the hazard will determine the measures taken to protect people from them. The various sources of non-mechanical hazards include the following:

- Electricity - electric shock and burns.
- Hot surfaces - burns and source of ignition.
- Noise and vibration - noise induced hearing loss; vibration white finger.
- Biological - viral and bacterial.
- Chemicals that are toxic, irritant, flammable, corrosive, explosive.
- High/low temperatures - burns to hands.
- Ionising and non ionising radiation - nausea, vomiting, death.
- Access - slips, trips and falls; obstructions and projections.
- Manual handling - work-related upper limb disorders.

SUMMARY OF MACHINERY HAZARDS

Mechanical	Mechanical examples	Non-mechanical examples
Entanglement	Auger drill, drilling machine	Electricity
Friction and abrasion	Grinding wheel	Hot surfaces/fire
Cutting	Sharp edges of circular saw	Noise
Shear	Scissor lift mechanism	Vibration
Stabbing and Puncture	Nail gun	Noise/vibration
Impact	Moving arm of an excavator	Chemicals
Crushing	Platform of a hoist, folding arms of MEWP	Radiation
Drawing in	Rollers of a surface roller	Access
Injection	High pressure hydraulic oil system	Manual handling
Ejection	Disc cutter - dust and particles	Extremes of temperature

Figure 5-32: Summary - machinery hazards.

Source: RMS.

Hazards presented by a range of equipment

OFFICE MACHINERY

Photocopier

Hazards are drawing-in, hot surfaces, fumes, toner dust, electrical, manual handling, noise and glare. These hazards are more likely to be encountered by people who carry out unauthorised maintenance work.

Document shredder

The main hazards are drawing-in, cutting or crushing, also cuts from paper handling and electrical dangers. Although these machines are well designed and, therefore guarding is adequate, care has to be taken to ensure that loose clothing such as ties and scarves do not get caught in the blades. If the equipment is fitted with an interlock, there should be regular inspections to ensure that the device has not moved out of adjustment or has been overridden. Unauthorised electrical repairs should not be carried out.

Figure 5-33: Abrasive wheel (grinder). *Source: RMS.*

Figure 5-34: Document shredder. *Source: www.axminster.co.uk.*

WORKSHOP MACHINERY

Bench-top grinder

Bench-top grinders are typically found in workshops and are suitable for indoor use. Bench-top grinders are used for sharpening of tool bits (drills, chisels and blades), shaping steel, and de-burring cut steel components. Hazards include friction and abrasion from contact with the moving abrasive wheel, entanglement, drawing-in and possible ejections when parts of the wheel or work piece break and sparks are thrown off. Other hazards are electricity, heat and noise.

Pedestal drill

Hazards in setting up the equipment include failure to remove the chuck-key (which will be ejected if the equipment is stated) and failure to secure the guard to drive pulleys. Hazards when the equipment is in use include entanglement, puncture and flying waste metal (swarf).

Bench-mounted circular saw

Cutting is the main hazard; together with electricity, noise, sawdust, splinters and musculoskeletal disorders related to posture and materials handling.

Figure 5-35: Pedestal drill. *Source: RMS.*

Figure 5-36: Bench cross-cut circular saw. *Source: RMS.*

Hand fed power planer

Hazards include noise, cuts and severs, dust, impact from flying debris, fire and electrocution.

Spindle moulding machine

Spindle moulding machines are widely used in woodworking activities for the high speed machining of timber, multi-spindle machines allow machining on all four sides. Typical products include squared stock, tongued and grooved boarding, skirting board, etc. Virtually all these machines produce noise levels in excess of 85 dB and noise levels up to 105 dB have been recorded at the in-feed operator's position. It is known that many operators of spindle moulding machines are exposed to noise levels well in excess of 85 dB even when the machines are provided with noise enclosures. Hazards include noise, cuts, entanglement and risk of fire.

Figure 5-37: Hand fed power planer. *Source: Screwfix.*

Figure 5-38: Spindle moulding machine. *Source: Axminster Power Tool Centre Ltd.*

CONSTRUCTION SITE MACHINERY

Compressor

Pneumatic compressors are a source of power for a variety of portable equipment used in construction activities. Tools that can source power from compressors include drills and chisels, saws, nail guns, mixing equipment and plasterer's surface scotchers. Whilst this list of tools is not exhaustive, the principle remains the same in that power is delivered through a high pressure airline to the tool and converted into mechanical power. Pneumatic compressors are typically large pieces of mobile plant that attach to the towing bar of a road going works vehicle. When at site, a compressor is free standing, only attached to the tool by the pressure airline.

Figure 5-39: Compressor. *Source: Atlas Copco.*

Hazards arise from the fuelling of the plant (normally diesel) where contact with the skin can occur, splashes into eyes, inhalation of fumes and the possible risk of fire where hot temperatures are involved. In operation, the compressor produces exhaust gases from the motor which may, in addition to the fuel, require an assessment in compliance with the Control of Substances Hazardous to Health Regulations (COSHH) 2002. The exhaust gases are a particular hazard in confined areas. Noise and vibration at high levels may be produced from the compressor although these levels may vary dependent upon the effectiveness of the soundproofing material incorporated into the plant in addition to the condition of the equipment and frequency of maintenance programmes that may exist. This equipment also involves pressure lines that provide a hazard of injection and trip hazard.

Cement mixer

Cement mixers are portable construction plant used for mixing a variety of aggregates and cement used in the construction process. The main benefit of this equipment is removing a significant volume of the manual labour aspect of the mixing process although a significant amount of labour intensive activities remain. The equipment consists of a motor (electric, petrol or diesel) linked through a gear box and drive shaft to a rotating drum that incorporates internal mixing blades to aid the mixing process.

The assembly may vary from a complete unit that pivots on a central bar or a two part system where the mixer is seated onto a plinth or stand and pivots forward to enable emptying of the drum when the mixture is complete.

Figure 5-40: Cement mixer. *Source: RMS.*

Hazards arise from the source of power when electricity is combined with the water used in the mixing process. In order to control this risk, a low voltage power supply should be used, with suitable heavy duty cable and cable covers when there is a risk of running over them with vehicles or plant. Used with a residual current protection device a good level of protection can be obtained. When the fuel source is diesel or petrol there is a risk of fire, which increases during refuelling operations when the exhaust system may still be hot or people may be smoking in the close vicinity of the equipment. The rotating drum and drive shaft poses an entanglement risk with personal protective equipment and other tools. If covers are removed they can expose drive belts or gearing with the associated risk of drawing in. Operatives loading mixers should be warned of the dangers of shovels and trowels becoming caught in the mixer blades and snatching the hand tool out of the operatives hand with force, which may result in personal injury to limbs and muscles. Loading the mixer is a manual task which can result in injury from repetitive, twisting motion when emptying shovels or gauging buckets into the mixer. Job rotation should be planned.

Assessments as required by the COSHH 2002 Regulations may be required for the fumes and dusts involved in the mixing process. Often the mixing activity is a slow process; operatives tend to leave the mixer running alone until the mix is ready. If the equipment is left running and unattended there is a risk of unauthorised access to the mixer and injuries to third parties. As the mixing process proceeds there is a likelihood of build-up of materials on the floor, leading to a risk of slips and trips and a possibility of falling onto the moving equipment.

Plate compactor

Plate compactors are simple machines used for consolidating aggregates or loose materials. They are also used for securing block paviors into position by applying a heavy downward force through a flat plate where the force is increased by the vibrating motion. They operate on the principle of a motor that rotates a cam through a drive belt which provides the vibration force. Upon first appearances from a distance, operators would appear to look as though they are operating a lawn mower as the equipment is walked up and down the surface to be compacted, with the vibration providing the drive, assisted by the operator. Hazards arise from the source of power, typically petrol, which has associated fire risks that are increased through refuelling operations when the exhaust system is still hot. This equipment, because of its purpose, has to be heavy which brings a risk of manual handling strain injuries when loading or unloading from a vehicle.

Figure 5-41: Plate compactor. *Source: HSS Hire Service Group Ltd.*

Ground consolidation equipment

Ground consolidation equipment serves the same purpose as a plate compactor. However, a plate compactor is generally for lighter duty than the large types of ground consolidation equipment such as man riding rollers or manual rollers. This heavy duty type of equipment requires competence and authorisation in order to use it on site.

Ground consolidation equipment moves at a greater speed than lighter duty equipment and its power drives the equipment directly through the roller wheel. The potential harm from the drawing in/crush hazards are high, a drawing in/crush sustained from a piece of this plant could more easily lead to a major injury or fatality.

Figure 5-42: Ground consolidation equipment. *Source: RMS.*

Portable circular saw

A portable circular saw is a powerful tool that can cross cut and rip timber. It is a versatile piece of equipment used for small woodworking tasks. Commonly the blade can cut to a depth of 55 mm (2in). The main hazards relate to cuts from the blade, which revolves at high speed. Typical other hazards are electric shock from damaged cables, cuts or injury from flying waste materials and dust. Vibration and noise, particularly when used in confined work areas indoors can be significant.

Figure 5-43: Circular saw. *Source: HSS Hire Service Group Limited.*

Road-marking equipment

Road marking usually involves the application of a hot plastic based substance to the surface of a road. The equipment used will often have its own supply of fuel in the form of liquefied petroleum gas (LPG). This is used to maintain the marking substance at a suitable working temperature in a holding vessel.

Direct hazards from the equipment include the hazard of drawing in/crush involving the wheels of the equipment, contact with the hot marking substance and potential overheating of the marking substance leading to a fire. Other hazards include exhaust gases and falls from the equipment.

Figure 5-44: Thermoplastic hand marking barrow. *Source: Maxigrip Surfacing Ltd.*

Figure 5-45: Road Marking vehicle. *Source: Maxigrip Surfacing Ltd.*

Electrical generators

Diesel/petrol powered electrical generators are used for powering portable power tools and other construction equipment. Smaller generators are often used to power road breakers; large versions may be used to provide electricity for site welfare arrangements. They may be equipped with 240V and 110V sockets or provide electricity to a 415 volt distribution system. The main hazards are electrocution, fire, noise and asphyxiation from carbon dioxide and carbon monoxide present in the exhaust gases. Other hazards include risks related to handling the fuel and, where they are portable, manual handling hazards related to moving them into the position needed.

Figure 5-46: Petrol 110v generator.   *Source: RMS.*

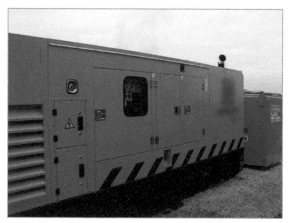

Figure 5-47: Large diesel generator.   *Source: RMS.*

5.4 - Control measures for machinery hazards

Machinery guarding

OBJECTIVE OF MACHINERY GUARDING

- To prevent workpeople from coming into contact with dangerous parts of machinery.
- To prevent physical injury from power driven and manually operated machines.
- To enable machines to be operated safely without interference with production.

PUWER REGULATION 11 - DANGEROUS PARTS OF MACHINERY

PUWER 1998, Regulation 11, sets out the following requirements with regard to dangerous parts of machinery:

"(1) Every employer shall ensure that measures are taken in accordance with paragraph (2) which are effective:

- *(a) To prevent access to any dangerous part of machinery or to any rotating stock-bar.*
- *(b) To stop the movement of any dangerous part of machinery or rotating stock-bar before any part of a person enters a danger zone.*

(2) *The measures required by paragraph (1) shall consist of:*

(a) *The provision of fixed guards enclosing every dangerous part or rotating stock-bar where and to the extent that it is practicable to do so, but where or to the extent that it is not.*

(b) *The provision of other guards or protection devices where and to the extent that it is practicable to do so, but where or to the extent that it is not.*

(c) *The provision of jigs, holders, push-sticks or similar protection appliances used in conjunction with the machinery where and to the extent that it is practicable to do so.*

(d) *The provision of information, instruction, training and supervision as is necessary.*

(3) *All guards and protection devices provided under sub-paragraphs (a) or (b) of paragraph (2) shall:*

(a) *Be suitable for the purpose for which they are provided.*

(b) *Be of good construction, sound material and adequate strength.*

(c) *Be maintained in an efficient state, in efficient working order and in good repair.*

(d) *Not give rise to any increased risk to health or safety.*

(e) *Not be easily bypassed or disabled.*

(f) *Be situated at sufficient distance from the danger zone.*

(g) *Not unduly restrict the view of the operating cycle of the machinery, where such a view is necessary.*

(h) *Be so constructed or adapted that they allow operations necessary to fit or replace parts and for maintenance work, restricting access so that it is allowed only to the area where the work is to be carried out and, if possible, without having to dismantle the guard or protection device.*

(4) *All protection appliances provided under sub-paragraph c) of paragraph (2) shall comply with sub-paragraphs (a) to (d) and (g) of paragraph (3).*

(5) *In this regulation - "danger zone" means any zone in or around machinery in which a person is exposed to a risk to health or safety from contact with a dangerous part of machinery or a rotating stock-bar; "stock-bar" means any part of a stock-bar which projects beyond the headstock of a lathe."*

Regulation 11(2) gives the measures that an employer should take to fulfil the duty under regulation 11(1) a combination of measures may be necessary to satisfy Regulation 11. When deciding on the appropriate level of safeguarding, risk assessment criteria (likelihood of injury, potential severity of injury, numbers at risk) need to be considered both in relation to the normal operation of the machinery and other operations such as maintenance, repair, setting, tuning, adjustment etc. Regulation 11(3) (c) applies to the maintenance of guards and protection devices and will include those which are not attached to the machine itself, for example, perimeter fences.

The principles, merits and limitations of protection methods

HIERARCHY OF MEASURES FOR DANGEROUS PARTS OF MACHINERY

■ Prevent access to dangerous parts by means of **F**ixed guard (preferably fully enclosing).

■ When the above is not practicable protect by other guards (**I**nterlock, **A**utomatic) or safety devices (for example, **T**rip device).

■ When the above is not practicable protect by using safety appliances (for example, push stick or jig).

The various guards and safety devices can be summarised as follows:

Fixed   **I**nterlock   **A**utomatic (including self-closing)   **T**rip devices

FIXED GUARDS

A fixed guard/fence must be fitted such that it cannot be removed other than by the use of specialist tools which are not available to operators of the equipment.

A fixed guard may be designed to enable access by authorised personnel for maintenance or inspection, but only when the dangerous parts of the machine have been isolated.

A common example of a fixed guard is shown *(see figure ref 5-48)*. Not all fixed guards are of solid construction, some are made of mesh. The holes in a mesh guard are of sufficient size to allow air circulation to cool the drive belt, but small enough to prevent the finger of the hand from penetrating the mesh and result in injury from the belt.

Figure 5-48: Total enclosure fixed guard. *Source: RMS.*

Distance (fixed) guard

Fixed guards do not always completely cover the danger point but place it out of normal reach.

The larger the opening (to feed in material) the greater must be the distance from the opening to the danger point. A tree shredding machine uses a fixed distance guard design to prevent operators reaching the dangerous part of a machine when in use.

Merits of fixed guards

- Create a physical barrier.
- Require a tool to remove.
- May not protect against non-mechanical hazards such as dust/fluids which may be ejected.
- No moving parts - therefore they require very little maintenance.

Limitations of fixed guards

- Do not disconnect power when not in place, therefore machine can still be operated without guard.
- May cause problems with visibility for inspection.
- If enclosed, may create problems with heat which, in turn, can increase the risk of explosion.

Figure 5-49: Fixed guard - panel removed.   *Source: RMS.*

Figure 5-50: Fixed guard over fan - mesh too big. *Source: RMS.*

INTERLOCKING GUARDS

An interlocking guard is similar to a fixed guard, but has a movable (usually hinged) part, so connected to the machine controls that if the movable part is in the open/lifted position the dangerous moving part at the work point cannot operate.

This can be arranged so that the action of closing the guard activates the working part (to speed up work efficiently); for example, the front panel of a photocopier or the gates of a platform hoist. Interlocked guards are useful if operators need regular access to the danger area. Everyday examples of interlocking guards are those found on domestic equipment such as dish washers, microwave cookers and automatic washing machines.

In *figure ref 5-51*, the electrical interlock is positioned halfway down the right hand side of this panel.

The panel is made from transparent material to allow easy visual checks of the products that are manufactured by this equipment.

Merits of interlocking guards

- Connected to power source, therefore machine cannot be operated with guard open.
- Allow regular access.

Limitations of interlocking guards

- Have moving parts therefore need regular maintenance.
- Can be over-ridden.

Figure 5-51: Interlocking guard.   *Source: RMS.*

- If interlock is in the form of a gate, a person can step inside and close the gate behind them (someone else could then re-activate the machine)
- Dangerous parts of machinery may not stop immediately the guard is opened, therefore a delay timer or brake might need to be fitted as well. For example, the drum on a spin drier does not stop instantly, and therefore a delay is fitted to prevent the door being opened until the drum is stationary.

SELF-ADJUSTING GUARD

These are guards that close themselves over the dangerous parts and prevent accidental access by the operator, but allow entry of the material to the machine in such a way that the material forms part of the guarding arrangement itself. For example, a hand held circular saw.

Merits of self-adjusting guards

- Close over the dangerous parts to provide protection without the need of the operator to do anything.

Limitations of self-adjusting guards

- May obscure visibility when in use.
- Are vulnerable to damage in the operation of the equipment.

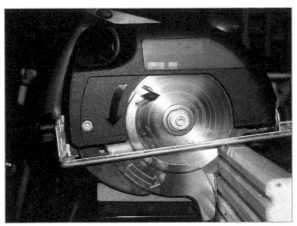

Figure 5-52: Self adjusting (fixed) guard.   *Source: RMS.*

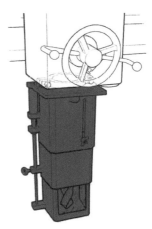

Figure 5-53: Adjustable (fixed) guard. *Source: BS EN ISO 12100.*

ADJUSTABLE GUARD

Adjustable guards are a fixed guard that incorporates an adjustable element (which remains fixed for the duration of a particular operation). For example, the crown guard of a bench circular saw or a pedestal drill chuck/drill bit guard.

Merits of adjustable guards

- Can be adjusted by operator to provide protection.

Limitations of adjustable guards

- Are reliant on the operator to adjust to the correct position.
- May obscure visibility when in use.

SENSITIVE PROTECTIVE EQUIPMENT/TRIP DEVICE

Sensitive protective equipment (sometimes called a trip device) comprises a sensitive rod, cable or other mechanism, which causes the device to activate a further mechanism which either stops or reverses the machine. It is important to note that this is not classed as a guard. A guard is something that physically prevents access to the hazard whereas sensitive protective equipment detects the person in the danger zone and responds to this, for example, a pressure sensitive mat.

Merits of sensitive protective equipment

- ***Can be used as an additional risk control measure.***
- ***Can minimise the severity of injury.***

Limitations of sensitive protective equipment

- Can be over-ridden.
- May not prevent harm from occurring.
- May cause production delays and increase stress in users with false 'trips'.

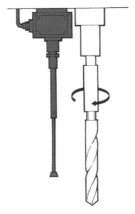

Figure 5-54: Trip device. *Source: BS EN ISO 12100.*

Figure 5-55: Trip device on radial drill.   *Source: RMS.*

TWO-HAND CONTROL (2HC) DEVICE

They provide a level of protection where other methods are not practicable, helping to ensure the operator's hands remain outside the danger area. A two-hand control is a device that requires both hands to operate it, the controls must be operated simultaneously and help to assure that both hands are kept away from the dangerous parts. '2HC' devices protect only the operator. An everyday example of use of two hand controls are those fitted to a hedge trimmer.

Merits of two hand control devices

- Ensures both of the operator's hands are out of danger area when the machine is operated.

Limitations of two hand control devices

- Only protects the operator from harm.
- May limit speed of operation with delays if controls are not pressed at exactly same time.

HOLD-TO-RUN

The principle of this device is that the operator has to "hold" a button, stick or foot pedal to "run" a piece of equipment.

Figure 5-56: Two-hand control on hedge trimmer.   *Source: RMS.*

A common application of this device is on a domestic lawn mower or hedge trimmer. It is essential that the hold-to-run device, which when released stops the machine, is located far enough away from the danger area to prevent the operator getting access to the moving parts without releasing it.

Merits of hold-to-run devices

- Ensures the operator is out of the danger area when the machine is operated.
- Provides distance between operator and hazard.

Limitations of hold-to-run devices

- Only protects the operator from harm.
- There may be residual movement of dangerous parts once the device has been released.

JIGS, HOLDERS AND PUSH-STICKS

When the methods of safeguarding mentioned above are not practicable then protection appliances such as jigs, holders and push-sticks must be provided. They will help to keep the operator's hands at a safe distance from the danger area. There is no physical restraint to prevent the operator from placing their hands in danger.

Figure 5-57: Notched push-stick. *Source: http://images.google.co.uk/.*

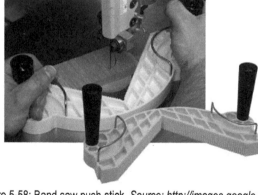

Figure 5-58: Band saw push-stick. *Source: http://images.google.co.uk/.*

Merits of protection appliances

- Provide distance between operator and hazard.
- Inexpensive and easily replaced if damaged.
- May be shaped to suit work being carried out.

Limitations of protection appliances

- Harm may still occur from other non-mechanical hazards.
- Some designs can be awkward to use and may result in a lack of control.
- Continuing adjustments have to be made for example, when using different sizes of wood.
- Failure of protection appliance (for example, breaking or kickback) may present additional hazard to operator.

Figure 5-59: Fixed guard and push-stick.   *Source: Lincsafe.*

EMERGENCY STOP CONTROLS

The function of an emergency stop control device is to provide a means to bring a machine to a rapid halt. It is provided in such circumstances where it would be of benefit and should be readily available to the operator and/or others. It should be easy to operate and clearly discernible from other controls. Emergency stop controls should be easily reached and actuated. Common types are mushroom-headed buttons, bars, levers, kick plates, or pressure-sensitive cables. Emergency stops are intended to effect a rapid response to potentially dangerous situations and they should not be used as functional stops during normal operation.

Merits	Limitations

Merits

- Removes power immediately.
- Equipment has to be reset after use.
- Prevents accidental restarting of the equipment.

Limitations

- Does not prevent access to the danger area.
- May be incorrectly positioned.

PERSONAL PROTECTIVE EQUIPMENT (PPE)

The Personal Protective Equipment at Work (PPER) Regulations 1992 governs the provision of PPE. PPE is a last resort and should only be relied upon when other controls do not adequately control risks. The use of machinery presents a number of mechanical hazards and care has to be taken that PPE is not used in situations where they present an increased risk of entanglement or drawing in to machinery, such as might happen with loose overalls and gloves. Main examples are:

- Eye protection (safety spectacles/glasses, goggles and face shields) - protection for the eyes and face from flying particles, welding glare, dust, fumes and splashes.
- Head protection (safety helmets or scalp protectors i.e. bump caps) - protection from falling objects, or the head striking fixed objects.
- Protective clothing for the body (overalls) - protection from a wide range of hazards, specialist clothing for chain saw hazards.
- Gloves (chain mail gloves and sleeves) - protection against cuts and abrasions when handling machined components, raw material or machinery cutters.
- Footwear (steel in-soles and toe-caps) - protection against sharp objects that might be stood on or objects dropped while handling them.
- Ear protection for noisy machine operations.

Merits

- Easy to see if it is being worn.
- Provides protection against a variety of hazards.

Limitations

- Only protects the user.
- May not give adequate protection.
- May pose additional hazards, for example, gloves becoming entangled.

INFORMATION, INSTRUCTION, TRAINING AND SUPERVISION

PUWER 1998 requires every employer to ensure that all persons who use work equipment and any of his employees who supervises or manages the use of work equipment have available to them adequate health and safety information and, where appropriate, written instructions and appropriate training pertaining to the use of the work equipment.

This includes information and, where appropriate, written instructions that are comprehensible to those concerned on:

- The conditions in which and the methods by which the work equipment may be used.
- Foreseeable abnormal situations and the action to be taken if such a situation were to occur.
- Any conclusions to be drawn from experience in using the work equipment.

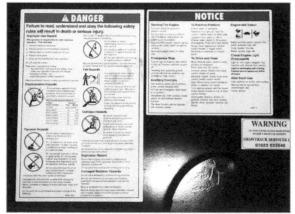

Figure 5-60: Information and instruction. *Source: RMS.*

Figure 5-61: PPE and supervision. *Source: RMS.*

Similarly, PUWER 1998 requires employers to ensure that all persons who use work equipment and any of his employees who supervises or manages work equipment have received training in any risks which such use may entail and precautions to be taken.

It is a requirement of both the HASAWA 1974 and PUWER 1998 Regulation 11 that supervision is provided as necessary. This will require extra supervision for new, inexperienced or less capable users of equipment.

Merits

- Easy to reach a wide audience on a variety of subjects.
- Can be applied immediately and adapted to suit specific needs of the user.

Limitations

- Supervision may not prevent contact with the hazard.
- Relies on the person concerned to follow the instruction.
- May be misunderstood.
- Supervision is needed to a sufficient degree to ensure health and safety, and a high degree of supervision may be required for some equipment.

Application of protection methods to a range of equipment

To meet the requirements of the syllabus, protection methods are discussed in this section. Specific *hazards* of the equipment listed are covered in *Section 5.3 - Machinery hazards*.

OFFICE MACHINERY

Photocopier

Because access to the moving parts by the user are likely to be required to remove paper jams the use of interlocking guard is appropriate for these access panels. Fixed guards may also protect some dangerous parts inside the panels, such as heating elements. Appropriate additional precautions are to avoid loose clothing i.e. ties, signage for hot components, well ventilated/suitable extraction, gloves, training in good practice when removing paper jams etc.

Shredder

Appropriate precautions are the use of interlocking guards that identify the removal of the shredding element of the equipment from the shredded paper collection area. Where the shredder has a large opening to the moving parts of the shredder to feed material in, it may be necessary to protect this with sensitive protective equipment that will detect the presence of the user's hand or clothing.

WORKSHOP MACHINERY

Bench grinder

Control measures include an adjustable fixed guard that is fitted over as much of the grinding wheel as is practicable, a work-piece rest, trained and competent users, high impact resistant goggles, respiratory protective equipment (depending on task) and personal hearing protection.

Pedestal drill

Appropriate precautions for pre-use are:

- Drive pulley entanglement prevented by isolation from power when adjusting speeds.
- Check that chuck key is removed before use.

Appropriate precautions during use are:

- Interlocking guard to cover the drive pulley and belts.
- Adjustable (fixed) guard provided round the chuck and drill bit, face shield/goggles for protection from flying metal pieces from the cutting process (swarf).
- Prevent entanglement - close fitting clothing, control of long hair and removal of jewellery.
- Puncture prevented by jigs or clamping devices.

Bench-mounted circular saw

Appropriate precautions are:

- Guarding for crown and front of the saw, and for the part of the saw below the bench.
- Riving knife fitted at rear of the saw above the bench.
- Use of jigs/holders or push sticks where appropriate.
- Need for a table extension to ensure distance of at least 1.2 m between edge of saw and end of table if another person assistants at the back of the bench.

Hand fed power planer

Appropriate precautions are:

- Use of a suitable bridge guard, adjusted according to the operation being undertaken.
- Use clamps to secure to a stable platform.
- Keep tools sharp and clean.

Spindle moulding machine

No single type of guard or other safety device can deal adequately with the variety of work that can be done on a spindle moulding machine. Each job must be considered individually to provide the most effective protection. Comprehensive guidance is contained in the HSE Information Sheet (Woodworking Sheet No. 18) "Safe Working Practices at Vertical Spindle Moulding Machines".

CONSTRUCTION SITE MACHINERY

Compressor

Appropriate precautions are:

- Over-pressure relief valve.
- Pressure gauge.
- Hose couplings fitted with pins or chains.
- Hose couplings inspected as part of daily plant inspection.
- Noise control equipment fitted to compressor.

Cement mixer

Fixed guards must be provided around drive mechanisms. Motor covers should be closed when in use. Operators should be warned of the dangers of shovels and trowels becoming caught in the mixer blades when charging. Electrical hazards are reduced by the use of low voltage (110 volts) power (or residual current circuit breaker if 240 volt supply), with suitable heavy duty protected cable. If petrol or diesel driven, equipment should be allowed to cool (for example, exhaust system) before refuelling, no smoking should be observed. Other controls include manual handling training, good housekeeping of spilt materials, and avoidance of exposure to dust and fume.

Plate compactor

Appropriate precautions are:

- Use a remote-control rather than a hand-guided compactor to reduce risks from hand-arm vibration.
- Take regular breaks to reduce exposure or rotate use among several people.
- A safe system of work for handling this equipment may be required, which could include a hoist on site vehicles and a trolley to manoeuvre around the site.

Ground consolidation equipment

Control measures include segregation of pedestrians and plant using barriers, warning signs and close supervision.

Portable circular saw

Appropriate precautions include provision and use of fixed and self-adjusting guards. Precautions also include ensuring material being cut is held firm to prevent movement on contact with the saw blade and during the cutting process. Support of the material being cut is advisable to prevent excess side pressure on the blade, particularly on completion of the cut. Care should be taken to ensure the blade has stopped revolving and self-adjusting guard covers the blade before putting the saw down. Eye and hearing PPE should be worn to reduce the risk of noise induced hearing loss and eye injuries from the waste wood cuttings. Portable mounted saws should be fitted with suitable local exhaust ventilation equipment, where possible. Respiratory protection may also be necessary particularly when cutting hardwoods. Regular rest breaks should be taken for hand held equipment to reduce the effects of vibration on the user.

Road-marking equipment

This equipment requires special training and authorisation for its safe use. Where this equipment is being used, barriers, warning signs and lighting is to be used, in addition to supervision. When this equipment is being used it is normally a requirement to have refuelling facilities available on site. When this is the case suitable isolation from sources of heat should be ensured, with only authorised operatives allowed to carry out refuelling activities.

Electrical generators

Diesel or petrol generators should always be used outdoors to prevent the risk of carbon monoxide accumulation. They should not be sited below scaffolds or near trenches where people are working, because there is a continuous risk of build-up of carbon dioxide whilst the compressor is running. They should never be refuelled when hot and noise limiting covers should remain closed when in use. The compressor must be installed and maintained by a competent person. The compressor must be of sufficient capacity for the total load required (electrical motors typically require three times their rated wattage on start-up). This should be taken into account before selection and use.

Basic requirements for guards and safety devices

PUWER 1998 REGULATION 11 - EFFECTIVE GUARDS AND DEVICES

PUWER 1998, Regulation 11, paragraph 3 sets out the following requirements with regard to guards and devices: *"All guards and protection devices provided under sub-paragraphs (a) or (b) of paragraph (2) shall:*

*(a) Be **suitable** for the purpose for which they are provided.*

*(b) Be of **good construction**, sound material and adequate strength.*

*(c) Be **maintained** in an efficient state, in efficient working order and in good repair.*

(d) Not give rise to any increased risk to health or safety.

*(e) Not be **easily bypassed** or disabled.*

(f) *Be situated at **sufficient distance** from the danger zone.*

(g) *Not unduly **restrict the view** of the operating cycle of the machinery, where such a view is necessary.*

(h) *Be so constructed or adapted that they allow operations necessary to fit or replace parts and for maintenance work, restricting access so that it is allowed only to the area where the work is to be carried out and, if possible, without having to dismantle the guard or protection device".*

COMPATIBILITY WITH PROCESS

Compatibility with the material being processed - this is particularly important in the food processing industry where the guard material should not constitute a source of contamination of the product. Its ability to maintain its physical and mechanical properties after coming into contact with potential contaminants such as cutting fluids used in machining operations or corrosive agents used in cement processing machinery is also very important. In selecting an appropriate safeguard for a particular type of machinery or danger area, it should be borne in mind that a fixed guard is simple, and should be used where access to the danger area is not required during operation of the machinery or for cleaning, setting or other activities. As the need for access arises and increases in frequency, the importance of safety procedures for removal of a fixed guard increases until the frequency is such that interlocking should be used.

ADEQUATE STRENGTH

Guard mounting should be compatible with the strength and duty of the guard. In selecting the material to be used for the construction of a guard, consideration should be given to the following:

- Its ability to withstand the force of ejection of parts of the machinery or material being processed, where this is a foreseeable danger.
- Its ability to provide protection against hazards identified. In many cases, the guard may fulfil a combination of functions such as prevention of access and containment of hazards. This may apply where the hazards include ejected particles, liquids, dust, fumes, radiation, noise, etc. and one or more of these considerations may govern the selection of guard materials.

MAINTAINED

All guards must be maintained in effective order to perform their function. This will require a planned approach to checks on guards and work such as checking the security of fixed guards.

ALLOW FOR MAINTENANCE WITHOUT REMOVAL

Its weight and size are factors to be considered in relation to the need to remove and replace it for routine maintenance. If a guard has to be removed in order to carry out maintenance work, it increases the risks for maintenance workers and also increases the chances that the guard will not be replaced. This is especially the case if a piece of equipment has a history of regular break down.

NOT INCREASE RISK OR RESTRICT VIEW

Any guard selected should not itself present a hazard such as trapping or shear points, rough or sharp edges or other hazards likely to cause injury. Power operated guards should be designed and constructed so that a hazard is not created or restrict the view of the process or machine by the user.

NOT EASILY BY-PASSED

Guards or their components must not be easily by-passed, in particular by operators. There is always a temptation to do so when under production or similar pressures. When positioning such protective devices as interlock switches; it is best to locate them away from the operator and preferably within the guard.

Sample assessment questions

1. The Provision and Use of Work Equipment Regulations 1998 require that work equipment used in hostile environments is inspected at suitable intervals.

    Identify the items on a small dumper truck that should be the subject of such an inspection. (8)

2. **Outline** practical ways of reducing the risk to employees when using an electrical powered cement mixer on site. (8)

3. **Outline** the control measures that should be adopted when cutting paving slabs with a petrol disc cutter. (8)

Please refer to back of assessment section for answers.

Electrical safety

Learning outcomes

On completion of this element, candidates should be able to demonstrate understanding of the content through the application of knowledge to familiar and unfamiliar situations. In particular they should be able to:

6.1 Outline the principles, hazards and risks associated with the use of electricity in the workplace.

6.2 Outline the control measures that should be taken when working with electrical systems or using electrical equipment.

6.3 Outline the control measures to be taken when working near or underneath overhead power lines.

Content

Sources of reference

Avoidance of danger from overhead electrical lines, GS6(rev), HSE Books, ISBN 978-0-7176-1348-9

Avoiding danger from underground services, HSG47 (Second edition), HSE Books, ISBN 978-0-7176-1744-9

Electrical safety on construction sites, HSG141, HSE Books, ISBN 978-0-7176-1000-6

Electricity at Work - Safe Working Practices, HSG85, second edition 2007, HSE Books, ISBN 978-0-7176-2164-4

Guidance on Safe Isolation procedures: www.select.org.uk/downloads/publications/Select%20-%20Safe%20Isolation%20Procedures.pdf

Health and Safety Toolbox, online resource, HSE, www.hse.gov.uk/toolbox/index.htm

IET Wiring Regulations 17th Edition (first amendment), BS 7671:2008+A1:2011, ISBN 978-1-84919-269-9

Maintaining Portable and Transportable Electrical Equipment, HSG107, second edition 2004, HSE Books ISBN 978-0-7176-2805-6

Memorandum of guidance on the Electricity at Work Regulation 1989, Guidance on Regulations, HSR25, second edition 2007, HSE Books ISBN 978-0-7176-6228-9

Relevant statutory provisions

Electricity at Work Regulations (EWR) 1989

Health and Safety (First-aid) Regulations (FAR) 1981

Reporting of Injuries, Diseases and Dangerous Occurrences Regulations (RIDDOR) 2013

6.1 - Hazards and risks associated with electricity

Principles of electricity

Electricity is a facility that we have all come to take for granted, whether for lighting, heating, as a source of motive power or as the driving force behind the computer. Used properly it can be of great benefit to us, but misused it can be very dangerous and often fatal.

Electricity is used in most industries, offices and homes and our modern society could now not easily function without it. Despite its convenience to the user, it has a major danger. The normal senses of sight, hearing and smell will not detect electricity. Making contact with exposed conductors at the domestic supply voltage, 230V can be lethal.

Unlike many other workplace accidents, the actual number of electrical notifiable accidents is small. However, with a reported 10-20 fatalities each year, the severity is high. Accidents are often caused by complacency, not just by the normally assumed ignorance. It must be recognised by everyone working with electricity that over half of all electrical fatal accidents are to skilled/competent persons.

In order to avoid the causes of electric injury, it is necessary to understand the basic principles of electricity, what it does to the body and what controls are necessary.

BASIC CIRCUITRY

The flow of electrons through a conductor is known as a current. Electric current flows due to differences in electrical "pressure" (or potential difference as it is often known), just as water flows through a pipe because of the pressure behind it.

Differences in electrical potential are measured in volts. In some systems the current flows continually in the same direction. This is known as direct current (DC). However the current may also constantly reverse its direction of flow. This is known as alternating current (AC). Most public electricity supplies are AC.

The UK system reverses its direction 50 times per second and it is said to have a frequency of 50 cycles per second or 50 Hertz (50Hz). DC is little used in standard distribution systems but is sometimes used in industry for specialist applications. Although there are slight differences in the effects under fault and shock conditions between AC and DC it is a safe approach to apply the same rules of safety for the treatment and prevention of electric shock.

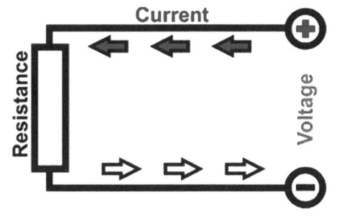

Figure 6-1: A basic electrical circuit.   *Source: RMS.*

As a current passes round a circuit under the action of an applied voltage it is impeded in its flow. This may be due to the presence in the circuit of resistance, inductance or capacitance, the combined effect of which is called impedance and is measured in ohms.

RELATIONSHIP BETWEEN VOLTAGE, CURRENT AND RESISTANCE

There is a simple relationship between electrical pressure (volts), current and resistance represented by Ohm's Law: voltage (**V**) = current (**I**) multiplied by the circuit resistance (**R**).

$$V = I \times R \text{ or } I = \frac{V}{R}$$

Hence, given any two values the third can be calculated. Also, if one value changes the other two values will change accordingly. This basic electrical equation can be used to calculate the current that flows in a circuit of a given resistance.

This will need to be done to determine, for example, the fuse or cable rating needed for a particular circuit. Similarly, the current that will flow through a person who touches a live conductor can be calculated.

By Ohm's law:

Current = $\dfrac{\text{Voltage}}{\text{Resistance}}$ or $I = \dfrac{V}{R}$

Resistance in a circuit is dependent on many factors. Most metals, particularly precious metals (silver, gold and platinum), allow current to pass very easily. These have a low resistance and are used as conductors.

Other materials such as plastics, rubber and textiles have a high resistance and are used as insulators.

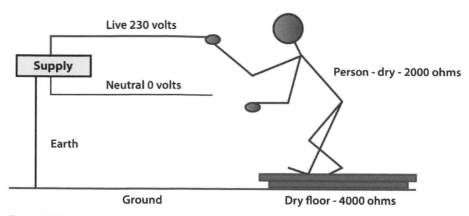

Figure 6-2: Basic electrical circuitry.   Source: RMS.

If the person is on a dry concrete floor, resistance in the body will only be about 2,000 Ohms and the resistance in the floor about 4,000 Ohms, therefore the combined resistance would be 6,000 Ohms.

Presuming the person is in contact with a live electrical supply at 230 Volts the current flowing through the person in this fault condition can be calculated.

$$I = \frac{V}{R} = \frac{230 \text{ Volts}}{2,000 + 4,000 \text{ Ohms}} = 0.038 \text{ Amperes}$$

The current flowing through the operator will then be about 0.04 Amperes or 40mA (40 milliAmperes). This could result in a fatal shock. *(See figure ref 6-2)*.

Risks of electricity

ELECTRIC SHOCK AND ITS EFFECT ON THE BODY

The term electric shock is used to describe the unwanted or undesirable exposure to electricity at a detectable level (typically 1mA AC at 50Hz).

When an electric current passes through a material, the resistance to the flow of electrons dissipates energy, usually in the form of heat. If the material is human tissue and the amount of heat generated is sufficient, the tissue may be burnt. The effect is similar to damage caused by an open flame or other high-temperature source of heat, except that electricity has the ability to *burn* tissue well beneath the skin, including internal organs.

Nerve cells communicate by creating electrical signals (at very small voltages and currents) in response to the input of certain chemical compounds called neurotransmitters. If the electric shock current is of sufficient magnitude it will override the electrical impulses normally generated by the neurons, preventing both reflex and volitional (controlled by conscious choice or decision) signals from being able to operate muscles. These effects may be felt as *pain*.

Muscles may also be triggered by a shock current, which will cause them to involuntarily *contract*. The forearm muscles responsible for bending fingers tend to be better developed than those muscles responsible for extending fingers. If both sets of muscles attempt to contract the "bending" muscles will be stronger and clench the fingers into a fist.

If the conductor delivering a shock current touches the palm of the hand, the clenching action will force the hand to grasp the conductor firmly, securing contact with the conductor and it will not be possible for the victim to release their grasp. Even when the current is stopped, the victim may not regain voluntary control over their muscles for a while, as the neurotransmitter chemistry will be in disarray. Involuntary muscle contraction is called tetanus. Shock-induced tetanus can only be interrupted by stopping the current passing through the body.

Electric current is able to affect more than just skeletal muscles; it can also affect breathing and heart function, particularly if the path is across the chest. The diaphragm muscle controlling the lungs and the heart muscle can also be caused to be in a state of tetanus by a shock current, leading to *respiratory failure* of the lungs and *fibrillation* of the heart or *cardiac arrest*.

Fibrillation is a condition where all the heart muscles start moving independently in a disorganised manner, rather than in a coordinated way. It affects the ability of the heart to pump blood, resulting in brain damage and eventual cardiac arrest.

Factors influencing severity of the effects of electric shock on the body

The factors influencing the severity of the effects of electric shock on the body include the following:

■   Voltage.
■   Frequency.
■   Duration.
■   Impedance/resistance.

- Current and current path.
- Direct/indirect shock.

The amount of current that flows through the body for a given voltage will depend on the frequency of the supply voltage, on the level of the voltage that is applied and on the state of the point of contact with the body, particularly the moisture condition. The effect of electricity on the body and severity of electric shock results from a combination of the current level and the time duration of the passage of that current. The voltage level is relevant mainly in that it causes the passage of the current.

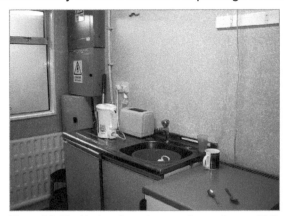

Figure 6-3: Electrical equipment near water. *Source: RMS.*

Figure 6-4: Contact with high voltage buried cable. *Source: RMS.*

Voltage

Voltage is the driving force behind the flow of electricity, in the same way that pressure in a water pipe influences the amount of water that flows. The correct name for this term is potential difference, as a voltage is the measure of the difference in electrical energy between two points. Any electrical charge that is free to move will move from the higher energy point to the lower one, taking a quantity of that energy difference with it.

Frequency

Alternating current (AC) is preferred over direct current (DC) for power generation/transmission systems and is used domestically, in industry and commerce, but AC is 3 to 5 times more dangerous than DC at the same voltage and amperage. AC at frequencies of 50 to 60 Hz produces a series of muscle contractions (tetany), which will, if the point of contact is the palm of the hand, cause the hand to grasp the source and prolonging the exposure. DC is most likely to cause a single convulsive contraction. AC has a greater tendency to cause fibrillation of the heart muscles, whereas DC tends to make the heart muscles stand still. Once the shock current is halted, a still heart has a better chance of regaining a normal beat pattern than one that is in fibrillation. Defibrillating equipment, used by paramedics, utilises a DC shock current to halt fibrillation to enable the heart to recover its normal beat. Though both AC and DC shocks may be fatal, more DC is required to have the same effect as AC, for example, the 'no let go' threshold for DC is reported to be 4-5 times that of AC.

Duration

For an electric shock to have an effect a person needs to be in contact with the current for sufficient time. At low current levels the body tolerates the current so the time is not material; however at higher current levels, for example, 50 mA, the person has to remain in contact for sufficient time for the heart to be affected, in the order of milliseconds. In general, the longer a person is in contact with the current the more harm may be caused.

Resistance

The amount of resistance in a circuit influences the amount of current that is allowed to flow, as explained by Ohm's law. It is possible for a person to be in contact with a circuit and to present sufficiently high resistance that very little current is allowed to flow through their body. The example shown in *figure ref 6-2* illustrates this. It should be noted that the level of current flow is also dependent on the voltage; at high voltages an enormous amount of resistance is needed to ensure current flow will remain at a safe level. In an electric shock situation the human body contributes part of the resistance of the circuit, and the amount it contributes depends on the current path taken and other factors such as personal chemical make-up (a large portion of the body is water), moisture on and thickness of skin, and any clothing that is being worn, such as shoes and gloves.

Current path

The effect of an electric shock on the body is particularly dependent on the current path through the body. Current has to flow through from one point to another as part of a circuit. If the flow was between two points on a finger the effect on the body would be concentrated between the two points. If the current path is between one hand and another, across the chest, this means the flow will pass through major parts of the body, such as the heart, and may cause fibrillation or cardiac arrest.

In a similar way, a contact between hand and foot (feet), across the chest, can have serious effects on a great many parts of the body, including the heart. These latter current paths tend to be the ones leading to fatal injuries. However, a current path from hand to foot down the one side of the body may not affect the heart and therefore may not be fatal. Although many people may experience shock from 230 volts this may not be fatal if they were, for example, standing on or wearing some insulating material. This may be a matter of fortune and, as a rule; protection should not be relied on.

The amount of current flow through the body has a significant influence on the effect of the electric shock. At low levels of current flow no effect may be experienced; however at progressively higher levels of current flow the larger muscles of the body may be affected.

The heart, being made of large muscles, requires a significant current to affect it. At high current levels burns may occur at the point of current entry and exit from the body, as well as points along the route the current takes through the body.

Current (mA)	Length of time	Likely effects
0 - 1	Not critical	Threshold of feeling. Undetected by person.
2 - 15	Not critical	Threshold of cramp. Independent loosening of the hands no longer possible, 'no let go' condition exists.
16 - 30	Minutes	Cramp like pulling together of the arms, breathing difficult. Limit of tolerance.
31 - 50	Seconds to minutes	Strong cramp like effects, loss of consciousness due to restricted breathing. Longer time may lead to fibrillation.
51 - 500	Less than one heart period (750 ms)	No fibrillation. Strong shock effects.
	Greater than one heart period	Fibrillation. Loss of consciousness. Burn marks.
Over 500	Less than one heart period	Fibrillation. Loss of consciousness. Burn marks.

Figure 6-5: Effects of alternating current flowing in the human body.   *Source: RMS.*

Direct/indirect shock

Direct shock

Direct shock relates to when a person makes contact with a charged or energised conductor that is intended to be charged or energised. In these circumstances the electrical system is operating in its normal or proper condition. This may occur when someone is working on equipment where conductors are exposed and in the live condition.

Indirect shock

Indirect shock relates to when a person makes contact with electrical conducting material that is normally at a safe potential, but has become dangerously live through a fault condition. Conductive parts of equipment that may become live in a fault condition include the conducting casing of equipment and trunking around electrical cables.

These are normally safe to touch, but under fault conditions could become dangerously live. For example, where the casing of equipment has a poor connection to earth, and when a fault occurs on the equipment, the casing may become live.

ELECTRICAL BURNS

External burns

When electrical current makes contact with the skin, it becomes part of the electrical circuit and can cause the point of entry to reach a high temperature creating immediate tissue damage and charring. The point of entry tends to be limited to small areas and will often appear sunken or hollowed whereas the exit wound is more extensively damaged and open.

Internal burns

The severity of the damage caused internally by electrical burns will depend upon the pathway the current flows. In the human body the pathways of least resistance being firstly blood vessels, nerves, muscle, then skin, tendon, fat, and finally bone.

Whilst there are likely to be burn marks on the skin at the point of contact there may also be a deep seated burning within the body, which is painful and slow to heal. As the outer layer of skin is burnt the resistance decreases and so the current will increase. The current flowing through the body can cause major injury to internal organs and bone marrow as it passes through them.

ELECTRICAL FIRES

Common causes

Much electrical equipment generates heat or produces sparks and this equipment should not be placed where this could lead to the uncontrolled ignition of any substance.

The principal causes of electrical fires are:

■ Wiring with defects such as insulation failure due to age or poor maintenance or physical damage.

■ Overheating of cables or other electrical equipment through overloading with currents above their design capacity (for example, a coiled extension lead will have a much lower current carrying capacity than one that is fully uncoiled and will rapidly overheat if this is exceeded).

■ Too high a fuse rating for the circuit to be protected (for example, 13A fuse used for a circuit with a load capacity of 3A).

■ Poor connections due to the effects of use/lack of maintenance or unskilled personnel (for example, cables not secured by a cable grip inside a drill casing).

Electrical equipment may itself explode or arc violently and it may also act as a source of ignition of flammable vapours, gases, liquids or dust through electric sparks, arcs or high surface temperatures of equipment.

Other causes are heat created by poorly maintained or defective motors, heaters and lighting.

Figure 6-6: Used coiled up - risk of overheating.   *Source: RMS.*

Figure 6-7: Max current capacity exceeded.   *Source: RMS.*

Figure 6-8: Worn cable - risk of electrical fire.   *Source: RMS.*

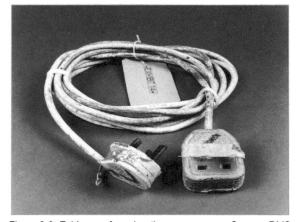

Figure 6-9: Evidence of overheating.   *Source: RMS.*

Static electricity

Static electricity is different to mains power electricity as static electricity can be generated naturally. It is familiar in everyday life as the crackling sound when we remove a woollen sweater and the tiny blue sparks seen in the dark.

It is also evident in the clinging together of clothing, paper or sheets of material or the sharp shock when we rub and separate from a dissimilar surface, such as when getting out of a car and then touching the body work.

Static electricity may be generated during the following situations:

■ The flow of liquids and powders through pipes, for example, when refuelling with petrol.

■ The pouring of powders from insulating plastic bags.

■ Spraying.

■ The unwinding of rolled insulating foils.

■ The movement of dust or liquids through air.

■ The pouring of liquids, granules or powders from insulated containers.

Static electricity build-up is particularly a problem where materials that are not very conductive are in contact with each other, for example, plastics and paper, and where two surfaces are rapidly separated.

Danger occurs, in particular, when a static spark is created in a flammable or explosive atmosphere. Given the right mix of flammable material and oxygen, a static spark with sufficient energy can start a fire or explosion.

WORKPLACE ELECTRICAL EQUIPMENT INCLUDING PORTABLE ELECTRICAL EQUIPMENT

Conditions and practices likely to lead to electrical accidents

Unsuitable equipment

- Unsuitable apparatus for the duty or the conditions.
- Misuse.
- Failure to follow operating instructions.
- Wrong connection of system - supply phase, neutral or earth reversed.
- Wrong voltage or rating of equipment.

Inadequate maintenance

- Inadequate maintenance of the installation and the equipment.
- Wrong or broken connection to portable apparatus.
- Inadequate earthing.
- Poor maintenance and testing.
- No defect reporting system.

Figure 6-10: Hazard - fuse wired out. *Source: RMS.*

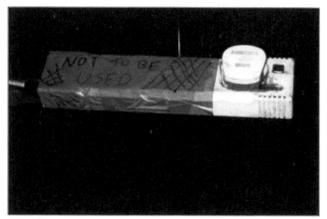

Figure 6-11: Continued use of defective equipment. *Source: RMS.*

Use of defective apparatus

- Faulty cables, notably extension leads.
- Plugs and sockets.
- Damaged plug or socket.
- Protection devices, such as fuses or circuit breaker, incorrect rating, damaged or missing.
- Overloaded leading to damage or over-heating.
- Short circuit leading to damage, overheating or movement.
- Isolation procedures or systems of work wrong.
- Bad circuit connections.

General

- Lack of competence.
- Poor access, lighting and emergency procedures.
- No work planning, for example, permit-to-work.

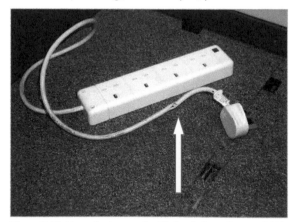

Figure 6-12: Hazard - damaged cable insulation. *Source: RMS.*

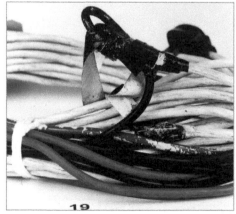

Figure 6-13: Hazard - taped joints. *Source: RMS.*

SECONDARY EFFECTS OF CONTACT WITH ELECTRICITY

These occur where the injury results from the flow of electricity through the body's nerves, muscles and organs and causes abnormal function to occur. Muscular spasm may be severe, particularly if the leg muscles are affected, causing a person to be thrown several metres. Injuries may result from dislocation, impact with surrounding objects or fall from a height. In addition, a tool may be dropped causing such injuries as burns or impact injury to the user or others nearby.

High risks associated with electricity

USE OF POORLY MAINTAINED ELECTRICAL EQUIPMENT

Regulation 4 of the Electricity at Work Regulations (EWR) 1989 sets out requirements for the maintenance of electrical systems.

> *"All systems shall at all times be of such construction as to prevent, so far as reasonably practicable, such danger". As may be necessary to prevent danger, all systems shall be maintained so as to prevent, so far as reasonably practicable, such danger".*

Figure 6-14: Regulation 4 of EWR 1989.   *Source: The Electricity at Work Regulations (EWR) 1989.*

Many deaths and injuries result from poorly maintained electrical equipment and fires started by faulty electrical appliances. Around 1,000 electrical accidents at work are reported to the Health and Safety Executive each year, of these, 24 people die of their injuries.

All electrical equipment should be maintained and checked at appropriate intervals (HSE Guidance "INDG236 Maintaining portable electrical equipment in offices and other low risk environments" gives some advice on inspection intervals) to ensure it is safe and in good repair. In particular, managers (and others, such as landlords) responsible for electrical equipment maintenance should ensure:

- Equipment is maintained in a safe condition.
- Information is available to equipment users to ensure safety.
- Safe procedures for inspection and testing are used.
- Records of inspection and testing are maintained.

WORK NEAR OVERHEAD POWER LINES

Contact with live overhead power lines kills a significant number of people and causes serious injuries every year. A high proportion - about one third - of inadvertent line contacts prove fatal. Overhead power lines may be confused with telephone lines, which can lead people not to identify the risk from contact. Lines may be hard to see at night or against a dark or very bright background. Power lines carry electricity at between 230 and 33,000 volts, even contact with a 230 volt line can kill. They are not normally covered in insulation so direct contact can easily be made. Contact can lead to current passing through a person, and the item that contacted the line, on a path to earth. Rubber-soled shoes would not provide protection from current flow and shock. Actual contact with a power line is not necessary to result in electric shock; a close approach to the line conductors may allow an arc to take place. The risk of arcing increases as the line voltage increases.

Many construction occupations may require workers to perform their job tasks near overhead power lines. Scaffold erectors, truck drivers, excavation equipment operators, tree service workers, mobile material handling equipment operators, tower crane operators and others find themselves carrying out their work in the vicinity of live overhead power lines. They may not be trained to recognise the dangers of electrocution if their bodies, equipment, tools, work materials or vehicles come near to an overhead power line.

CONTACT WITH UNDERGROUND POWER CABLES DURING EXCAVATION WORK

Underground power cables are present in most locations that excavations are conducted, in the high street, on construction or re-development sites and even in the country. Their location may be marked, not identified or not known of at all. Their presence is not obvious when conducting a visual site survey and so the likelihood of striking a power cable when excavating, drilling or piling is increased. The results of striking an underground power cable can include shock, electrocution, explosion and burns. As with overhead power lines, any underground service should be treated as live until confirmed dead by a power authority. Maps showing the location of underground power cables need to be taken as an indication of their location not as 'pin-point' accuracy, which means that careful testing needs to take place until indicated power cables are located. Even then some degree of caution needs to be taken in case unmarked power cables are encountered.

WORK ON MAINS ELECTRICAL SUPPLIES (230 VOLT)

Mains electricity supplies can be treated complacently because of their prevalence and their relatively low voltage; however a number of deaths occur each year of people working on mains electricity supplies.

WORK ON LIVE AND DEAD ELECTRICAL SUPPLIES

It is never absolutely safe to work on live electrical equipment. There are few circumstances where it is necessary to work live, and this must only be done after it has been determined that it is unreasonable for the work to be done dead. Even if working live can be justified, many precautions are needed to make sure that the risk is reduced 'so far as is reasonably practicable'.

Each year about 1,000 accidents at work involving electric shock or burns are reported to the Health and Safety Executive. Around 24 of these are fatal. Some of the high risk work associated with these deaths involves work on live and dead electrical supplies.

Work on live electrical supplies represents a high risk as the conductors being worked on are live and others nearby may also be live. There is a significant risk that tools used in live work could contact the different conductors or that a circuit is made between a live conductor and the frame of the equipment, causing a short circuit.

Additionally, when working on a live conductor the tool used and worker could provide an easy path for the current to pass to earth. The resultant shock of the current passing through the worker's body could lead to fatal injuries. Non-fatal shocks can cause severe and permanent injury, including burns and fractures. In addition, there is a risk of explosive vaporisation of metal conductors when they are accidentally short circuited by non-insulated tools.

In construction activities, electrical work may involve work on dead electrical circuits that may become live. This could be due to changes in the circuitry made during the progress of construction work that lead to a dead circuit becoming unexpectedly energised.

USE OF ELECTRICAL EQUIPMENT IN WET ENVIRONMENTS

Use of electrical equipment in wet conditions increases the risk of harm because the wet conditions increase the conductivity of surrounding surfaces. Where a fault exists on electrical equipment in a wet environment it may not be necessary to make direct contact with it to receive an electric shock, the wet substance may act as a conductor making a circuit between the faulty equipment and the person. These conditions may exist where, for example, a plasterer plasters a wall around a faulty light socket or a pressure water cleaner has a damaged cable lying in the water run-off from the cleaning operation.

USE OF ELECTRICAL EQUIPMENT IN FLAMMABLE/EXPLOSIVE ENVIRONMENTS

The failure to use correctly rated electrical equipment (international protection (IP) rating) in areas where explosive atmospheres exist or may exist may result in ignition of flammable dust, gases or vapours with explosive results. The spread of ignited material to other areas where fires might be initiated, far from the original source of ignition, may also result in additional explosions, propagating the fire to adjacent areas. This will result in damage to property and individuals within the vicinity, resulting in severe burns, physical damage to the body and hearing/sight sensory organs.

6.2 - Control measures

Selection and suitability of equipment for use in construction activities

PROTECTION OF CONDUCTORS

Conductors, whether live, neutral or earthed require protection from accidental or deliberate contact, interference, misuse or even abuse. This is often in the form of insulation. *Insulators* are materials that do not readily conduct electricity. Some common insulator materials are glass, plastic, rubber, air, and wood. Where conductors that are insulated are exposed to a higher risk of damage they may be further protected by a metal casing, which provides re-enforcement around the insulation, or ducting which provides a protective location for it to be placed.

CABLES AND LEADS

Insulation appropriate to the environment should be used to give resistance to abrasion, chemicals, heat and impact. The insulation must be in good condition. Flexible, multi-strand cables are required for portable tools and extension leads. Cables must be secured by the outer sheath at their point of entry into the apparatus, including plugs. The individual conductor insulation should not show through the sheath and conductors must not be exposed. Extension leads must be fused.

Temporary wiring should be used in compliance with standards and properly secured, supported and mechanically protected against damage. Taped joints in cables are not allowed and proper line connectors must be used to join cables. Connectors should be kept to a minimum to reduce earth path impedance.

Many cables are set up on a temporary basis, but these improvised arrangements can get left for a considerable time. Care should be taken to identify true short term temporary arrangements and those that warrant full longer term arrangements, such as being placed in trunking for better protection.

Conductors across roads or pedestrian ways should be covered to protect them from damage. Where they are to cross a doorway this is usually best done by taking it around the door instead of trailing it across the floor. Overhead cables likely to be hit by vehicles or persons carrying ladders, pipes etc. should be highlighted by the use of appropriate signs.

Regular examination should be made for deterioration, cuts (these are best identified by using the technique of systematic bending of short sections of cable by hand, progressing along the length of the cable). Cuts will be opened by this process revealing the conductor, kinks or bend damage (particularly near to the point of entry into apparatus), exposed conductors, overheat or burn damage, trapping damage, insulation embrittling or corrosion.

STRENGTH AND CAPABILITY OF EQUIPMENT

Regulation 5 of the Electricity at Work Regulations (EWR) 1989 sets out requirements for strength and capability of electrical equipment.

"No electrical equipment shall be put into use where its strength and capability may be exceeded in such a way as may give rise to danger".

Figure 6-15: Regulation 5 of EWR 1989.   Source: *The Electricity at Work Regulations (EWR) 1989.*

Strength and capability in this context has a wide meaning. This includes the requirement that any electrical equipment needs to be capable of standing normal and fault currents without failure.

In order for equipment to remain safe when subjected to sustained fault conditions it may require the inclusion of protective devices which detect the fault and break the circuit containing the fault.

It is also important to ensure that all electrical equipment is suitable for what it is used for in terms of its strength and capability. For example, if it is to be used for outdoor work on a construction site in conditions that it might get wet, equipment providing protection from the ingress of water must be selected. Many tools are designed and provided for use in a domestic situation and they may not be suitable for use in the more arduous conditions of a construction site, for example, cable entry grips may be more secure and outer protection of cables thicker on equipment designed for construction work.

The British Standard BS 7671, the Institute of Electrical Engineers (IEE) 17th edition requirements, Chapter 13 - 'Fundamental principles for safety' - specifies the following needs. Good workmanship and proper materials shall be used. Construction, installation, inspection, testing and maintenance shall be such as to prevent danger.

Equipment shall be suitable for the power demanded and the conditions in which it is installed. Additions and alterations to installations shall comply with regulations. Equipment which requires operation or attention shall be accessible.

The Low Voltage (Safety) Regulations place a duty on the supplier of equipment to ensure that equipment using between 50 and 100 volts ac is safe. Construction, including flexible cables and cords, must be to European Union (EU) accepted good engineering practice standards. The Regulations are deemed satisfied if the equipment bears a recognised standard mark, certificate or other acceptable authorisation. Supply of unsafe equipment or components is prohibited.

PLANNING AND INSTALLATION OF A PROGRESSIVELY EXTENDING ELECTRICAL SYSTEM ON SITE

Electricity in construction brings numerous hazards that require stringent planning and control systems. Prior to starting construction activities, at the planning stage consideration must be given to factors including buried services, electricity sub-stations or proximity to overhead cables. A site may have existing buildings and tests must be made to determine whether existing services are live or dead. At the planning stage, a full site survey will include identifying the location of any electrical sources or conductors.

Planning also provides the ideal opportunity to ensure that where electricity is involved, the correct measures are implemented to control risk. This may include location of plant, planning cable runs or ducts, whether high or low voltage is required, control features when in use (switch panels, isolation, and lock off), protection devices (earthing arrangements, trip switches, residual current devices, panel housings, warnings and instructions). Maintenance should play a key part in the planning stage, with consideration given to access, isolation, lock-off and security.

When construction activities start heavy mechanical plant will be introduced that may operate in close proximity to sources of electricity. Safe systems should be introduced to include ensuring that sufficiently safe distances are maintained from overhead cables to prevent electrical 'arc' (discharge) from the uninsulated cables.

Safe systems may include permits-to-work, 'goal post' type visual barriers, information for site workers and signs. There may be activities that involve explosive atmospheres that require intrinsically safe equipment to be used (for example, work is sewers or chambers).

Most industrial installations work on high voltage systems due to increased consumption of electricity during the many different processes. Owing to economic advantages, industrial sites commonly include their own dedicated power sub-stations that operate at voltages typically in ranges of 11kV. This high voltage is then transformed down into values more commonly in the range of 415v. When working with high voltage circuitry, staff must be 'high voltage' trained and work under a permit to work system.

It is essential that the planning and installation of electrical systems reflect not only the power needs but the lighting needs of the site as well. The plan should include anticipated needs or demand as the site changes, for example, extending provision as a structure is built or orderly withdrawal of provision as a structure is demolished. Planning should ensure power is available at key points as close to where work is carried out that requires it, thus minimising the need for extension cables to run for long distances. Planning should take account of where it is not practicable to provide a permanent system and where local power generation is more suitable. In this case the same planning is required to ensure the system provided is adequate for the demands. In some cases this will require the provision of a quantity of small generators to ensure the right amount of power is available where it is needed.

Figure 6-16: Construction site generator.   *Source: RMS.*

Figure 6-17: Construction site power supply panel. *Source: RMS.*

If work is to be conducted in someone else's building that is occupied and power is to be obtained by adapting the system within the building, consideration has to be given to the effects on the host's power supply of this additional demand. Care should be taken to ensure that power is drawn from agreed points and at agreed, safe voltages. Where practicable systems provided for construction work should run at 110V or lower and should be set into place at the earliest safe opportunity; in many cases this can be integrated into ground works that is planned for the site. If systems are to be left in place at the end of the work, and they do not form part of the system for the structure constructed, care should be taken to identify them on plans and if they are to be left 'dead' they should be checked to ensure this is the case.

Figure 6-18: 110v generator.   *Source: RMS.*

Figure 6-19: 110v extension lead.   *Source: RMS.*

PERMIT TO WORK PROCEDURES AND REQUIREMENTS

A permit to work is an official, documented safe system of work that is used for controlling high risk activities. Implementation is required prior to work beginning to ensure that all precautions are taken and are securely in place to prevent danger to the workforce. When managed correctly, a permit to work prevents any mistakes or deviations through poor communication; by stating the specific requirements of the task. For electrical systems, a permit to work is typically used for those rated at or in excess of 240v or where there is more than one point or means of isolation.

The authorised person issues the permit to work and will sign the document to declare that all isolations are made and remain in place throughout the duration of the task.

Figure 6-20: Power supply isolation.   *Source: RMS.*

In addition to this, the authorised person will make checks to ensure that all controls to be implemented by the acceptor are in place before work commences.

The acceptor of the permit to work assumes responsibility for carrying out the work on the electrical system. The acceptor signs the document to declare that the terms and conditions of the permit to work are understood and will be complied with fully at all times by the entire work team. Compliance with a permit to work system includes ensuring the required safeguards are implemented and that the work will be restricted to only the equipment stated within the document.

Items included in the electrical permit to work are:

■ Permit issue number.
■ Authorised person identification.
■ Points at which isolation is made.
■ Test procedure and confirmation of dead circuitry.
■ Warning information sign locations.
■ Earth connection points.
■ Details of the work to be carried out.
■ Signature of authoriser.
■ Signature of acceptor.
■ Signature for works clearance/extension/handover.
■ Signature for cancellation.

Other precautions include risk assessments, method statements, and personal protective equipment.

REQUIREMENTS FOR TEMPORARY ELECTRICAL SUPPLIES

The supply of electricity on a construction site will normally be provided by one or both of the following:

■ A public supply from the local electricity company.
■ A site generator, where public supply is not practical or economic.

Public supply

The public supply company will require the installation of a suitable facility for the incoming cables to be connected to. The facility may be a temporary structure or a permanent substation which may be required for the site development. The supply will be connected to isolation switch gear, monitoring equipment and in accordance with the supplier requirements for earthing.

Generators

Where generators are required, these will either be petrol or diesel powered and will need to be sited to reduce the effects of noise and emissions on the site workers or others on neighbouring facilities. Generating equipment should be installed by a competent person in accordance with BS7375:2010; a code of practice that gives recommendations for the distribution of electricity on construction sites. The sites covered in the standard are areas where any of the following take place:

■ Construction work of new buildings.
■ Repair, alteration, extension, demolition of existing buildings or parts of existing buildings.
■ Engineering works.
■ Earthworks.
■ Work of similar nature.

If the generator is rated above 55 volts AC, it must be earthed and the effectiveness of the earth checked by a competent person. Generators that operate at or below 55 volts AC do not require an earth. Not all portable generators available have a centre tapped earth output of 110 volts, giving 55 volts at point of use *(see also - Element 6.2 - Reduced low voltage systems)*. This is common with generators with dual voltage output selection. Where there is a site distribution system the metal framework of the generator should be connected to a common earth.

Figure 6-21: Earth provided to generator.   *Source: RMS.*

Figure 6-22: Earthed distribution equipment.   *Source: RMS.*

Electrical contractors should not switch on the electricity until they have a written request from the main contractor or the main contractor's agent; the circuits have been fully inspected and tested and are safe to use. When the electricity is switched on, the main contractor is legally responsible for making sure that everyone working on site is aware of any live circuits in an area. They are also responsible for making sure that their electrical subcontractors use safe isolation procedures before working on any circuits that could possibly be live. The electrical subcontractor has the same duty and responsibility to use safe isolation practices when required.

ADVANTAGES AND LIMITATIONS OF PROTECTIVE SYSTEMS

Fuses

This is a device designed to automatically cut off the power supply to a circuit within a given time when the current flow in that circuit exceeds a given value. A fuse may be a rewirable tinned copper wire in a suitable carrier or a wire or wires in an enclosed cartridge.

In effect it is a weak link in the circuit that melts when heat is created by too high a current passing through the thin wire in the fuse case. When this happens the circuit is broken and no more current flows. A fuse usually has a rating in the order of Amperes rather than milli Amps which means it has **limited usefulness in protecting people from electric shock.** The fuse will operate (break the circuit) relatively slowly if the current is just above the fuse rating. Using too high a fuse means that the circuit will remain intact and the equipment will draw power. This may cause it to overheat leading to a fire or if a fault exists the circuit will remain live and the fault current may pass through the user of the equipment when they touch or operate it.

The following formula should be used to calculate the correct rating for a fuse:

Current (Amperes) = $\dfrac{\text{Power (watts)}}{\text{Voltage (volts)}}$

For example, the correct fuse current rating for a 2-kilowatt kettle on a 230-volt supply would be:

$\dfrac{2,000 \text{ W}}{230 \text{ V}}$ = 8.69A

Typical fuses for domestic appliances are 3, 5, 10 and 13 Ampere ratings.

The nearest fuse just above this current level is 10A.

	Typical examples of power ratings are:	Suitable fuses at 230 Volts:
Computer processor.	350 Watts.	3 Amperes.
Electric kettle.	1,850 - 2,200 Watts.	10 - 13 Amperes.
Dishwasher.	1,380 Watts.	10 Amperes.
Refrigerator.	90 Watts.	3 Amperes.

Summary

A fuse is:

- A weak link in the circuit that melts slowly when heat is created by a fault condition. However, this usually happens too slowly to protect people.
- Easy to replace with wrong rating.
- Needs tools to replace.
- Easy to override by replacing a fuse with one of a higher rating or putting in an improvised 'fuse', such as a nail, that has a high rating.

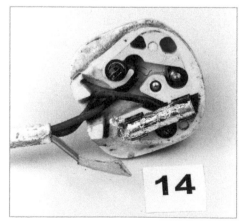

Figure 6-23: Plug-foil fuse no earth. *Source: RMS.*

Figure 6-24: Earthing. *Source: RMS.*

Earthing

A conductor called an earth wire is fitted to the system; it is connected at one end to a plate buried in the ground and the other end connected to the metal casing of the equipment. If for any reason a conductor touches the casing so that the equipment casing becomes 'live' the current will flow to the point of lowest potential, the earth. The path to this point (earth) is made easier as the wire is designed to have very little resistance. This *may prevent electric shock* provided it is used in association with a correctly rated fuse, or better still a residual current device (RCD), and no one is in contact with the equipment at the time the fault occurs.

It should be remembered that earthing is provided where the casing can become live. If the equipment is designed so that this cannot be the case, such as double insulated equipment where the user touches non-conducting surfaces, earthing of the equipment is no advantage. In summary, earthing provides a path of least resistance for "stray" current and provides protection against indirect shock.

Isolation of supply

Isolation of an electrical system is an excellent way of achieving safety for those that need to work on or near the system; for example, isolation of a power supply into a building that is to be refurbished or isolation of plant that is to be maintained. In its simplest form it can mean switching off and unplugging a portable appliance at times it is not in use. Care must be taken to check that the isolation has been adequate and effective before work starts; this can include tests on the system. It is also important to ensure the isolation is secure; 'lock off' and 'tag out' systems will assist with this.

Reduced and low voltage systems

One of the best ways to reduce the risk from electricity is to reduce the voltage. This is frequently achieved by the use of a transformer (step down) which will reduce the voltage. A common reduction is from the mains voltage of 230V to 110V. Normally, transformers that are used to reduce voltage are described as "centre tapped to earth". In practice this means that any voltage involved in an electrical shock will be 55V.

Using the earlier example of Ohms Law, if the voltage is 230V then:

$$I = \frac{V}{R} = \frac{230 \text{ Volts}}{2,000+4,000 \text{ Ohms}} = 0.038 \text{Amperes or } 38 \text{ mA}$$

However, if a centre tapped to earth transformer is used then,

$$I = \frac{V}{R} = \frac{55 \text{ Volts}}{2,000+4,000 \text{ Ohms}} = 0.009 \text{ Amperes or } 9 \text{ mA}$$

Reference to *figures 6-2 and 6-5* will clearly show how this *reduces the effects of electric shock* on the body.

Figure 6-25: 110V centre tapped earth transformer. *Source: RMS.*

Figure 6-26: 110V powered drill. *Source: RMS.*

An alternative to reduction in voltage by means of a transformer is to provide battery-powered equipment; this will commonly run on 12V to 24V, but voltages may be higher. The common method is to use a rechargeable battery to power the equipment which eliminates the need for a cable to feed power to the equipment and gives a greater flexibility of use for the user, for example, for drills and power drivers.

Residual current device (RCD)

An electro-mechanical switching device is used to automatically isolate the supply when there is a difference between the current flowing into a device and the current flowing from the device. Such a difference might result from a fault causing current leakage, with possible fire risks or the risk of shock current when a person touches a system and provides a path to earth for the current. RCDs can be designed to operate at low currents and fast response times (usually 30 mA and 30 mSeconds) and thus they *reduce the effect of an electric shock*. Though they do not prevent the person receiving an electric shock they are very sensitive and operate very quickly and reduce some of the primary effects of the shock. It is still possible for a person to receive injury from the shock, not least some of the secondary injuries referred to earlier. But the use of this type of device means the fault current should be isolated before sustained shock, and therefore before fibrillation, occurs. The equipment needs to be de-energised from time to time in order to be confident it will work properly when needed. This can easily be done by a simple test routine before use, as equipment is plugged into the RCD.

Summary of features of RCD

A residual current device is:

- Rapid and sensitive.
- Difficult to defeat.

- Easy and safe to test and reset.
- Not able to prevent shock, but reduces the effect of a shock.

Figure 6-27: Residual current device. *Source: RMS.*

Figure 6-28: Plug-in residual current device. *Source: RMS.*

Double insulation

This is a common protection device and consists of a layer of insulation around the live electrical parts of the equipment and a second layer of insulated material around this, commonly the casing of the equipment. Since the casing material is an insulator and does not conduct electricity, equipment having this type of protection does not normally have an earth wire.

To make sure that the double insulation is not impaired, it must not be pierced by conducting parts such as metal screws. Nor must insulating screws be used, because there is the possibility that they will be lost and will be replaced by metal screws. Any holes in the enclosure of a double Insulated appliance, such as those to allow ventilation, must be so small that fingers cannot reach live parts.

Each layer of insulation must be sufficient in its own right to give adequate protection against shock. Equipment which is double insulated will carry the symbol shown in *figure ref 6-30*.

Double insulated equipment has two layers of insulating material between the live parts of the equipment and the user. If a fault occurs with the live parts and a conductor touches the insulating material surrounding it no current can pass to the user, therefore *no shock occurs.*

Figure 6-29: Double insulated 230V drill. *Source: RMS.*

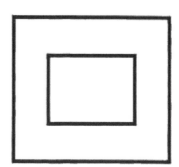

Figure 6-30: Double insulation symbol. *Source: HSE, HSG107.*

Use of competent persons

It is particularly important that anyone who undertakes electrical work is able to satisfy the requirements of the Health and Safety at Work etc. Act (HASAWA) 1974 and the Electricity at Work Regulations (EWR) 1989.

For work on electrical systems below 1,000 volts AC they should be able to work within the guidelines set out in BS 7671 'Requirements for electrical installations, IEE Wiring Regulations, 17th edition'. Other work should be carried out according to the guidelines set out in the relevant industry standard.

Those who wish to undertake electrical testing work would normally be expected to have more knowledge and to be able to demonstrate competence through the successful completion of a suitable training course. More complex electrical tasks such as motor repair or maintenance of radio frequency heating equipment should only be carried out by someone who has been trained to do them.

Work on higher voltage systems must be carried out by specialist electrical engineers trained for this purpose. Work on live electrical systems must be controlled and requires specialist competence and systems of work to ensure safety.

Use of safe systems of work

LIVE ELECTRICAL WORK

The Electricity at Work Regulations (EWR) 1989 sets out requirements for live electrical work.

"No person shall be engaged in any work activity on or so near any live conductor that danger may arise, unless it is unreasonable in all the circumstances for it to be dead".

Figure 6-31: Work on live conductors, Regulation 14.   *Source: The Electricity at Work Regulations (EWR) 1989.*

This duty means that if danger could be present, work where possible, should be carried out with the electrical system dead. If it is necessary to work on live conductors, very strict controls must be in place and a safe system of work adhered to.

These will include:

- A full justification of why there is no reasonably practicable alternative to live working.
- A Live Electrical Permit to Work which will be valid for the stated task only.
- At least two competent persons must be present during the work and the more senior of these will sign off the permit when the work is complete and after all equipment has been restored to a fully safe condition.
- Restriction of work area to these competent people.
- Protection of the work area from other hazards, such as vehicles.
- Protection of workers from non-essential live conductors, by isolation or screening.
- Provision of information on the system and task.
- Use of suitable, insulated test equipment and tools.
- Adequate lighting and clear space to work.
- First-aid service immediately available.
- Competent supervision.

ISOLATION

The Electricity at Work Regulations (EWR) 1989 sets out requirements for isolation.

"'Isolation' means the disconnection and separation of the electrical equipment from every source of electrical energy in such a way that this disconnection and separation is secure".

Figure 6-32: Isolation, Regulation 12 of EWR 1989.   *Source: The Electricity at Work Regulations (EWR) 1989.*

Health and Safety Executive (HSE) booklet 'Electricity at Work - Safe Working Practices (HSG85)' provides information on isolation procedures when working on both Low Voltage (LV) and High Voltage (HV) systems.

The requirement of the Electricity at Work Regulations (EWR) 1989 means that any isolation method used must be adequate and secure. This means that turning equipment off at a general on off switch or other mechanism is not adequate. Isolation therefore requires disconnection at the primary isolation mechanism for the equipment or circuit.

In order to ensure a high level of security if work on the circuit or equipment takes the person away from constant site of the isolator mechanism, a lock may be added. Isolation procedures often referred to as 'lockout/tagout', in conjunction with a 'Permits-to-work' often form part of a 'Safe System of Work'. Various competences are required to ensure full compliance with these procedures, with specialist training and supervision required.

Figure 6-33: Multi-lock system.   *Source: RMS.*

If multi-lock systems are used *(see figure ref 6-33)* there must be a contingency plan to deal with the likelihood that someone will lose a key or even leave at the end of a shift without removing their personal pad lock.

LOCATING BURIED SERVICES

Excavation operations should not begin until all available service location drawings have been identified and thoroughly examined. Record plans and location drawings should not be considered as totally accurate but serve only as an indication of the likelihood of the presence of services, their location and depth.

It is possible for the position of an electricity supply cable to alter if previous works have been carried out in the location due to the flexibility of the cable and movement of surrounding features since original installation of the cable.

In addition, plans often show a proposed position for the services that does not translate to the ground, such that services are placed in position only approximately where the plan says.

Before groundwork is due to commence it is common and good practice to check for presence of any of the services or hazards by using a detection device. A common detection device used is the cable avoidance tool more commonly known as a CAT scanner. It is important that 'service location devices' such as a cable avoidance tool (CAT) are used by competent, trained operatives to assist in the identification and marking of the actual location and position of buried services. When identified it is essential that physical markings be placed on the ground to show where these services are located.

Figure 6-34: Marking of services.   Source: RMS.

PROTECTION AGAINST OVERHEAD CABLES

Contact with live overhead lines kills people and causes serious injuries every year.

It is important, where possible, to eliminate the danger by:

- Avoidance - carrying out as much work as is possible remote from the lines.
- Diversion - diverting all overhead lines clear of the work area.
- Isolation - make lines dead while the work is in progress.
- Insulation.

If the danger cannot be eliminated, the risk must be managed by controlling access to, and work beneath, overhead power lines. For lower voltage cables it may be possible to temporarily isolate the supply and fit insulation to prevent contact with the live conductor when power is restored.

The following precautions may also be needed to manage the risk:

- Isolate the supply.
- Erect 'goal-post' barriers to define clearance distances.
- Clearly mark danger zones with signs and/or bunting.
- Ensure safe access under lines.
- Use banksman or marshals where appropriate.
- Restrict the use of metal equipment such as ladders and scaffolds.

See also - Element 6.3 - Control measures for working near overhead power lines.

INSPECTION AND MAINTENANCE STRATEGIES

The Electricity at Work Regulations (EWR) 1989, Regulation 4(2) sets out requirements for the owner to maintain electrical systems.

> *"As may be necessary to prevent danger, **maintain** all systems so as to prevent, so far as is reasonably practicable, such danger".*

Figure 6-35: Regulation 4(2) of EWR 1989.   *Source: The Electricity at Work Regulations (EWR) 1989.*

Danger is defined as the risk of injury from electric shock, electric burn, fire of electrical origin, electric arcing or explosion initiated or caused by electricity.

In order to identify what systems will need maintenance, they should be listed. This same listing can be used as a checklist, recording that the appropriate checks have been done. It may also include details of the type of equipment, as well as the checks and tests to be carried out. The list should include any equipment that is, or may be, connected to a common source of electrical energy. The requirements apply similarly to the permanent installation in a building, including wiring and fixed equipment such as a bench mounted circular saw and portable equipment such as sanders or drills.

Maintenance is a general term that in practice can include visual inspection, repair, testing and replacement. Maintenance will determine whether equipment is fully serviceable or needing repair.

It further suggests that cost effective maintenance can be achieved by a combination of:

- Checks by the user.
- Visual inspections by a person appointed to do this.
- Combined inspection and tests by a competent person or by a contractor.

User checks

A procedure should be established by which the user brings faults to the attention of a supervisor and/or a competent person who might rectify the fault. The user of portable electrical equipment should, after basic training, look critically at equipment and its source of power and if any defects are found, the equipment should be marked and quarantined and not be used again before examination by a competent person.

Checks by the user should be aimed at identifying the following:

- Damaged cable sheaths.
- Damaged plugs. Cracked casing or bent pins.
- Taped or other inadequate cable joints.
- Outer cable insulation not secured into plugs or equipment.
- Faulty or ineffective switches.

- Burn marks or discolouration.
- Damaged casing.
- Loose parts or screws.
- Wet or contaminated equipment.
- Loose or damaged sockets or switches.

Formal inspection and tests

Visual inspection

The maintenance system should always include formal visual inspection of all portable electrical equipment and electrical tests.

The frequency depends on the type of equipment and where it is used. The inspection can be done by a member of staff who has been trained in what to look for and has basic electrical knowledge. They should know enough to avoid danger to themselves or others.

Visual inspections are likely to need to look for the same types of defects as user checks but should also include the following.

Opening plugs of portable equipment to check for:

- Use of correctly rated fuse.
- Effective cord grip.
- Secure and correct cable terminations.

Inspection of fixed installations for:

- Damaged or loose conduit, trunking or cabling.
- Missing broken or inadequately secured covers.
- Loose or faulty joints.
- Loose earth connections.
- Moisture, corrosion or contamination.
- Burn marks or discolouration.
- Open or inadequately secured panel doors.
- Ease of access to switches and isolators.
- Presence of temporary wiring.

User checks and a programme of formal visual inspections will find the majority of faults.

Testing

Faults such as loss of earth or broken wires inside an installation or cable cannot be found by visual inspection, so some apparatus needs to have a combined inspection and test. This is particularly important for all earthed equipment and leads and plugs connected to hand held or hand operated equipment. The system should be tested regularly in accordance with Institute of Electrical Engineers (IEE) requirements; tests may include earth continuity and impedance tests and tests of insulation material.

Frequency of inspection and testing

Question:	*"I have been told that I have to have my desk lamp tested every six months. Is this correct?"*
Answer:	*"No. The law requires it to be maintained. It does not require any elaborate or rigorous system of frequent electrical testing".*

Figure 6-36: Testing frequency.   *Source: HSE Note INDG 160L.*

Deciding the frequency

Many approaches to establishing frequency suggest that they should be done regularly. As can be seen above, the word 'regularly' is not specified in terms of fixed time intervals for all systems; a management judgment must be made to specify an appropriate timetable.

In effect, the frequency will depend on the condition the system is used in; for example, a test of office portable equipment may be sufficient if conducted every 3 years, whereas equipment used on a construction site may need to be tested every 3 months.

The system as a whole rather than just portable equipment must also be tested periodically and again this will depend on the conditions of use and may vary from 10 years to 6 months.

Factors to be considered when deciding the frequency include:

- Type of equipment.
- Whether it is hand held.
- Manufacturer's recommendations.

- Frequency of use.
- Duration of use.
- Foreseeable use.

- Its initial integrity and soundness.
- Age.
- Working environment.
- Likelihood of mechanical damage.

- Who it is used by and if it is used continuously by different workers.
- Modifications or repairs.
- Past experience.

Records of inspection and testing

In order to identify what systems and equipment will need inspection and testing they should be listed. This same listing can be used as a checklist recording that the appropriate checks, inspections and tests have been done.

It would be usual to include details of the type of the equipment, its location and its age. It is important that a cumulative record of equipment and its status is held available to those that are responsible for using the equipment as well as those that are conducting the inspection or test. In addition, it is common practice to add a label to the system or part of the system (for example, portable appliances) to indicate that an inspection and/or test has taken place and its status following this.

Figure 6-37: PAT labels. Source: RMS.

Some labels show the date that this took place; others prefer to show the date of next inspection or test.

On construction sites, employees may bring to work their own electrically powered equipment, including tools to do their work and equipment for welfare reasons, for example, radios and kettles. All such equipment should be recorded, inspected and tested by a competent person before use and at regular intervals, as if it were company property.

Advantages and limitations of portable appliance testing (PAT)

The purpose of portable appliance testing is to periodically confirm the critical aspects of the electrical integrity of portable appliances. Three levels of inspection should be included in a maintenance and inspection strategy for portable electrical appliances:

- The first level of inspection would be that carried out by the operator before the appliance is used and would consist of an informal check of the condition of the appliance and its cable and plug.
- The second check would be supplemented by a more formal visual inspection by an appointed person which would follow a set down procedure and include other matters such as the correctness of the rating of the fuses fitted, security of cable grips, earth continuity, impedance and insulation.
- The third strategy would include the periodic combined inspection and testing of the appliance by a competent person.

It is important to keep centralised records of the results of portable appliance testing within an organisation. Such records can then be used for setting the frequency for appliance testing, to verify whether unlabelled equipment had been tested or had merely lost its label and to provide a record of past faults on all appliances that had been reported. This approach will demonstrate that the employer is in compliance with the regulations.

The limitation with portable appliance testing is that people may have an over-reliance on the apparent assurance that the test indicates. They may be tempted to see it as a permanent assurance that the equipment is safe. This can lead to users not making their own pre-use checks of the appliance. In effect it is only a test, and therefore assurance, at a point in time. It does not assure that someone has not, for example, altered the fuse and put one in with an incorrect rating or that the cable grip has not come loose.

It must also be recognised that there is little benefit in having a perfect portable appliance if it is plugged into a defective socket which may be without proper insulation, with a switch that does not work properly, with the polarity reversed or with a high resistance earth connection.

EMERGENCY PROCEDURES FOLLOWING AN ELECTRICAL INCIDENT

Anyone working around electrical systems should be aware of what needs to be done for a casualty of electrical shock.

If someone is lying unconscious and in contact with conductors the following actions should be taken in an order depending on the circumstances:

- Assess the situation.
- Summon help, including qualified medical support.
- If possible shut off the power.
- Do not touch the casualty - there may be enough voltage across the body of the casualty to shock the would-be rescuer. The problem with this rule is that the source of power may not be known, or easily found in time to save the casualty from shock.

- Remove the power. If possible prove the system is discharged and dead. If this is not possible take the following action.
- Remove the casualty from the power. It may be possible to dislodge the casualty from the circuit with a dry wooden board or piece of non-metallic material or using a jacket as a loop around the person, holding both sleeves and pulling away.
- Reassess the situation and any remaining danger to yourself and the casualty.
- Once the casualty has been disconnected from the source of electric power, the immediate medical concerns for the casualty should be respiration and circulation (breathing and pulse). If the rescuer is trained in cardio pulmonary resuscitation (CPR), they should follow the appropriate steps of checking breathing (including the airway) and pulse, then applying CPR as necessary to keep the casualty's body from de-oxygenating.
- If the casualty is conscious, lay them in the recovery position and keep them warm to reduce the chances of physiological shock until qualified medical personnel arrive on the scene.
- Keep the casualty under observation for secondary effects. Cool burns with water.

Figure 6-38: First-aid sign. *Source: RMS.*

Further considerations:

- Do not go near the casualty until the electricity supply is proven to be off. This is especially important with overhead high voltage lines: keep yourself and others at least 18 metres away until the electricity supply company personnel advise otherwise.
- Do not delay - after 3 minutes without blood circulation irreversible damage can be done to the casualty.
- Do not wait for an accident to happen - train in emergency procedures and first-aid, plan procedures for an emergency (calling for help, making calls to the emergency services, meeting ambulances and leading them to the casualty) and hold emergency drills.
- Establish if the incident has to be reported under the Reporting of Injuries, Diseases and Dangerous Occurrences Regulations (RIDDOR) 2013.

6.3 - Control measures for working near overhead power lines

Control measures

Every year people are seriously hurt by coming into contact with overhead power lines, so it is important to identify the overhead cables and implement adequate control measures. Any lines found on a construction site should always be treated as live until they are proved to be otherwise.

Control measures might include diversion of the power lines, temporary isolation of supply, safe access points, restricted vehicle movements, barriers and fencing.

AVOIDANCE WHERE POSSIBLE

It may be possible to have the overhead power lines diverted away from the site while work is carried out. Access routes to sites should be sited a safe distance away from overhead cables; if this is not possible then the adequate control measures should be adopted.

PRE-PLANNING AND CONSULTATION WITH SERVICE PROVIDER

Planning and consultation with service providers is essential and forms part of the safe system of work, as it may be necessary to isolate the supply in the event of an incident. Access routes should be established in consultation and these should be away from overhead cables. They should be clearly identified, signed and marked. Where this is not possible, then clear passing places with clear goal posts erected at both ends should be established, clearly signed, including clearance height and notice to driver to lower jibs. Lighting may be required if work is to take place after sunset.

Isolation/diversion of supply

The supply may need to be isolated at some point in the event of heavy equipment movements on or around the site. Where isolation is not practical then arrangements will need to be made with the utility suppliers, to divert the supply away from the site in order to maintain continuous supply to local consumers.

Therefore, it is essential that this has been adequately planned and a procedure has been adopted and approved with the electricity supplier.

GROUND LEVEL BARRIERS, GOAL POSTS AND CORRECT CLEARANCE DISTANCES

If work is to be carried out near overhead lines then barriers should be used, along with warning signs. The recommended distance for the position of the barriers is 6 metres (horizontally) from the nearest line. Some construction vehicles have jib's or telescopic arms that extend long distances, therefore the measurement should be taken with the reach of the jib (maximum outreach) measured (horizontally) from the position of the ground barrier. For very high voltages these distances may be increased significantly. Bunting may also be required to show drivers of these vehicles the position of the lines. The bunting should be placed at a height of 3 to 6 metres. The barriers should be sturdy enough so that they cannot be moved easily and should be coloured coded with red and white stripes.

Types of barrier commonly used include:

- 200 litre drums filled with rubble or concrete.
- Railway sleepers.
- A raised earth bank to 1 metre and marked by posts to prevent vehicle entry.
- A tension wire fence with flags attached (this should be earthed in consultation with the electricity supplier).

Access and egress routes beneath overhead cables should be clearly marked with clearance distances using a vertical pole each side of the opening and a height limiting barrier above and between. This work practice is commonly referred to as cross under 'goal posts'.

The safe clearance distance from the overhead line depends on the level of voltage of the line as it possible for electricity to arc between the line and any conducting material in contact with an earth.

This means the correct clearance may have to be determined by consultation with the electrical service provider responsible for the overhead line.

Figure 6-39: Working near power lines.   *Source: HSE, HSG150.*

RESTRICTION OF EQUIPMENT/VEHICLE REACH

There may be a requirement to restrict certain equipment, for example, rough terrain fork-lift trucks or cranes from working under power lines, due to the possibility of jibs or forks coming into contact with lines or near enough to form an arc from the power lines.

Similarly, the reach of telescopic cranes may be restricted by the application of electronic or mechanical restraints.

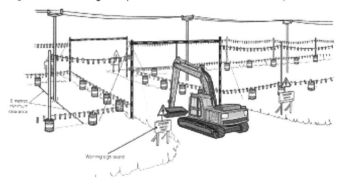

Figure 6-40: Overhead cable protection on traffic route.
Source: HSE, HSG144.

Sample assessment questions

1. **Describe** how the following two protective measures reduce the risk of electric shock **AND**, in **EACH** case, give an example of their application.

    (a)   Reduced low voltage. (4)

    (b)   Double insulation. (4)

2. Ground works are being planned on a site crossed by high voltage overhead power lines. The work will involve the use of excavators and tipper lorries to remove spoil from the site.

    Outline control measures to reduce the risk from contact with the overhead power lines.   (8)

3. Hand-held electric drills are commonly used on construction sites.

    (a)   **Outline** the checks that should be carried out by the user of a drill to reduce the likelihood of electric shock. (4)

    (b)   Other than electricity, **identify FOUR** hazards associated with the use of hand-held electric drills. (4)

Please refer to back of assessment section for answers.

Fire safety

Learning outcomes

On completion of this element, candidates should be able to demonstrate understanding of the content through the application of knowledge to familiar and unfamiliar situations. In particular they should be able to:

7.1 Describe the principles of fire initiation, classification and spread and the additional fire risks caused by construction activities in an existing workplace.

7.2 Outline the principles of fire risk assessment.

7.3 Outline the principles of fire prevention and the prevention of fire spread in construction workplaces.

7.4 Identify the appropriate fire detection, fire alarm system and firefighting equipment for construction activities.

7.5 Outline the requirements for an adequate and properly maintained means of escape in the construction workplace.

7.6 Outline the factors which should be considered when implementing a successful evacuation of a construction workplace in the event of a fire.

Content

Sources of reference

Storage of dangerous substances, Dangerous Substances and Explosives Atmospheres Regulations 2002, ACOP and guidance, L135, HSE Books, ISBN 978-0-7176-2200-9

Fire safety in construction work, HSG168, HSE Books ISBN 978-0-7176-6345-3

Fire Safety Risk Assessment series, Communities and Local Government Publications, https://www.gov.uk/workplace-fire-safety-your-responsibilities/fire-safety-advice-documents:

> Fire Safety Risk Assessment - Offices and shops, ISBN-13 978-1-8511-2815-0
>
> Fire Safety Risk Assessment - Factories and warehouses, ISBN-13 978-1-8511-2816-7
>
> Fire Safety Risk Assessment - Sleeping accommodation, ISBN-13 978-1-8511-2817-4
>
> Fire Safety Risk Assessment - Residential care premises, ISBN-13 978-1-8511-2818-1
>
> Fire Safety Risk Assessment - Educational premises, ISBN-13 978-1-8511-2819-8
>
> Fire Safety Risk Assessment - Small and medium places of assembly, ISBN-13 978-1-8511-2820-4
>
> Fire Safety Risk Assessment - Large places of assembly, ISBN-13 978-1-8511-2821-1
>
> Fire Safety Risk Assessment - Theatres, cinemas and similar premises, ISBN-13 978-1-8511-2822-8
>
> Fire Safety Risk Assessment - Open air events and venues, ISBN-13 978-1-8511-2823-5
>
> Fire Safety Risk Assessment - Healthcare premises, ISBN-13 978-1-8511-2824-2
>
> Fire Safety Risk Assessment - Transport premises and facilities, ISBN-13 978-1-8511-2825-9

Safe use and handling of flammable liquids, HSG140, HSE, ISBN 978-0-7176-0967-3

Storage of dangerous substances, Dangerous Substances and Explosive Atmospheres Regulations 2002, ACoP and guidance, L135, HSE Books, ISBN 978-0-7176-2200-9

The storage of flammable liquids in containers, Second edition, HSG51, HSE Books, ISBN 978-0-7176-1471-4

Relevant statutory provisions

Construction (Design and Management) Regulations (CDM) 2007

Dangerous Substances and Explosives Atmospheres Regulations (DSEAR) 2002

Fire Safety (Employees' Capabilities) (England) Regulations 2010

Fire Safety (Employees' Capabilities) (Wales) Regulations 2012

Fire (Scotland) Act (FSA) 2005

Fire Safety (Scotland) Regulations 2006

Health and Safety (Safety Signs and Signals) Regulations (SSSR) 1996

Management of Health and Safety at Work Regulations (MHSWR) 1999

Regulatory Reform (Fire Safety) Order (RRFSO) 2005

7.1 - Fire initiation, classification and spread

Basic principles of fire

THE FIRE TRIANGLE

In order for combustion to take place the three essential elements of a fire have to be brought together - fuel, oxygen and source of ignition (heat) - this is called the fire triangle.

In order to prevent fires these elements, particularly the fuel and ignition sources, are kept apart. When they are brought together in the right proportions combustion takes place. It should be noted that it is only the vapour from a fuel that burns. A solid or liquid must be heated to a temperature where the vapour given off can ignite before combustion takes place.

This principle is important when considering combustible dusts as this combustion process happens so quickly it becomes an explosion.

Figure 7-1: Fire triangle.   •   *Source: RMS/Corel.*

This explosion can be caused by a source of ignition, for example, a spark; a small dust explosion can often disturb more dust to fuel a bigger explosion. The other important aspect of this combustion principle is that if one or more of these elements of the fire is removed the fire will be extinguished. This can be done by:

Cooling   The fire to remove the heat - by applying water to the fire.

Starving   The fire of fuel - by moving material from the area of a fire or closing off an area of combustible material from the fire, for example, Isolating a gas valve to extinguish a gas fire.

Smothering   The fire by limiting its oxygen supply - by closing a lid on a metal bin that contained a fire, covering a fire with a fire blanket or applying an extinguishing medium such as foam.

SOURCES OF IGNITION

Any source of heat is a possible ignition source. Examples could be:

- Discarded smokers' materials (not such a big problem now that smoking is prohibited in the workplace).
- Naked flames.
- Fixed or portable heaters - particularly those that use liquid fuel.
- Hot processes for example, welding, cutting and grinding.
- Burning of vegetation or rubbish on site.
- Lighting.
- Cooking.
- Electrical equipment - overloading electrical circuits.
- Machinery - sparks, overheating of drive belts due to over tightening.
- Static electricity - most commonly from lightning strikes although sparks from static charges are very dangerous in flammable and explosive atmospheres.

Figure 7-2: Illicit smoking.   *Source: FSTC Ltd.*

Figure 7-3: Festoon lighting: an incorrect fixing creates a potential source of ignition. *Source: HSE, HSG168.*

SOURCES OF FUEL

Anything that burns is a fuel for a fire:

- Flammable liquids, for example, petrol storage areas.
- Plastics, rubber and foam, for example, liners and sealant.

- Flammable gases, for example, liquefied petroleum gas (LPG) heater cylinders.
- Flammable chemicals, for example, paints and solvents.
- Wood, for example, pallets, packing material and dust from carpentry processes.
- Paper and card, for example, packing and office stationery.
- Insulating materials, for example, polystyrene foam in walls and partition components.
- Waste materials, chemicals, waste packing, and general waste.

The structure of the building should also be considered. The building itself could be made from wood or other flammable material or may contain flammable materials as part of the decoration, for example, wallpaper, etc.

SOURCES OF OXYGEN

The main source of oxygen for a fire is in the air around us. In an enclosed building this is provided by the ventilation system in use. This generally falls into one of two categories; either natural airflow through doors, windows and other openings; or mechanical air conditioning systems and air handling systems. In many buildings there will be a combination of systems, which will be capable of introducing/extracting air to and from the building.

Leaks from cylinders or piped oxygen supplies, combined with poor ventilation, can lead to an oxygen enriched atmosphere. Materials that ordinarily will burn only slowly will burn very vigorously in an oxygen-enriched atmosphere. Others such as greases and oils may burst into flames in this kind of atmosphere. As well as the precautions outlined above for flammable gases, the following points should be remembered:

- Never use oxygen instead of compressed air.
- Never use oxygen to improve air quality in a working area or confined space.
- Never use grease or oil on equipment containing oxygen.

Classification of fires

A basic understanding of the classes of fire needs to be achieved because many fire extinguishers state the classes of fire on which they may be used.

Class A	Fires involving solids - wood, paper or plastics (usually material of an organic nature).
Class B	Fires involving liquids or liquefiable solids - petrol, oil, paint, fat or wax.
Class C	Fires involving gases - liquefied petroleum gas, natural gas, acetylene, methane, etc.
Class D	Fires caused by burning metals that combust easily on contact with air, such as magnesium and lithium. Such specialised fires require a specialised metal powder fire extinguisher to deal with them, and will be required in scientific labs or where manufacturing processes involve the risk of metal fires. For example, aluminium dust or swarf can catch fire, so any process involving cutting, drilling or milling aluminium holds potential risk.
Electrical fires	Though this is not a class of fire electricity is often a source of ignition and the presence of electricity is a very serious consideration where water is used as the extinguishing medium.
Class F	Fires involving cooking oils and fats usually found in commercial kitchens such as restaurants and fast food outlets.

Figure 7-4: Classification of fires.

Source: RMS.

Principles of heat transmission

There are four methods by which heat may be transmitted:

1) Convection

The movement of hotter gases up through the air (hot air rises). Convection can quickly move hot gases to another part of a building where they raise the temperature of combustible materials to a point that combustion takes place, for example, hot gases rising up a staircase through an open door.

Control measure: protection of openings by fire doors and the creation of fire resistant compartments in buildings.

2) Conduction

The movement of heat through a material (usually solid). Some materials, such as metal can absorb heat readily and transmit it to other rooms by conduction, where it can set fire to combustible items that are in contact with the heated material, for example, metal beam or pipe transmitting heat through a solid wall.

Control measure: insulation of the surface of a beam or pipe with heat resistant materials.

3) Radiation

Transfer of heat as invisible waves through the air (the air or gas is not heated, but solids and liquids in contact with the heat are). Any material close to a fire will absorb the heat, in the form of energy waves, until the material starts to smoulder and then burn. For example, a fire in a waste skip stored too near to a building may provide enough radiant heat to transfer the fire to the building.

Control measure: separation distances or fire resistant barriers.

4) Direct burning

Combustible materials in direct contact with a naked flame, for example, curtains or carpet tiles may be consumed by combustion and enable fire to be transferred along them to other parts of a building.

Control measure: the use of fire retardant materials.

Reasons why fires spread

FAILURE OF EARLY DETECTION

Early detection of fire spread can be delayed by:

- No detection system or patrols.
- No alarm system in place.
- People not knowing or confusing the sound of an alarm.
- Not being able to extinguish the fire promptly due to lack of hoses or extinguishers.
- Fire starting in an unoccupied area.
- Fire starting out of normal work hours.
- Building material waste being burnt as a normal routine and smoke and other signs of fire not seen as unusual.
- Numerous hot working tasks conducted - therefore smells of burning ignored.
- Frequent occurrence of small, local fires caused by hot work, and not seen as significant.

ABSENCE OF COMPARTMENTS IN BUILDING STRUCTURE

Fire spread within a building can result from an absence of compartments:

- An open plan layout.
- False ceilings.
- Still being under construction or alteration incomplete; reducing the separation between levels and/or sections on a level.

COMPARTMENTS UNDERMINED

Fire spread within a building can result from compartments being undermined:

- Fire doors wedged open.
- Poor maintenance of door structure.
- Holes may be designed to pass through compartments and are waiting fitment of services and subsequent sealing.
- Holes cut for ducts or doorways or to provide temporary access to locate/remove equipment.
- Compartments may be progressively created in buildings under alteration, thus increasing the risk of fire spread.

MATERIALS INAPPROPRIATELY STORED

Inappropriate storage of materials can cause fire spread:

- Flammable liquids not controlled - too much or in unsuitable containers.

Figure 7-5: Compartment undermined-holes cut.   *Source: RMS.*

- Boxes in corridors.
- Off cuts of wood and sawdust left in the areas where work has taken place.
- Packing materials used in the process, such as shredded paper, polystyrene, bubble wrap etc.
- Pallets and plastic covering left near to ignition sources.

Figure 7-6: No fire door fitted. *Source: HSE, HSG168.*

Figure 7-7: Materials inappropriately stored.   *Source: RMS.*

Common causes and consequences of fire during construction activities

CAUSES

Causes may be split into the following four main groups.

1) Careless actions and accidents

Careless actions and accidents relate to hot works conducted inappropriately, such as welding, cutting and grinding; discarded lighted cigarette end or match; smouldering waste; unattended burning of bonfires or poor electrical connections.

2) Misusing equipment

Misusing equipment relates to overloading electrical circuits and/or using fuses of too high a rating, failure to follow servicing instructions, failure to repair faulty machinery/equipment promptly or use beyond its capacity causing overheating.

3) Defective machinery or equipment

Defective machinery or equipment relates to electrical short circuits, an electrical earth fault can cause local overheating and electrical insulation failure may occur when affected by heat, damp or chemicals.

4) Deliberate ignition (arson)

Deliberate ignition is the crime of maliciously and intentionally, or recklessly, starting a fire or causing an explosion, for example, insurance fraud, aggrieved persons, concealment of another crime, political activists or vandalism.

Figure 7-8: Careless action - hot work. *Source: RMS.*

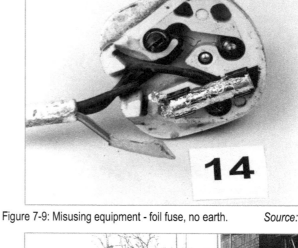

Figure 7-9: Misusing equipment - foil fuse, no earth. *Source: RMS.*

Figure 7-10: Defective electrical equipment. *Source: RMS.*

Figure 7-11: Potential for deliberate ignition. *Source: RMS.*

CONSEQUENCES

Consequences may be split into four main groups.

1) Human harm

The UK Statistics Authority reported that in 2008 (published 2010) there were 451 fire-related deaths in the UK, up from 443 in 2007. There were no fire-related firefighter fatalities in 2008 - compared with 6 in 2007. The long term trend in fire-related deaths has been downward.

The most common identified cause of death from a fire incident is being overcome by gas or smoke. In 2008, fire and rescue services reported that 189 people died this way, accounting for 42 per cent of all deaths. A further 76 (17%) deaths were attributed jointly to both burns and being overcome by gas or smoke, whilst 115 (25%) were due to burns alone.

The fire fatality rate is defined as the number of deaths per million population, abbreviated to pmp. The fatality rate last peaked at 13 pmp in 1995, since then there has been a general downward trend to 7.3 pmp in 2008. Though most of these fatalities do not occur in the workplace, fire has the potential for major loss of life in the workplace due to direct contact with heat and flame or from the effects of smoke and toxic gases.

The radiant heat of a fire and contact with flames can give rise to the risk of heat stroke or burns. The degree of exposure to the heat or flames will influence greatly the effect on the body each will have; they could quickly lead to shock, coma or death.

Both the hot gases and smoke involved in fires represent separate hazards to a person involved in a fire. The hot gases and smoke can present a direct effect on the lungs causing restriction in breathing. In addition, toxic gases may be liberated as part of a fire; these may include carbon monoxide, which if breathed in sufficient quantities can lead to asphyxiation. Other toxic products of combustion can include hydrogen cyanide and chlorine.

2) Economic effects

The Association of British Insurers (ABI) established that fire damage claims in the first half of 2009 cost £639 million - £3.6 million each day. This follows on from the £1.3 billion fire losses in 2008, a 16 percent rise on 2007 and the most expensive year ever. Between 2002 and 2008 the cost of the average fire claim for both commercial and domestic fires doubled, to £21,000 and £8,000 respectively. When fires do occur in the workplace the business is usually so badly affected it does not resume business again. The occurrence of a fire during construction activities can have a disastrous effect on the organisation commissioning the construction work. Business plans and objectives may fail to be achieved and services not provided. The effects may be particularly pronounced in situations where the construction activity is taking place alongside the organisation's normal activities. These normal business activities may suffer greatly because of the fire.

3) Legal effects

There is a legal requirement under the Regulatory Reform (Fire Safety) Order (RRFSO) 2005 in England and Wales and the Fire (Scotland) Act (FSA) 2005/Fire Safety (Scotland) Regulations (FSSR) 2006 in Scotland to prevent fire, protect employees and other relevant persons from the effects of fire and to mitigate the effect of fire on anyone in the vicinity of premises on fire. Failure to comply with legislation could result in prosecutions and, if found guilty, fines.

4) Environmental harm

Large uncontrolled fires create pollutants, such as smoke, that enter the atmosphere. The fire itself may cause damage to storage areas with the subsequent leakage of chemicals onto land or into water courses and the run-off from fire hoses may ultimately enter the water system. *See figure ref 7-12 and 7-13* which show some of the damage caused by the Buncefield oil storage depot disaster in December 2005. The plume of smoke was so large it could be seen from space.

Figure 7-12: Buncefield - run-off from fire hoses. *Source: Chiltern Air Support.*

Figure 7-13: Buncefield oil storage depot disaster. *Source: Chiltern Air Support.*

7.2 - Fire risk assessment

Requirement and matters to be addressed in carrying out the assessment

The purpose of a fire risk assessment (FRA) is to identify where fire may start in the workplace, the people who would be put at risk, and to reduce the risk where possible.

Specific legal duties to conduct risk assessments are set out in the Regulatory Reform (Fire Safety) Order (RRFSO) 2005 and the Fire Safety (Scotland) Regulations (FSSR) 2006, which require the 'Responsible Person' (Employer, Person in control or Owner) to make a suitable and sufficient assessment of:

■ The risks to the health and safety of his employees to which they are exposed whilst they are at work.
■ The risks to the health and safety of persons not in his employment (Relevant Persons) arising out of or in connection with the conduct by him of his undertaking.

Similarly, the self-employed must make a suitable and sufficient assessment of:

■ The risks to their *own* health and safety to which they are exposed whilst at work.
■ The risks to the health and safety of *persons not in his employment* (Relevant Persons), arising out of or in connection with the conduct by them of their undertaking.

This will require fire risk assessments to be conducted at the project planning stage of construction to determine what the risks are related to both the construction activities and the final constructed item. The choice of materials and building/structure design can have a major influence on the risk of fire during and after construction. All phases of construction must be considered in the risk assessment process. The scope of the assessment should include consideration of the effects of construction work on existing premises as well as temporary site accommodation, which may be used for office, welfare or sleeping purposes. It is important that risk assessments are maintained in the light of changes planned and those that take place. The process may require co-operation with clients whose premises may be affected by the construction activities,

Factors to be considered in carrying out the risk assessment

Depending upon the work to be carried out there will be different things to consider, for example, for new builds compared to the refurbishment of an existing building.

For a new build, consideration will need to be given to its location and proximity to other buildings, the type of construction materials and methods to be used. During construction and before final fire protection is in place the building will be more vulnerable to fire, for example, a timber framed structure is more vulnerable to fire before the external finishes are in place.

Existing buildings should meet fire protection standards required by the Building Regulations (BR) 2011. However, before a refurbishment project can be undertaken consideration will need to be given to the age and construction of the premises. For example, an older building is likely to have a relatively heavy fire load due to the materials used in its construction, including lath and plaster ceilings and walls, wooden panelling and floors. There may also have been changes to the fabric of the building that could have significant consequences in a fire. The assessments must, at least, identify the measures needed to satisfy the 'General Fire Precautions' of the RRFSO 2005 or the FSSR 2006. The legislation requires fire and other emergency provisions to be in place; as such, risk assessments must be conducted to determine fire risks and the provisions necessary for the protection of people and the environment. The measures would include:

■ Reduction of the risk of fire.
■ Prevention of fire spread.
■ Adequate means of escape from fire.
■ Maintenance measures to ensure means of escape available at all times.

■ Means to fight fire.
■ Means to detect and warn of fire.
■ Fire actions/instructions and training.
■ Actions to mitigate the effects of a fire.

Step 1 - Identify fire hazards

■ *Identify sources of ignition* - smokers' materials, naked flames, heaters, hot processes, cooking, machinery, boilers, faulty or misused electrical equipment, lighting equipment, hot surfaces, blocked vents, friction, static electricity, metal impact and arson.
■ *Identify sources of fuel* - flammable liquids, flammable chemicals, wood, paper and card, plastics, foam, flammable gases, furniture, textiles, packaging materials, waste materials including shavings, off cuts and dust.
■ *Identify sources of oxygen* - natural ventilation, doors, windows, forced ventilation systems, air conditioning, oxidising materials, oxygen cylinders or piped oxygen systems.

Step 2 - Identify people at risk

■ Consider people in the premises - staff, visitors, contractors, public, old, young, disabled, and their level of discipline and training. Contractors in sleeping accommodation on site would be a particular group to identify.
■ Consider how fire, heat or smoke could spread to areas that people occupy, for example, by convection, conduction, radiation or direct burning.
■ Identify where the people are that may be at risk, for example, people carrying out noisy tasks, placed high at the top of a building or crane, conducting work in confined spaces, nearby workers or the public.
■ Identify people who are especially at risk, for example, new sub-contractors, visitors or people with language difficulties.
■ Consider how people will be warned of fire and determine whether people could be trapped by fire.
■ Consider members of the fire service that might be at risk when fighting the fire.

Step 3 - Evaluate, remove, or reduce and protect from risk

The way the site is managed will affect the precautions that will need to be put in place.

With a new build the person in control may be the principal contractor, whereas for refurbishment work part of the site may remain occupied during the work. This may involve the need to work with managing agents or building owners. In multiple occupancy buildings, all those with some control must co-operate to reduce the risk to an acceptable level.

Risk reduction by prevention

- *Reduce sources of ignition* - remove unnecessary sources of heat or replace with safer alternatives, ensure electrical fuses are of the correct rating, ensure safe and correct use of electrical equipment, enforcing a 'hot work' permit system, safe smoking policy, arson reduction measures.
- *Minimise potential fuel for a fire* - remove or reduce amount of flammable materials, replace materials with safer alternatives, ensure safe handling, storage and use of materials, safe separation distances between flammable materials, use of fire-resisting storage, repair or replace damaged or unsuitable furniture, control and removal of flammable waste, care of external storage due to arson, good housekeeping.
- *Reduce sources of oxygen* - close all doors and windows not required for ventilation particularly out of working hours, shutting down non-essential ventilation systems, not storing oxidising materials near heat sources or flammable materials, controlling the use of oxygen cylinders and ensuring ventilation to areas where they are used. During new build and refurbishment activities close doors, windows and other openings not required for ventilation, particularly out of working hours.

Risk reduction by protection

Consider existing fire safety measures, risk reduction by protection (controls), in the workplace and consider possible improvements.

- Reducing unsatisfactory structural features.
  - Remove, cover or treat large areas of combustible wall and ceiling linings, improve fire resistance of workplace, install fire breaks into open voids.
- Fire detection and warning.
  - Can fire be detected quickly enough to allow people to escape?
  - Can means of warning be recognised and understood?
  - Do staff know how to operate the system?
  - Will staff know what to do if the alarm operates?
  - Are fire notices posted around workplace?
- Means of escape.
  - How long will it take for people to escape once they are aware of a fire?
  - Is this time reasonable?
  - Are there enough exits?
  - Are exits in the right places?
  - Is there suitable means of escape for all people, including disabled?
  - Could a fire happen that would affect all escape routes?
  - Are escape routes easily identifiable?
  - Are exit routes free from obstructions and blockages?
  - Are exit routes suitably lit at all times?
  - Have staff been trained in the use of the escape routes?
- Means of fighting fire.
  - Is the firefighting equipment suitable for the risk?
  - Is it suitably located?
  - Is it signed where necessary?
  - Have people been trained to use equipment where necessary?
- Maintenance and testing.
  - Check all fire doors, escape routes, lighting and signs.
  - Check all firefighting equipment.
  - Check all fire detectors and alarms.
  - Check any other equipment provided to help means of escape arrangements.
  - Are there relevant instructions to staff regarding maintenance and testing?
  - Are those who carry out maintenance and testing competent?
- Fire procedures and training.

- Is there an emergency plan?
- Does the emergency plan take account of all reasonably foreseeable circumstances?
- Are all employees familiar with the plan, trained in its use, and involved in testing it?
- Is the emergency plan made available to staff?
- Are fire procedures clearly indicated throughout the workplace?
- Have all people likely to be present, been considered?

Step 4 - Record, plan, inform, instruct and train

Where the employer employs five or more employees they must record the significant findings (actions already taken, plus actions that will be taken) of the assessment and any group of employees identified by it as being especially at risk. A record must also be kept of measures that have been or will be taken by the responsible person.

Emergency plans

Following completion of the fire risk assessment, an emergency plan should be devised. The plan should include the following:

- Action on discovery of fire.
- Action on hearing alarm.
- Details of the fire warning system.
- Details of the evacuation process.
- Means of escape - travel distances.
- Location of assembly points.
- Identification of escape routes - signs, emergency lighting.

- Details of firefighting equipment.
- Specific staff duties.
- Safe evacuation of people who need assistance to escape.
- Safe working practices in high risk areas.
- Procedures for calling Fire Service.
- Staff training needs and arrangements for providing training.

Step 5 - Review and monitor

The assessment and the fire safety measures must be reviewed regularly. In addition, a review should be done when:

- At each significant stage of construction to determine what effect the previous stage may have on the fire risk assessment of the next phase.
- When failure of fire precautions occurs, for example, fire-detection and alarm systems.
- Changes to workplace are proposed, for example, increased storage of flammable materials or alterations to the building, including the internal layout.
- Changes to work process/activity are proposed, for example, introducing a new night shift.
- Changes to number or type of people present are proposed, for example, public are invited on site.
- A near miss or a fire occurs.

Additional risk assessment factors related to construction

TEMPORARY WORKPLACES AND CHANGES TO WORKPLACES

Many serious fires occur in existing buildings during maintenance and construction work. Due to the increased fire risks during these periods of time, additional fire precautions may be needed. Dependent upon the nature of the work to be carried out and the size and use of the workplace, it may be necessary to carry out a new fire risk assessment to include all the new hazards that will be created during the construction work.

Fire risk assessments must be conducted for all workplaces, even for temporary workplaces. It may be possible to utilise a generic fire risk assessment approach if the construction activities are simple consistent and short term. However, it is important to ensure the generic risk assessment is appropriate to each temporary workplace as small changes in location of the workplace may make a significant difference. A temporary construction workplace in the grounds of a school may be significantly different to one in the grounds of communication equipment located in the countryside.

Figure 7-14: Misleading fire exit signage, exit no longer available.
Source: HSE, HSG168.

Changes made to existing workplaces during construction must be considered as part of the risk assessment. The changes may affect others occupying the workplace as well as construction workers and increase the risk of fire. In some cases the increased risk will be due to the increase of sources of ignition or additional materials. In other cases it will be due to the effect on the controls in place at the premises. Some work may require the isolation of smoke detectors or an alarm system. Normally well controlled escape routes may become cluttered by equipment, materials or workers. Attention should be paid to:

- Accumulation of flammable waste and building materials.
- The obstruction or loss of exits and exit routes.
- Fire doors being propped open, wedged open or removed.
- Openings created in fire-resisting structures.
- Isolation of fire detection, or fixed firefighting systems.
- Introduction of additional electrical equipment, or other sources of ignition.
- Use of hot work process.
- Introduction of flammable products, for example, adhesives or flammable gases.
- The additions of new people to the premises that may be unfamiliar with fire arrangements, for example, alarm, routes, roll calls, assembly points.
- People working in unusual locations, for example, the roof, basement or duct areas.
- People working outside normal working hours.

NEED FOR CONTINUAL REVIEW AS WORK PROGRESSES

In all workplaces there is a need to actively review and revise the fire risk assessment. This may lead to changes to the fire safety measures that apply and the fire/emergency plans. This aspect of fire safety is absolutely vital in construction sites or any other workplace where layout changes are constantly taking place. Dependent upon the state of the build, fire risks should be reviewed frequently, possibly weekly or daily depending on work progress. Checks and assessment should be made to ensure that the risk control measures for means of escape are still appropriate and that the following fire safety measures are not being compromised, leading to increased risk:

- Escape routes.
- Access to fire alarms.
- Audibility of fire alarm systems.
- Access and availability of firefighting equipment.
- Suitability of fire safety signage.
- Need for and suitability of escape lighting.
- New staff and the need for 'fire induction'.

- Fire protection/fire resistant structures within the building.
- Introduction of new fire hazards, for example, hot works.
- Correct storage/use of flammable materials.
- Site security/arson prevention.

If, as a result of any construction work that needs to be carried out, fire safety standards may be reduced the effects should be identified, assessed and additional compensating factors introduced. For example, if detector heads need to be covered to prevent false alarms a fire watch system of patrols may be introduced to compensate. As can be seen, fire safety is a constantly changing factor that must be integral to the everyday management of site safety.

CONSIDERATION OF SHARED WORKPLACES

Under the Management of Health and Safety at Work Regulations (MHSWR) 1999, Regulation 11 - "Co-operation and coordination", employers who work together in a common workplace have a duty to co-operate to discharge their duties under relevant statutory provisions. They must also take all reasonable steps to inform their respective employees of risks to their health or safety that may arise out of their work. Specific arrangements must be made to ensure compliance with fire legislation, including the assessment of risk. Regulation 10 of MHSWR 1999 sets out that clear instruction must be provided concerning any preventative or protective control measures; this would include those relating to serious and imminent danger and fire assessments. Details of any competent persons nominated to discharge specific duties in accordance with the regulations must also be communicated as should risks arising from contact with other employers activities.

SITE SPECIFIC EMERGENCY PLANS

The site emergency plan is one of the control measures used to manage fire risk and should be evaluated at the time of conducting the fire risk assessment, to determine if it is suitable and sufficient to provide effective control of the risk. Just as risk assessments should be site specific, it is important that a site specific emergency plan that includes fire risks is drawn up. Generic emergency plans that are designed to suit all sites may remain insufficient in detail to be effective.

A copy of the emergency plans should be available at the point of entry to the site. The plan should be updated from time to time to reflect any changes made to the site during each stage of the build or demolition phase to reflect changes in access and storage. Site plans should contain the name and details of how to contact the responsible person in the event of an emergency. Consideration will need to be given to ensure there is a responsible person available (24 hours, 7 days) until the construction work is completed and handed back to the client. The content of emergency plans will vary, but typically will contain information on what to do in the event of a fire, including raising the alarm, evacuation and assembly. It will usually also include the location and names of first-aiders, site entry restrictions, location of flammable materials etc., location of any streams or buried services.

7.3 - Fire prevention and prevention of fire spread

Control measures to minimise the risk of fire in a construction workplace

USE AND STORAGE OF FLAMMABLE AND COMBUSTIBLE MATERIALS

Where possible employers should seek to eliminate the use of flammable materials in the workplace, for example, replacing adhesives that have a flammable content with those that are water based. Where this is not possible the amount used should be reduced and kept to the minimum.

Quantities of material stored in the workplace must be in suitable containers and controlled to the minimum for immediate work needs. Flammable materials not in use should be removed to a purpose designed store in a well-ventilated area, preferably outside the building but in a secure area. Lids should be kept on containers at all times when they are not in immediate use.

Any waste containers, contaminated tools or materials should be treated in the same way and removed to a store in fresh air, until dealt with. Containers and contaminated materials need to be disposed of in a controlled manner so that they do not present a risk of fire.

Care has to be taken to control the delivery and therefore the storage of flammable and combustible materials to site. There is a temptation to have large quantities all delivered at the same time, but where possible deliveries should be staggered to reflect the rate of use in order to minimise the amount stored on site.

Terms used with flammable and combustible materials

Flashpoint

'Flashpoint' is defined as the lowest temperature at which, in a specific test apparatus, sufficient vapour is produced from a liquid sample for momentary or flash ignition to occur.

It must not be confused with ignition temperature which can be considerably lower.

Flammable

Liquids with a flash point between 32°C and 55°C are classified as flammable.

Highly flammable

Liquids with a flash point below 32°C are classified as highly flammable. The flash points of some common solvents are:

- Ethanol   +12°C.
- Toluene   +4°C.

- Methyl ethyl ketone - 9°C.
- Acetone   -19°C.

General principles for storage and use of flammable liquids

When considering the storage or use of flammable liquids, the following safety principles should be applied:

V   Ventilation - plenty of fresh air.

I   Ignition - control of ignition sources.

C   Containment - suitable containers and spillage control.

E   Exchange - try to use a less flammable product to do task.

S   Separation - keep storage away from process areas, by distance or a physical barrier, for example, a wall or partition.

CONTROL OF IGNITION SOURCES

Welding

- Only use competent trained staff.
- Regulators should be of a recognised standard.
- Colour code hoses:

    Blue   -   oxygen.

    Red   -   acetylene.

    Orange   -   propane.

- Fit non-return valves at blowpipe/torch inlet on both gas lines.
- Fit flashback arrestors incorporating cut-off valves and flame arrestors fitted to outlet of both gas regulators.
- Use crimped hose connections not jubilee clips.
- Do not let oil or grease contaminate oxygen supply due to explosion hazard.
- Check equipment visually before use, and check new connections with soapy water for leaks.
- Secure cylinders in upright position.

Figure 7-15: Welding equipment.   Source: RMS.

- Keep hose lengths to a minimum.
- Follow a permit to work system.
- Do not store standby gases that are not connected to welding apparatus in the workplace.

Hot work

Hot work has been responsible for causing many fires. One of the most tragic fires due to hot work was Dusseldorf Airport Fire in 1996. The fire was started by welding on an open roadway and resulted in damage in excess of £200 million, several hundred injuries and 17 deaths.

It is imperative that good safe working practices are utilised. Combustible materials must be removed from the area or covered over. Consideration must be given to the effects of heat on the surrounding structure, and where sparks, flames, hot residue or heat will travel to. It is often necessary to have a fire watcher to spot any fires that may be started. Fire extinguishers need to be immediately available and operatives must know how to use them. The work area must be checked thoroughly for some time after the completion of work to ensure there are no smouldering fires. Strong consideration should be given to the use of hot work permits.

Smoking

It is now against the law to smoke inside any public buildings (includes the workplace). Prohibition of smoking may lead to illicit smoking and extra vigilance may be needed. Where smoking is allowed, provide easily accessible, non-combustible receptacles for cigarette ends and other smoking material and empty daily. Smoking should cease half an hour before close down.

Arson

Arson is the single greatest cause of fire (the arson detection rate is only 8 percent, compared to 24 percent for other offences) and as such simple but effective ways to deter the arsonist are by giving attention to security, both external and internal, which should encompass the following:

External security

- Control of people having access to the building/site.
- Use of patrol guards.
- Lighting the premises at night - linked to closed circuit television (CCTV).
- Safety of keys.
- Structural protection.
- Siting of rubbish bins/skips at least 8m from buildings.

Internal security

- Good housekeeping and clear access routes.
- Inspections and audits.
- Visitor supervision.
- Control of sub-contractors.
- Control door access by keypad or electronic locks, **see figure ref 7-17**.

Figure 7-16: Control arson by external security. *Source: RMS.*

Figure 7-17: Control arson by internal security. *Source: RMS.*

SYSTEMS OF WORK

Systems of work combine people, equipment, materials and the environment to produce the safest possible climate in which to work. In order to produce a safe system of work, it is essential to make an assessment of the area to determine where the hazards and risks arise and how best to control them. The requirement to carry out a fire risk assessment should address the following:

- Identify potential fire hazards.
- Decide who may be in danger, and note their locations.
- Evaluate the risks and carry out any necessary improvement measures.
- Record findings and action taken.
- Keep assessment under review.

In addition to the fire risk assessment carried out, other measures may include implementing the following strategies.

1) A safe place

A safe place begins with ensuring that the fabric of the building is designed or planned in a way that will prevent ignition, suppress fire spread and allow for safe, speedy unobstructed evacuation with signs to direct people. Factors to consider will include compartmentalisation, fire resistant materials, proper and suitable means of storage, means of detection, means of raising the alarm good housekeeping and regular monitoring and review.

2) Safe person

A safe person begins with raising awareness to individuals of any risk of loss resulting from outbreak of fire. Information can be provided that will identify where to raise the alarm, what the alarm sounds like, how to evacuate and where to muster, responsibility for signing in and out of the site register, fire drill procedures, trained authorised fire appointed persons, use and storage of flammable materials, good housekeeping and use of equipment producing heat or ignition (including hot processes i.e. welding).

3) Safe materials

Safe materials begin with providing information and ensuring safe segregation and storage for materials and sources of ignition/heat. In addition, providing information on the correct way to handle materials and substances, including a substances register that will detail methods of tackling a fire involving hazardous substances, is necessary.

4) Safe equipment

Safe equipment begins with user information and maintenance to ensure good working and efficient order. Information should also provide the user with a safe method for use and the limitations of and risks from the equipment. Supervision may be necessary to ensure correct use and prevent misuse that may lead to short circuiting or overheating that could result in fire. Where work involves hot processes by nature (welding, grinding, casting, etc) then permit-to-work procedures may be necessary in order to tightly control the operations.

Other equipment required in relation to fire hazards and control may include smoke or heat detection equipment, alarm sounders/bells, alarm call points and appropriate fire extinguishing apparatus. It should be noted that in the event of a fire alarm, all the passenger lifts should not be used. Under normal circumstances the lift will return to the ground floor and remain in that position with the doors locked in the open position. All equipment should be regularly tested to ensure its conformity and be accompanied with a suitable certificate of validity.

Safe systems must also include consideration of who is at risk, including those persons with special needs such as the young, elderly, infirm or disabled. There may be a requirement to prevent smoking in the workplace or employ appointed persons to take control of the situation and coordinate emergency responses in the event of an alarm. If the building relies solely on internal artificial lighting, then the requirement to install emergency back-up lighting will be needed. All systems must be regularly monitored in order to reflect changes to the environment and put remedies in place to ensure full preparedness in the event of a fire.

PERMIT TO WORK PROCEDURES

A permit to work is an official, documented safe system of work that is used for controlling high risk activities. Implementation is required prior to work beginning to ensure that all precautions are taken and securely in place to prevent danger to the workforce.

When managed correctly, a permit to work prevents any mistakes or deviations through poor verbal communication by stating the specific requirements of the project. For fire control, a permit to work is typically used where there is a requirement to use flammable materials or when hot work or processes are being carried out.

The authorised person shall issue the permit to work and will sign the document to declare that all isolations are made and remain in place throughout the duration of the project. In addition to this, the authorised person will make checks to ensure that all controls to be implemented by the acceptor are in place before work begins

The acceptor of the permit to work shall assume responsibility for carrying out the works. The acceptor shall sign the document to declare that the terms and conditions of the permit to work are understood and will be complied with fully at all times by the entire work team.

Compliance with a permit to work system includes ensuring the required safeguards are implemented and that the work will be restricted to the equipment only stated within the document.

Items included in a permit to work are:

- Permit issue number.
- Authorised person identification.
- Locations of firefighting equipment.
- Locations of flammable materials.
- Warning information sign locations.
- Emergency muster points.
- Details of the work to be carried out.

- Signature of authoriser.
- Signature of acceptor.
- Signature for works clearance/extension/handover.
- Signature for cancellation.
- Other precautions (risk assessments, method statements, PPE).

HOT WORK PERMITS

Hot work permits are formal management documents that control and implement a safe system of work whenever methods of work that utilise heat or flame systems are used. If the risk of fire is low, it may not be necessary to implement a hot work permit; however they should always be considered.

The hot work permit should be issued by an Authorised Person who ensures that the requirements stated in them are complied with before the permit is issued, and during duration of the work. Hot work permits should be issued for a specific time, for a specific place, for a specific task, and are issued to a designated competent person.

Figure 7-18: Hot work.   Source: Speedy Hire Plc.

STORAGE, TRANSPORT AND USE OF LIQUEFIED PETROLEUM AND OTHER GASES IN CYLINDERS

Liquefied petroleum gas (LPG) is a term that relates to gas stored in a liquefied state under pressure; common examples are propane and butane. LPG and other gas cylinders should be stored in line with the principles detailed below:

Storage

- Storage area should preferably be in clear open area outside.
- Stored in a secure compound - 2m high fence.
- Safe distance from toxic, corrosive, combustible materials, flammable liquids or general waste.
- Stored safe distance from any building.
- If stored inside building, kept away from exit routes, consideration should be given to fire-resisting storage.
- Well ventilated area - 2.5% of total floor and wall area as vents, high and low.
- Oxygen cylinders at least 3m away from flammable gas cylinders.
- Acetylene may be stored with LPG if quantity of LPG less than 50 Kg.

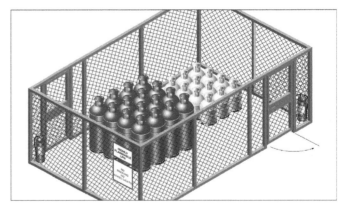

Figure 7-19: Secure LPG storage.   Source: HSE, HSG168.

- Access to stores should be controlled to prevent LPG etc. being stored unsafely in the general workplace.
- More than one exit (unlocked) may need to be available from any secure storage compound where distance to exit is greater than 12m.
- Lock storage compound when not in use.
- Protection from sunlight.
- Flameproof lighting.
- Empty containers stored separate from full.
- Fire extinguishers located nearby - consider powder and water types.

Transport

- Upright position.
- Secured to prevent falling over.
- Protection in event of accident, for example, position on vehicle.
- Transport in open vehicle preferably.

- Avoid overnight parking while loaded.
- Park in secure areas.
- 'Trem card' and warning signs.
- Driver training.
- Firefighting equipment.

Use

General use

- Cylinder connected for use may be stored in the general workplace; any spare cylinders must be secured in a purpose built store until required for use.
- Fixed position to prevent falling over, or on wheeled trolley - chained.
- Well ventilated area.
- Away from combustibles.
- Kept upright unless used on equipment specifically designed for horizontal use, for example, gas powered lift truck.
- Handled carefully - do not drop.
- Allow to settle after transport and before use.

- Consider manual handling and injury prevention.
- Turn off cylinder before connecting, disconnecting equipment.
- Check equipment before use.
- Any smell of gas during use, turn off cylinder and investigate.
- Use correct gas regulator for equipment/task.
- Use equipment in line with manufacturers' instructions.

Use in huts

- Only allow cylinders in a hut if it is part of a heater (cabinet heater).
- Pipe into site huts from cylinder located outside where possible.
- If cylinder is outside the hut use the shortest connecting hose as possible.
- Hut to be adequately ventilated high and low.
- Heaters fitted with flame failure devices.
- Turn off heater and cylinder after use and overnight.
- Be aware of danger of leaks inside huts, especially overnight as a severe risk of fire or explosion may occur.
- Keep heaters away from clothing and other combustibles.

Figure 7-20: Gas cylinders for huts, located outside.   Source: RMS.

GOOD HOUSEKEEPING

Housekeeping means the general tidiness and order of the building. At first sight, this may seem a strange matter to discuss when considering fire safety, but as housekeeping affects so many different aspects of this subject, it cannot be ignored.

Housekeeping and its effect on fire safety

Fires need fuel. A build-up of redundant combustible materials, rubbish and stacks of waste materials provide that fuel. All combustible materials cannot be eliminated, but they can be controlled.

Any unnecessary build-up of rubbish and waste should be avoided. If a fire starts in a neatly stacked pile of timber pallets, around which there is a clear space, the fire may be spotted and extinguished before it can spread.

However, if the same pile were strewn around in an untidy heap, along with adjacent rubbish, the likelihood is that fire would spread over a larger area and involve other combustible materials.

Figure 7-21: Accumulated combustible site rubbish.
Source: HSE, HSG168.

Poor housekeeping can also lead to:

- Blocked fire exits.
- Obstructed escape routes.
- Difficult access to fire alarm call points/extinguishers/hose reels.
- Obstruction of vital signs and notices.
- A reduction in the effectiveness of automatic fire detectors and sprinklers.

Checklists

Fire Prevention is a matter of good routine and the checklists following are a guide as to what to look out for:

List A - Routine checks

Daily at the start of business - including:

- Doors which may be used for escape purposes - unlocked and escape routes unobstructed.
- Free access to hydrants, extinguishers and fire alarm call points.
- No deposits on electric motors.

List B - Routine checks

Daily at close-down - including:

- Inspection of whole area of responsibility - to detect any incipient smouldering fires.
- Fire doors and shutters closed.
- All plant and equipment safely shutdown.
- Waste bins emptied.

- No accumulation of combustible process waste, packaging materials or dust deposits.
- Safe disposal of waste.
- Premises left secure from unauthorised access.

List C - Periodic inspection

During working hours - weekly/monthly/quarterly as decided:

- Goods neatly stored so as not to impede firefighting.
- Clear spaces around stacks of stored materials.
- Gangways kept unobstructed.
- No non-essential storage in production areas.
- Materials clear of light fittings.
- Company smoking rules known and enforced.

Storage of small quantities of highly flammable/flammable liquids

The objective in controlling the risk from these materials is to remove all unnecessary quantities from the workplace to a recognised storage area outside the building. This may be done as part of a close down routine at the end of the day. It is accepted that quantities of this material may need to be available in a workplace during normal working. This should not exceed 50 litres in any work area unless a full scale purpose constructed store is used. In other cases local small scale storage of up to *50 litres of highly flammable* or up to *250 litres of flammable* liquids may be kept within the workplace provided it is controlled and placed in a suitable store container. Highly flammable or flammable liquids removed from storage must be in suitable containers to prevent spills and loss of vapours.

Figure 7-22: Poor storage of flammable liquids.   *Source: RMS.*

Figure 7-23: Storage of flammable materials.   *Source: RMS.*

STORAGE IN THE WORKPLACE

- In a suitable sealed container.
- In a suitable cabinet, bin or other store container.
- In a designated area of the workplace.
- Away from ignition sources, working or process areas.
- Capable of containing any spillage.
- In a 30 min fire resistant structure.
- Provided with hazard warning signs to illustrate the flammability of the contents.
- Prohibition signs for smoking and naked flame.
- Not contain other substances or items.

STORAGE IN THE OPEN AIR

- Formal storage area on a concrete pad, with a sump for spills.
- Bunded all around to take content of largest drum plus an allowance of 10%.
- Away from other buildings.
- Secure fence and gate 2m high.
- Marked by signs warning of flammability.
- Signs prohibiting smoking or other naked flames.
- Protection from sunlight.
- If lighting is provided within store it must be flameproof.
- Provision for spill containment materials.

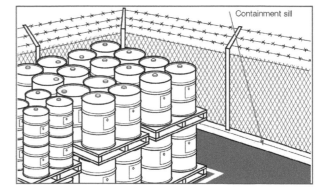

Figure 7-24: Outdoor storage of flammable liquids. *Source: HSE, HSG51.*

- Fire extinguishers located nearby - consider powder type.
- Full and empty containers separated.

- Clear identification of contents.

Structural measures to prevent spread of fire and smoke

PROPERTIES OF COMMON BUILDING MATERIALS

Brickwork/blockwork

Both brickwork and blockwork perform well in fires. Dependent upon the materials, workmanship, thickness, and the load carried, fire resistance of 30 minutes to 2 hours may be achieved.

Steelwork

Steel and other metals are extensively used in modern building structures. Generally they can be affected by fire at relatively low temperatures unless they are protected from the effects of the fire by some form of fire retardant materials. This may be done by encasing in concrete, fire retardant boards or spray coatings.

Timber

Timber performs very well in fires as long as it is of sufficient size that, as its outer coat burns away, there is still sufficient strength to do its task. Generally timber does not fail rapidly in a fire, unlike steel.

Glass

Glass generally performs poorly in a fire unless it is fire resistant glass. At high temperatures glass will melt and sag, which is why the traditional fire resistant glass has wire within it.

STRUCTURAL MEASURES TO PREVENT SPREAD

Measures to prevent spread of fire and smoke include:

- Fire-resisting structures.
- Compartmentalisation to confine the fire to a predetermined size.
- Fire stopping of ducts, flues and holes in fire resistant structures.
- Fire-resisting doors.
- Smoke seals and intumescent (a material which expands and insulates the surface, when heat is applied) materials on doors.
- Early and rapid detection of a fire by use of 'intelligent' fire alarm systems.
- Sprinklers in large compartments, in particular 'rapid response' systems to limit the size of the fire.
- Control of smoke and toxic fumes by ventilation systems, so that clear air is maintained at head height level, to enable persons to escape.

Figure 7-25: Magnetic door holder linked to alarm. *Source: RMS.*

Figure 7-26: Door stop with automatic release. *Source: RMS.*

PROTECTION OF OPENINGS AND VOIDS

Consideration should be given to the protection of openings and voids by the use of fire barriers such as fire shutters, cavity barriers and fire curtains. It is important that when construction or maintenance work takes place it is managed to minimise the effect on the structure being worked on to keep fire precautions intact as much as possible.

This will involve planning for the prompt re-instatement of protection of openings and voids as soon after their breach to do work as is possible. The temptation to leave all breaches to the end of work and then re-instate them should be avoided - the longer that breaches are left open the higher the risk from fires.

Use of suitable electrical equipment in flammable atmospheres

The Dangerous Substances and Explosive Atmospheres Regulations (DSEAR) 2002 apply to most workplaces where a potentially explosive atmosphere may occur. DSEAR 2002 requires employers to eliminate or control the risks from potentially explosive atmospheres.

CLASSIFICATION OF AREAS WHERE EXPLOSIVE ATMOSPHERES MAY OCCUR

Employers must classify areas where hazardous explosive atmospheres may occur into zones. The classification given to a particular zone, and its size and location, depends on the likelihood of an explosive atmosphere occurring and its persistence if it does occur. Schedule 2 of DSEAR 2002 contains descriptions of the various classifications of zones for gases and vapours and for dusts.

There are three zones for gases and vapours:

Zone 0   Flammable atmosphere highly likely to be present - may be present for long periods or even continuously.

Zone 1   Flammable atmosphere possible but unlikely to be present for long periods.

Zone 2   Flammable atmosphere unlikely to be present except for short periods of time - typically as a result of a process fault condition.

Similarly, there are three zones for dusts:

Zone 20   Dust cloud likely to be present continuously or for long periods.

Zone 21   Dust cloud likely to be present occasionally in normal operation.

Zone 22   Dust cloud unlikely to occur in normal operation, but if it does, will only exist for a short period.

SELECTION OF EQUIPMENT AND PROTECTIVE SYSTEMS

Areas classified into zones must be protected from sources of ignition. Electrical equipment for use in hazardous explosive atmospheres needs to be designed and constructed in such a way that it will not provide a source of ignition. Equipment intended to be used in zoned areas should be selected to meet the requirements of the Equipment and Protective Systems Intended for Use in Potentially Explosive Atmospheres Regulations (EPS) 1996. Zone zero and zone 20 are the zones with the highest likelihood of an explosive atmosphere occurring and persisting; electrical equipment for this zone needs to be very well protected against providing a source of ignition. There are a number of ways in which electrical equipment can be designed to prevent ignition of explosive atmospheres, each achieves this in different ways. The types of protection include intrinsically safe (cannot produce a spark with sufficient energy to cause ignition), flameproof (ingress of explosive atmosphere is controlled and any ignition is contained in the equipment) and Type 'E' equipment (do not produce sparks or hot surfaces).

7.4 - Fire detection, fire alarm and firefighting equipment

Common fire detection and alarm systems

FIRE DETECTION

Heat detection

Sensors operate by the melting of a metal (fusion detectors) or expansion of a solid, liquid or gas (thermal expansion detectors).

Radiation detection

Photoelectric cells detect the emission of infra-red/ultra-violet radiation from the fire.

Smoke detection

Using ionising radiations, light scatter (smoke scatters beams of light), obscuration (smoke entering a detector prevents light from reaching a photoelectric cell).

Figure 7-27: Smoke detector.   *Source: RMS.*

Flammable gas detection

Measures the amount of flammable gas in the atmosphere and compares the value with a reference value.

ALARM SYSTEMS

The purpose of a fire alarm is to give an early warning of a fire in a building for two reasons:

- To increase the safety of occupants by encouraging them to escape to a place of safety.
- To increase the possibility of early extinction of the fire thus reducing the loss of or damage to the property.

There are a number of methods of operation for fire alarm systems including:

Voice   Simplest and most effective type but very limited because it is dependent upon the size of the workplace and background noise levels.

Hand operated Rotary gong, hand bell or triangle and sounder but limited by the scale of the building.

Call points with sounders	Standard system, operation of one call point sounds alarm throughout workplace.
Automatic system	System as above, with added fire detection to initiate the alarm.

Single-stage alarm

The alarm sounds throughout the whole of the building and calls for total evacuation.

Two-stage alarm

In certain large/high rise buildings it may be better to evacuate the areas of high risk first, usually those closest to the fire or immediately above it. In this case, an evacuation signal is given in the affected area, together with an alert signal in other areas. If this type of system is required, early consultation with the Fire Service is essential.

Figure 7-28: Easy operation alarm call point.   *Source: RMS.*

Figure 7-29: Alarm point identified and well located.   *Source: RMS.*

Staff alarms

In some premises, an immediate total evacuation may not be desirable, for example, nightclubs, shops, theatres, cinemas. A controlled evacuation by the staff may be preferred, to prevent distress and panic to the occupants. If such a system is used, the alarm must be restricted to the staff and only used where there are sufficient members of staff and they have been fully trained in the action of what to do in case of fire. Alarms must make a distinctive sound, audible in all parts of the workplace (sound levels should be 65 dB (A) or 5dB (A) above any other noise - whichever is the greater). The meaning of the alarm sound must be understood by all. They may be manually or automatically operated.

Portable firefighting equipment

SITING

Portable fire extinguishers should always be sited:

- On the line of escape routes.
- Near, but not too near, to danger points.
- Near to room exits inside or outside according to occupancy and/or risk.
- In multi-storey buildings, at the same position on each floor, for example, top of stair flights or at corners in corridors.
- Where possible in groups forming fire points.
- So that no person need travel more than 45 metres to reach an extinguisher.
- With the carrying handle about one metre from the floor to facilitate ease of handling, removal from wall bracket, or on purpose designed floor stand.
- Away from excesses of heat or cold.

MAINTENANCE AND INSPECTION

Any firefighting equipment provided must be properly maintained and subject to examination and test at intervals such that it remains effective.

Maintenance

This means service of the fire extinguisher by a competent person. It involves thorough examination of the extinguisher (internal/external) and this is usually done annually.

Inspection

A monthly check should be carried out to ensure that extinguishers are in their proper place and have not been discharged, lost pressure or suffered obvious damage. It may be necessary to increase the frequency of checks made for fire extinguishers on a construction site to a weekly basis, due to the less structured or controlled work environment that they are sited in. This could mean that there is a higher risk of them being damaged or used without notification.

FIREFIGHTING EQUIPMENT TRAINING REQUIREMENTS

The 'Responsible Person' must take measures for firefighting as necessary. They should nominate competent persons to implement these measures and provide training and equipment accordingly. It would be good practice to make sure that those that may need to take a lead in operating fire extinguishers can do this competently and for most people this would mean practising how to use them in a situation that reproduces the circumstances of a fire. Training should include:

- Understanding of principles of combustion and classification of fires.
- Identification of the various types of fire extinguisher available to them.
- Principles of use and limitations of extinguishers.
- Considerations for personal safety and the safety of others.
- How to identify if the extinguisher is appropriate to the fire and ready to use.
- How to attack fires with the appropriate extinguisher(s).
- Any specific considerations related to the environment the extinguishers are kept or used in.

Training has to clarify the general and specific rules for use of extinguishers:

General - aim at the seat of the fire and move the extinguisher across the fire to extinguish it - this is particularly appropriate for Class A fires.

Specific - if using a foam extinguisher for Class B fires the foam is allowed to drop onto the fire by aiming just above it. If this is for a flammable liquid fire contained in an open tank it is possible to get good results by this process or aiming it to the back of the tank and allowing the foam to float over the liquid. For other specific limitations or approaches to the use of individual types of extinguishing media see next section.

Extinguishing media

WATER (PORTABLE EXTINGUISHER - COLOUR CODE - RED)

Water should only be used on Class A fires - those involving solids like paper and wood. Water works by cooling the burning material to below its ignition temperature, therefore removing the heat part of the fire triangle, and so the fire goes out. Water is the most common form of extinguishing media and can be used on the majority of fires involving solid materials. It must not be used on liquid fires or in the vicinity of live electrical equipment.

Figure 7-30: Fire point sign. *Source: BCW Office Products.*

Figure 7-31: Water extinguisher colour coded red by label and sign. *Source: RMS.*

Figure 7-32: Fire point sign. *Source: Warning Signs Direct.*

Figure 7-33: Cream colour coded extinguisher. *Source: Low Cost Fire.*

FOAM (PORTABLE EXTINGUISHER - COLOUR CODE - CREAM)

Foam is especially useful for extinguishing Class B fires - those involving burning liquids and solids which melt and turn to liquids as they burn. Foam works in several ways to extinguish the fire, the main way being to smother the burning liquid, i.e. to stop the oxygen reaching the combustion zone. Foam can also be used to prevent flammable vapours escaping from spilled volatile liquids and also on Class A fires. It is worth noting that the modern spray foams are more efficient than water on a Class A fire. *It must not be used in the vicinity of live electrical equipment, unless electrically rated.*

DRY POWDER (PORTABLE EXTINGUISHER - COLOUR CODE - BLUE)

Designed for Class A, B and C fires but may only subdue Class A fires for a short while. One of the main ways in which powder works to extinguish a fire is the smothering effect, whereby it forms a thin film of powder on the burning liquid, thus excluding air. The extinguishing media is also excellent for the rapid knock down (flame suppression) of flammable liquid spills. Powders generally provide extinction faster than foam, but there is a greater risk of re-ignition. If used indoors, a powder can cause problems for the operator due to the inhalation of the powder and obscuration of vision. This type of extinguishing media may be used on live electrical equipment.

Figure 7-34: Fire point sign.
Source: Warning Signs Direct.

Figure 7-35: Blue colour coded extinguisher. *Source: The Sharpedge.*

Figure 7-36: Fire point sign.
Source: BCW Office Products.

Figure 7-37: Black colour coded extinguisher. *Source: Blazetec Fire Protection.*

CARBON DIOXIDE (CO₂) (PORTABLE EXTINGUISHER - COLOUR CODE - BLACK)

Carbon dioxide (CO_2) is safe and excellent for use on live electrical equipment. It may also be used for small Class B fires in their early stages of development, indoors or outdoors with little air movement. CO_2 replaces the oxygen in the atmosphere surrounding the fuel and the fire is extinguished. CO_2 is an asphyxiant and should not be used in confined spaces. As it does not remove the heat there is the possibility of re-ignition. CO_2 extinguishers are very noisy due to the rapid expansion of gas on release; this can surprise people when they operate a portable extinguisher. This expansion causes severe cooling around the discharge horn and can freeze the skin if the operator's hand is in contact with the horn. As most carbon dioxide portable extinguishers last only a few seconds, only small fires should be tackled with this type of extinguisher.

EXTINGUISHING MEDIA FOR SPECIFIC CLASSES OF FIRE

Class C fires

Except in very small occurrences, a Class C fire involving gas should not normally be extinguished. If a gas fire is to be extinguished, then isolation of the gas supply must also take place.

Class D fires

Class D metal fires are a specialist type of fire and they cannot be extinguished by the use of ordinary extinguishing media. In fact, it may be dangerous to attempt to fight a metal fire with ordinary extinguishing media as an explosion of the metal may take place or toxic fumes may be produced. Metal fires can be extinguished by smothering them with dry sand. However, the sand must be absolutely dry or an explosion may occur. Other extinguishing media used are pyromet, graphite, talc or salt. All of these extinguishing media basically operate by the smothering principle.

Figure 7-38: Fire point sign. *Source: Midland Fire Ltd.*

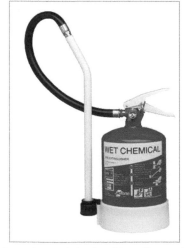

Figure 7-39: Yellow colour coded extinguisher. *Source: Midland Fire Ltd.*

Class F fires (Wet chemical) (Portable extinguisher - Colour code - Yellow)

New style wet chemical extinguishing media have been designed to specifically deal with Class F cooking oil fires. This type of extinguishing media congeals on top of the oil and excludes the oxygen. It may also be used on Class A fires depending upon the manufacturer's instructions.

SUMMARY MATRIX - FIRE EXTINGUISHING MEDIA

	Method	Class 'A'	Class 'B'	Class 'C'	Class 'D'	Electric	Class 'F'
Water	Cools	Yes	No	No	No	No	No
Spray foam	Smothers	Yes	Yes	No	No	No	No
Wet chemical	Chemical	Some manufacturers	No	No	No	No	Yes
Dry powder	Smothers and Chemical	Limited	Yes	Yes and Isolate	Special Powders	Yes - Low Voltage	No
Vapourising liquids	Chemical and Smothers	Special uses					
Carbon dioxide	Smothers	No	Yes - Small Fires	No	No	Yes	No

Figure 7-40: Summary matrix - fire extinguishing media. *Source: RMS.*

7.5 - Means of escape

General requirements for means of escape

The Regulatory Reform (Fire Safety) Order (RRFSO) 2005 requires the responsible person to "make and give effect to such arrangements as are appropriate, having regard to the size of his undertaking and the nature of its activities, for the effective planning, organisation, control, monitoring and review of the preventive and protective measures". The RRFSO 2005 also sets out the type of requirements necessary with regard to emergency routes and exits. An adequate means of escape is essential for all premises. The following general factors should be taken into consideration when planning means of escape.

TRAVEL DISTANCES

Travel distance is a significant component of a successful means of escape plan. Travel distances are judged on the basis of distance to a place of safety in the open air and away from the building; the distance needs to be kept to the minimum. The distance includes travel around obstructions in the workplace and may be greatly affected by any work in progress on a construction site. If someone is outside on a scaffold it is unlikely to be considered as a place of safety and the distance would usually be taken as that to reach the ground away from the building (for example, at an assembly point).

The route must be sufficiently wide and of a sufficiently short distance to allow speedy and safe evacuation. There should normally be alternative routes leading in different directions. Everyone should be able to escape unaided (if able bodied). The distance between work stations and the nearest fire exit should be minimised.

Figure 7-41: Fire escape - hazard of falling on exit due to height from ground. *Source: RMS.*

Table 1 Maximum travel distances

	Fire hazard		
	Lower	*Normal*	*Higher*
Enclosed structures:			
Alternative	60 m	45 m	25 m
Dead-end	18 m	18 m	12 m
Semi-open structures:			
Alternative	200 m	100 m	60 m
Dead-end	25 m	18 m	12 m

Notes:

Semi-open structures are completed or partially constructed structures in which there are substantial openings in the roof or external walls, which would allow smoke and heat from any fire to readily disperse, and which are not at risk of exposure from radiation or direct impingement from a fire on the site.

Figure 7-42: Maximum travel distances. *Source: HSE, HSG168.*

STAIRS

Staircases form an integral part of the means of escape from fire in most buildings. If they are to be part of the escape route, the following points must be ensured:

- Fire resistant structure.
- Fitted with fire doors.
- Doors must not be wedged open.
- Wide enough to take the required number of people.
- Must lead direct to fresh air, or to two totally separate routes of escape.
- Non slip/trip and in good condition.
- No combustible storage within staircase.

External escape stairs and ladders

External temporary escape stairs may be required, if an internal protected stairway is not available. Stairways can be constructed from scaffolding.

The external wall against which the stairway is erected should be fire resistant without openings onto the stairway with 30 minutes fire resistance for 9 m vertically below the stairway and 1.8 m either side or above, as measured from the stair treads. All doors, apart from the uppermost one leading onto the external stairway, should have 30 minutes' fire resistance and be self-closing. Any other openings, including windows, which are not of fire-resisting construction, should be suitably protected, for example, with plasterboard, proprietary mineral fibre-reinforced cement panels or steel sheets.

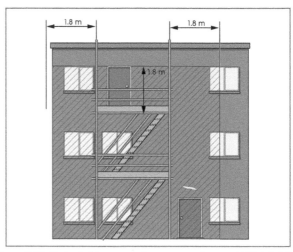

Figure 7-43: Protected temporary fire escape. *Source: HSE, HSG168.*

PASSAGEWAYS

- The route should lead directly to the open air via a protected route (where necessary).
- Route to be kept unobstructed.

DOORS

- Exit doors are to open outwards easily (unless small numbers of people involved).
- Provide fire doors along the escape route.
- Fire doors along with fire resistant structures serve two purposes:
  - Prevent the spread of fire.
  - Ensure that there is means of escape for persons using the building.
- They should not be wedged open.
- Lead to open air - safety.

EMERGENCY LIGHTING

Emergency lighting should be considered if escape is likely to be required in dark conditions. This could mean late afternoon in winter time, not just at night time.

EXIT AND DIRECTIONAL SIGNS

Fire escape signs are provided to guide escape from wherever people are in a building, via a place of relative safety (the escape route) to the place of ultimate safety (the assembly area).

Fire escape signs are not needed on the main route into or out of a building (the one used by people for normal arrival and exit), but alternative escape routes and complicated escape routes do need to be signed.

It must not be assumed that everyone will know all safe routes through the building or that once people are out of the building they will know how to get to the assembly point.

Signs directing to the assembly point will also be needed.

Figure 7-44: Fire escape sign. *Source: RMS.*

ASSEMBLY POINTS

The assembly point is a place of safety where people wait whilst any incident is investigated, and where confirmation can be made that everyone has evacuated the premises.

The main factors to consider are:

- Safe distance from building.
- Sited in a safe position.
- Not sited so that staff will be in the way of Fire Brigade.
- Must be able to walk away from assembly point and back to a public road.
- Clearly signed.
- More than one provided to suit numbers and groups of people.

Figure 7-45: Assembly point.   *Source: RMS.*

- Communications should be provided between assembly points.
- Measures provided to decide if evacuation successful.
- Person must be in charge of assembly point and identified.
- Person to meet/brief the fire and rescue service.

NEED FOR CONTINUAL REVIEW AS CONSTRUCTION ACTIVITY PROGRESSES

In all workplaces there is a need to actively review and revise the fire safety measures that relate to means of escape. This aspect of fire safety is absolutely vital in construction sites as the layout may change as construction activities progress.

Dependent upon the state of the build, fire means of escape may need to be reviewed on a weekly or even daily basis. Checks and assessment should be made to ensure that the means of escape are still appropriate and that they have not being compromised:

- Travel distances remain within limits.
- Egress via stairs or passageways is achievable without restriction.
- Doors have not been filled in, moved or become unusable.
- Exit and directional signs still relate to the actual escape route.

- Emergency lighting has not become obscured by processes that could contaminate the surface or screened by new structures.
- Assembly points remain accessible and in place, for example, not built over.

7.6 - Evacuation of a construction workplace

Emergency evacuation procedures

Article 15 of the RRFSO 2005 sets out requirements for the responsible person to establish emergency evacuation procedures.

> *"Establish and, where necessary, give effect to appropriate procedures, including safety drills, to be followed in the event of serious and imminent danger to relevant persons".*

Figure 7-46: Article 15 of RRFSO 2005.   *Source: The Regulatory Reform (Fire Safety) Order (RRFSO) 2005.*

Furthermore, it sets out a requirement to nominate a sufficient number of competent persons to implement evacuation procedures.

The danger that may threaten people if an emergency occurs at work depends on many different factors; consequently it is not possible to construct one model procedure for action in the event of fire and emergency for all premises. Evacuation procedures need to reflect the type of emergency, the people affected and the premises involved. Many of the different issues to consider for different emergencies have common factors, for example, evacuation in an efficient/effective manner, an agreed assembly location (which may be different for different emergencies) and checks to ensure people are safe. These factors are considered below with regard to fire emergencies.

ROLE AND APPOINTMENT OF FIRE MARSHALS

In all premises a person should be nominated to be responsible for coordinating the fire evacuation plan. This may be the same person that organises fire instruction and training and drills and coordinates the evacuation at the time of the fire. They may appoint persons such as fire marshals to assist them in fulfilling the role. This involves the appointment of certain staff to act as fire marshals to assist with evacuation. The way in which they assist will vary between organisations; for example, some will check areas of the building in the event of a fire to ensure no person is still inside and others will lead the evacuation to show where to go. The fire marshals' appointment should be made known to workers and they should be clearly identifiable at the time of emergency so that those that are asked to evacuate understand the authority of the person requiring them to do so. The appointment of fire marshals contributes to an employer's compliance with the requirement to establish competent persons to assist with health and safety.

FIRE INSTRUCTION NOTICES

At conspicuous positions in all parts of the location, and adjacent to all fire alarm actuating points (for example, break glass operated call points), printed notices should be exhibited stating, in concise terms, the essentials of the action to be taken upon discovering a fire and on hearing the fire alarm. It is usual to also state what someone must do when they discover a fire.

Fire action

The action in the event of a fire and upon discovery needs to be immediate, and a simple fire action plan should be put into effect. A good plan of action would include the following points.

On discovering a fire

■ Sound the fire alarm (to warn others).
■ Call the fire service.
■ Go to the assembly point.
■ On hearing the alarm
■ Leave the building by the nearest exit.
■ Close doors behind you.
■ Go to the assembly point.
■ Get out of the building and stay out.

On evacuation

■ Do not take risks.
■ Do not stop for personal belongings.
■ Do not use lifts.
■ Do not return to the building unless authorised to do so.
■ Report to assembly point.
■ Consider the wording on notices that are posted and ensure that workers are instructed and trained to do what is asked of them.

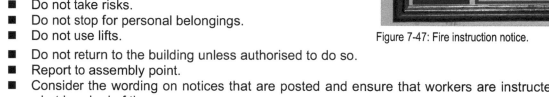

Figure 7-47: Fire instruction notice.   *Source: RMS.*

FIRE TRAINING

Typical issues to be included in a fire training programme relating to emergency action are:

■ Fire prevention.
■ Recognition of fire alarms and the actions to be taken.
■ Understanding the emergency signs.
■ Location of fire escape routes and assembly points.
■ Requirements for safe evacuation (for example, non-use of lifts, do not run etc.).
■ Location and operation of call points and other means of raising the alarm.
■ How the fire service is called.
■ Location, use and limitations of firefighting equipment.
■ Consideration of people with special needs.
■ Identity and role of fire marshals.

FIRE DRILLS

A fire drill is intended to ensure, by means of training and rehearsal, that in the event of fire:

■ The people who may be in danger act in a calm, orderly and efficient manner.
■ Those designated with specific duties carry them out in an organised and effective manner.
■ The means of escape are used in accordance with a predetermined and practised plan.
■ An opportunity for management leadership.

The fire drill enables all people involved in the evacuation to practice and learn under as near realistic circumstances as possible. This can identify what works well in the evacuation procedure and what does not. Practice in the form of a drill helps people to respond quickly to the alarm and, because they have done it before, to make their way efficiently to the assembly point. At least once a year a practice fire drill should normally be carried out simulating conditions in which one or more of the escape routes from the building are obstructed. This will assist in developing an awareness of the alternative exits that can be taken and assist in ensuring people understand the unpredictability of fires.

ROLL CALL

The traditional method of undertaking a roll call is by use of a checklist of names. Very few workplaces can now operate this system as they do not have such a static workforce as this system requires. Where they can operate they will provide a speedy and efficient means of identifying who has arrived at the assembly point and who has not.

Where strict security control to a construction site is used, with signing in and out, this may make this process more viable. This requires people on site to report to their allocated assembly point and for someone (for example, a fire marshal) to confirm that they have arrived safely and determine if anyone is missing.

If it is not known exactly who is in a building a system of fire marshals who can make a check of the building at the time of their own evacuation (without endangering their own safety) may be employed. This can assist with the process and may identify people that have not evacuated. However, this system may not be able to provide an absolute confirmation that everyone has evacuated as there may be limited opportunity for the fire marshal to check the whole of the area allocated to them. Any doubt or confirmed missing persons should be reported to the person nominated to report to the fire service, who in turn will provide a report to the fire service as soon as they arrive.

PROVISIONS FOR THE INFIRM AND DISABLED

When planning a fire evacuation system employers need to consider who may be in the workplace, their abilities and capabilities.

Any disability for example, hearing, vision, mental or mobility impairment must be catered for. Some of the arrangements may be to provide the person with a nominated assistant(s) to support their speedy escape, for example, with the use of a specially designed evacuation chair to enable them to make their way out of a building down emergency exit stairs.

Part of the provision is to make sure they are capable of knowing that an emergency exists. This may mean providing them with special alarm arrangements that cater for their disability, for example, a visual and or vibrating alert for the hearing impaired.

Figure 7-48: Fire refuge sign for disabled people.
Source: Safety Selector.

In some cases, disabled people may need to use a refuge area, a relatively safe waiting area for short periods. A refuge area is separated from the fire by a fire-resisting structure and has access via a safe route to a fire exit. It provides a temporary space for disabled people to wait for others who will help them to evacuate. Some buildings may be equipped with an evacuation lift, which has been specifically designed within a fire-resisting enclosure and having a separate power supply.

Sample assessment questions

1. (a) **Identify TWO** flammable gases contained in cylinders that might be found on a construction site. (2)

   (b) **Outline** precautions that should be taken to prevent fires and explosions during the transport and use of flammable gases contained in cylinders. (6)

2. Arson on a construction site is a common cause of fire.

   (a) **Give** reasons why some construction sites may be vulnerable to arson attacks. (4)

   (b) **Identify** ways of reducing the risk of arson on a construction site. (4)

3. A major hazard on a refurbishment project is fire.

   (i) **Identify THREE** activities that represent an increased fire risk in such a situation. (3)

   (ii) **Outline** the precautions that may be taken to reduce the risk of a fire occurring. (5)

Please refer to back of assessment section for answers.

This page is intentionally blank

Chemical and biological health - hazards and risk control

Learning outcomes

On completion of this element, candidates should be able to demonstrate understanding of the content through the application of knowledge to familiar and unfamiliar situations. In particular they should be able to:

8.1 Outline the forms of, and classification of, and the health risks from exposure to, hazardous substances.

8.2 Explain the factors to be considered when undertaking an assessment of the health risks from substances encountered in construction workplaces.

8.3 Explain the use and limitations of Workplace Exposure Limits including the purpose of long term and short term exposure limits.

8.4 Outline control measures that should be used to reduce the risk of ill-health from exposure to hazardous substances.

8.5 Outline the hazards, risks and controls associated with specific agents.

8.6 Outline the basic requirements related to the safe handling and storage of waste on construction sites.

Content

Sources of reference

Asbestos essentials task manual, HSG210, Third Edition, HSE Books, ISBN 978-0-7176-6503-7

Asbestos: The Survey Guide, HSG264, HSE Books, ISBN 978-0-7176-6502-0

Control of Substances Hazardous to Health (fifth edition), ACoP and guidance, L5, HSE Books, ISBN 978-0-7176-2981-7

Controlling Airborne Contaminants at Work: A Guide to Local Exhaust Ventilation, HSG258, second edition 2011, HSE Books ISBN 978-0-7176-6415-3

Information on the Control of Asbestos Regulations 2012 www.hse.gov.uk/asbestos/regulations.htm

Managing and working with asbestos. Control of Asbestos Regulations 2012, ACOP and guidance, L143, HSE Books, ISBN 978-0-7176-6618-8

Managing Asbestos in Buildings: A brief guide, INDG223 (rev5) 2012, HSE Books

Occupational Exposure Limits, EH40/2005, HSE Books ISBN 978-0-7176-6446-7

Personal Protective Equipment at Work (second edition), Personal Protective Equipment at Work Regulations 1992 (as amended), L25, Guidance on Regulations, HSE Books, ISBN 978-0-7176-6139-3

Respiratory Protective Equipment at Work - A Practical Guide, HSG53, third edition 2005, HSE Books ISBN 978-0-7176-2904-6

Step by Step Guide to COSHH Assessment, HSG97, second edition 2004, HSE Books, ISBN 978-0-7176-2785-1

The management of asbestos in non-domestic premises, Regulation 4 of the Control of Asbestos Regulations 2006, Approved Code of Practice and guidance (L127), ISBN 978-0-7176-6209-8

Workplace exposure limits, EH40, HSE Books (updated annually), ISBN 978- 0-7176-6446-7

Relevant statutory provisions

Chemicals (Hazard Information and Packaging for Supply) Regulations (CHIP 4) 2009

Control of Asbestos Regulations (CAR) 2012

Control of Substances Hazardous to Health Regulations (COSHH) 2002

Personal Protective Equipment at Work Regulations (PPER) 1992

8.1 - Health risks from hazardous substances

Forms of chemical agent

The form taken by a hazardous substance is a contributory factor to its potential for harm. Principally the form affects how easily a substance gains entry to the body, how it is absorbed into the body and how it reaches a susceptible site.

Chemical agents take many forms, the most common being the primary forms or states - solids, liquids, gases - and the derivative forms - dusts, fibres, fumes, smoke, mists/aerosols and vapours.

SOLIDS

Solids are materials which are solid at normal temperature and pressure.

LIQUIDS

Liquids are substances which are liquid at normal temperature and pressure.

GASES

Gases are formless fluids usually produced by chemical processes involving combustion or by the interaction of chemical substances. A gas will normally seek to fill the space completely into which it is liberated - for example, chlorine gas, carbon monoxide, methane, etc.

DUSTS

Dusts are solid airborne particles, often created by operations such as grinding, crushing, milling, sanding or demolition - for example, silica, asbestos, cotton fibres, flour, cement, etc.

FIBRES

Dust may be created that is made up of tiny fibres for example, mineral wool and asbestos.

FUMES

Fumes are solid particles formed by condensation from the gaseous state - for example, lead fume, welding fume.

SMOKE

Smoke is particles that result from incomplete combustion. They are a combination of gases and very small particles that can be in either solid or liquid state.

MISTS

Mists are finely dispersed liquid droplets suspended in air. Mists are mainly created by spraying, foaming, pickling and electro-plating - for example, mists from a water pressure washer, paint spray, pesticide, oil, etc.

VAPOUR

Vapour is the gaseous form of a material normally encountered in a liquid or solid state at normal room temperature and pressure. Typical examples of vapours are those released from solvents - for example, Toluene which releases vapours when the container holding it is opened.

Forms of biological agents

FUNGI

Fungi are a variety of organisms that act in a parasitic manner, feeding on organic matter. Most are either harmless or positively beneficial to health; however a number could cause harm to humans and may be fatal. An example of a fungi organism is the mould from rotten hay called Aspergilla, which causes Aspergillosis (Farmer's Lung). Farmer's lung is an allergic reaction to the mould. This occurs deep in the lungs, in the alveoli region. It leads to shortness of breath, which gets progressively worse at each exposure. The resulting attack is similar to asthma. Aspergilla can also cause short-term effects of irritation to the eyes and nose and coughing. Other fungi can cause ringworm and Athlete's Foot.

BACTERIA

Bacteria are single cell organisms. Most bacteria are harmless to humans and many are beneficial. The bacteria that can cause disease are called pathogens. Examples of harmful bacteria are leptospira (causing Weil's disease), bacillus anthracis (causing anthrax), and legionella pneumophila (causing legionnaires disease).

VIRUSES

Viruses are the smallest known type of biological agent. They invade the cells of other organisms, which they take over and make copies of themselves, and while not all cause disease many of them do. Examples of viruses are hepatitis, which can cause liver damage, and the Human Immunodeficiency Virus (HIV), which causes acquired immune deficiency syndrome (AIDS).

Main classification of substances hazardous to health

CHIP refers to the Chemicals (Hazard Information and Packaging for Supply) Regulations 2009, which came into force on 6 April 2009. These regulations are also known as CHIP 4.

CHIP applies to suppliers of dangerous chemicals. Its purpose is to protect people and the environment from the effects of those chemicals by requiring suppliers to provide information about the dangers and to package them safely. CHIP requires the supplier of a dangerous chemical to:

- Identify the hazards (dangers) of the chemical. This is known as 'classification'.
- Give information about the hazards to their customers. Suppliers usually provide this information on the package itself (for example, a label).
- Package the chemical safely.

Currently, CHIP 4 continues to apply in the UK, but will be repealed in full in the UK when the new European Union (EU) Regulation on classification, labelling and packaging of chemical substances and mixtures (CLP) is fully in force, on 1st June 2015.

CHIP and its supporting guidance will be amended as the transitional period progresses and the revised EU CPL Regulation begins to apply the United Nations Globally Harmonised System of Classification and Labelling of Chemicals (GHS) requirements.

Indication of danger	Symbol (orange background)	Category of danger	Characteristic properties and body responses
Irritant	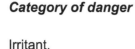	Irritant.	A non-corrosive substance which, through immediate, prolonged or repeated contact with the skin or mucous membrane, can cause inflammation for example, butyl ester, a severe irritant which can cause abdominal pain, vomiting and burning of the skin and eyes.
		Sensitising (by contact).	May cause an allergic skin reaction which will worsen on further exposures (allergic dermatitis), for example, nickel or epoxy resin.
Corrosive		Corrosive.	May destroy living tissues on contact, for example, sulphuric (battery) acid or sodium hydroxide (caustic soda).
Harmful		Harmful.	If inhaled or ingested or it penetrates the skin, has an adverse effect on health, for example, some solvents causing narcosis or central nervous system failure.
		Sensitising (by inhalation).	May cause an allergic respiratory reaction, which will progressively worsen on further exposures (asthma), for example, flour dust, isocyanates.
		Carcinogenic (category 3).	Only evidence is from animals, which is of doubtful relevance to humans, for example, benzyl chloride.
		Mutagenic (category 3).	Evidence of mutation in Ames Test and possible somatic cell mutation.
		Toxic to reproduction (category 3).	Animal data, not necessarily relevant.
Toxic		Toxic.	If inhaled or ingested or it penetrates the skin, may involve serious acute or chronic health risks and even death, for example, arsenic, a systemic poison.
		Mutagenic (categories 1 and 2).	May cause genetic defects, for example, 2-Ethoxyethanol may impair fertility.

Figure 8-1: Harmful, toxic.   *Source: RMS.*

		Toxic to reproduction (categories 1 and 2).	May cause harm to the unborn child, for example, lead suspected of causing restricted development of the brain of the foetus.
Very toxic			If inhaled or ingested or it penetrates the skin, may involve extremely serious acute or chronic health risks and even death, for example, cyanide, a severe irritant and systemic poison.
Carcinogenic		Category 1. Substances known to cause cancer on the basis of human experience. Category 2. Substances which it is assumed can cause cancer, on the basis of reliable animal evidence.	May, if inhaled or it penetrates the skin, induce uncontrolled cell division (cancer) or increase its incidence, for example, benzene affects bone marrow causing leukaemia. Carries the risk phrase R45.
		Category 3.	Not included in the COSHH definition of carcinogen although they are subject to the general requirements of COSHH. If purchased from a supplier carries the "harmful" (Xn) symbol and the Risk Phrase R40 (limited evidence of a carcinogenic effect).

Figure 8-2: Classification by harm to health.   *Source: CHIP 4 2009, Schedule 1 and 2.*

Difference between acute and chronic health effects

The effect of a substance on the body depends not only on the substance, but also on the dose, and the susceptibility of the individual. No substance can be considered non-toxic; there are only differences in degree of effect.

ACUTE EFFECT

An acute effect is an immediate or rapidly produced, adverse effect, following a single or short term exposure to an offending agent, which is usually reversible (the obvious exception being death). Examples of acute effects are those from exposure to solvents, which affect the central nervous system causing dizziness and lack of co-ordination or carbon monoxide, which affects the level of oxygen in the blood causing fainting.

CHRONIC EFFECT

A chronic effect is an adverse health effect produced as a result of prolonged or repeated exposure to an agent. The gradual or latent effect develops over time and is often irreversible. The effect may go unrecognised for a number of years. Examples of chronic effects are lead or mercury poisoning, cancer and asthma.

Other common terms used in the context of occupational health are:

Toxicology	The study of the body's responses to substances. In order to interpret toxicological data and information, the meaning of the following terms should be understood.
Toxicity	The ability of a chemical substance to produce injury once it reaches a susceptible site in or on the body. A poisonous substance (for example, organic lead), which causes harm to biological systems and interferes with the normal functions of the body. The effects may be acute or chronic, local or systemic.
Dose	The level of environmental contamination multiplied by the length of time (duration) of exposure to the contaminant.
Local effect	Usually confined to the initial point of contact. Possible sites affected include the skin, mucous membranes or the eyes, nose or throat. Examples are burns to the skin by corrosive substances (acids and alkalis), solvents causing dermatitis.
Systemic effect	Occurs in parts of the body other than at the point of initial contact. Frequently the circulatory system provides a means to distribute the substance round the body to a target organ/system.
Target organs	An organ within the human body on which a specified toxic material exerts its effects, for example, lungs, liver, brain, skin, bladder or eyes.
Target systems	Central nervous system, circulatory system, and reproductive system.

Examples of substances that have a systemic effect and their target organs/systems are:

Alcohol   -   central nervous system, liver.

Lead   -   bone marrow and brain damage.

Mercury   -   central nervous system.

It must be noted that many chemicals in use today can have both an acute and chronic effect. A simple everyday example is alcohol. The acute effect of drinking too much wine in a single evening is vomiting and headache whereas the chronic effect of drinking wine in smaller quantities, but over a prolonged period is cirrhosis, a systemic effect with the liver as the target organ.

8.2 - Assessment of health risks

Routes of entry of hazardous substances into the body

INHALATION

The most significant industrial entry route is inhalation. It has been estimated that at least 90% of industrial poisons are absorbed through the lungs. Harmful substances can directly attack the lung tissue causing a local effect or pass through to the blood system, to be carried round the body and affect target organs, such as the liver. Typical effects of substances that enter the body through inhalation are:

Local effect

A local effect is where the hazardous substance has an effect on the body where it first contacts the body. For example, Silicosis, caused by inhalation of silica dust - where dust causes scarring of the lung leading to inelastic fibrous tissue to develop and reducing lung capacity.

Systemic effect

A systemic effect is where the hazardous substance has an effect on the body at another site to that where it first contacts the body. For example, Anoxia, caused by inhalation of carbon monoxide - the carbon monoxide replaces oxygen in the bloodstream affecting the nervous system.

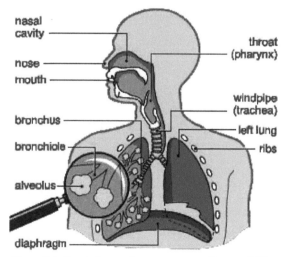

Figure 8-3: Respiratory system.   *Source: BBC.*

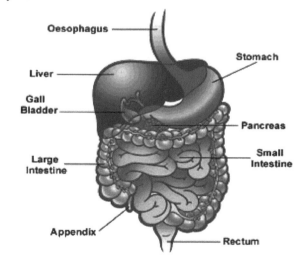

Figure 8-4: Digestive system.   *Source: STEM.*

INGESTION

The ingestion route normally presents the least problem as it is unlikely that any significant quantity of harmful liquid or solid will be swallowed without deliberate intent. However, accidents will occur where small amounts of contaminant are transferred from the fingers to the mouth if eating, drinking or smoking in chemical areas is allowed or where a substance has been decanted into a container normally used for drinking. The sense of taste will often be a defence if chemicals are taken in through this route, causing the person to spit it out.

If the substance is taken in, vomiting and/or excretion may mean the substance does not cause a systemic problem, though a direct effect, for example, ingestion of an acid, may destroy cells in the mouth, oesophagus or stomach.

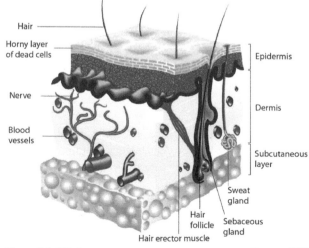

Figure 8-5: Skin layer.   *Source: SHP.*

Where hazardous substances are ingested, they may pass into the digestive system and be absorbed through the intestine to the blood system and may cause harm in another part of the body.

ABSORPTION (SKIN CONTACT)

Substances can enter through the skin, cuts or abrasions and conjunctiva of the eye, this is called absorption. Solvents such as organic solvents, for example, toluene and trichloroethylene, can enter due to accidental exposure or if they are used for washing. The substance may have a local effect, such as de-fatting of the skin resulting in inflammation and cracking of the horny layer, or pass through into the blood system causing damage to the brain, bone marrow and liver.

Dermatitis

Dermatitis is caused by exposure to substances which interfere with normal skin physiology leading to inflammation of skin, usually on the hands, wrists and forearms.

Figure 8-6: Dermatitis.   *Source: SHP.*

The skin turns red and in some cases may be itchy. Small blisters may occur and the condition may take the form of dry and cracked skin.

Contact dermatitis (irritant contact dermatitis)

If a person's skin is frequently in contact with some substances or is exposed for a long duration the persistent contact can lead to irritation and then dermatitis. There are many chemicals used in the construction industry that may irritate the skin leading to this condition; including cement, soaps, detergents, epoxy resins and hardeners, acrylic sealants, bitumen and solvents used in paints or glues.

Removal from contact with the substance usually allows normal cell repair. A similar level of repeat exposure results in the same response. This class of dermatitis is called contact dermatitis.

Sensitisation dermatitis (allergic contact dermatitis)

A second form of dermatitis is called sensitisation dermatitis. In cases of sensitisation dermatitis a person exposed to the substance develops dermatitis in the usual way.

When removed from exposure to the substance the dermatitis usually repairs, but the body gets ready for later exposures by preparing the body's defence mechanisms. A subsequent small exposure is enough to cause a major response by the immune system. The person will have become sensitised and will no longer be able to tolerate small exposures to the substance without a reaction occurring. Though the range of substances an individual may become sensitised to varies, some substances have the tendency to cause sensitisation in a large number of people. For example, cement may contain two well known sensitisers chromate and cobalt. Epoxy resins of the type used in the construction industry also have a tendency to cause sensitisation.

Dermatitis can be prevented by:

- Clean working conditions and properly planned work systems.
- Careful attention to skin hygiene principles.
- Prompt attention to cuts, abrasions and spillages onto the skin.
- Use of protective equipment.
- Barrier cream can help.
- Pre-employment screening for sensitive individuals.

INJECTION

Injection is a forceful breach of the skin, perhaps as a result of injury, which can carry harmful substances through the skin barrier. For example, handling broken glass, that cuts the skin and transfers a biological or chemical agent. On construction sites there are quite a few items that present a hazard of penetration, such as nails in broken up false work that might be trodden on and penetrate the foot presenting a risk of infection from tetanus.

In addition, some land or buildings being worked on may have been used by intravenous drug users and their needles may present a risk of injection of a virus, such as hepatitis. The forced injection of an agent into the body provides an easy route past the skin, which usually acts as the body's defence mechanism and protects people from the effects of many agents that do not have the ability to penetrate.

When identifying possible routes of entry, it must be remembered that many substances have multiple possibilities. Trichloroethylene, for example, is denoted "sk" in the HSE document that lists approved workplace limits (EH40), that is, it will absorb through the skin. However, it should be remembered that when in use, it also gives off very harmful vapours that may be inhaled and, because it is liquid, there is the possibility of accidental ingestion.

BODY RESPONSE TO AGENTS AND PROTECTIVE MECHANISMS

The body's response against the invasion of substances likely to cause damage can be divided into external or superficial defences and internal or cellular defences.

Superficial defence mechanisms

Respiratory (inhalation):

Nose	On inhalation many substances and minor organisms are successfully trapped by nasal hairs, for example, the larger wood dust particles.
Respiratory tract	The next line of defence against inhalation or substances harmful to health begin here, where a series of reflexes activate the coughing and sneezing mechanisms to forcibly expel the triggering substances.
Ciliary escalator	The passages of the respiratory system are also lined with mucus and well supplied with fine hair cells which sweep rhythmically towards the outside and pass along large particles. The respiratory system narrows as it enters the lungs where the ciliary escalator assumes more and more importance as the effective defence. Smaller particles of agents, such as some lead particles, are dealt with at this stage. The smallest particles, such as organic solvent vapours, reach the alveoli and are either deposited or exhaled.

Gastrointestinal (ingestion):

Mouth	For ingestion of substances. Saliva in the mouth provides a useful defence to substances which are not excessively acid or alkaline or in large quantities.
Gastrointestinal tract	Acid in the stomach also provides a useful defence similar to saliva. Vomiting and diarrhoea are additional reflex mechanisms which act to remove substances or quantities that the body is not equipped to deal with.

Skin (absorption):

Skin	The body's largest organ provides a useful barrier against the absorption of many foreign organisms and chemicals (but not against all of them). Its effect is, however, limited by its physical characteristics. The outer part of the skin is covered in an oily layer and substances have to overcome this before they can damage the skin or enter the body.
	The outer part of the epidermis is made up of dead skin cells. These are readily sacrificed to substances without harm to the newer cells underneath. Repeated or prolonged exposure could defeat this. The skin, when attacked by substances, may blister in order to protect the layers beneath. Openings in the skin such as sweat pores, hair follicles and cuts can allow entry and the skin itself may be permeable to some chemicals, for example, toluene.

Cellular mechanisms

The cells of the body possess their own defence systems.

Scavenging action	A type of white blood cell called macrophages attack invading particles in order to destroy them and remove them from the body. This process is known as phagocytosis.
Secretion of defensive substances	Is done by some specialised cells. Histamine release and heparin, which promotes availability of blood sugar, are examples.
Prevention of excessive blood loss	Reduced circulation through blood clotting and coagulation prevents excessive bleeding and slows or prevents the entry of bacteria.
Repair of damaged tissues	Is a necessary defence mechanism which includes removal of dead cells, increased availability of defender cells and replacement of tissue strength, for example, scar tissue caused by silica.
The lymphatic system	Acts as a 'form of drainage system' throughout the body for the removal of foreign bodies. Lymphatic glands or nodes at specific points in the system act as selective filters preventing infection from entering the blood system. In many cases a localised inflammation occurs in the node at this time.

Other measures to complement the body's protection mechanisms

Practical measures include:

- Good personal hygiene.
- Do not apply cosmetics in the workplace.
- No eating or drinking in the workplace.
- Proper containers/storage for food and drink.
- Provision and use of appropriate personal protective equipment.
- Taking care when removing contaminated protective clothing.

Factors to be taken into account when assessing health risks

In order to assess the risks to health it is necessary to know and take into account the following factors:

- The form the substance is in: solid, liquid, gas, dust, etc.
- The classification of the hazard: very toxic, toxic, corrosive, etc.
- How much of the substance will be present and its concentration.
- The routes of entry onto and into the body: inhalation, ingestion, skin pervasion, absorption.
- Whether the substance has an acute or chronic affect or both.
- The extent to which the body's defences will deal with the substance.
- The first signs of damage or ill-health.
- The vulnerability of the people involved in the process: young persons, pregnant workers; anyone who has existing health problems, such as skin problems or bronchitis.
- The effectiveness of existing control measures.

Considering these factors will help the assessor decide whether the risks to health are tolerable or acceptable or further controls are needed.

Sources of information

PRODUCT LABELS

Requirements under CHIP 4

CHIP 4 refers to the Chemicals (Hazard Information and Packaging for Supply) Regulations 2009, which came into force on 6 April 2009. CHIP 4 applies to suppliers of dangerous chemicals. Its purpose is to protect people and the environment from the effects of those chemicals by requiring suppliers to provide information about the dangers of the chemicals and to package them safely. CHIP 4 requires the supplier of a dangerous chemical to:

- Identify the hazards (dangers) of the chemical. This is known as 'classification'.
- Give information about the hazards to their customers. Suppliers usually provide this information on the package itself (for example, a label).
- Package the chemical safely.

All substances available for use in the workplace should be labelled in accordance with the CHIP 4, for example, toxic, harmful, corrosive, irritant, and sensitising. Where a dangerous chemical is supplied in a package, the package must be labelled. Packaging must be safe and able to withstand the conditions it is exposed to during supply. The label must state the hazards and precautions required. More useful information to help ensure the safe use of dangerous substances comes in the form of risk phrases and safety phrases. These are often displayed either on the container label (if it is large enough) or in the safety data sheet. There are currently 122 risk phrases and 74 safety phrases. Some examples can be seen in the following table and detailed information can be found in the approved guide to CHIP 4 produced by the Health and Safety Executive (HSE), L131.

	Risk phrase		Safety phrase
R3	Extreme risk of explosion by shock, friction, fire or other sources of ignition.	S2	Keep out of reach of children.
R20	Harmful by inhalation.	S20	When using do not eat or drink.
R30	Can become highly flammable in use.	S25	Avoid contact with eyes.
R45	May cause cancer.	S36	Wear suitable protective clothing.
R47	May cause birth defects.	S41	In cases of fire and/or explosion do not breathe fumes.

Figure 8-7: Risk and safety phrase table.   *Source: CHIP 4.*

The absence of hazard symbols or risk and safety advice does not mean the item is harmless.

Currently, CHIP 4 continues to apply in the UK, but will be repealed in full in the UK when the new European Union (EU) Regulation on classification, labelling and packaging of chemical substances and mixtures (CLP) is fully in force, on 1st June 2015. CHIP and its supporting guidance will be amended as the transitional period progresses and the revised EU CPL Regulation begins to apply the United Nations Globally Harmonised System of Classification and Labelling of Chemicals (GHS) requirements.

European Regulation on classification, labelling and packaging of chemical substances

The European Union (EU) Regulation on classification, labelling and packaging of chemical substances and mixtures (CLP) introduces throughout the EU a new system for classifying and labelling chemicals based on the United Nations' Globally Harmonised System (UN GHS).

CLP is concerned with the hazards of chemical substances and mixtures and how to inform others about them.

It is the responsibility of manufacturers to establish what the hazards of substances and mixtures are before they are placed on the market, and to classify them in line with the identified hazards. When a substance or a mixture is hazardous, it has to be labelled so that workers are informed about its effects it is used. Note that "mixture" is the same as the term "preparation", which has been used previously.

Transition to CLP

From entry into force, not all of the provisions of the CLP Regulation will be obligatory immediately. There are transitional provisions until 1st June 2015. The transitional arrangements establish timelines for manufacturers to comply with CLP requirements and notify the European central inventory of the classification of hazardous substances and mixtures. *See figure ref 8-8* which illustrates the timelines. The European Union Dangerous Substances Directive (DSD), which established requirements under CHIP, was repealed and immediately re-instated under Table 3.2 of Part 3 of Annex VI to the CLP Regulation for the transition period.

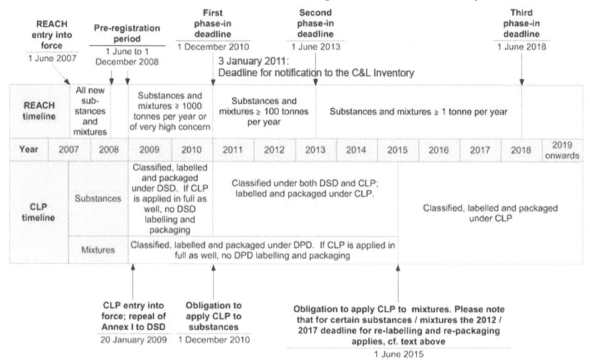

Figure 8-8: Transition to CLP Regulation requirements.   *Source: European Chemical Agency (ECHA).*

Harmonised warning pictograms

Under CLP, United Nations' globally harmonised warning pictograms for labels will replace the existing CHIP 4 requirements.

CHIP 4 (DSD) symbol   CLP symbol

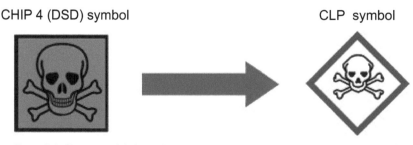

Figure 8-9: Changes to labels, toxic.   *Source: HSE.*

CLP symbol	Description
⟨!⟩	This pictogram refers to less serious health hazards such as skin irritancy/sensitisation and applies to many circumstances where the CHIP symbol is applied.
⟨person⟩	This pictogram reflects serious longer term health hazards such as carcinogenicity and respiratory sensitisation.

Figure 8-10: Changes to labels.   *Source: HSE.*

Harmonised hazard and precautionary statements

New, globally harmonised, hazard and precautionary statements for labels, will replace the existing risk and safety phrases.

	Hazard statements		Precautionary statements
H240	Heating may cause an explosion.	P102	Keep out of reach of children.
H320	Causes eye irritation.	P271	Use only outdoors or in well-ventilated area.
H401	Toxic to aquatic life.	P410	Protect from sunlight.

Figure 8-11: Hazard and precautionary statements table.   *Source: CLP.*

HSE GUIDANCE NOTE EH40

EH40, which is prepared and published annually by the Health and Safety Executive (HSE), contains the lists of Workplace Exposure Limits (WEL) for use with the Control of Substances Hazardous to Health Regulations (COSHH) 2002, a description of the limit setting process, technical definitions and explanatory notes. EH40 is mostly guidance but does contain sections of special legal status; some sections have been approved by the Health and Safety Executive (HSE) and are statutory requirements that must be complied with.

MANUFACTURERS' HEALTH AND SAFETY DATA SHEETS

Section 6 of the Health and Safety at Work etc Act (HASAWA) 1974 requires manufacturers, importers and suppliers to provide information on substances for use at work; this is usually provided in the form of a data sheet. REACH (Registration, Evaluation, Authorisation and restriction of Chemicals) is the system for controlling chemicals in Europe. It became law in the UK on the 1st June 2007. REACH adopts some of the older aspects of the chemicals system in Europe, including Safety Data Sheets (SDS).

INFORMATION TO BE INCLUDED BY SUPPLIER

Safety Data Sheets established in accordance with REACH and provided to users by the supplier require the following to be included:

- Identification of the substance/mixture and of the company/undertaking.
- Hazards identification.
- Composition/information on ingredients.
- First-aid measures.
- Firefighting measures.
- Accidental release measures.
- Handling and storage.
- Exposure controls/personal protection.

- Physical and chemical properties.
- Stability and reactivity.
- Toxicological information.
- Ecological information.
- Disposal considerations.
- Transport information.
- Regulatory information.
- Other information.

SDS information does not have to be provided for:

- The offer or sale of dangerous substances or mixtures to the general public provided sufficient information is provided to enable users to take the necessary measures as regards safety, protection of human health and the environment.
- Unless a SDS is requested by a downstream user or distributor.
- If the substances/mixtures are supplied in the UK and not classified as dangerous.
- For certain products intended for the final user, for example, medicinal products or cosmetics.

LIMITATIONS OF INFORMATION IN ASSESSING RISKS TO HEALTH

Information provided by manufacturers and contained within the HSE Guidance Note EH40 may be very technical and require a specialist to explain its relevance to a given activity. Some substances have good toxicological information, usually gained from past experience of harm; many others have a limited amount of useful toxicological information available to guide us as to the harm it may produce. This can lead to a reliance on data that is only our best understanding at the time and this may have to be revised as our knowledge on the substance changes. This is reflected in the use of WELs. Individual susceptibility of workers differs by, for example, age, gender or ethnic origin. Exposure history varies over the working life of an individual and current exposure may not indicate that the individual may suffer due to a cumulative effect from the earlier exposures. For example, an individual may have been or be engaged in a number of processes within a variety of workplaces or personal pastimes.

Role and limitations of hazardous substance monitoring

The role of hazardous substance monitoring is to determine the level of likely exposure of workers to substances in order to establish the likely effects on the worker. Hazardous substance monitoring can help to determine what controls are required, if current controls are adequate to limit exposure and assist in choosing appropriate personal protective equipment (PPE). Monitoring can also confirm compliance with workplace exposure limits (WEL).

As described previously, the health effects of exposure to toxic substances can be acute or chronic. It is therefore necessary to use appropriate methods of measurement to distinguish these effects. It is also important to understand the limitation of any hazardous substance monitoring method used, for example, the risk of cross contamination of similar substances being measured and the fact that general workplace monitoring may not represent specific worker exposure.

When embarking upon a monitoring campaign to assess the risk to which an individual may be exposed, it is necessary to ask several questions.

1) What to sample?

This involves a review of the materials, processes and operating procedures being used within a process, coupled with discussions with management and health and safety personnel. A brief 'walk-through' survey can also be useful as a guide to the extent of monitoring that may be necessary.

Health and safety data sheets are also of use. When the background work has been completed it can then be decided what is to be measured.

2) On whom?

This depends on the size and diversity of the group that the survey relates to. From the group of workers being surveyed the sample to be monitored should be selected; this must be representative of the group and the work undertaken. Selecting the individual with the highest exposure can be a reasonable starting point. If the group is large then random sampling may have to be employed, but care has to be exercised with this approach. The group should also be aware of the reason for sampling.

3) How long should the sample be for?

There are many considerations when answering this question, including the applicable control limits for the substance; the type of hazard (acute or chronic); the limit of detection of the equipment and the resources that are available.

4) How is monitoring done?

The particular sampling strategy, based on the hazard presented, is outlined in the following table:

Measurements to determine	*Suitable types of measurement*
Chronic hazard.	Continuous personal dose measurement. Continuous measurements of average background levels. Short term readings of containment levels at selected positions and times.
Acute hazard.	Continuous personal monitoring with rapid response. Continuous background monitoring with rapid response. Short term readings of background contaminant levels at selected positions and times.
Environmental control status.	Continuous background monitoring. Short term readings of background contaminant levels at selected positions and times.
Whether area is safe to enter.	Direct reading instruments.

Figure 8-12: Sampling strategy.   *Source: RMS.*

Basic monitoring equipment

SHORT TERM SAMPLERS

Stain tube detectors (multi-gas/vapour)

Simple devices for the measurement of contamination on a grab (short term) sampling basis. It incorporates a glass detector tube, filled with inert material. The material is impregnated with a chemical reagent which changes colour ('stains') in proportion to the quantity of contaminant as a known quantity of air is drawn through the tube.

There are several different manufacturers of detector tubes including Dräger and Gastec. It is important that the literature provided with the pumps and tubes is followed. These provide a quick and easy way to detect the presence of a particular airborne contaminant. However they possess inherent inaccuracies and tube manufacturers claim a relative standard deviation of 20% or less (i.e. 1ppm in 5ppm).

Types of tube construction

- Commonest is the simple stain length tube, but it may contain filter layers, drying layers, or oxidation layers.
- Double tube or tube containing separate ampoules, avoids incompatibility or reaction during storage.
- Comparison tube.
- Narrow tube to achieve better resolution at low concentrations.

The previously shown list illustrates the main types of tubes; however there are more variations and the manufacturer's operating instructions must be read and fully understood before tubes are used.

Pumps

There are four types:

- Bellows pump.
- Piston pump.
- Ball pump.
- Battery operated pump.

Pumps and tubes of different manufacturers should not be missed.

How to use tubes

- Choose tube to measure material of interest and expected range.
- Check tubes are in date.
- Check leak tightness of pump.
- Read instructions to ensure there are no limitations due to temperature, pressure, humidity or interfering substances.
- Break off tips of tube, prepare tube if necessary and insert correctly into pump. Arrows normally indicate the direction of air flow.
- Draw the requisite number of strokes, to cause the given quantity of air to pass through the tube.
- Immediately, unless operating instructions say otherwise, evaluate the amount of contaminant by examining the stain and comparing it against the graduations on the tube. If there is any doubt when reading the tube, always err on the safe side (higher end of the scale of discolouration).
- Remove tube and discard according to instructions.
- Purge pump to remove any contaminants from inside the pump.

Figure 8-13: Gas detector pump. *Source: Drager.*

Advantages of short term samplers:

- Quick and easy to use.
- Instant reading without further analysis. Does not require much expertise to use.
- Relatively inexpensive.

Disadvantages of short term samplers:

- Tubes can be cross sensitive to other contaminants.
- Accuracy varies - some are only useful as an indication of the presence of contaminants.
- Is only a grab sample (taken at a single location point and may not represent the workplace as a whole).
- Relies on operator to accurately count pump strokes (manual versions).
- Only suitable for gases and vapours (not dusts).

Direct reading dust sampler

Simple methods are by direct observation of the effect of the dust on a strong beam of light, for example, using a Tyndall Lamp. High levels of small particles of dust show up under this strong beam of light. Other ways are by means of a direct reading instrument. This establishes the level of dust by, for example, scattering of light. Some also collect the dust sample. The advantages and disadvantages are:

Advantages of direct reading dust samplers:

- Instant reading.
- Continuous monitoring.
- Can record electronically.
- Can be linked to an alarm.
- Suitable for clean room environments.

Disadvantages of direct reading dust samplers:

- Some direct reading instruments can be expensive.
- Does not differentiate between dusts of different types.
- Most effective on dusts of a spherical nature.

LONG TERM SAMPLERS

Static sampling

These devices are stationed in the working area. They sample continuously over the length of a shift, or longer period if necessary. Mains or battery-operated pumps are used. Very small quantities of contaminant may be detected. The techniques employed include absorption, bubblers, and filtration; they are similar in principle to personal samplers, but the equipment is tailored to suit static use.

Advantages of long term samplers:

■ Will monitor the workplace over a long period of time.
■ Will accurately identify 8 hour time weighted average.

Disadvantages of long term samplers:

■ Will not generally identify a specific type of contaminant.
■ Will not identify multiple exposure i.e. more than one contaminant.
■ Does not identify personal exposure.
■ Unless very sophisticated, will not read peaks and troughs.

Personal samplers

Passive personal samplers

Passive samplers are so described to illustrate the fact that they have no mechanism to draw in a sample of the contaminant, but instead rely on passive means to sample. As such they take a time to perform this function, for example, acting as an absorber taking in contaminant vapours over a period of a working day. Some passive samplers, like gas badges, are generally fitted to the lapel and change colour to indicate contamination.

Active personal samplers

Filtration devices are used for dusts, mists and fumes. A known volume of air is pumped through a sampling head and the contaminant filtered out. By comparing the quantity of air with the amount of contaminant a measurement is made.

Sampling head in consistent position (eg mid point on shoulder seam)

Battery operated sampling pump

Figure 8-14: Personal sampling equipment. *Source: ROSPA OS and H.*

The filter is either weighed or an actual count of particles is done to establish the amount, as with asbestos. The type of dust can be determined by further laboratory analysis. Active samplers are used in two forms, for personal sampling and for static sampling.

SMOKE TUBES

Smoke tubes are simple devices that generate a 'smoke' by means of a chemical reaction. A tube similar in type to those used in stain tube detectors is selected, its ends broken (which starts the chemical reaction) and it is inserted into a small hand bellows. By gently pumping the bellows smoke is emitted. By watching the smoke air flow can be studied. This can be used to survey extraction and ventilation arrangements to determine their extent of influence.

8.3 - Workplace exposure limits

Purpose of workplace exposure limits

The purpose of workplace exposure limits is to control the exposure of workers to a variety of substances which can have harmful effects. If exposure is not controlled this can lead to many forms of ill-health. Therefore, it is important to know in advance how to protect people at work. The Health and Safety Executive set Workplace Exposure Limits (WELs) for hazardous substances and these are published in EH40, which is updated annually. These WEL's establish limits that employers work to when controlling exposure of workers to substances.

Workplace exposure limits (WELs) are occupational exposure limits set under the Control of Substances Hazardous to Health Regulations (COSHH) 2002 (amended) to protect the health of persons in the workplace. They are concentrations (either parts per million or per cubic metre of air) of airborne substances averaged over a period of time known as a Time Weighted Average (TWA). The two periods that are used are 8-hours and 15-minutes. The 8-hour TWA is known as an LTEL (long-term exposure limit), used to help protect against chronic ill-health effects. 15-minute STELs (short-term exposure limits) are to protect against acute ill-health effects such as eye irritation, which may happen in minutes or even seconds of exposure. Many substances have both a LTEL and STEL allocated to them.

Airborne substances can be solid (dust), liquid (mist/aerosol), gas, vapours or fumes. Solids and liquids can be measured by weight (milligrams - mg); therefore the WEL for cement dust is expressed as 10 mg/m^3.

Gas, vapours and fumes are weightless. Therefore, the WEL is expressed as a concentration in the atmosphere - the long term WEL for trichloroethylene is 100 parts per million (PPM). COSHH 2002 (amended) states that exposure to hazardous substances should be prevented where it is reasonably practicable. Where this cannot be done by, for example, changing the process, substituting it for something safer or enclosing the process, exposure should be reduced by other methods.

TOTAL INHALABLE DUST AND RESPIRABLE DUST

'Total inhalable dust' approximates to the fraction of airborne material, which enters the nose and mouth during breathing and is, therefore, available for deposition in the body. 'Respirable dust' approximates to the fraction, which penetrates to the gas exchange region of the lung. Where dusts contain components which have their own assigned occupational exposure limits, all the relevant limits should be complied with. Many cases of exposure can consist of a complex mixture of chemicals, such as a welding fume. The effects of these can be difficult to assess as simultaneous exposure to two or more chemicals may alter toxicity in several ways. In additive effects the combined effects are equal to the sum of its parts. EH40 provides advice on assessing the effects of mixed exposures.

Long-term and short-term exposure limits

LONG-TERM EXPOSURE LIMITS

LTEL   These are WELs that are concerned with the total intake averaged over a reference period (usually 8 hours) and is therefore appropriate for protecting against the effects of long term exposure (chronic effects). Some examples:

Benzene	1ppm
Formaldehyde	2ppm
Chlorine	0.5ppm
Phenol	2ppm
Trichloroethylene	100ppm
Trichloroethylene	550 mg/m^3

SHORT-TERM EXPOSURE LIMITS

STEL   These are WELs primarily aimed at avoiding the acute effects or at least reducing the risk of occurrence. They are averaged over a 15 minute reference period. Some examples:

Phosgene	0.02ppm
Trichloroethylene	150 ppm
Trichloroethylene	820 mg/m^3

It can be seen from the examples shown that trichloroethylene has both a long and short term WEL to accommodate its acute effect (narcosis) and its chronic effect (possible cancer). It is also expressed as parts per million to protect from its harmful vapours and, because processes that use trichloroethylene can create mists, it is also regulated by milligrams per cubic metre.

Limitations of exposure limits

There are many reasons why control of exposure should not be based solely on WELs:

- **Inhalation only.** Many substances (for example, trichloroethylene) have the ability to absorb through the skin. WELs do not account for these compound routes of entry.
- **Personal susceptibility.** The majority of the work has been based on the average male physiology from the countries in which studies were conducted. Some work has been done where specific health related effects have been noted amongst females, for example, exposure to lead compounds.
- **Adopted from American TLV.** Work done to date has been based upon exposure to individuals in the developed countries, for example, Europe and USA.
- **Variations in control.** Local exhaust ventilation systems may not always work consistently because of lack of maintenance, overwhelming levels of contamination, etc.
- **Errors in monitoring.** Measuring microscopic amounts of contamination requires very accurate and sensitive equipment. Lack of maintenance and misuse can lead to inaccuracies in monitoring.
- **Synergistic effects.** The standards that are available relate to single substances and the effects of multiple substances in the workplace need to be considered.

Reducing exposure levels

Though WELs may be set for substances the Health and Safety at Work Act (HASAWA) 1974 and COSHH 2002 require reduction of exposure to **as low as is reasonably practicable.** Existing data on exposure limits may not reflect the safe levels that should be achieved to ensure the health of people exposed to substances in the workplace. It is important to review work practices and control strategies to reduce levels of exposure whenever possible. Control strategies should be constantly reviewed to ensure the lowest levels of exposure are achieved. If the levels of exposure are to be maintained below the WEL, with confidence, it will be necessary to work below them sufficiently to account for changes in work situation. This is particularly important with those WELs that are set for substances that are carcinogens or sensitisers. By working "at the limit" employers do not allow for sensitive people who may be affected by relatively low exposures. Nor do they account for variations or inaccuracies in monitoring, sudden surges of contaminant or partial failures of control measures.

Regulation 7 (7) of COSHH 2002 sets out the criteria that controls must conform to in order to be considered adequate.

(a) The principles of good practice for the control of exposure to substances hazardous to health set out in Schedule 2A are applied.

(b) Any workplace exposure limit approved for that substance is not exceeded.

(c) For a substance:

   (i) Which carries the risk phrase R45, R46 or R49 (i.e. carcinogens), or for a substance or process that is listed in Schedule 1.

   (ii) Which carries the risk phrase R42 or R42/43 (i.e. respiratory sensitisers), or which is listed in section C of HSE publication "Asthmagen? Critical assessments of the evidence for agents implicated in occupational asthma", exposure is reduced to as low a level as is reasonably practicable.

Figure 8-15: Regulation 7 (7) of COSHH 2002.   *Source: The Control of Substances Hazardous to Health Regulations (COSHH) 2002 (amended).*

8.4 - Control measures

Duty to prevent exposure or adequately control it

"Every employer shall ensure that the exposure of his employees to substances hazardous to health is either prevented or, where this is not reasonably practicable, adequately controlled".

Figure 8-16: Regulation 7 (1) of COSHH 2002.   *Source: The Control of Substances Hazardous to Health Regulations (COSHH) 2002 (amended).*

The eight principles of good practice for the control of exposure to substances hazardous to health are set out in Schedule 2A of the Control of Substances Hazardous to Health Regulations (COSHH) 2002 (as amended) ACOP and guidance. A summary of the main points is given here and further detail can be found in the section **'Principles of good practice as regards control of exposure' later in this element**.

- Design and operate processes and activities to minimise emission, release and spread of substances hazardous to health.
- Take into account all relevant routes of exposure - inhalation, skin absorption and ingestion - when developing control measures.
- Control exposure by measures that are proportionate to the health risk.
- Choose the most effective and reliable control options that minimise the escape and spread of the substances hazardous to health.
- Where adequate control of exposure cannot be achieved by other means, provide, in combination with other control measures, suitable personable protective equipment.
- Check and review regularly all elements of control measures for their continuing effectiveness.
- Inform and train all employees on the hazards and risks from the substances with which they work and the use of control measures developed to minimise the risks.
- Ensure that the introduction of control measures does not increase the overall risk to health and safety.

Ensuring the workplace exposure limit is not exceeded

If exposure cannot be prevented, preferably by avoiding the use of a hazardous substance, then employers must adequately control exposure.

To achieve this, the employer must apply protection measures appropriate to the activity and consistent with the priority order specified by COSHH 2002:

- Provision of a high level of inherent health and safety by careful design, selection and use of appropriate work processes, systems and engineering controls, and use of suitable work equipment and materials, for example, systems and processes which reduce to the minimum required for the work the amount of hazardous substance used or produced, or equipment which totally encloses the process.
- Controlling exposure at source, for example, by including adequate ventilation systems and appropriate organisational measures such as reducing to a minimum the number of employees exposed and the level and duration of their exposure.
- Using personal protective equipment in addition to the previous measures where those measures alone cannot achieve adequate control.

The selection of protection measures should be determined by the level of the ill-health risk resulting from exposure to the hazardous substance and the scope for reducing the risk to a minimum. It is important to ensure that protection measures are put in place that protects those directly affected by the substance and maintenance workers. Protection measures need to be supported by the provision of information, instruction, training and supervision to ensure exposure limits are met and protection measures not undermined. It is essential that the protection measures are monitored for effectiveness by the provision of workplace and worker monitoring.

Principles of good practice as regards control of exposure

The principles of good practice are detailed in schedule 2A of COSHH 2002. Employers have a responsibility to manage and minimise the risks from work activities. They must develop suitable and sufficient control measures and ways of maintaining them. They should:

- Identify hazards and potentially significant risks.
- Take action to prevent and control risks.
- Keep control measures under regular review.

To be effective in the long-term, control measures must be practical, workable and sustainable. Principles of good practice in the control of substances hazardous to health are outlined in the forthcoming sections.

MINIMISING EMISSION, RELEASE AND SPREAD OF HAZARDOUS SUBSTANCES

It is important, where possible to minimise emission, release and spread of hazardous substances by effective design and operation of processes and task activities. A useful approach to control exposure to hazardous substances is to reduce the actual quantity of the substance which can become airborne; for example, prevention of large volumes of airborne vapours by use of a paint brush rather than an aerosol can of paint or paint spraying equipment. In the case of disposal of acids, the risk of acid burns or corrosion will be removed by neutralisation with a suitable alkali.

Changes in work patterns can ensure that fewer employees are exposed. It might be possible that some work takes place at night or weekend when fewer people are present.

Change of work patterns to reduce length of time of exposure forms the basis of occupational exposure limits, i.e. long-term exposure limits (8 hours time weighted average value) and short-term exposure limits (15 minutes weighted average value). This is particularly relevant when considering shift patterns, where 12 hour shifts are common and the individual operators' work arrangements may need to be rotated, within a shift, to ensure 8 hours time weighted averages are not exceeded.

Remove contaminant at source so that its range of contamination is minimised. Removal is usually achieved by mechanical air handling. Local exhaust ventilation or dilution ventilation are the options available depending on the amount and toxicity of the contaminant.

TAKING INTO ACCOUNT ROUTES OF EXPOSURE AND CONTROL OPTIONS

It is important to take into account all relevant routes of exposure, along with the effectiveness and reliability of control options.

Exposure can occur through, inhalation; to or through the skin; or by ingestion. When selecting control options consideration will therefore need to be given to the:

- Way the substances are used and how exposure occurs.
- Degree of exposure.
- Health effects that the substances can cause.

When all sources and routes of exposure have been identified these should be ranked in order of importance.

In many case it will be found that not all routes of exposure will occur, for example, for people potentially exposed to crystalline silica, when cutting stone or concrete, the only relevant route of entry is by inhalation.

Whereas, for those handling a low volatility substance, such as diesel, the primary route of entry will be through the skin. In this way, control can be directed at the main sources and routes of exposure.

Where inhalation is the most relevant route, the main focus for control will be sources of emission to air. Where the main concern is ingestion or effects on, or as a result of penetration through, the skin the main focus for control will be sources of contamination of surfaces or clothing and direct contamination of the skin. For example, controls may then include training users in the correct techniques for putting on and taking their gloves off to avoid skin contamination. Other controls to limit ingestion would include making sure people have clean areas to rest, eat and drink. This can be supplemented by the provision of adequate and accessible welfare facilities for washing and changing; with segregation of clean and dirty areas if the risk of contamination is severe.

EXPOSURE CONTROL TO BE PROPORTIONAL TO HEALTH RISK

The principle of "so far as is reasonably practicable" allows employers to balance cost against the degree of risk. This principle has to be applied when selecting adequate control measures to protect employees from harmful exposures.

Control measures have to take into account the nature of the hazard, the frequency and duration of exposure and the number and type of people exposed. If the risk is low and not likely to cause long-term harm, the control measures may be simple procedural issues such as replacing the lid tightly on tins and vessels or a regime of regular cleaning. However, if the consequences are likely to be diseases such as dermatitis, asthma or cancer then more robust and reliable measures must be implemented.

CHOOSING THE MOST EFFECTIVE AND RELIABLE CONTROL OPTIONS

It is important to choose the most effective and reliable control options for the circumstances and direct these at the main sources and causes of exposure. Some control options are inherently more reliable and effective than others.

For example, the protection afforded by personal protective equipment (PPE) is dependent upon good fit and attention to detail. In contrast, a very reliable form of control is changing the process so that less of the hazardous substance is emitted or released.

A set of integrated control measures that are effective and reliable enough to control exposure adequately has to be developed. Some control measures are more reliable than others are. However, it is important that the 'hierarchical' approach to reliability and effectiveness is not viewed so rigidly that some control options are seen as 'good', while others are seen as ineffective. There is a general hierarchy of controls available:

- *Elimination of the substance* - This is the most effective though least realistic option. If elimination can be achieved it means that no exposure can take place and there is no residual risk to manage.
- *Reduction of exposure* - By substituting a less harmful substance or reducing the number of people exposed and/or the frequency and duration of exposure. This method protects all employees but there will be residual risk to deal with.
- *Isolation of the substance* - Secure storage facilities with limited access.
- *Controls* - Engineering controls such as local exhaust ventilation. These have to be carefully monitored to ensure, for example, that the captor hood is correctly positioned.
- *Personal protective equipment* - Or other devices worn by individuals such as exposure monitors. The main disadvantage of this method is that it only protects the user. Furthermore, it will only protect the user if the equipment/device is worn correctly, if at all.

The important consideration is that there is a hierarchy of reliability of control options and this is often linked to their effectiveness. Always consider elimination first. If this is not possible, a reliable form of control is to change the process so that it releases less substance. Controls applied to the process might be as effective, but will require maintenance and are unlikely to be as reliable.

There is a range of control options available. Each will have its own characteristics as to when it is appropriate to be applied, how much it can reduce exposure, and how reliable it is likely to be. It is important not to be too fixed in one's thinking as, in many cases, an effective set of control measures will turn out to be a mix of options; some more reliable than others.

Control options, such as change of process or applied controls, are likely to be more effective and reliable than PPE, and be cheaper in the long term, but it may take longer to plan and organise them. It is important not to rely solely on PPE as the only control option and believe exposure is adequately, effectively and reliably controlled.

Employers should also consider the consequences of failure of the control measure when making their selection. If failure of the control measure would lead to exposure of workers to a high risk of harm and failure of the control measure to control harm was likely, it would be preferable to use a control that was more reliable.

Decisions to use personal protective equipment as a control measure should be taken with regard to its likely level of success in preventing harm. When working with high risk substances it would be preferable to use controls that are more reliable than personal protective equipment.

Whoever designs control measures needs appropriate knowledge, skills and experience. The competencies required will depend on the scope and complexity of the exposure problems to be addressed and solved.

USE OF PERSONAL PROTECTIVE EQUIPMENT IN CONJUNCTION WITH OTHER MEASURES

When adequate control of exposure cannot be achieved by other means, a combination of control measures and personal protective equipment may be applied. This will provide more effective protection of workers in the circumstances that the control measures provide limited protection or protection is required where their reliability may mean they fail.

An example of this may be where the control measure provided is local exhaust ventilation (LEV). In this situation, the LEV will provide a degree of effective removal of the contaminant, but to increase the effectiveness of protection the worker may also wear respiratory protective equipment (RPE), such as a respirator.

The use of personal protective equipment is considered in more detail later in this element and also in NGC1 - Element 4 - Health and safety management systems 3 - planning.

CHECKS AND REVIEW OF CONTROL MEASURES TO CONFIRM EFFECTIVENESS

All control measures require regular checks and review to ensure their continued effectiveness and efficiency. There are a number of reasons why this approach should be adopted.

- Statutory obligations.
- To comply with WELs.
- Provision of information to employees.
- To indicate the need for health surveillance.
- For insurance purposes.
- To develop in-house exposure standards.

Exactly what checks should be carried out depends on such factors as:

- The control measures in use.
- The reliability of the controls.
- The consequences of failure.

PROVISION OF INFORMATION AND TRAINING

It is important to ensure the Provision of information and training to those working with hazardous substances. For control measures to be effective, people need to know how to use them. Furthermore, employees should be consulted during the development of control measures.

Employees who have been actively involved in the design of controls are more likely to appreciate the need for their use and, therefore, more likely to use them correctly.

Regulation 12 of COSHH 2002 requires:

"That the instruction and training must ensure that people at work on the premises do not put themselves, or others at risk through exposure to substances hazardous to health. In particular, the instruction must be sufficient and suitable for them to know:

(a) How and when to use the control measures.

(b) The defined methods of work.

(c) How to use the personal protective equipment and especially respiratory protective equipment, for example, the correct method of removing and refitting gloves and masks and determining how long protective gloves should be worn before any liquid contamination is liable to permeate them.

(d) The cleaning, storage and disposal procedures they should follow, why they are required and when they are to be carried out, for example, cleaning contaminated PPE with water or a vacuum fitted with a high-efficiency particulate arrester (HEPA) filter, and not with an airline, or the risks of using contaminated PPE.

(e) The procedures to be followed in an emergency.

Figure 8-17: Regulation 12 of COSHH 2002.   *Source: The Control of Substances Hazardous to Health Regulations (COSHH) 2002 (amended).*

Training should include elements of theory as well as practice. Training in the use and application of control measures and PPE should take account of recommendations and instructions supplied by the manufacturer.

CONTROL MEASURES NOT TO INCREASE OVERALL RISK TO HEALTH AND SAFETY

People designing control measures have to consider the possibility that the new measures might introduce new risks. For example, personal protective equipment can affect mobility and interfere with the senses. The introduction of local exhaust ventilation means that it will have to be maintained and, therefore, will introduce the hazards attendant to maintenance operations and the use of enclosures might increase the chances of an explosion.

Common measures used to implement principles of good practice

REDUCED TIME EXPOSURE AND SIGNIFICANCE OF TIME WEIGHTED AVERAGES

There is a close relationship between exposure and time. At a fixed level of contamination the effect will be proportional to the time exposed. This is the basis of occupational exposure limits, i.e. long-term exposure limits (8 hours time weighted average value) and short-term exposure limits (15 minutes weighted average value). Acceptable concentrations of airborne substances may be averaged over a period of time, known as a Time Weighted Average (TWA).

The 8-hour TWA is known as an LTEL (long-term exposure limit), used to help protect against chronic ill-health effects. 15-minute STELs (short-term exposure limits) are to protect against acute ill-health effects such as eye irritation, which may happen after minutes or even seconds of exposure.

It may be possible to organise work so that exposure to any one person is controlled by means of job/task rotation.

ENCLOSURE OF HAZARDS

In its simplest sense this can mean putting lids on substances that have volatile vapours, such as tins of solvent based products. In this way the strategy is to enclose the hazard so that vapours are not given off. In this case, this is best done when the substance is not in use, this does not just mean at the end of the day but at intervals when the substance is not actually in use. It makes a very simple and effective control of exposure to hazards.

SEGREGATION OF PROCESS

This strategy is based on the containment of an offending substance or agent to prevent its free movement in the working environment. It may take a number of forms, for example, pipelines, closed conveyors, laboratory fume cupboards. In construction situations, this is used in processes such as asbestos removal where the work being done is enclosed in plastic sheeting in order to segregate the work process from the surrounding areas. In a similar way, this may be suitable for building cleaning processes using shot or for spray protection being applied to a structure.

SEGREGATION OF PEOPLE

Segregation is a method of controlling the risks from toxic substances and physical hazards such as biological or toxic substances. It can take a number of forms, including physical separation and segregation by worker characteristics.

By physical separation

This can be a relatively simple method such as where the minimum number of employees are working with biological or toxic substances and are distanced (segregated) from the general workforce. If the hazards cannot be enclosed close to their source it may be preferable that the workforce be segregated from the hazard by providing physical separation in the form of a refuge, for example, a control room of a chemical process.

By worker characteristics

The protection of young workers in certain trades is still valid today, a good example being lead. In this case the Control of Lead at Work Regulations (CLAW) 2002 excludes the employment of young persons in lead processes. There remains the possibility of gender linked vulnerability to certain toxic substances such as lead; segregation affords a high level of control in these circumstances. In addition, workers that have shown a susceptibility to substances may be segregated to ensure they are not exposed to them, for example, respiratory sensitisers like flour dust.

LOCAL EXHAUST VENTILATION

General applications and principles

Various local exhaust ventilation (LEV) systems are in use in the workplace, for example:

- Receptor hoods such as are used in fume cupboards and kilns.
- Captor hoods (used for welding and milling operations). *See figure ref 8-19*, which shows the fixed captor hood, flexible hose and rigid duct.
- High velocity low volume flow systems, for example, as used on a grinding tool.

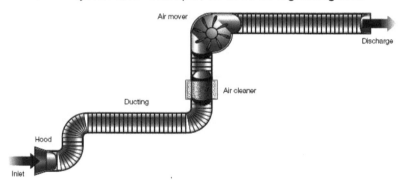

Figure 8-18: Common elements of a simple LEV system.   *Source: HSE indg408.*

Components of a basic system

- *Hood(s)* to collect airborne contaminants at, or near, where they are created (the source).
- *Ducts* to carry the airborne contaminants away from the process. *See figure ref 8-23* which shows the length of ducting with curves not corners.
- *Air cleaner* to filter and clean the extracted air.
- *Fan* must be the right size and type to deliver sufficient 'suck' to the hood. *See figure ref 8-20* as it clearly shows the size of a fan and motor required for industrial scale LEV.
- *Discharge* the safe release of cleaned, extracted air into the atmosphere.

Figure 8-19: Captor system on circular saw.   *Source: RMS.*

Figure 8-20: LEV fan and motor.   *Source: RMS.*

Figure 8-21: Flexible hose and captor hood.   *Source: RMS.*

Figure 8-22: Portable self contained unit.   *Source: RMS.*

Factors that reduce a LEV system's effectiveness

The efficiency of LEV systems can be affected by many factors including the following:

- Damaged ducting.
- Unauthorised alterations.
- Incorrect hood location. *See figure ref 8-21* which shows how a captor hood can be repositioned to suit the work activity by the use of a flexible hose.

- Too many bends in ducts.
- Blocked or defective filters.
- Leaving too many ports open.
- Process changes leading to overwhelming amounts of contamination.
- Fan strength or incorrect adjustment of fan.

The cost of heating make up air may encourage some employers to reduce extraction rates. When arranging installation of LEV it is vital that the pre and post ventilation contamination levels are specified and the required reduction should be part of the commissioning contract.

Figure 8-23: Length of ducting with curves.   *Source: RMS.*

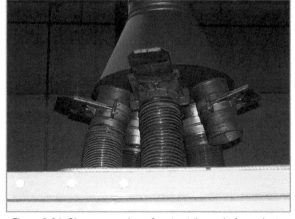
Figure 8-24: Shows a number of ports at the end of one duct - not all ports being used. *Source: RMS.*

Requirements for inspection

COSHH 2002 Regulation 9(2) and schedule 4 set out requirements for inspection of LEV systems. A thorough examination and test must take place once every 14 months (more frequently for those processes listed in schedule 4). Records must be kept available for at least 5 years from the date on which it was made.

The majority of ventilation systems, although effective in protecting workers' health from airborne contaminants, can create other hazards. One of the main hazards that need to be considered when designing LEV systems is that of noise. Even if it has been considered as a design feature when establishing LEV systems, it should be monitored on a periodic basis.

USE AND LIMITATIONS OF DILUTION VENTILATION

Dilution ventilation is a system designed to induce a general flow of clean air into a work area. A particularly simple approach to providing dilution ventilation is to open a window and door and allow natural air flow to dilute the workplace air. This is not a reliable means of dealing with toxic contaminants and may be over relied on in the construction industry. On its own it may prove inadequate but supported by respiratory protection equipment it may be acceptable for some substances.

Dilution ventilation may be achieved by driving air into a work area, causing air flow around the work area, dilution of contaminants in the work area and then out of the work area through general leakage or through ventilation ducts to the open air.

A variation on this is where air may be forcibly removed from the work area, but not associated with a particular contaminant source, and air is allowed in through ventilation ducts to dilute the air in the work area. Sometimes a combination of these two approaches is used; an example may be general air conditioning provided into an office environment.

Because dilution ventilation does not target any specific source and it relies on dispersal and dilution instead of specific removal, it can only be used with nuisance contaminants that are themselves fairly mobile in air. Dilution ventilation systems will only deal with general contamination and will not prevent contaminants entering a person's breathing zone. Local exhaust ventilation is the preferred means of controlling a person's exposure to substances.

Dilution ventilation may only be used as the sole means of control in circumstances where there is:

- Non toxic contaminant or vapour (not dusts).
- Contaminant which is uniformly produced in small, known quantities.
- No discrete point of release.
- No other practical means of reducing levels.

RESPIRATORY PROTECTIVE EQUIPMENT

Purpose, application and effectiveness

Damage to health and death can be caused by breathing in hazardous substances, such as dusts, fumes, vapours, gases or even micro-organisms. If direct prevention or control of exposure is not possible then respiratory protective equipment (RPE) may be needed; this should always be seen as a measure of last resort in the hierarchy of control measures. RPE includes a very wide range of devices from simple respirators offering basic protection against low levels of nuisance dusts to self-contained breathing apparatus.

The effectiveness of respiratory protection depends on using the proper equipment for the specific task. Before selecting respiratory protection equipment, the following issues should be considered:

- Operations and work sites where there is any kind of contamination.
- Jobs where a lack of oxygen is a problem.
- Specific contaminants that are present at the work site.
- Harmful properties of the contaminants.
- Form of the contaminant material: dust, mist, spray, gas, vapour, fume, or some combination of these.
- Concentrations of each contaminant.

Types of respiratory protection equipment

There are two main categories of respiratory protection:

1) Respirators.
2) Breathing apparatus.

Respirators

Respirators filter the air breathed but do not provide additional oxygen. There are a number of types of respirator that provide a variety of degrees of protection from dealing with nuisance dusts to high efficiency respirators for solvents or asbestos.

Some respirators may be nominated as providing non-specific protection from contaminants whereas others will be designed to protect from a very specific contaminant such as solvent vapours. There are five main types of respirators:

1) Filtering face piece.
2) Half mask respirator.
3) Full face respirator.
4) Powered air purifying respirator.
5) Powered visor respirator.

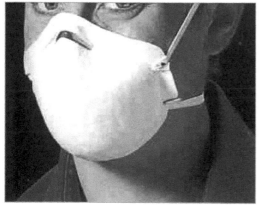

Figure 8-25: Paper filter respirator. *Source: Haxton Safety.*

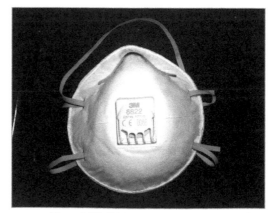

Figure 8-26: 3M disposable respirator. *Source: RMS.*

Advantages

■ Unrestricted movement.
■ Often lightweight and comfortable.
■ Can be worn for long periods.

Limitations

■ Purify the air by drawing it through a filter to remove contaminants. Therefore, can only be used when there is sufficient oxygen in the atmosphere.
■ Requires careful selection by a competent person.
■ Requires regular maintenance.
■ Knowing when a filter or cartridge is at the end of its useful life.
■ Requires correct storage facilities.
■ Can give a 'closed in'/claustrophobic feeling.
■ Relies on user for correct fit/use etc.
■ Incompatible with other forms of personal protective equipment (PPE).
■ Performance can be affected by beards and long hair.
■ Interferes with other senses, for example, sense of smell.

Breathing apparatus

Breathing apparatus provides a separate source of supply of air (including oxygen) to that which surrounds the person. Because of the self-contained nature of breathing apparatus it may be used to provide a high degree of protection from a variety of toxic contaminants and may be used in situations where the actual contaminant is not known or there is more than one contaminant.

There are three types of breathing apparatus:

1) Fresh air hose apparatus - clean air from uncontaminated source.

2) Compressed air line apparatus from compressed air source.

3) Self-contained breathing apparatus - from cylinder.

Figure 8-27: Full face canister respirator. *Source: Haxton Safety.*

Figure 8-28: Breathing apparatus. *Source: Haxton Safety.*

Advantages

■ Supplies clean air from an uncontaminated source. Therefore, can be worn in oxygen deficient atmospheres.
■ Has high assigned protection factor (APF). Therefore may be used in an atmosphere with high levels of toxic substance.
■ Can be worn for long periods if connected to a permanent supply of air.

Limitations

■ Can be heavy and cumbersome which restricts movement.
■ Requires careful selection by competent person.
■ Requires special training.
■ Requires arrangements to monitor/supervise user and for emergencies.
■ Can give a 'closed in'/claustrophobic feeling.

■ Relies on user for correct fit/use etc.
■ Incompatible with other forms of PPE.
■ Performance can be affected by, for example, long hair.
■ Interferes with other senses, for example, sense of smell. Requires correct storage facilities.

Selection, use and maintenance

There are a number of issues to consider in the selection of respiratory protective equipment (RPE) not least the advantages and limitations shown in the previous list.

A general approach must not only take account of the needs derived from the work to be done and the contaminant to be protected from but must include suitability for the person. This will include issues such as face fit and the ability of the person to use the equipment for a sustained period, if this is required. One of the important factors is to ensure that the equipment will provide the level of protection required.

This is indicated by the assigned protection factor (APF) given to the equipment by the manufacturers - the higher the factor the more protection provided. With a little knowledge it is possible to work out what APF is needed using the following formula.

$$APF = \frac{\text{Concentration of contaminant in the workplace}}{\text{Concentration of contaminant in the face-piece}}$$

It is important to understand that this factor is only an indication of what the equipment will provide. Actual protection may be different due to fit and the task being conducted. Every employee must use any personal protective equipment provided in accordance with the training and instructions that they have received. Where respiratory protective equipment (other than disposable respiratory protective equipment) is provided the employer must ensure that thorough examination and where appropriate testing, of that equipment is carried out at suitable intervals.

OTHER PROTECTIVE EQUIPMENT AND CLOTHING

Hand/arm protection including gloves

There are numerous types of glove and gauntlet available that offer protection from hazards:

- Chemical hazards such as acids, alkalis etc.
- Thermal hazards such as hot surfaces.
- Mechanical hazards in the form of splinters and sharp edges.

The materials used in the manufacture of these products are an essential feature to consider when making the selection. There are several types of rubber (latex, nitrile, PVC, butyl) all giving different levels of protection against aqueous chemicals; leather affords protection against heat , splinters and cuts; space age technology in the form of Kevlar (a tough, lightweight material) protects against cuts from knife blades and is used in the sleeves of jackets for those using chainsaws.

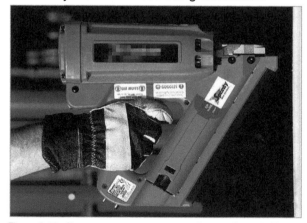

Figure 8-29: Gloves.   *Source: Speedy Hire plc.*

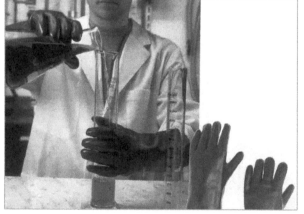

Figure 8-30: Protective clothing - gloves.   *Source: Haxton Safety.*

Protective clothing - overalls

1) Head protection - safety helmets or scalp protectors (bump caps) - scalp protectors give limited protection and are unsuitable for confined spaces. Safety helmets have a useful life of three years and this can be shortened by prolonged exposure to ultra-violet light. There is specific legal requirement on construction sites to wear head protection where there is risk of injury from falling objects.
2) Protective outer clothing - normally PVC, often high-visibility to alert traffic.
3) Protective inner clothing - overalls, aprons.

Eye protection

When selecting suitable eye protection, some of the factors to be considered are:

- Type and nature of hazard (impact, chemical, ultra violet (UV) light, etc.)
- Type/standard/quality of protection.
- Comfort and user acceptability issues.
- Compatibility.
- Maintenance and training requirements.
- Cost.

Figure 8-31: Eye and ear protection.   *Source: Speedy Hire plc.*

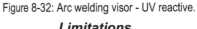

Figure 8-32: Arc welding visor - UV reactive.   *Source: RMS.*

Types	*Advantages*	*Limitations*
Spectacles	■ Lightweight, easy to wear. ■ Can incorporate prescription lenses. ■ Do not 'mist up'.	■ Do not give all round protection. ■ Relies on the wearer for use.
Goggles	■ Give all round protection. ■ Can be worn over prescription lenses. ■ Capable of high impact protection. ■ Can protect against other hazards, for example, dust, molten metal.	■ Tendency to 'mist up'. ■ Uncomfortable when worn for long periods. ■ Can affect peripheral vision.
Face shields (visors)	■ Gives full face protection against splashes. ■ Can incorporate a fan which creates air movement for comfort and protection against low level contaminants. ■ Can be integrated into other PPE, for example, head protection.	■ Require care in use, otherwise can become dirty and scratched. ■ Can affect peripheral vision. ■ Unless the visor is provided with extra sealing gusset around the visor, substances may go underneath the visor to the face.

Footwear - safety boots/shoes

The importance of foot protection is illustrated by the fact that around 21,000 foot and ankle injuries are reported annually. Inadequate protection and a lack of discipline on the part of the wearer commonly cause these. There are many types of safety footwear on the market, many of them offering different types of protection. It is vital that the nature of the hazard is considered when selecting appropriate footwear.

Here are some common examples:

■ Falling objects   - steel toe-caps.
■ Sharp objects   - steel in-soles.
■ Flammable atmospheres - anti-static footwear.
■ Spread of contamination - washable boots.
■ Electricity   - rubber soles.
■ Wet environments   - impermeable wellingtons.
■ Slippery surfaces   - non-slip soles.
■ Cold environments   - thermally insulated soles.

Figure 8-33: Personal protective equipment.   *Source: RMS.*

Ear protection

See also - Element 9 - Physical and psychological health - hazards and risk control, for details of ear protection.

PERSONAL HYGIENE AND PROTECTION REGIMES

Personal hygiene and good housekeeping have an important role in the protection of the health and safety of people at work. Laid down procedures and standards are necessary for preventing the spread of contamination.

The provision of adequate washing/showering facilities is important to remove contamination from the body. The provision of laundry facilities for overalls and PPE reduces the effect of contamination. Barrier creams and suitable hand protection are important considerations for chemical and biological risks.

Where personal hygiene is critical, for example, when stripping asbestos, a 'three room system' is employed. Workers enter the 'clean end' and put work clothes on, leaving by means of the 'dirty end'. When work has been completed they return by means of the 'dirty end', carry out personal hygiene and leave by means of the 'clean end'.

Vaccination

Where construction workers work in the vicinity activities like water treatment/sewage and medical treatment there is a higher than average risk from some biological hazards. Where segregation is not possible consideration may have to be given to those involved being immunised against common high risks, for example, hepatitis B. Whilst vaccination can be an effective way of preventing ill-health as a result of exposure to biological agents, it is important that employers are aware of problems that can arise. In the first instance, vaccination is intrusive.

Employers need the permission of employees before adopting this method - this may not always be forthcoming. Secondly, it is possible that some people will suffer adverse effects from the vaccination. Finally, not all diseases are treatable by vaccination and, for those that are, vaccination might not be available.

HEALTH SURVEILLANCE AND BIOLOGICAL MONITORING

Health surveillance

The Management of Health and Safety at Work Regulations (MHSWR) 1999, Regulation 6, deals with health surveillance and gives employers a duty to provide it where it is appropriate. Further details on health surveillance are contained in other Regulations, for example, COSHH 2002. *(Details can be found in the Approved Code of Practice Schedule 6; Extracts from the ACOP follow).*

Substances for which health surveillance is appropriate		Processes
Vinyl Chloride Monomer (VCM).		In manufacturing, production, reclamation, storage, discharge, transport, use or polymerization.
Nitro or amino derivatives of phenol and of benzene or its homologues.		In the manufacture of nitro or amino derivatives of phenol and of benzene or its homologues and the making of explosives with the use of any of these substances.
Orthotolidine and its salts.	Dianisidine and its salts. Dichlorbenzidene and its salts.	In manufacture, formation or use of these substances.
Auramine.	Magenta.	In manufacture.
Carbon Disulphide. Disulpher Dichloride. Benzene, including benzol.	Carbon Tetrachloride. Tricholoroethylene.	Process in which these substances are used, or given off as a vapour, in the manufacture of indiarubber or of articles or goods made wholly or partially of indiarubber.
Pitch.		In manufacture of blocks of fuel consisting of coal, coal dust, coke or slurry with pitch as a binding substance.

Figure 8-34: Schedule 6 medical surveillance.   *Source: COSHH ACoP.*

Though construction workers are not engaged in the manufacture of these substances they may work in locations where manufacture takes place. Other than the cases stated in the COSHH 2002 schedule, surveillance may be appropriate where exposure to hazardous substances is such that an identifiable disease or adverse health effect may be linked to the exposure. There must be a reasonable likelihood that the disease or effect may occur under the particular conditions of work prevailing and that valid techniques exist to detect such conditions and effects. The employer must keep records of surveillance in respect of each employee for at least 40 years. This requirement still applies where companies cease to trade, in which case the records must be offered to the HSE.

Biological monitoring guidance values

Biological monitoring may be particularly useful in circumstances where:

■ There is likely to be significant skin absorption and/or gastrointestinal tract uptake following ingestion.
■ Control of exposure depends on respiratory protective equipment.
■ There is a reasonably well-defined relationship between biological monitoring and effect.

- It gives information on accumulated dose and target organ burden which is related to toxicity.

Biological Monitoring Values (BMGVs) are set where they are likely to be of practical value, suitable monitoring methods exist and there are sufficient data available. BMGVs are non-statutory and any biological monitoring undertaken in association with a guidance value needs to be conducted on a voluntary basis (i.e. with the fully informed consent of all concerned). Where a BMG is exceeded it does not necessarily mean that any corresponding airborne standard has been exceeded nor that ill-health will occur. It is intended that where they are exceeded this will give an indication that investigation into current control measures and work practices is necessary. Similarly, a low BMGV should not suggest that there is no need to reduce workplace exposure further.

Table 2 EH40/2005 lists BMGVs; a few examples of common substances can be seen in *figure ref 8-35.*

Substance	Biological monitoring guidance value	Sampling time
Butan-2-one.	70µmol butan-2-one/L in urine.	Post shift.
Carbon monoxide.	30ppm carbon monoxide in end-tidal breath.	Post shift.
Lindane. (Organo chlorine pesticide).	35nmol/L (10µg/L of Lindane in whole blood (equivalent to 70nmol/Lidane in plasma).	Random.
Xylene, o-, m-, p- or mixed isomers.	650 mmol methyl hippuric acid/mol creainine in urine.	Post shift.

Figure 8-35: Biological Monitoring Values (BMGVs).   *Source: EH40/2005 Workplace exposure limits.*

Control of substances with specific effects

CARCINOGENS

Carcinogens are substances that have been identified as having the ability to cause cancer. Examples of these include arsenic, hardwood dusts and used engine oils.

OCCUPATIONAL ASTHMA

Occupational asthma is caused by substances in the workplace that trigger a state of specific airway hyper-responsiveness in an individual, resulting in breathlessness, chest tightness or wheezing. These substances are known as asthmagens and respiratory sensitisers. Exposure to these substances should be prevented, and where that is not possible, kept as low as reasonably practicable. Control measures used should take account of long term time weighted averages and short term peak exposures to the substance. If an individual develops occupational asthma, their exposure must be controlled to prevent any further attacks. Employees who work with asthmagens must have regular health surveillance to detect any changes in respiratory function.

GENETIC DAMAGE

Substances known as mutagens have been identified that cause changes to DNA, increasing the number of genetic mutations above natural background levels. These changes can lead to cancer in the individual affected or be passed to their offspring as genetic material, for example, thalidomide and plutonium oxide.

Due to the serious and irreversible nature of cancer and genetic changes, an employer's first objective must be to prevent exposure to carcinogens and mutagens. These substances should not be used or processes carried out with them, if a safer alternative less hazardous substance can be used instead. Where this is not feasible suitable control measures should include:

- Totally enclosed systems.
- Where total enclosure is not possible, exposure to these substances must be kept to as low a level as possible through the use of appropriate plant and process control measures such as handling systems and local exhaust ventilation (these measures should not produce other risks in the workplace).
- Storage of carcinogens/mutagens must be kept to the minimum needed for the process, in closed, labelled containers with warning and hazard signs, including waste products until safe disposal.
- Areas where carcinogens/mutagens are present must be identified and segregated to prevent spread to other areas.
- The number of people exposed and the duration of exposure must be kept to the minimum necessary to do the work.
- Personal protective equipment is considered a secondary protection measure used in combination with other control measures.
- Measures should be in place for monitoring of workplace exposure and health surveillance for work involving carcinogens and mutagens.

8.5 - Specific agents

Health risks and controls associated with other specific agents

BLOOD BORNE VIRUSES

Blood borne viruses (BBVs) are mainly found in blood or bodily fluids. The main BBVs of concern in the workplace are Human Immunodeficiency Virus (HIV), Hepatitis B and Hepatitis C.

HIV

HIV is transmitted through contact with body fluids, in particular blood, semen, vaginal secretions and breast milk. It is not transmitted through casual contact, coughing, sneezing, by sharing a toilet, by eating utensils, or by consuming food or beverages handled or prepared by someone with HIV. The main method of transfer at work is through laceration or puncture of the skin or contamination of the eyes; therefore, a co-worker with HIV in the workplace is not a risk to others.

Hepatitis

Hepatitis means inflammation of the liver. Viruses can cause this by infecting the liver. There are a number of different hepatitis viruses. Two of the most common are Hepatitis B and C.

Hepatitis B and C are easily transmitted through contaminated blood. Most people do not know if they are infected. They may live for many years without symptoms. A proportion take 20 to 30 years to develop severe liver disease, some recover completely with treatment, others recover without any treatment at all. A small proportion develops liver cancer.

Hepatitis B is mainly transmitted through contact body fluids, such as, blood, semen, vaginal fluid and breast milk. Importantly, there is an effective vaccination against Hepatitis B.

Hepatitis C is mainly transmitted through blood, with a low risk of transmission through semen and vaginal fluid. There is no vaccine against Hepatitis C and current treatments for it are not effective in all cases.

Workers who come into contact with bodily fluids from other humans are at risk from BBVs, particularly if their work also involves sharp or abrasive implements or substances that may break the skin. Healthcare workers are at an obvious risk. Less obvious, perhaps, are those who work for cleansing or recreation/parks departments and staff who conduct bodily searches or searches of personal effects. Staff which work in these circumstances may come into contact with used needles.

The level of risk will depend on:

- Frequency and scale of contact with bodily fluids.
- The type of fluid or material they come into contact with.
- The activity the person must conduct in relation to the infectious material.
- The nature of the infection contained in the material.

Where a risk of exposure to BBVs has been identified, simple, inexpensive measures to prevent or control risks can be taken:

- Ensure good personal hygiene practices are observed, in particular hygienic hand-washing.
- Use procedures such as avoiding the use of sharps such as needles, blades, glass, etc.
- Also consider using equipment with built-in safety devices.
- Use personal protective equipment such as gloves, eye protection, face masks, etc.
- Ensure contaminated waste is disposed of in a safe manner, for example, sharps disposal bin.
- Use disposable equipment where there is a risk of BBV contamination, otherwise decontamination procedures must be strictly complied with.
- Ensure employees are aware of immediate steps to be followed upon contamination with blood or other body fluids.

ORGANIC SOLVENTS

Organic solvents include highly volatile/flammable cleaning agents such as acetone, organo chlorides such as trichloroethylene (used for commercial degreasing) or carbon tetrachloride used in dry cleaning processes. In the construction industry they may be encountered as residual contents of storage tanks or may be used as convenient cleaning substances to remove adhesives. Trichloroethylene is capable of absorption through the skin, it is a narcotic and classified "harmful". If the vapours are inhaled, it can cause drowsiness very quickly, depressing the central nervous system and leading to liver failure and death if exposure is for prolonged periods.

Controls for organic solvents include consideration of the use of an alternative process that does not use organic solvents. If substitution is not feasible then the process should be totally enclosed, which will enable solvent vapours to be collected and recovered. If it is not reasonably practicable to enclose the process, for example, an open-topped tank containing solvents for degreasing, care should be taken to operate the tank in accordance with current good working practice. This would usually involve ensuring the maximum solvent level was not exceeded and temperature control of the solvent was closely monitored and kept to a minimum.

Tanks used for degreasing would usually be fitted with condensers and local exhaust ventilation in order to control the vapours given off by the process. The surface area available for evaporation of the solvent should be kept to a minimum, large tanks may be provide with floating balls that cover the surface or covers for when it is not in use.

Smaller containers should be provided with a lid or similar method to limit vapour release. It is important that processes are conducted in controlled conditions that enable good general ventilation and sufficient fresh air for the workers exposed.

Regular monitoring of vapour levels and the use of respirators, protective gloves and clothing will also need to be considered carefully. Where flammable solvents are used, ensuring minimum quantities are in use in the workplace and the control of ignition sources will be additional factors to consider when establishing controls.

CARBON DIOXIDE

Carbon dioxide (CO_2) is a simple asphyxiant that can displace oxygen in the air that we breathe, resulting in insufficient oxygen reaching the brain. CO_2 at levels of 1.5% can cause hyperventilation and headaches, whilst at levels of 10% and above it can lead to collapse and death.

Carbon dioxide may be encountered during construction activities in fixed firefighting installations in buildings and as a By-product of the work being conducted in the premises being worked on, for example, in brewing processes and the manufacture of carbonated soft drinks. In addition, it may be encountered in confined spaces, such as trenches, particularly in chalky soil where carbon dioxide is evolved naturally from the chalk deposits. The gas is heavier than air and tends to gather in low areas.

Areas where CO_2 is likely to occur should be monitored whilst workers are exposed. Fixed and portable carbon dioxide detectors with alarm functions are inexpensive and readily available.

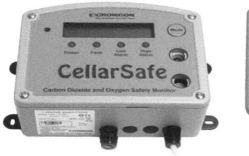    

Figure 8-36: CO_2 Detector for fixed applications. *Source: Safelinks Ltd.*   Figure 8-37: CO_2 Portable detector. *Source: Safelinks Ltd.*

NITROGEN

Nitrogen (N_2) is a simple asphyxiant gas. When nitrogen is released into a confined area it displaces a proportion of oxygen in the air and can, like carbon dioxide, lead to reduced amounts of oxygen reaching the brain, causing dysfunction, collapse and death. This may happen with very few warning symptoms or signs, since the human carotid body (a small cluster of receptors that measure oxygen and carbon dioxide levels in the blood) does not detect low-oxygen (hypoxia) levels very quickly. Two or three deep breaths of nitrogen are sufficient to cause the average person to cease breathing.

Direct skin contact with liquid nitrogen causes severe frostbite (cryogenic burns) within moments to seconds, although not instantly on contact, depending on the form of liquid nitrogen (liquid or mist) and surface area of the nitrogen-soaked material.

Nitrogen may be encountered in construction activities relating to premises that have manufactured or used the chemical, for example, it is commonly used to purge air in chemical plant. In addition, it is used as part of the proof testing processes that are used to test the integrity of tanks and vessels after construction or installation, for example, fuel storage tanks or chemical storage vessels.

Controls include education of workers regarding the risks, control over vessel entry, monitoring the atmosphere where it is likely to be present and training in the use of emergency respirators where bulk supplies are used continuously. In addition, first-aiders qualified to resuscitate those collapsed from nitrogen inhalation and appropriate equipment should be available. The provision of air or pure oxygen will not resuscitate on its own, the victim must be treated with a mixture of oxygen and carbon dioxide to trigger the breathing response.

ISOCYANATES

The principal health risks from isocyanates are that they are sensitising agents, in particular they sensitise the lungs and skin. Toluene di-isocyanate (TDI) and methylene bisphenyl di-isocyanate (MDI) are highly toxic in very small amounts (parts per billion) and inhalation will result in a severe respiratory reaction.

TDI and MDI are heavier than water and may gather in the bottom of tanks or other enclosed vessels filled with water. Isocyanates rapidly decompose in contact with water above 50°C with explosive potential if the material is contained before mixing.

Isocyanates may be encountered in construction activities related to the manufacture of resins and urethane foams, where common compounds are toluene di-isocyanate (TDI) and methylene bisphenyl di-isocyanate (MDI). TDI is an extremely volatile vapour and is evolved during the manufacture of foams. In addition, they are used in some glues and specialised paints that use the isocyanate as a hardener and in some expanding foams that may be used as a filler for gaps in building structures. Thermal decomposition of polyurethane materials may lead to the evolution of free isocyanate. Construction tasks that may involve exposure to isocyanates due to the heating of polyurethanes include soldering wire coated with polyurethane plastic, "hotwire" cutting of polyurethane foam, welding pipes lagged with polyurethane foam and burning off polyurethane paint.

Depending on the type of isocyanate used, controls will range from the use of respirators, through to local exhaust ventilation and breathing apparatus and full body secondary protection. If handling isocyanates, care will need to be taken to prevent skin contact by using handling/mixing aids and wearing gloves. The presence of isocyanates should be identified before engaging in hot work that might evolve isocyanates. Covered storage should be provided and procedures need to be in place to ensure early detection and handling of damaged containers.

LEAD

Lead is a poisonous metal that can damage nerve connections in the body (especially in young children) and cause blood and brain disorders. Lead poisoning typically results from ingestion of food or water contaminated with lead, but may also occur after accidental ingestion of contaminated soil, dust, or lead based paint. Similarly, lead poisoning can also develop from exposure to inhaled lead dust. Long-term exposure to lead or its salts (especially soluble salts or the strong oxidant PbO_2) can cause kidney damage, and colic-like abdominal pains. The main target for lead toxicity is the nervous system. Long-term exposure can result in decreased mental performance and weakness in fingers, wrists, or ankles, increases in blood pressure and can cause anaemia. In the case of pregnant women, high levels of exposure to lead may cause miscarriage and it reduces fertility in males.

Lead may be encountered in construction work on premises that use or used lead in their processes. It is widely used in the manufacture of lead-acid batteries, bullets and shots, weights, solders, pewters and crystal glass. Exposure to lead that has been left over from previous processes may occur during site remediation activities. Demolition of premises that conducted work using lead could lead to high levels of exposure, as could the disturbing of lead paint through its removal or cutting sections of a structure coated with lead paint. In addition, lead may be encountered as part of construction materials used for roofing.

Controls include prohibition of eating, drinking and smoking in workplaces, provision of washing and separate washing facilities. The presence of lead deposits or paint should be identified during a pre-remediation or pre-demolition survey and measures taken to limit exposure of workers by the use of the above controls, accompanied by the use of personal protective equipment. Work clothing should be kept separate from other clothing and laundered by a specialised industrial laundry.

It may be necessary to remove lead dust deposits as part of the construction activities. Because leaded dust is so small, it cannot be seen by the naked eye. Special cleaning methods are needed to make sure all harmful dust is removed. All visible and invisible particles need to be removed. Lead dust is hard to remove with an ordinary vacuum cleaner, particularly in poorly maintained buildings with rough and ageing surfaces. An ordinary vacuum will send lead dust through the work area because holes in the filter are not small enough to filter the dust out. A HEPA (High Efficiency Particulate Air) vacuum is equipped with a special filter that removes lead dust particles from the vacuums exhaust air stream that would otherwise be sent throughout the workplace.

CARBON MONOXIDE

Carbon monoxide is a colourless, odourless, toxic, flammable gas which is slightly lighter than air. Carbon monoxide has a great affinity (200 times that of oxygen) for the haemoglobin red blood cells and will reduce the red blood cells available for oxygen uptake. This causes asphyxiation, leading to collapse and death. Because of the chemical interaction of carbon monoxide with haemoglobin red blood cells it is classed as a chemical asphixiant.

The earliest symptoms of exposure to carbon monoxide, especially from low level exposures, are often non-specific and readily confused with other illnesses, typically flu-like viral syndromes, depression, chronic fatigue syndrome, and migraine or other headaches. This often makes the diagnosis of carbon monoxide poisoning difficult. If suspected, the diagnosis can be confirmed by measurement of blood carboxyhemoglobin. Common problems encountered are difficulty with higher intellectual functions and short-term memory, dementia, irritability, gait disturbance, speech disturbances, parkinson-like syndromes, cortical blindness, and depression. Upon removal from exposure, the symptoms usually resolve themselves.

Carbon monoxide is produced as a by-product of incomplete combustion of carbon fuels, for example, fuels used in gas water heaters, compressors, pumps, dumper trucks or generators, it is a particular risk when the equipment is operated in poorly ventilated confined areas. Carbon monoxide emission from equipment in this way may mean workers are exposed, over time, to increasing levels.

Controls include ensuring that any work carried out in relation to gas appliances in premises is undertaken by a Gas Safe Registered engineer, competent in that area of work. The HSE strongly recommends the use of audible carbon monoxide (CO) alarms as a useful back-up precaution, but they must not be regarded as a substitute for proper installation and maintenance of gas appliances by a Gas Safe Registered engineer. Always make sure there is enough fresh air when using any internal combustion engine or gas appliance, for example, generators, pumps, petrol driven tools such as circular saws and where any gas welding is carried.

CEMENT

Cement is used extensively in the construction industry as part of the mix for mortar and concrete. It is mildly corrosive and can cause harm in the following ways:

- Skin contact - causing contact dermatitis. If it is trapped inside a worker's boot or glove then it can cause severe chemical burns.
- Eye contact - causing irritation and inflammation.
- Inhalation - causing irritation of the nose and throat. Possible long term respiratory problems.

The accompanying image shows severe burns a worker sustained from kneeling in wet cement for 3 hours; his right leg had to be amputated.

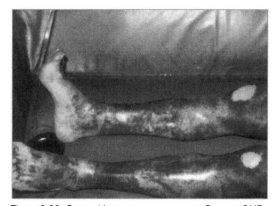

Figure 8-38: Cement burns.   Source: SHP.

Precautions include the correct use of gloves, protective overalls, boots and masks should be worn. Wash skin thoroughly after contact with cement; launder overalls which have become contaminated.

LEGIONELLA/LEGIONNAIRES' DISEASE

Legionella/Legionnaires' disease is a type of pneumonia caused by Legionella Pneumophila, a bacterium. The organism is ubiquitous in water and frequently present in water cooling systems and domestic hot water systems. Large workplace buildings are therefore susceptible to infected water systems, especially hotels and hospitals.

The organism is widespread in the environment, but needs certain conditions to multiply, for example, the presence of sludge, scale, algae, rust and organic material plus a temperature of 20-50°C. Transmission is from inhalation of the organism in contaminated aerosols. Smoking, age and alcohol may increase susceptibility. Symptoms are aching muscles, headaches and fever followed by a cough. Confusion, emotional disturbance and delirium may follow the acute phase. The fatality rate in the UK is about 12%.

The greatest risk areas are from showers used for bathing, air conditioning sprays, water cooling towers, fountains and recirculating water cooling systems.

The hazard can be controlled by proper design of water systems i.e. locating hot and cold water supply pipework separate from each other, avoiding the use of water storage tanks, use of plastic tanks instead of metal to avoid rust deposits and hot water being heated to 55-60°C. Regular use of biocides is necessary for cleaning open water systems, such as cooling towers. Showers should be designed to drain water completely after use, to avoid stagnant water retention.

LEPTOSPIRA

The bacteria Leptospira, spiral shaped bacteria, penetrates the skin and causes leptospirosis (Weil's Disease). Rodents represent the most important reservoir of infections, especially rats (also gerbils, voles, and field mice).

Other sources of infection are dogs, hedgehogs, foxes, pigs, and cattle. These animals are not necessarily ill, but carry leptospires in their kidneys and excrete it in their urine. Infection can be transmitted directly via direct contact with blood, tissues, organs or urine of one of the host animals or indirectly by contaminated environment. Infection enters through broken skin or mucous membrane. Symptoms vary but include flu-like illness, conjunctivitis, liver damage (including jaundice), kidney failure and meningitis. If untreated infection may be fatal.

Construction workers are most at risk when they work where rats prevail. This will include water and sewage work, demolition or refurbishment of old unoccupied buildings, and those working on sites adjoining rivers and other watercourses. The bacteria survival depends on protection from direct sunlight, so it survives well in water courses and ditches protected by vegetation.

Precautions include increasing exposed worker understanding of the risks, symptoms and the need to avoid eating, drinking or smoking without prior washing or using anti-bacterial wash on the hands first. These controls should be supported by measures to limit exposure of the skin to the bacteria; which includes covering cuts and the use of personal protective clothing. Cards are available for employees to show to a physician, if they develop flu like symptoms, to show they may be at risk. Early diagnosis, by blood analysis, is essential to prevent fatal symptoms developing.

SILICA

Inhalation of silica can result in silicosis, a fibrosis of the lung. *Silicosis* (also known as Grinder's disease and Potter's rot) is a form of occupational lung disease caused by inhalation of crystalline silica dust, and is marked by inflammation and scarring in forms of nodular lesions in the upper lobes of the lungs. Silicosis (especially the acute form) is characterised by shortness of breath, fever, and cyanosis (bluish skin). It may often be misdiagnosed as pulmonary oedema (fluid in the lungs), pneumonia, or tuberculosis.

Silica exists naturally as crystalline minerals. A common variety is quartz (tridymite, cristobalite). Industrially silica is used in the morphous (after heating) form, for example, fumed silica, and silica gel. In construction activities it may be encountered in stone work or work with quartz based materials, such as tiles.

Precautions include increasing exposed worker understanding of the risks, the use of appropriate local exhaust ventilation (LEV) and or respiratory protection equipment when using fumed silica or cutting stone or concrete materials.

FIBRES

Fibres include man-made mineral fibres, for example, extruded glass fibres, glass wools and ceramic fibres. They also include other fibres, like synthetic organic fibres made from gypsum and calcium carbonate.

These fibres are commonly used within the construction industry as insulation materials, used in roofs, walls and voids.

Exposure to these fibres must be controlled by the use of personal protective equipment, for example, suitable respiratory protective equipment, eye protection, gloves and long sleeved overalls.

HEPATITIS

See blood borne viruses earlier.

TETANUS

Tetanus is a life-threatening disease caused by toxins produced by the bacterium Clostridium tetani, which often enters and grows at the site of a cut or wound while working with soil or even from a bite from an animal.

There is greater risk of developing tetanus if the wound is deep or if it gets dirty with soil or manure, but even small wounds such as a prick from a thorn can allow enough bacteria to get into the body to cause tetanus.

Muscles in the jaw first become stiff, and then rigidly fixed (lockjaw). This can progress to other parts of the skeletal muscles causing the body to shape into a characteristic form called opisthotonos (behind tension) of the spine.

Figure 8-39: Tension of the spine.   *Source: Painting by Charles Bell.*

Prevention includes skin protection, such as gauntlet gloves and tough material leggings and boots. Medical attention is required for any contaminated deep cuts. Exposed workers can be vaccinated against tetanus; this should be done every 10 years or at the time of injury.

HYDROGEN SULPHIDE

Hydrogen sulphide (H_2S) is a colourless, highly flammable gas that is heavier than air. Hydrogen sulphide is very poisonous. It has the characteristic odour of rotten eggs, which can be detected at very low concentrations, typically 0.0005 parts per million (ppm). This is well below the threshold to causes harm; H_2S has an 8 hour exposure limit of 5ppm. The toxicity of H_2S is comparable with that of hydrogen cyanide, but H_2S can be detected in minute quantities compared with hydrogen cyanide. On inhalation H_2S forms a complex bond with essential maintenance cells preventing cellular repair and respiration. The human body produces small amounts of H_2S and has a tolerance to very small concentrations; low levels of H_2S may be tolerated indefinitely.

Early symptoms of low toxic exposure include eye irritation, a sore throat and cough, nausea, shortness of breath, and fluid in the lungs. Exposure in excess of 300 ppm leads to increased fluid in the lungs and ultimately death.

Hydrogen sulphide is produced by anaerobic (without oxygen) bacterial digestion of organic matter. The gas is present in gas released from land fill sites, excavations in soils rich in organic material, sewers and some well waters. Large quantities of H_2S are produced in oil refineries where it is used to produce the element sulphur, which is primarily used in fertilisers and the production of sulphuric acid.

Precautions include the early detection of the gas at low levels. Many personal safety gas detectors, such as those used by petrochemical and sewage workers, are set to alarm at 5 to 10 ppm and to go into high alarm at

15 ppm. Additional measures are the use of respiratory protection and the absence of ignition sources where the material is handled or may be found naturally.

Generation and control of dust on a construction site

CEMENT DUST

Cement dust is generated when handling the dry product in bags and when opening the bags in preparation for mixing. In addition, it may be generated during scabbling processes and when using cut off saws for cutting concrete, for example, curb stones or paving slabs.

Control of cement dust should be achieved by working in a way that avoids dusty methods of work. For example, scabbling, which is often carried out to ensure an adequate bond between successive concrete pours and the amount of scabbling can be reduced by larger pours.

The need to cut or break hardened concrete can be reduced by designing work so as to allow for tolerances, by not relying on perfect fit or cutting away to make things fit, by leaving positive gaps and specifying expanding grout, mastic or resilient materials as joint fillers.

Work should be carried out in such a way that minimises the amount of dust produced. Bags of cement should be opened with care and mixed carefully. Dry dusty materials like cement should be handled in a well-ventilated area. Workers must be provided with and wear clothing to protect their skin from cement and cement mixtures, for example:

- Gloves.
- Overalls with long sleeves and full-length trousers.
- Waterproof boots.

Clothing should be worn so as to avoid 'traps' for fresh mortar or concrete to fall in, i.e. with sleeves over the gloves and trouser legs over the boots - not tucked inside. If 'trapping' does happen, steps should be taken immediately to clean the contaminated skin and protective clothing with copious amounts of clean water.

Suitable respiratory protective equipment should be used if work in dusty conditions cannot be avoided. Suitable eye protection must be worn when conditions give rise to a risk of eye injury (for example, opening cement sacks, during mixing where splashing might occur).

WOOD DUST

Exposure to wood dust has long been associated with a variety of adverse health effects, including dermatitis, allergic respiratory effects, mucosal and non-allergic respiratory effects, and cancer. Contact with the irritant compounds in wood sap can cause dermatitis and other allergic reactions.

The respiratory effects of wood dust exposure include asthma, hypersensitivity pneumonitis (inflammation of the air sacks in the lungs), and chronic bronchitis.

The main construction activities likely to produce high dust levels are:

- Machining operations, particularly sawing, routing and turning.
- Sanding, by machine and by hand.
- Using compressed air lines to blow dust off wood products that have been worked on before spraying.

Controls will include the use of local exhaust ventilation, the use of respiratory protective equipment and the removal of dust deposits from flat surfaces at all levels especially at height. Compressed air should not be used to displace dust; instead a suitable vacuum system should be available for all cleaning tasks.

Health risks and controls associated with asbestos

HEALTH RISKS

Asbestos related diseases include pneumoconiosis, lung cancer and mesothelioma.

The term "pneumoconiosis" refers to a group of lung diseases caused by the inhalation and retention in the lungs of dusts. Pneumoconiosis derived from exposure to asbestos is statistically significant and incidence is often reported separately from other diseases in the group.

Asbestos fibres are a particular form of fibrous dust that readily become airborne when disturbed and may enter the lungs, where they cause fibrosis (scarring and thickening) of the lung tissue (asbestosis) or pleura (diffuse pleural thickening).

The pleura is a two-layered membrane that surrounds the lungs and lines the inside of the rib cage.

Figure 8-40: Asbestos label. *Source: Scaftag.*

Whilst asbestos fibres may have a direct effect on the lungs, some asbestos fibres inhaled into the lungs work their way out to the pleura and may cause fibrosis or scarring to develop there, which causing the pleura to thicken. These forms of pneumoconiosis typically take more than 10 years to develop.

The HSE reported that there were 429 deaths in 2011 where asbestosis is described as the underlying cause of death on the death certificate and there were 460 new cases of disablement benefit for diffuse pleural thickening in 2012.

"The annual number of new cases of asbestosis according to the Department of Work and Pensions (DWP) Industrial Injuries and Disablement Benefit (IIDB) scheme (which compensates workers for prescribed occupational diseases) has risen erratically since the early 1980s, with the trend strongly increasing since the early 1990s reaching the current level of 2125 in 2012. This is likely to be an underestimate of the total number of cases".

Figure 8-41: Annual incidence of asbestosis.   *Source: HSE.*

The HSE also reported that the trend in diffuse pleural thickening cases has increased over recent years, although this may due to the acceptance of claims under the IIDB scheme for unilateral (affecting only one lung) cases and other changes in data collection methods.

In addition, exposure to asbestos can lead to lung cancer and mesothelioma (cancer of the pleura). Mesothelioma is a type of cancer that affects the mesothelial cells. These cells cover the outer surface of most of our internal body organs, including the lungs and abdomen, forming a lining that is sometimes called the mesothelium. Cancer affecting the lining of the lungs is known as pleural mesothelioma and may arise out of exposure to asbestos. Lung cancers or mesotheliomas may not appear until 20 to 50 years after exposure.

The HSE reported that the annual number of mesothelioma deaths had increased since 1968, where annual recorded deaths were 153, reaching 2291 deaths in 2011. The expected number of deaths amongst males is predicted to increase to a peak of 2500 in the year 2016. The HSE also reported that there it was likely that there were around as many asbestos related lung cancer deaths in Great Britain annually as there are mesothelioma deaths. In the majority of cases mesothelioma is rapidly fatal following diagnosis so mesothelioma death statistics give a clear indication of the disease incidence.

Diagnosis for asbestos related diseases is generally made on the basis of clinical features, X-ray appearances or CT scan and a history of asbestos exposure. It is generally recognised that heavy asbestos exposures are required in order to produce clinically significant asbestosis within the lifetime of an individual. Current trends of identified cases of asbestosis therefore still largely reflect the results of heavy exposures in the past. This may not reflect the occurrence of mesothelioma as it is asserted that it could result from a single fibre, though risks are greater if the worker is exposed to large amounts of asbestos over a period of time. Cancer Research UK reported that approximately 1 in 10 people exposed to asbestos develop mesothelioma in the pleural membranes.

The HSE identified that the ten male occupations found to have the highest risk of asbestos related diseases were carpenters, plumbers, electricians, labourers in other construction trades, metal plate workers, pipe fitters, construction operatives, managers in construction, construction trades and energy plant operatives.

CONTROLS

If asbestos containing materials are in good condition they may be left in place and their condition monitored and managed.

- The presence of asbestos must be identified and must be labelled.
- An assessment must be done of work which exposes employees to asbestos.
- Training is mandatory for those that may be exposed to asbestos fibres at work, including maintenance workers, cable installers or others that may come into contact with or disturb asbestos.
- A written plan of work is required for work with asbestos.

The Control of Asbestos Regulations (CAR) 2012 Regulation 3 requires that employers who work with asbestos must be licensed unless the circumstances are that:

(a) The exposure of employees to asbestos is sporadic and of low intensity.

(b) It is clear from the risk assessment that the exposure of any employee to asbestos will not exceed the control limit.

(c) The work involves:

    (i) Short, non-continuous maintenance activities.

    (ii) Removal of materials in which the asbestos fibres are firmly linked in a matrix.

    (iii) Encapsulation or sealing of asbestos-containing materials which are in good condition.

    (iv) Air monitoring and control, and the collection and analysis of samples to ascertain whether a specific material contains asbestos.

- Work with asbestos other than that listed previously must be notified to the employer's enforcing authority.
- Exposure must be prevented or reduced by controls.
- Controls must be used and maintained.

■ The employer is responsible for the cleaning of personal protective equipment and clothing.

Duty to manage asbestos

The duty to manage asbestos is covered by Regulation 4 of the Control of Asbestos Regulations (CAR) 2012. In many cases, the duty holder is the person or organisation that has clear responsibility for the maintenance or repair of non-domestic premises through an explicit agreement such as a tenancy agreement or contract. Where there are domestic premises such as flats the duty holder will be responsible for common areas such as corridors or walkways.

The duty holder has the responsibility to:

■ Take reasonable steps to find out if there are materials containing asbestos in non-domestic premises and if so, amount, location and condition.

■ Presume materials contain asbestos unless there is strong evidence that they do not.

■ Record the location and condition of the asbestos containing materials or materials which are presumed to contain asbestos.

■ Assess the risk of anyone being exposed to fibres from the materials identified.

■ Prepare a plan that sets out in detail how the risks from these materials will be managed.

■ Take the necessary steps to put the plan into action.

■ Periodically review and monitor the plan.

■ Provide information on the location and condition of the materials to anyone who is liable to work on or disturb them.

There is also a requirement on anyone to co-operate as far as is necessary to allow the duty holder to comply with the requirements shown previously.

ASBESTOS IDENTIFICATION

There are three main types of asbestos, which is a naturally occurring mineral. It can be amphibole asbestos which includes crocidolite (blue) and amosite (brown) asbestos, or serpentine asbestos which is chrysotile (white) asbestos.

All three of these main types have been used in Great Britain at some time.

Types of survey

Management survey

This is the standard survey used to identify the presence and extent of any asbestos containing materials (ACMs) in the building which could be damaged or disturbed during normal occupancy, including foreseeable maintenance and installation, and to assess their condition.

A management survey might involve minor intrusive work and some disturbance which will vary between premises and depend on what is reasonably practicable for individual properties.

Management surveys can involve a combination of sampling to confirm asbestos is present or presuming asbestos to be present.

Refurbishment and demolition surveys

A refurbishment and demolition survey will be needed before any work of this type is carried out. This survey will be used to locate and describe all ACMs in the area where the work will take place or in the whole building if demolition is planned. This type of survey is fully intrusive and involves destructive inspection to gain access to all areas, including those that may be difficult to reach. A refurbishment and demolition survey may also be required in other circumstances, for example, when more intrusive maintenance and repair work will be carried out or for plant removal or dismantling.

Who can undertake them

An independent expert/specialist organisation must:

■ Have adequate training and be experienced in survey work.

■ Able to demonstrate independence, impartiality and integrity.

■ Have an adequate quality management system.

■ Carry out any asbestos survey work in accordance with recommended HSE guidance HSG264 "Asbestos: The survey".

HSG264 states that organisations offering an asbestos survey service should be able to demonstrate their competence by holding United Kingdom Accreditation Service (UKAS) accreditation to ISO/IEC 17020 and individuals to ISO/IEC 17024.

Competence for assessment

The HSE guidance - "Work with materials containing asbestos" states:

"Whoever carries out the assessment should:

Have adequate knowledge, competence, training and expertise in understanding the risks from asbestos and be able to make informed decisions about the risks and precautions that are needed.

> *Know how the work activity may disturb asbestos; be familiar with the asbestos regulations and understand the requirements of the ACOP (Approved Code of Practice).*
>
> *Have the ability and the authority to collate all the necessary, relevant information.*
>
> *Be able to assess other non-asbestos risks on site".*

Figure 8-42: Work with materials containing asbestos.   *Source: HSE guidance.*

Where it can be located

Asbestos has a number of valuable properties; these include physical strength, resistance to chemicals, non-combustibility and good thermal and electrical insulation. Asbestos is commonly mixed with other materials and is typically used in the following applications:

- As yarn or cloth - for protective clothing, etc.
- Insulation boards - for protection of buildings against fire.
- Asbestos cement products - for construction of buildings and pipes.
- Asbestos resins - for clutch faces and brake linings.
- Various other applications - in gaskets, filters, floor tiles and decorative plasterwork in old buildings.
- Asbestos spraying for thermal and acoustic insulation of buildings and plant, and for fire resistance in structural steelwork, is no longer carried out, although it is encountered as a problem when being removed.
- Atmospheric contamination of workplace and neighbourhoods may occur during building work involving asbestos products or during work to repair or remove such products. Slow disintegration of materials containing asbestos may also cause contamination. There is a hazard whenever airborne fibres are released.

It should be noted that uses of sprayed coating ceased in 1974 and asbestos lagging is unlikely to be found in buildings constructed after 1975.

PROCEDURE FOR THE DISCOVERY OF ASBESTOS DURING CONSTRUCTION ACTIVITY

Employers must have prepared procedures which can be put into effect in the case an incident or emergency that could put people at risk should occur. Information and instruction should be made available to emergency services attending the incident so that they can adequately protect themselves.

REQUIREMENTS IF PERSONS ARE ACCIDENTALLY EXPOSED TO ASBESTOS MATERIALS

Regulation 15 of the Control of Asbestos Regulations (CAR) 2012 requires employers to have arrangements in place to deal with accidents, incidents and emergencies.

These procedures must include means of raising the alarm and means of evacuation. People not wearing personal protective equipment (PPE) must leave the work area. If people have been contaminated then arrangements must include means of decontaminating. (Contaminated PPE should be treated as contaminated waste). The contaminated area must be cleaned thoroughly by employees wearing PPE. Supervisors and managers must make sure that the work has been carried out.

Figure 8-43: Asbestos cement sheets. *Source: www.risk-it.co.uk.*

Figure 8-44: Asbestos pipe lagging. *Source: www.risk-it.co.uk.*

REQUIREMENTS FOR REMOVAL

Non Licensed Work

Most asbestos work must be undertaken by a licensed contractor but any decision on whether particular work is licensable is based on the risk. To be exempt from needing a licence the work must be:

- Sporadic and low intensity.
- Carried out in such a way that the exposure of workers to asbestos will not exceed the legal control limit of 0.1 asbestos fibres per cubic centimetre of air (0.1 f/cm3).
- A short non-continuous maintenance task.
- A removal task, where the ACMs are in reasonable condition and are not being deliberately broken up.
- A task where the ACMs are in good condition and are being sealed or encapsulated.

- An air monitoring and control task to check fibre concentrations in the air, or it's the collection and analysis of asbestos samples to confirm the presence of asbestos in a material.

Notifiable Non Licensed Work

From April 2012, some non-licensed work, where the risk of fibre release is greater, is subject to three additional requirements:

1) Notification of work.
2) Medical examinations.
3) Record keeping (the requirement for medical examinations does not come into force until April 2015).

This work is known as notifiable non-licensed work (NNLW).

To decide if the work is NNLW, employers will need to consider the type of work that will be carried out, the type of material to be worked on and its condition:

- Decide what type of work will be done.
- Consider the asbestos type.
- Consider the material's condition.

Licensed

Certain types of work with ACMs can only be done by those who have been issued with a licence by HSE. This is work which meets the definition of 'licensable work with asbestos' in regulation 2(1). That is work:

- Where worker exposure to asbestos is not sporadic and of low intensity.
- Where the risk assessment cannot clearly demonstrate that the control limit (0.1 f/cm3 airborne fibres averaged over a four-hour period) will not be exceeded.
- On asbestos coating (surface coatings which contain asbestos for fire protection, heat insulation or sound insulation but not including textured decorative coatings)
- On asbestos insulation or AIB where the risk assessment demonstrates that the work is not sporadic and of low intensity, the control limit will be exceeded and it is not short duration work.

Short duration means the total time spent by all workers working with these materials does not exceed two hours in a seven-day period, including time spent setting up, cleaning and clearing up, and no one person works for more than one hour in a seven-day period.

If licensable work is to be carried out then the appropriate enforcing authority must be notified of details of the proposed work. Employers must carry out a risk assessment of the work. This assessment must be kept at the place where work is being carried out. For licensable work, the plan of work *(see following section)* should be site specific and contain the following information:

- The scope of work as identified in the risk assessment.
- Details of hygiene facilities, transit route, vacuum cleaners, air monitoring, protective clothing, respiratory protection equipment (RPE), and communication between the inside and outside of the enclosure.
- Use of barriers and signs, location of enclosures and airlocks, location of skips, negative pressure units, cleaning and clearance certification, emergency procedures.

A decision flow chart is available from the HSE at www.hse.gov.uk/asbestos/essentials/index.htm.

Notification and plan of work

If carrying out licensable work, it must be notified to the appropriate enforcing authority 14 days in writing before work commences (the authority may allow a shorter period in an emergency if there is a serious risk to health). For any work involving asbestos, the employer must draw up a written plan of work. The plan of work must include the following information:

- Nature and duration of the work.
- Number of persons involved.
- Address and location of the work.
- Methods used to prevent or reduce exposure.
- Type of equipment used to protect those carrying out the work and those present or near the worksite.

Work must not take place unless a copy of the plan is readily available on site.

RESPIRATORY EQUIPMENT

If, despite other control measures an employee's exposure is likely to exceed the control limit or exceed 0.6f/cm3 peak level measured over ten minutes, the employer must provide suitable RPE.

RPE must be matched to:

- The exposure concentrations (expected or measured).
- The job.
- The wearer.
- Factors related to the working environment.

Suitable RPE means:

- It provides adequate protection (i.e. reduces the wearer's exposure to asbestos fibres as low as is reasonably practicable, and anyway to below the control limits) during the job in hand and in the specified working environment (for example, confined spaces).
- It provides clean air and the flow rate during the whole wear period at least conforms to the minimum recommended by the manufacturer.
- The face piece fits the wearer correctly.
- It is properly maintained.
- The chosen equipment does not introduce additional hazards that may put the wearer's health and safety at risk.

PROTECTIVE CLOTHING

Protective clothing must be adequate and suitable. Cuffs, ankles and hoods should be elasticated and provide a tight fit at the face and neck. Pockets or other attachments which could trap dust should be avoided. Where disposable overalls are used they should be Type 5 (under BS EN ISO 13982-1).

TRAINING

Asbestos awareness training should be given to all employees who could foreseeably be exposed to asbestos. In particular, training should be given to employees whose work is likely to disturb the fabric of the building. The training should include the following topics:

- The properties of asbestos and its effects on health.
- The types, uses and likely occurrence of asbestos.
- Emergency procedures.
- How to avoid the risks from asbestos.

AIR MONITORING

Air testing is required for a number of reasons, such as to certify clearance after asbestos has been removed (a regulatory requirement in most cases), to ensure that leaks do not occur during asbestos treatment or removal and to provide reassurance that nobody has been placed at risk. Personal air monitoring is also necessary to ensure that RPE is providing the appropriate level of protection. Records must be kept for 5 years or, where employees are under health surveillance, for 40 years.

MEDICAL SURVEILLANCE

Regulation 22 of the Control of Asbestos Regulations (CAR) 2012 requires all employers to ensure that all employees who are exposed to asbestos are under adequate health surveillance.

For work with asbestos, which is not licensable work with asbestos, and is not exempted by regulation 3(2), the requirements in paragraphs (1)(a) to (c) apply and:

(a) a medical examination in accordance with paragraph (1)(c) and (2)(a) must take place on or before 30 April 2015;

(b) on or after 1 May 2015, a medical examination in accordance with paragraph (1)(c) and (2)(a) must take place not more than 3 years before the beginning of such exposure; and

(c) a periodic medical examination in accordance with paragraph (1)(c) and (2)(b) must take place at intervals of at least once every 3 years, or such shorter time as the relevant doctor may require while such exposure continues.

The employer must keep health records for a minimum of 40 years after the last entry made in it. It is not a medical confidential record. It contains job exposure information and dates of previous medical examinations.

REQUIREMENTS FOR DISPOSAL

Licensed carrier

Health and Safety Executive (HSE) requirements on the licensed contractor has means that each company must have in place an up to date standard operating procedure manual, which should contain all of the details relating to the safe removal and disposal of asbestos. This manual must also be sent to the local HSE inspector and constantly updated to reflect changes in guidance and legislation. Waste carriers licence involves a simple application and anyone looking to transport waste asbestos will need to be a Registered Waste Carrier.

Notification

Employers must notify the appropriate enforcing authority 14 days before carrying out any licensable work. This can be done on form FOD ASB5.

Licensed disposal site

Any facility looking to accept waste asbestos has to apply to the Environment Agency for a site licence. This will set out the range and volumes of wastes that can be accepted on the site, the site control and management systems, engineering and infrastructure, manning and qualification requirements and reporting and monitoring regimes.

8.6 - Safe handling and storage of waste

Basic environmental issues relating to waste disposal and effluent

Environmental pollution is a major issue today with the industrialised countries of the world concerned about the long-term effects on Earth's resources and on plant, animal and human life. Major concerns on health are often blamed on pollution and there are many pressure groups that focus on environmental issues, particularly pollution.

Neighbours of construction sites are affected by air pollutants, including those generated as By-products of combustion, for example, from diesel and petrol compressors and associated noise nuisance from the use of heavy machinery and other activities such as piling. Plant failure and accidents can lead to abnormal releases following higher than expected temperatures and pressures leading to uncontrolled venting to the environment. Lack of control when filling tankers with waste effluent can lead to losses through overfilling or bad coupling, either of which could lead to a release to the environment.

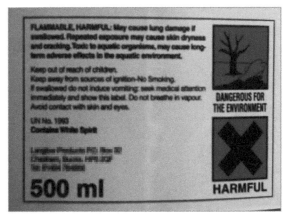

Figure 8-45: Hazard label - environment.   *Source: RMS.*

Figure 8-46: Environmental hazard.   *Source: RMS.*

PERSONAL PROTECTIVE EQUIPMENT

The hazards that might be encountered during the collection, storage and disposal of waste are:

- Chemicals.
- Biological agents.
- Gases, vapours and fumes.
- Dusts.
- Oil, grease.

- Paint, solvents.
- Asbestos.
- Flammable, explosive substances.
- Radioactive materials.

When selecting suitable personal protective equipment it is essential that these issues are considered.

SEPARATE STORAGE OF INCOMPATIBLE WASTE STREAMS

In addition to general safe storage practices, segregated storage of incompatible materials is a must. As a minimum, wastes should be segregated according to similar hazards, such as flammability, corrosively, sensitivity to water or air, and toxicity.

Figure 8-47: Measures to control pollution.   *Source: RMS.*

Figure 8-48: Measures to control pollution.   *Source: RMS.*

When establishing a storage scheme, the main consideration should be the flammability characteristics of the material. If the material will contribute significantly to a fire (i.e. oxidisers) it should be isolated from the flammables. If a fire were to occur, the fire would be more intense and may spread more quickly and would require far more water to be used to extinguish it. The response to the larger fire would produce extra run-off of contaminated water to be disposed of environmentally safely, than would have been the case if segregation had been done.

Consider the toxicity of the material, with particular attention paid to regulated materials. In some cases, this may mean that certain wastes will be isolated within a storage area, for instance, a material that is an extreme poison but is also flammable, should be locked away in the flammable storage area to protect it against accidental release.

There will always be some chemicals that will not fit singularly into one category or another, but with careful consideration of the hazards involved most of these cases can be handled in an appropriate manner. For the safety of all personnel and to protect the integrity of the facilities, hazardous materials must be segregated.

PRINCIPLES OF PROTECTION AGAINST ACCIDENTAL RELEASE

Leaking and spillage can result from a number of sources: faulty valves or flanges to pipework; containers such as tins, drums or bags; loss from tanks (typically one tonne) of solids and liquids; road or rail freight containers; cargo vessels etc. Typical techniques to contain spillage include: curbed areas for drum storage, tanker loading of liquids, bunded areas to contain sited tanks and drip trays at piped systems and drum decanting points.

Portable tanks are available with two skins (a tank within a tank) to contain any leaks from the internal tank. They are often used where there is a need for portability such as with storing fuels on construction sites. Similarly, cargo vessels may have double skinned tanks or hulls.

Bunding

A bund, sometimes called a secondary containment system, often consists of an area contained by a rectangular wall built upon a concrete slab. The bund floor and walls should be treated to be impervious to any spillage or water that may be present. Storage tanks are located within this confined area. The bund must provide storage of at least 110% of the tank's maximum capacity. If more than one tank is stored, the bund system must be capable of storing 110% of the volume of the biggest of the tank's capacity, or 25% of the total capacity of all the tanks within the bund, whichever is the greater.

It is necessary to consider the potential escape of any spillage beyond the bund area in the event of the tank developing a hole (known as jetting).

The risk of this can be minimised by:

- Keeping the primary container as low as possible.
- Increasing the height of the bund wall.
- Leaving sufficient space between the tank and bund walls.
- Not sitting one tank above another.
- Providing screens or curtains.
- Ensure there is no direct uncontrolled outlet connecting the bund to any drain, sewer, watercourse, yard or unmade ground.

Ideally, pipework should not pass through the bund wall. If unavoidable, the pipe should be sealed into the bund with a material that is resistant to attack by the substance stored, to ensure the bund remains leak-proof.

See also Element 2 - Construction site hazards and risk control, '2.2 - Appropriate general site control measures'.

Sample assessment questions

1. Insulation board tiles that contain asbestos are to be removed from the ceiling of a store room located within a primary school.

   Outline factors which should be taken into consideration when planning the work. (8)

2. Silica can be found in various materials used in construction, and exposure to silica dust can lead to chronic health effects such as silicosis.

   (a) **Give** the meaning of the term 'workplace exposure limit'. (2)

   (b) **Outline** control measures that could be considered to control levels of silica dust in the workplace. (6)

3. **Identify FOUR** hazardous substances prevalent to the construction industry **AND give** the associated health risk for **EACH**. (8)

Please refer to back of assessment section for answers.

Physical and psychological health - hazards and risk control

Learning outcomes

On completion of this element, candidates should be able to demonstrate understanding of the content through the application of knowledge to familiar and unfamiliar situations. In particular they should be able to:

9.1   Outline the health effects associated with exposure to noise and appropriate control measures.

9.2   Outline the health effects associated with exposure to vibration and appropriate control measures.

9.3   Outline the health effects associated with ionising and non-ionising radiation and the appropriate control measures.

9.4   Outline the causes and effects of stress at work and appropriate control measures.

Content

Sources of reference

Controlling Noise at Work, The Control of Noise at Work Regulations, Guidance on Regulations, second edition 2005, L108, HSE Books, ISBN 978-0-7176-6164-4

Essentials of Health and Safety at Work, HSE Books, ISBN 978-0-7176-6179-4

Health and Safety Toolbox, online resource, HSE www.hse.gov.uk/toolbox/index.htm

Hand-arm vibration, Control of Vibration at Work regulations 2005, Guidance on Regulations, L140, HSE Books, ISBN 978-0-7176-6125-1

HSE Stress Management Standards www.hse.gov.uk/stress/standards

Lighting at work, HSG38, HSE Books, ISBN 978-0-7176-1232-1

Managing the causes of work-related stress; A step by step approach to using the management standards, HSG218, second edition 2007, HSE Books, ISBN 978-0-7176-6273-9

Personal Protective Equipment at Work (second edition), Personal Protective Equipment at Work Regulations 1992 (as amended), Guidance on Regulations, HSE Books, ISBN 978-0-7176-6139-3

Radon in the workplace www.hse.gov.uk/radiation/ionising/radon.htm#testingradon

Safe use of work equipment, Provision and Use of Work Equipment Regulations 1998, ACOP and guidance, L22, HSE Books, ISBN 978-0-7176-6295-1

Upper Limb Disorders in the Workplace - A Guide, second edition 2002, HSG60, HSE Books, ISBN 978-0-7176-1978-8

Whole-body vibration; The Control of Vibration at Work Regulations 2005, Guidance on Regulations, L141, HSE Books, ISBN 978-0-7176-6126-8

Workplace health, safety and welfare, Workplace (Health, Safety and Welfare) Regulations 1992. ACOP and guidance, L24, HSE Books, ISBN 978-0-7176-6583-9

Work with display screen equipment, Guidance, L26, HSE Books, ISBN 978-0-7176-2582-6

Relevant statutory provisions

Control of Noise at Work Regulations (CNWR) 2005

Control of Vibration at Work Regulations (CVWR) 2005

Construction (Design and Management) Regulations (CDM) 2007

Health and Safety (Display Screen Equipment) Regulations (DSE) 1992

Ionising Radiations Regulations (IRR) 1999

Personal Protective Equipment at Work Regulations (PPER) 1992

Provision and Use of Work Equipment Regulations (PUWER) 1998

Physical Agents (Artificial Optical Radiation) Directive (2006/25/EC)

9.1 - Noise

Physical and psychological effects on hearing of exposure to noise

The ear senses **sound**, which is transmitted in the form of pressure waves travelling through a substance, for example, air, water, metals etc. Unwanted sound is generally known as **noise**.

The ear has 3 basic regions **see figure ref 9-1**:

a) The **outer** ear channels the sound pressure waves through to the eardrum.

b) In the **middle** ear, the vibrations of the eardrum are transmitted through three small bones (hammer, anvil and stirrup) to the inner ear.

c) The cochlea in the **inner** ear is filled with fluid and contains tiny hairs (nerves) which respond to the sound. Signals are then sent to the brain via the acoustic nerve.

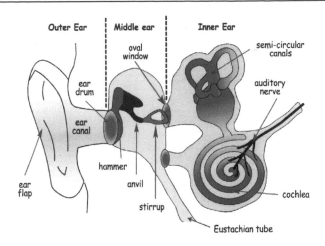

Figure 9-1: Inner ear diagram.   Source: www.echalk.co.uk.

PHYSICAL EFFECTS

Excessive noise over long periods of time can cause damage to the hairs (nerves) in the cochlea of the ear. This results in **noise induced hearing loss (deafness)**, which can be of a temporary or permanent nature. Also, a single high pressure event can damage the ear by dislocation of a bone or rupturing the ear drum. It has been shown that high levels of noise can cause, or increase the onset of, **tinnitus** ('ringing in the ears').

PSYCHOLOGICAL EFFECTS

Noise is often linked with adverse psychological effects such as stress, sleep disturbance or aggressive behaviour, and is frequently cited as the cause of friction between workers, particularly in a noisy office environment where there is a need for some individuals to concentrate on complex issues but they find this difficult or impossible because of background noise levels.

The meaning of common sound measurement terms

SOUND POWER AND PRESSURE

For noise to occur power must be available. It is the sound power of a source (measured in Watts) which causes the sound pressure (measured in Pascals) to occur at a specific point.

INTENSITY AND FREQUENCY

The amplitude of a sound wave represents the intensity of the sound pressure. When measuring the **amplitude** of sound there are two main parameters of interest **as shown in figure ref 9-2**. One is related to the energy in the sound pressure wave and is known as the 'root mean square' (RMS) value, and the other is the 'peak' level. We use the rms sound pressure for the majority of noise measurements, apart from some impulsive types of noise when the peak value is also measured.

Sound waves travel through air at the **'speed of sound'** which is approximately equal to 344 m/s.

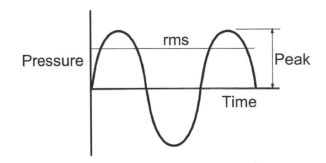

Figure 9-2: Rms and peak levels of a sound wave. *Source: RMS.*

A sound can have a **'frequency'** or **'pitch'**, which is measured in cycles per second (Hz).

THE DECIBEL SCALE

The ear can detect pressures over a very wide range, from 20 µPa to 20 Pa (Pascals). To help deal with this wide range, the **deciBel (dB)** is used to measure noise. A decibel is a unit of sound pressure (intensity) measured on a logarithmic scale from a base level taken to be the threshold of hearing (0dB). Typical noise levels include:

Source	dB	Source	dB
Night club	110	Radio in average room	70
Smoke detector at 1 metre	105	Library	30
Machine Shop	90	Threshold of hearing	0

Figure 9-3: Typical noise levels.   *Source: RMS.*

A problem with decibels is that they are based on a logarithmic scale and cannot be added together in the conventional way, for example:

- 2 dB + 2 dB = 5 dB (deciBel Arithmetic).
- 85 dB + 85 dB = 88 dB (deciBel Arithmetic).

Weighting scales - the terms dB(A) and dB(C)

The human ear can hear sound over a range of frequencies, from 20 Hz up to approximately 20,000 Hz (20 kHz). However, the ear does not hear the same at all frequencies; it naturally reduces (attenuates) low frequencies and very high frequencies to the range of speech. To take account of the response of the human ear sound level meters use weighting scales or filters. The most widely used sound level filter is the A scale. Using this filter, the sound level meter is thus less sensitive to very high and very low frequencies. Measurements made on this scale are expressed as dB(A) or referred to as 'A weighted'. The majority of measurements are made in terms of dB(A), although there are other weightings that are used in some circumstances. One of these is the C scale, which is used to assess the acoustic emissions of machines, in the selection of hearing protectors and analysis of environmental noise. The C scale is used to determine peak sound pressure levels and is particularly useful for impact or explosive noises. It has a broader spectrum than that of the A weighted scale and is more accurate at higher levels of noise. Measurements made on this scale are expressed as dB(C). There is also a (rarely used) B weighting scale, intermediate between A and C.

The range of frequencies that we encounter is often divided into **Octave Bands**. A noise can be measured in each octave band and these levels can be used when assessing the attenuation of hearing protectors, or when diagnosing noise problems.

Other noise units

In most situations the noise level varies with time. When measuring noise we need to determine the average, or 'equivalent continuous level', over a period of time. This is known as the **Leq**. Not all noise meters include a **Leq** function. Other noise units commonly encountered are shown in the following list:

L_{eq} the average, or 'equivalent continuous level'.

$L_{EP,d}$ daily personal exposure level, dB(A). This is equivalent to the L_{eq} over an 8-hour working day. The $L_{EP,d}$ is directly related to the risk of hearing damage.

L_{peak} peak pressure - pascals or dB(C). This is the peak level of the sound pressure wave with no time constant applied. For noise at work measurements the peak level should be C weighted.

The need for assessment of exposure

Employers have a duty under the Control of Noise at Work Regulations (CNWR) 2005 to reduce the risk of hearing damage to their employees by controlling exposure to noise. There is a further requirement that the employer obtain an adequate noise assessment, which will enable compliance with duties to control noise exposure. This will also help the employer when providing suitable hearing protection, marking out ear protection zones and giving information, instruction and training to employees.

The assessment should establish which employees are at risk of hearing damage, and the level of risk. It will also identify sources of noise that particularly contribute to the noise level employees are exposed to for example, equipment and specific activities. This will enable analysis of the options to control the noise at source or by other means. Re-assessment should be carried out after action to control exposure, or after a reasonable time, to establish the effectiveness of the controls.

In conducting the assessment the employer should assess the level of noise the workers are exposed to by:

- Observation.
- Reference to information on expected levels for work conditions and equipment.
- If necessary by measurement of the level of noise to which their employees may be exposed.

It is not always necessary to carry out measurements of noise exposure as part of the assessment; an estimate of noise levels may be enough to decide that controls are required. The Health and Safety Executive (HSE) suggest estimation by observation may be sufficient to indicate there is a noise problem. This is where the assessor determines how easy it is for two people to hold a conversation at a distance from each other, by using the 'one and two metre rule'.

Two metre rule: If the conversation is difficult (need to raise the voice or repeat words) at a distance of two metres apart the noise level is likely to be above 85 dB.

One metre rule: If the conversation is difficult (need to raise the voice or repeat words) at a distance of one metre apart the noise level is likely to be above 90 dB.

Similarly, it may be possible to determine if there is a potential noise problem by considering expected levels of noise for work conditions and equipment. This may be done by considering noise data provided by the manufacturer or alternatively the HSE provides the table *as shown in figure ref 9-4* to help indicate expected noise levels.

If it is necessary to be more certain whether noise exposure levels exceed the action or limit values, measurements of actual noise levels may be preferred.

Process	Work	Noise level
Working with concrete: chipping, drilling, floor finishing, grinding etc	Typical	85-90 dB
Labouring	General work	84 dB
	Shuttering	91 dB
	Shovelling hardcore	94 dB
	Concrete pour	97 dB
	Digging/scabbling	100 dB
Driving machines or vehicles	Typical	85-90 dB
Carpentry	Typical	92 dB
Angle grinding/cutting	Typical	90-100 dB
Piling	Machine operator	85 dB
	Piling worker	100 dB

Figure 9-4: Typical noise levels for a range of construction activities.   *Source: HSE.*

A detailed assessment should include consideration of:

- Level, type and duration of exposure, including any exposure to peak sound pressure.
- Effects of exposure to *noise* on employees or groups of employees whose health is at particular risk from such exposure.
- So far as is practicable, any effects on the health and safety of employees resulting from the interaction between noise and the use of toxic substances at *work*, or between *noise* and vibration.
- Indirect effects on the health and safety of employees resulting from the interaction between noise and audible warning signals or other sounds that need to be audible in order to reduce risk at *work*.
- Information provided by the manufacturers of *work* equipment.
- Availability of alternative equipment designed to reduce the emission of *noise*.
- Any extension of exposure to noise at the workplace beyond normal *working* hours, including exposure in rest facilities supervised by the employer.
- Appropriate information obtained following health surveillance, including, where possible, published information.
- Availability of personal hearing protectors with adequate attenuation characteristics.

Employees or their representatives must be consulted and significant findings and measures taken or planned to comply with the regulations have to be recorded.

ACTION AND LIMIT VALUES

Regulation 2 of the CNWR 2005 sets out the definition of 'daily average noise exposure' as the time weighted average of the noise to which a worker is exposed over an 8 hour working day, taking account of levels of noise and duration of exposure and including impulsive noises. Weekly noise exposure means the average of daily noise exposures over a week and normalised to five working days.

	Lower exposure action values	Upper exposure action values	Exposure limit values
Daily or weekly personal noise exposure (A-weighted).	80 dB	85 dB	87 dB
Peak sound pressure (C-weighted).	135 dB	137 dB	140 dB

Figure 9-5: Noise exposure values.   *Source: CNWR 2005.*

Under *Regulation 4 of CNWR 2005* if the exposure of the employee to noise in the workplace varies greatly the employer can choose to use weekly noise exposure instead of daily noise exposure in determining if values or limits are exceeded. The exposure can take into account personal hearing protection provided to the employee.

Lower exposure action values

Where an employee is likely to be exposed to noise at or above the lower exposure action values, the daily or weekly exposure of 80 dB(A) or a peak sound pressure level of 135 dB(C), the employer must make hearing protection available upon request and provide the employees and their representatives with suitable and sufficient information, instruction and training.

This shall include:

■ Nature of risks from exposure to noise.
■ Organisational and technical measures taken in order to comply.
■ Exposure limit values and upper and lower exposure action values.
■ Significant findings of the risk assessment, including any measurements taken, with an explanation of those findings.
■ Availability and provision of personal hearing protectors and their correct use.
■ Why and how to detect and report signs of hearing damage.
■ Entitlement to health surveillance.
■ Safe working practices to minimise exposure to noise.
■ The collective results of any health surveillance in a form calculated to prevent those results from being identified as relating to a particular person.

Figure 9-6: Noise hazard sign.   *Source: RMS.*

Upper exposure action values

Where the noise exposure of an employee is likely to be at or above the upper exposure action values, the daily or weekly exposure of 85 dB(A) or a peak sound pressure level of 137 dB(C), the employer shall:

Figure 9-7: Mandatory hearing protection sign. *Source: Stocksigns.*

■ Provide employees with hearing protection.
■ Ensure that the area is designated a hearing protection zone, fitted with mandatory hearing protection signs.
■ Ensure access to the area is restricted where practicable.
■ So far as reasonably practicable, ensure those employees entering the area wear hearing protection.

Exposure limit values

The employer must ensure that employees are not exposed to noise above an exposure limit value, the daily or weekly exposure of 87 dB(A) or a peak sound pressure level of 140 dB(C). If an exposure limit value is exceeded the employer must immediately:

■ Reduce exposure below the limit value.
■ Identify the reason for the limit value being exceeded.
■ Modify the organisational and technical measures to prevent a reoccurrence.

Basic noise control measures

Requirements for noise control set out in Regulation 6 of CNWR 2005 follow the general principles of prevention set out in the Management of Health and Safety at Work Regulations (MHSWR) 1999.

Employers must ensure that risk from the exposure of their employees to noise is either eliminated at source or, where this is not reasonably practicable, reduced to as low as is reasonably practicable.

Consideration should be made to:

■ Other ***working*** methods which reduce exposure to noise.
■ Choice of appropriate ***work*** equipment emitting the least possible ***noise***, taking account of the ***work*** to be done.
■ Design and layout of workplaces, ***work*** stations and rest facilities.
■ Suitable and sufficient information and training for employees, such that ***work*** equipment may be used correctly, in order to minimise their exposure to ***noise***.
■ Reduction of ***noise*** by technical means.
■ Appropriate maintenance programmes for ***work*** equipment, the workplace and workplace systems.
■ Limitation of the duration and intensity of exposure to ***noise***.
■ Appropriate ***work*** schedules with adequate rest periods.

The employer has to take care that noise levels in rest facilities are suitable for their purpose. The employer must adapt measures provided to suit a group or individual employee whose health is likely to be of particular risk from exposure to noise at work. Employees or their representatives must be consulted on the measures used. Noise can be controlled at different points in the following 'chain':

■ The source (for example, a noisy machine).
■ The path (for example, through the air).
■ The receiver (for example, the operator of a machine).

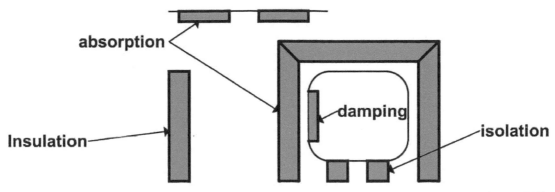

Figure 9-8: Basic layout of the main control methods.   *Source: RMS.*

The main methods of noise control are shown in the following list:

Isolation Positioning an absorbent element (for example, rubber mount etc.) in the path of vibration can isolate a noise radiating area from a vibration input.

Absorption When noise passes through porous materials (for example, foam, mineral, wool etc.) some of its energy is absorbed.

Insulation Imposing a barrier (for example, a brick wall, lead sheet etc.) between the noise source and the receivers will provide noise insulation.

Damping Mechanical vibration can be converted into heat by damping materials (for example, metal/plastic/metal panels).

Silencing Pipes/boxes can be designed to reduce air/gas noise (for example, engine exhaust silencers, duct silencers, etc.).

Other specialist control methods (***not*** examinable):

- **Force reduction** - reduce impacts by using rubber pads or lower drop heights.
- **Air exhaust and jet silencers** - proprietary silencers can be used.
- **Active** - equal but opposite phase noise can cancel a problem noise.

In addition to controlling the amplitude of noise the **exposure level** can be reduced by minimising the amount of time an employee is exposed to noise, for example, by job rotation.

Increasing the distance between noisy equipment and a work location can reduce the noise to which an employee is exposed.

Figure 9-9: Silenced diesel welder.   *Source: Speedy Hire Plc.*

When buying new plant and equipment; employers should adopt a purchasing policy which results in the quietest machines being sourced.

Personal hearing protection

PURPOSE

The purpose of personal hearing protection is to protect the user from the adverse effects on hearing caused by exposure to high levels of noise. All hearing protection must be capable of reducing exposure to below the upper exposure action value as required by CNWR 2005 (85 dB averaged over 8 hours). All types of personal ear protection should carry a CE mark.

APPLICATION AND LIMITATIONS OF VARIOUS TYPES

Earmuffs:	Application:	Limitations:
<ul><li>Banded.</li><li>Helmet mounted.</li><li>Communication muffs.</li></ul>	<ul><li>Worn on the outside of the ear so less chance of infection.</li><li>Clearly visible therefore easy to monitor.</li><li>Can be integrated into other forms of personal protective equipment (PPE) for example, head protection.</li></ul>	<ul><li>Can be uncomfortable when worn for long periods.</li><li>Incompatibility with other forms of PPE.</li><li>Effectiveness may be compromised by for example, long hair, spectacles etc.</li><li>Requires correct storage facilities and regular maintenance.</li></ul>

Ear plugs:	Application:	Limitations:
■ Pre-moulded. ■ User formable. ■ Custom moulded. ■ Banded plugs.	■ Easy to use and store - but must be inserted correctly. ■ Available in many materials and designs, disposable. ■ Relatively lightweight and comfortable. Can be worn for long periods.	■ They are subject to hygiene problems unless care is taken to keep them clean. ■ Correct size may be required. Should be determined by a competent person. ■ Interferes with communication. ■ Worn inside the ear, difficult to monitor.

Figure 9-10: Application and limitations of various types. *Source: RMS.*

Figure 9-11: Ear defenders. *Source: RMS.*

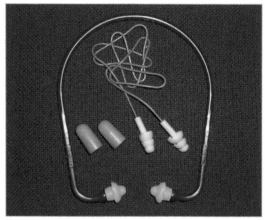

Figure 9-12: Disposable ear plugs. *Source: RMS.*

SELECTION

When selecting personal hearing protectors employers must take into consideration several factors, including:

- Noise attenuation (reduction) capability.
- Compatibility with other personal protective equipment.
- Suitability for the work environment.
- Readily available.
-

- Comfort and personal choice.
- Issue to visitors.
- Provision of information and training.
- Care and maintenance.

USE

All PPE should be used in accordance with employer's instructions, which should be based on manufacturer's instructions for use. PPE should only be used after adequate training has been given. Also, adequate supervision must be provided to ensure that training and instructions are being followed. Personal ear protection may not provide adequate protection due to any of the following reasons:

- Long hair, spectacles, earrings etc, may cause a poor seal to occur.
- Ear protectors are damaged, for example, cracked.
- Not fitted properly - due to lack of training.
- Not wearing ear protectors all of the time.
- Specification of protectors does not provide sufficient attenuation.

MAINTENANCE

Employers have a legal duty to ensure that any PPE is maintained in an efficient state, efficient working order and good repair. Simple maintenance can be carried out by the trained wearer, but more intricate repairs should only be done by specialist personnel. Maintenance in this context includes actions to keep personal hearing protection in use in good order. This will include the timely disposal of personal hearing protection that no longer affords adequate protection due to use.

ATTENUATION FACTORS

The attenuation (noise reduction) associated with personal hearing protectors must be supplied with the product. The information required is in terms of:

- SNR (Single Number Rating) values.
- HML (High, Medium and Low) values.
- Octave band values.

For example, a hearing protector might be designated with SNR 26, H=32, M=23, L=14. The estimated attenuation changes according to the noise spectrum of the environment in which the hearing protector is to be worn.

The SNR value is the result of a lengthy mathematical calculation; it gives a single-number rating of a hearing protector's attenuation for a specified percentage of the population. The SNR is significantly lower than the average attenuation across all of its test frequencies as the calculation contains correction factors to make it applicable to the broader population. While it is not the perfect measure of attenuation, SNR is a very useful standardised method for describing a hearing protector's attenuation in a single number. For example if an environment has a weighted noise measurement of 100 dB(C) then by using an earplug with a SNR rating of 25 dB it will reduce the noise to 75 dB(A).

Using HML values, H is for high-frequency noise environments, M for mid-frequency and L for low-frequency. Note that the HML designation does not refer to noise level, rather the spectrum of the noise frequencies. To determine the predicted noise attenuation (PNA) it is necessary that a noise reading be taken in both A weighting and C weighting mode, at the worker's ear. If the difference between the A weighted reading and the C weighted reading is greater than 2 a formula using the medium and low values is used; if it is less than or equal to 2 a formula using the high and medium value is used. This method enables the effects of the frequency of the noise to be taken into account by using a sound level meter with A and C weighting.

If readings have been taken using an octave band sound level meter the octave band method can be used to produce a more accurate reflection of the effectiveness of hearing protectors. This can assist with ensuring a close match of a particular hearing protector with the noise created by a particular noise source. It involves quite complicated mathematics, so to assist employers the Health and Safety Executive (HSE) has produced a calculator, which can be found at http://www.hse.gov.uk/noise/calculator.htm. Calculators are also available for SNR and HML methods.

Whichever method is used to determine the predicted noise attenuation of hearing protection, the HSE recommends the reduction of the value by 4 dB to reflect what they see as 'real world factors'. This takes account of variances with fit or other user factors that may limit the effectiveness of the hearing protection.

The role of monitoring and health surveillance

Construction work includes the demolition, maintenance, repair, erection, construction of buildings/roads and any work of engineering construction. A great deal of this type of these activities can involve workers being exposed to high noise levels.

Construction workers are not only exposed to the noise from construction machinery, but may also the excessive noise levels generated by heavy traffic when work is being carried out on the side of a busy road. Because of the changing noise exposure levels that arise during construction activities it is important to monitor the noise and the effects of noise through health surveillance.

MONITORING

The role of noise monitoring is to ensure that noise designated areas and working conditions in those areas are kept under review.

The main functions of monitoring are to:

- Check that areas have been correctly designated for hearing protection.
- Identify any changes to noise levels so that appropriate control measures for restricting exposure can be proposed.
- Detect breakdowns in controls or systems, so as to indicate whether conditions are satisfactory for continuing work in that area.
- Ensure workers use the controls provided and report any defects.
- Ensure workers use hearing protection where its use is designated as mandatory.
- Provide information on those who may be at risk and in need of health surveillance.

HEALTH SURVEILLANCE

The role of health surveillance is to provide early detection of work-related ill-health. It will assist with the identification of noise hazards and the evaluation of noise control measures. By conducting health surveillance from the start of an employee's employment it is possible to detect early signs of hearing loss and provide early intervention to limit the continuing effects. Health surveillance can assist with confirming the success of noise controls at source and support the promotion of personal hearing protection.

Regulation 9 of the CNWR 2005 states that if a risk assessment indicates a risk to the health and safety of employees who are, or are liable to be, exposed to noise, and then they must be put under suitable health surveillance (including testing of their hearing). The employer must keep and maintain a suitable health record. The employer will, providing reasonable notice is given, allow the employee access to their health record.

Where, as a result of health surveillance, an employee is found to have identifiable hearing damage the employer shall ensure that the employee is examined by a doctor. If the doctor, or any specialist to whom the doctor considers it necessary to refer the employee, considers that the damage is likely to be the result of exposure to noise, the employer must:

- Ensure that a suitably qualified person informs the employee accordingly.
- Review the risk assessment.

- Review any measure taken to comply with the regulations.
- Consider assigning the employee to alternative work.
- Ensure continued health surveillance.
- Provide for a review of the health of any other employee who has been similarly exposed.

Employees must, when required by the employer and at the cost of the employer, present themselves during working hours for health surveillance procedures.

9.2 - Vibration

The effects on the body of exposure to vibration

Occupational exposure to vibration may arise in a number of ways, often reaching workers at intensity levels disturbing to comfort, efficiency and health and safety. Long-term, regular exposure to vibration is known to lead to permanent and debilitating health effects such as vibration white finger, loss of sensation, pain, and numbness in the hands, arms, spine and joints. These effects are collectively known as hand-arm or whole body vibration syndrome.

In the case of whole body vibration it is transmitted to the worker through a contacting or supporting structure that is itself vibrating, for example, the seat or floor of a vehicle (for example, dumper truck or road preparation/laying machine).

Figure 9-13: Use of circular saw - vibration.   *Source: RMS.*

By far the most common route of harm to the human body is through the hands, wrists and arms of the subject - so called segmental vibration, where there is actual contact with the vibrating source.

HAND-ARM VIBRATION

Prolonged intense vibration transmitted to the hands and arms by vibrating tools and equipment can lead to a condition known as *Hand-arm Vibration Syndrome (HAVs).* These are a range of conditions relating to long term damage to the circulatory system, nerves, soft tissues, bones and joints. Probably the best known of these conditions is known as vibration white finger (VWF). Here the fingers go white and numb (known as *Raynaud's phenomenon*), leading to sharp tingling pains in the affected area and an often painful deep red flush. This seems to occur in response to a change in metabolic demand in the fingers induced, for example, by temperature change. It seems that the blood vessels are unable to dilate either at all or rapidly enough because of the thickened tissues that then become anoxic (lacking in oxygen).

Contributory factors

As with all work-related ill-health there are a number of factors which when combined result in the problem occurring. These include:

- Vibration frequency - frequencies ranging from 2 to 1,500 Hz are potentially damaging but the most serious is the 5 to 20 Hz range.
- Duration of exposure - this is the length of time the individual is exposed to the vibration.
- Contact force - this is the amount of grip or push used to guide or apply the tools or work piece. The tighter the grip the greater the vibration to the hand.
- Factors affecting circulation - including temperature and smoking.
- Individual susceptibility.

Examples of risk activities in construction

- The use of hand-held chain saws.
- The use of hand-held rotary tools in grinding, sanding or cutting.
- The use of hand-held percussive drills for drilling into concrete or similar materials.
- The use of vibrating compactors.
- The use of disc cutter/cut off saws and hand held saws or planners.
- The use of nail and other impact fixing guns.
- The use of scrabblers.
- The use of hand-held powered percussive drills or hammers.

The medical effects of sustained exposure to hand-arm vibration can be serious and permanent and are summarised in the following points:

- Vascular changes in the blood vessels of the fingers.
- Neurological changes in the peripheral nerves
- Muscle and tendon damage in the fingers, hands, wrists and forearms.

- Suspected bone and joint changes.
- Damage to the autonomic centres of the central nervous system in the brain influencing the endocrine, cardiac, vestibular and cochlear functions (not proven).

WHOLE BODY VIBRATION (WBV)

Whole-body vibration is vibration transmitted to the entire body via the seat or the feet, or both, often through driving or riding in vehicles (including fork-lift trucks, excavators, vehicles fitted percussion hammers and dumper trucks) or through standing on vibrating floors of equipment (including road preparation/laying equipment and concrete pumps).

Prolonged exposure can lead to considerable back pain and time off work and may result in permanent injury and having to give up work.

High-risk activities include driving construction site vehicles (for example dumper trucks) and the prolonged use of compactors.

Figure 9-14: Dumper truck seat, vibration mountings. *Source: RMS.*

The need for assessment of exposure, including limit and action values

RISK ASSESSMENT

Regulation 5 of CVWR 2005 requires the employer to make a suitable and sufficient assessment of the risk created by work that is liable to expose employees to risk from vibration. The assessment must observe work practices, make reference to information regarding the magnitude of vibration from equipment and, if necessary, measurement of the magnitude of the vibration.

Consideration must also be given to the type, duration, effects of exposure, exposures limit/action values, effects on employees at particular risk, the effects of vibration on equipment and the ability to use it, manufacturers' information, availability of replacement equipment, and extension of exposure at the workplace (for example, rest facilities), temperature and information on health surveillance. The risk assessment should be recorded as soon as is practicable after it is made and be reviewed regularly.

EXPOSURE ACTION AND LIMIT VALUES

Regulation 4 of the CVWR 2005 states the personal daily exposure limits and daily exposure action values, normalised over an 8-hour reference period.

	Daily exposure action values	*Daily exposure limit values*
Hand arm vibration	2.5 m/s2	5 m/s2
Whole body vibration	0.5 m/s2	1.15 m/s2

Figure 9-15: Vibration exposure action and limit values. *Source: CVWR 2005.*

Exposure action values

Where an employee is likely to be exposed to vibration at or above an exposure action values, the employer must place the employee under suitable health surveillance and provide the employee and their representatives with suitable and sufficient information, instruction and training.

Exposure limit values

In general, the employer must ensure that employees are not exposed to vibration above an exposure limit value. If an exposure limit value is exceeded the employer must immediately:

- Reduce exposure below the limit value.
- Identify the reason for the limit value being exceeded.
- Modify the measures taken to prevent a reoccurrence.

Where exposure to vibration is usually below the exposure action value but varies markedly from time to time, the exposure limit value may be occasionally exceeded, providing that:

- Any exposure to vibration averaged over one week is less than the exposure limit value.
- There is evidence to show that the risk from the actual pattern of exposure is less than the corresponding risk from constant exposure at the exposure limit value.
- Risk is reduced to as low a level as is reasonably practicable, taking into account the special circumstances.
- Employees concerned are subject to increased health surveillance.

Basic vibration control measures

PREVENTIVE AND PRECAUTIONARY MEASURES

Regulation 6 of CVWR 2005 states that the employer must seek to eliminate the risk of vibration at source or, if not reasonably practicable, reduce it to as low a level as is reasonably practicable. Where it is not reasonably practicable to take preventive measures which eliminate the risk at source and the personal daily exposure action value is likely to be reached or exceeded, the employer must reduce exposure by implementing a programme of organisational and technical measures. These precautionary measures include the use of other methods of work, improved ergonomics, maintenance of equipment, design and layout, rest facilities, information, instruction and training, limitation by schedules and breaks and the provision of personal protective equipment to protect from cold and damp. Measures must be adapted to take account of any group or individual employee whose health may be of particular risk from exposure to vibration.

The following precautionary measures should be considered when protecting people who work with vibrating equipment.

CHOICE OF EQUIPMENT

It is important to consider vibration characteristics when purchasing new equipment or selecting equipment for a task. Some equipment will provide better control of vibration at source; others will have damping measures provided to limit vibration transmission to the user. Many manufacturers claim to use composite materials that, when moulded into hand-grips and fitted onto vibrating power tools, reduce vibration by up to 45%. Some equipment may provide beneficial design that can limit the effects of vibration, such as the routing of exhaust gases of portable petrol driven equipment through the operating handles, to keep the user's hands warm in cold weather conditions.

MAINTENANCE

Equipment should be maintained to its optimum performance level, thereby reducing vibration to a minimum (for example the bearings of grinders).

LIMITING EXPOSURE

- Carry out a detailed assessment of hazardous tasks (for example, breaking asphalt with a road breaker). This should include duration and frequency of the task.
- The work schedule should be examined to reduce duration of vibration exposure and magnitude, either by alternating with non-vibration work or avoiding continuous vibration by, for example, scheduling ten minute breaks every hour. Where equipment creates a high magnitude of vibration this must be clearly identified and its use by a single worker limited to short periods. Care should be taken to organise work schedules so that rest periods from this high risk work happen naturally in the process. Where they do not, it may be necessary to use reminders in the form of timed alarms or supervision.
- Wearing gloves is recommended for safety and protection against the cold by the retention of heat. Gloves of this type will not absorb a significant fraction of the vibration energy which lies within the 30 - 300Hz range. Care needs to be taken to select appropriate gloves, as the absorbent material in some gloves for thermal insulation may introduce a resonance frequency which may increase the total energy input to the hands.
- Warm clothing can help workers exposed to vibration to maintain a good body core temperature, which will assist circulation to the hands. It may be necessary for workers to be provided with a warm location for rest breaks or periods when cold is affecting their circulation. Workers with established HAVS should avoid exposure to cold and thus minimise the number of blanching attacks.
- Workers with advanced HAVS, which health surveillance has determined as deteriorating, should be removed from further exposure. The medical priority of this action is to prevent finger tip ulceration (tissue necrosis).

Other precautionary measures

- The vibration characteristics of hand tools should be assessed and reference made to the BSI and ISO Guidelines.
- Development of a purchasing policy to include consideration of vibration and, where necessary, vibration isolating devices.
- Training of all exposed employees on the proper use of tools and the minimisation of exposure. The greater the coupling (hand and tool interface), the more energy enters the hand. Increasing grip force increases the coupling. There are working techniques for all tools and the expertise developed over time justifies an initial training period for new starters. Operators of vibrating equipment should be trained to recognise the early symptoms of HAVS and WBV and how to report them.
- A continuous review should be conducted with regard to the redesigning tools, rescheduling work methods, or automating the process until such time as the risks associated with vibration are under control.
- As with any management system, the controls in place for vibration should be subject to audit.

Regulation 8 of CVWR 2005 states that employers must provide information, instruction and training to all employees who are exposed to risk from vibration and their representatives. This includes any organisational and technical measures taken, exposure limits and values, risk assessment findings, why and how to detect injury, entitlement to and collective results of health surveillance and safe working practices.

Information, instruction and training shall be updated to take account of changes in the employer's work or methods. The employer shall ensure all persons, whether or not an employee, who carry out work in connection with the employer's duties have been provided with information, instruction and training.

Role of monitoring and health surveillance

MONITORING

The role of monitoring is to ensure where vibrating tools or equipment are used vibration exposure and control measures are kept under review.

The main functions of monitoring are to:

- Check that equipment identified as high risk or of lower risk has been correctly designated.
- Identify any changes to vibration exposure so that appropriate control measures for restricting exposure can be proposed.
- Detect breakdowns in controls or systems, so as to indicate whether conditions are satisfactory for continuing work with the equipment.
- Ensure workers use the controls provided and report any defects.
- Ensure equipment is maintained.
- Ensure equipment is used correctly for the purpose for which it was designed.
- Ensure workers are protected from cold windy and wet conditions.
- Ensure workers take regular rest breaks from vibration tasks.
- To provide information on those who may be at risk and in need of health surveillance.

HEALTH SURVEILLANCE

The role of health surveillance is to provide early detection of work-related ill-health; it will assist with the identification of symptoms of the effects of vibration on health. By conducting health surveillance from the start of an employee's employment it is possible to detect early signs of the effects of vibration and provide early intervention to limit the continuing effects.

Health surveillance can assist with confirming the success of vibration control measures. Surveillance for HAVS usually involves the worker or an occupational health specialist examining the hands to identify early signs of tingling or blanching. For whole body vibration, it can be a simple reporting method or questionnaire relating to experience of lower back discomfort or pain.

Regulation 7 of CVWR 2005 states that health surveillance must be carried out if there is a risk to the health of employees liable to be exposed to vibration. This is in order to prevent or diagnose any health effect linked with exposure to vibration. A record of health shall be kept of any employee who undergoes health surveillance. The employer shall, providing reasonable notice is given, provide the employee with access to their health records and provide copies to an enforcing officer on request.

If health surveillance identifies a disease or adverse health effect, considered by a doctor or other occupational health professional to be a result of exposure to vibration, the employer shall ensure that a qualified person informs the employee and provides information and advice. The employer must ensure they are kept informed of any significant findings from health surveillance, taking into account any medical confidentiality.

In addition the employer must also:

- Review risk assessments.
- Review the measures taken to comply.
- Consider assigning the employee to other work.
- Review the health of any other employee who has been similarly exposed and consider alternative work.

9.3 - Radiation

Differences between non-ionising and ionising radiation

Ionising radiation is that radiation, typically alpha and beta particles and gamma and x-rays, which has sufficient energy to produce ions by interacting with matter, whereas non-ionising radiation does not possess sufficient energy to cause the ionisation of matter.

Types and occupational sources of non-ionising radiation

Non-ionising radiation relates to the part of the electromagnetic spectrum covering two main regions, optical radiation (ultraviolet, visible and infrared) and electromagnetic fields (power frequencies, microwaves, and radio frequencies).

ULTRAVIOLET

Possible sources

There are many possible sources of Ultraviolet (UV) radiation to which people may be exposed at work:

- The sun.
- Electric arc welding.
- Insect killers.
- Sunbeds and sunlamps.
- Crack detection equipment.

- Tanning and curing equipment.
- Forgery detectors.
- Some lasers.
- Mercury vapour lamps.
- Tungsten halogen lamps.

Potential health effects

Much of the natural ultraviolet in the atmosphere is filtered out by the ozone layer. However, sufficient ultraviolet penetrates to cause sunburn and even blindness.

Its effect is thermal and photochemical, producing burns and skin thickening, and eventually skin cancer.

Electric arcs and ultraviolet lamps can produce an effect on the conjunctiva of the eyes resulting in inflammation (sometimes called "arc-eye") and cataract formation.

VISIBLE LIGHT (INCLUDING LASERS)

Possible sources

Any high intensity source of visible light can cause problems. Lasers are an obvious danger but so are light beams, powerful light bulbs and the sun. The danger is always due to direct or reflected radiation.

- Furnaces or fires.
- Molten metal or glass.
- Burning or welding.
- Heat lamps.
- Some lasers.
- The sun.

Potential health effects

Light in the visible frequency range can cause damage if it is present in sufficiently intense form. The eyes are particularly vulnerable but skin tissue may also be damaged.

Figure 9-16: UV - from welding.   *Source: Speedy Hire Plc.*

The eyes can be damaged in the cornea and lens, which may become opaque (cataract). Retinal damage may also occur if the radiation is focused. Indirect danger may also be created by employees being temporarily dazzled.

Exposure may also result in a thermal effect such as skin burning and loss of body fluids (heat exhaustion and dehydration).

RADIO FREQUENCY AND MICROWAVES

Possible sources

This type of radiation is produced by radio/television transmitters. It is used industrially for induction heating of metals and is often found in intruder detectors.

Potential health effects

- Burns can be caused if persons using this type of equipment allow parts of the body that carry jewellery to enter the radio frequency field.
- Microwaves can produce the same deep heating effect in live tissue as they can produce in cooking.

Figure 9-17: Radio mast.   *Source: RMS.*

Intense fields at the source of transmitters will damage the body and particular precautions need to be taken to isolate radio/television transmitters to protect maintenance workers.

Types and occupational sources of ionising radiation

Ionising radiation occurs as either electromagnetic rays, for example gamma rays or x-rays, or in particles, for example alpha and beta particles. Radiation is emitted by a wide range of sources and appliances used throughout industry, medicine and research. It is also a naturally occurring part of the environment. All matter is composed of **atoms**. Different atomic structures give rise to unique **elements**. Examples of common elements, which form the basic structure of life, are hydrogen, oxygen and carbon.

Atoms form the building blocks of nature and cannot be further sub divided by chemical means. The centre of the atom is called the **nucleus**, which consists of **protons** and **neutrons**. Electrons take up orbit around the nucleus.

Protons - Have a unit of mass and carry a positive electrical charge.

Neutrons - These also have mass but no charge.

Electrons - Have a mass about 2,000 times less than that of protons and carry a negative charge.

In an electrically neutral atom the number of electrons equals the number of protons (the positive and negative charges cancel out each other). If the atom loses an electron then a positively charged atom is created. The process of losing or gaining electrons is called **ionisation**.

If the matter which is ionised is a human cell, the cell chemistry will change and this will lead to functional changes in the body tissue. Some cells can repair radiation damage, others cannot. The cell's sensitivity to radiation is directly proportional to its reproductive function; bone marrow, and reproductive organs are the most vulnerable; muscle and central nervous system tissue are affected to a lesser extent.

> *"Ionising radiation is that radiation which has sufficient energy to produce ions by interacting with matter".*

Figure 9-18: Ionising radiation.   Source: RMS.

Ionising radiation found in industry are alpha, beta and gamma, and X-rays. Whilst X-rays may occur in nature, generally they are created in the work place either with knowledge, for example X-ray machines or sometimes without knowledge from high voltage equipment. The human body absorbs radiation readily from a wide variety of sources, mostly with adverse effects.

There are a number of different types of ionising radiation each with their different powers of penetration and effects on the body. Therefore, the type of radiation will determine the type and level of protection.

ALPHA PARTICLES

Alpha particles are comparatively large. Alpha particles travel short distances in dense materials, and can only just penetrate the skin. The principal risk is through ingestion or inhalation of a source for example, radon gas emits alpha particles. This might place the material close to vulnerable tissue such as the lungs; when this happens the high localised energy effect will destroy associated tissue of the organs affected.

BETA PARTICLES

Beta particles are much smaller and faster moving than alpha particles. They are smaller in mass than alpha particles, but have longer range, so they can damage and penetrate the skin. Whilst they have greater penetrating power than alpha particles, beta particles are less ionising and take longer to effect the same degree of damage.

GAMMA RAYS

These have great penetrating power. Gamma radiation passing through a normal atom will sometimes force the loss of an electron, leaving the atom positively charged; this is called an **ion**.

X-RAYS

X-rays are very similar in their effects to gamma rays. X-rays are produced by sudden acceleration or deceleration of a charged particle, usually when high-speed electrons strike a suitable target under controlled conditions. The electrical potential required to accelerate electrons to speeds where X-ray production will occur is a minimum of **15,000 volts**. X-rays and gamma rays have **high energy**, and **high penetration** power through fairly dense material. In low density substances, including air, they may travel long distances.

RADON

Radon is a naturally occurring radioactive gas that can seep out of the ground and enter buildings. It is also the most common source of exposure to radiation in Britain, easily exceeding exposure from nuclear power stations or hospital scans and X-rays. It is the second most common cause of lung cancer in the UK, tobacco smoking being the most common cause.

It occurs naturally from decaying uranium, and it is particularly abundant in regions with granite bedrock. Exposure is high in Cornwall, Devon and Somerset, because of these counties' underlying geology, and there are also 'hotspots' in Wales, the Cotswolds and the Pennines. However, the gas disperses outdoors so levels are generally very low.

Once inhaled into the lungs, the gas decays into other radioactive isotopes of lead, bismuth and polonium, including polonium 210, the poison that was used to kill the Russian former spy Alexander Litvinenko in London in 2006. Some decay products emit alpha particles which, when breathed in, can cause harm to the sensitive cells of the lungs.

SOURCES OF IONISING RADIATION

The most familiar examples of ionising radiation in the workplace are in hospitals, dentist surgeries and veterinary surgeries where X-rays are used extensively. X-ray machines are used for security purposes at baggage handling points in airports. In addition, gamma rays are used in non-destructive testing of metals, for example, site radiography of welds in pipelines.

In other industries ionising radiation is used for measurement, for example, in the paper industry for the thickness of paper, and in the food processing industry for measuring the contents of sealed tins.

The Health Protection Agency (HPA) and British Geological Survey have extensively surveyed the UK and the Government has defined the highest radon areas as radon affected areas.

Whilst all workplaces can be at risk from radon, workplaces at higher risk tend to be those located in affected areas. Underground workplaces such as mines and caves made available as tourist attractions are also at higher risk of increased radon levels, wherever their location might be.

POTENTIAL HEALTH EFFECTS OF IONISING RADIATION

The effects on the body of exposure to ionising radiation will depend on the type of radiation, the frequency and duration of exposure. Acute effects will include nausea, vomiting, diarrhoea and burns (either superficial skin burns or deep, penetrating burns causing cell damage). Long-term (chronic) effects such as dermatitis, skin ulcers, cataracts and cancers can also be expected.

The basic means of controlling exposures to ionising and non-ionising radiation

CONTROLS FOR NON-IONISING RADIATION

The Control of Artificial Optical Radiation at Work Regulations (CAOR) 2010 requires an employer to conduct a specific risk assessment and to eliminate or reduce risks. Optical radiation includes ultraviolet, visible light and infrared. Exposure limit levels are set for this form of radiation.

Information and training is to be provided to those that may be affected, which includes employees and others carrying out work on behalf of the employer. Medical examination and health surveillance is to be provided for those employees that receive over exposure.

Ultraviolet

Protection from natural sources of UV is relatively simple and includes the provision of outdoor workers with barrier creams, suitable lightweight UV rated clothing and head protection, and as appropriate eye protection. In addition, workers should be encouraged to take breaks in the shade where possible and consideration should be made to adjusting work schedules so outside tasks may be conducted at times of day that are less affected by UV.

Control of artificial sources of UV includes segregation of UV emitting processes and the use of warning signs. UV radiation emitted from industrial processes can be isolated by physical shielding such as partitions or plastic curtains. It should be borne in mind that some plastic materials differ in their UV absorption abilities and care should be taken in their selection.

Users of UV emitting equipment, such as welders, can protect themselves by the use of goggles and protective clothing - the latter to avoid "sunburn". Assistants in welding processes often fail to appreciate the extent of their own exposure, and require similar protection. Workers should check skin exposed to UV frequently to identify possible effects that might lead to skin cancer.

Visible light

The eye detects visible light. It has two protective control mechanisms of its own, the eyelids and the iris. These are normally sufficient to provide general protection, as the eyelid has a reaction of 150 milliseconds.

However, where this is not adequate because of the intensity of light or the sustained exposure of the eye to it other precautions should be considered, including confinement of high-intensity sources, matt finishes to nearby paint-work, and provision of optically-correct protective glasses for outdoor workers in snow, sand or near large bodies of water. Where the high intensity visible light is artificially created those not involved in the process must also be protected. Warning signs should be posted and access restricted to the process area.

Infrared

Controls to limit exposure include engineered measures, such as remote controls, screening, interlocks and clamps to hold material to enable the worker to be outside the exposure area. This can be supplemented by forms of personal protective equipment where exposure cannot be prevented, for example, face shields, goggles or other protective eyewear, coveralls and gloves.

The management of enforced maximum working periods should be used where exposure cannot be reduced to an acceptable level; this can include a routine change of activity/job rotation. It is important to protect others not directly involved in the process by using screens, curtains and restricted access.

Radio frequency and microwaves

Radio frequency and microwave radiation can usually be shielded at point of generation, to protect the users. If size and function prohibits this, restrictions on entry and working near an energised microwave device will be needed.

Metals, tools, flammable and explosive materials should not be left in the electromagnetic field generated by microwave equipment. Appropriate warning devices should be part of the controls for each such appliance.

CONTROLS FOR IONISING RADIATION

Reduced time

Reducing the duration of exposure through redesigning work patterns, giving consideration to shift working, job rotation etc. The dose received will also depend upon the time of the exposure. These factors must be taken into account when devising suitable operator controls.

Increased distance

Radiation intensity is subject to the inverse square law. Energy received (dose) is inversely proportional to the square of the distance from the source.

Shielding

The type of shielding required giving adequate protection will depend on the penetration power of the radiation involved. For example, it may vary from thin sheets of silver paper to protect from beta particles through to several centimetres of concrete and lead for protection against gamma or X-rays.

In addition to the previous specific controls, the following general principles must be observed:

- Radiation should only be introduced to the work place if there is a positive benefit.
- Safety information must be obtained from suppliers about the type(s) of radiation emitted or likely to be emitted by their equipment.
- Safety procedures must be reviewed regularly.
- Protective equipment provided must be suitable and appropriate, as required by relevant Regulations. It must be checked and maintained regularly.
- Emergency plans must cover the potential radiation emergency.
- Written authorisation by permit should be used to account for all purchase/use, storage, transport and disposal of radioactive substances.

The basic means of controlling exposures to radon

Control of radon exposure in new buildings can be done by installing a 'radon proof membrane' within the floor structure. In areas more seriously affected by radon it may be necessary to install a 'radon sump' to vent the gas into the atmosphere. A radon sump has a pipe connecting a space under a solid floor to the outside.

A small electric fan in the pipe continually sucks the radon from under the house and expels it harmlessly to the atmosphere. Modern sumps are often constructed from outside the building so there is no disruption inside. In existing buildings it is not usually possible to provide a radon proof barrier, so alternative measures are used to control the build-up of radon in the building and subsequent exposure to it.

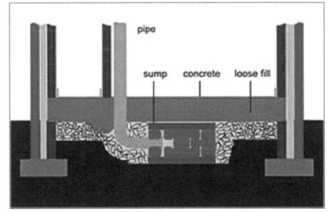

Figure 9-19: Radon sump.   *Source: HSE.*

Such measures include a mixture of active and passive systems such as improved under floor and indoor ventilation in the area, positive pressure ventilation of occupied areas, installation of radon sumps and extraction pipework and sealing large gaps in floors and walls in contact with the ground.

Basic radiation protection strategies

Basic radiation protection strategies include the application of the principles of time, distance and shielding. Exposure should be limited to as few people as possible and those individuals should be monitored and exposure levels maintained within limits.

Regulation 8 of the Ionising Radiation Regulations (IRR) 1999 sets out requirements for the employer to control exposure to ionising radiation:

> *"Every radiation employer shall, in relation to any work with ionising radiation that he undertakes, take all necessary steps to restrict so far as is reasonably practicable the extent to which his employees and other persons are exposed to ionising radiation".*

Figure 9-20: Regulation 8 of IRR 1999.   *Source: Ionising Radiation Regulations (IRR) 1999.*

In the case of ionising radiation, where possible only sealed sources should be used and a system developed to minimise dose levels to individuals. This work must be under the control of a radiation protection advisor.

RADIATION PROTECTION ADVISERS (RPA)

With the exception of the operations specified in Schedule 1 of the IRR 1999, at least one radiation protection adviser (RPA) must be appointed in writing by employers using ionising radiation. The numbers of RPA appointed must be appropriate to the risk and the area where advice is needed is to be stated. Employers must consult the RPA on:

- The implementation of controlled and supervised areas.
- The prior examination of plans for installations and the acceptance into service of new or modified sources of ionising radiation in relation to any engineering controls, design features, safety features and warning devices provided to restrict exposure to ionising radiation.
- The regular calibration of equipment provided for monitoring levels of ionising radiation and the regular checking that such equipment is serviceable and correctly used.
- The periodic examination and testing of engineering controls, design features, safety features and warning devices and regular checking of systems of work provided to restrict exposure to ionising radiation.

Adequate information and facilities must be provided by the employer to the RPA in order to allow them to fulfil their functions.

RADIATION PROTECTION SUPERVISOR

A radiation employer is required to appoint one or more radiation protection supervisors for the purpose of securing compliance with the regulations in respect of work carried out in any area subject to 'local rules for work in controlled or supervised areas'. Their area of work needs to be defined and they must be trained so that they understand the requirements of legislation and local rules insofar as they affect their area of work. They also need to understand the reasons for the precautions that need to be taken in their area of work, and they should command the respect of those they supervise.

CLASSIFIED WORKERS

Persons entering a controlled area should either be classified or be entering in accordance with 'written arrangements' designed to ensure that doses will not exceed, in cases of persons over 18, levels which would otherwise require the persons to be classified. In the case of other persons the relevant dose limit is applicable.

The role of monitoring and health surveillance

Regulation 19 of the Ionising Radiation Regulations (IRR) 1999 requires every employer who designates an area as a controlled or supervised area to ensure that levels of ionising radiation are adequately monitored for each such area and that working conditions in those areas are kept under review.

The main role of monitoring is to:

- Check that areas have been correctly designated.
- Help determine radiation levels and contamination from particular operations, so that appropriate control measures for restricting exposure can be proposed.
- Detect breakdowns in controls or systems, so as to indicate whether conditions are satisfactory for continuing work in that area.
- Provide information on which to base estimates of personal dose for non-classified persons.

Regulation 24(2) of the Ionising Radiation Regulations (IRR) 1999 requires every employer to ensure that each of his employees affected by the regulations is under adequate health surveillance by an appointed doctor or employment medical adviser to determine their fitness for the work with ionising radiation. Fitness in this sense is not restricted to possible health effects from exposure to ionising radiation. Those conducting the health surveillance will need to take account of specific features of the work with ionising radiation, such as the fitness of the individual. This will include such things as:

- Their ability to wear any personal protective equipment (including respiratory protective equipment) required to restrict exposure.
- Whether they have a skin disease which could affect their ability to undertake work involving unsealed radioactive materials.
- Whether they have serious psychological disorders which could affect their ability to undertake work with radiation sources that involves a special level of responsibility for safety.

9.4 - Stress

Causes

> "Stress is the adverse reaction people have to excessive pressures or other demands placed on them".

Figure 9-21: Definition of stress.   Source: HSE.

Stress in workers can be caused by a range of issues that relate to the organisation they work in and issues that are external to the organisation but influence the worker while they are at work, for example, personal relationship problems at home.

The issues that relate to the organisation can be considered using the structure depicted in the Health and Safety Executive (HSE) Management Standards for stress at work. The standards define the positive characteristics or culture of an organisation where stress is being managed effectively, but if these characteristics are absent they can be a cause of stress.

DEMAND

This includes issues like workload and work patterns, stress may be due to an individual not being able to cope with the demands of the job, for example heavy physical work or several revisions of a designers specification, and the work environment itself.

Work patterns that could lead to stress include shift working, excessive overtime and unsocial hours. If the work pattern or job demands are such that the worker does not get adequate breaks this can also lead to stress.

Typical environmental stressors are:

- Noise.
- Extremes of temperature.
- Poor lighting.

Excessive working hours

Workers may be encouraged to work longer hours to get the job done, for example, if the work is subject to a late penalties clause in the contract. The willingness to work excessive hours might be driven by employer threats about their future employment if they do not comply. Additional hours may be added to the days work if workers need to travel long distances to and from the site.

CONTROL

If an individual has little control over the pace and manner they work this can create stress. In particular, work that has repetitive or monotonous features that the worker has no ability to control or adjust may lead to stress.

SUPPORT

If a worker perceives a lack of encouragement or resources provided by the organisation, line management or co-workers a feeling of remoteness can be created.

The failure to provide support was highlighted in the landmark case, *Lancaster v Birmingham City Council (1999),* where liability was admitted when an employee had taken three periods of sick leave and had then been medically retired. She had been moved from her job as draughtswoman to work as a neighbourhood housing officer.

In addition to dealing with members of the public who were often intimidating and abusive, she was not given sufficient administrative support, and had a high workload, partly as a result of an unfilled vacancy. She said she was expected to do the job without ever having been given proper training. In July 1999 she was awarded more than £67,000 in compensation.

WORK RELATIONSHIPS

As long ago as 1994, Staffordshire University Business School published the results of a survey indicating that 1 in 2 UK employees have been bullied at work during their working life.

The Manufacturing, Science and Finance Union (MSF) have identified workplace bullying as:

> "Persistent, offensive, abusive, intimidating, malicious or insulting behaviour, abuse of power or unfair penal sanctions which make the recipient feel upset, threatened, humiliated, or vulnerable, which undermines their self confidence and which may cause them to suffer stress. Harassment, in general terms, is unwanted conduct affecting the dignity of men and women in the workplace. It may be related to age, sex, race, disability, religion, sexual orientation, nationality or any personal characteristic of the individual, and may be persistent or an isolated incident. The key is that the actions or comments are viewed as demeaning and unacceptable to the recipient".

Figure 9-22: Bullying.   Source: Cipd.

If relationships with co-workers, customers or suppliers are poor, this can put the worker under pressure, which may lead to stress. This is particularly so if the relationship involves such issues as harassment, discrimination or bullying. If the relationship part of the work includes the fear of violence, this can put the worker under significant pressure when conducting their job, particularly if they feel they can do nothing to manage the risk. Poor work relationships can lead to poor communications, and vica versa, which can cause the worker to feel isolated or unprepared for the work they are doing. In the same way, if workers are not consulted or involved in processes that might affect them and their work, like risk assessment, they may feel under additional pressure because they do not understand or accept the outcomes from the process.

ROLE

If workers do not understand their role in the organisation, or have conflicting roles, this can increase the potential for stress. In particular, undertaking new or difficult work without first achieving the appropriate skills to complete it successfully or safely could put the individual under pressure.

CHANGE

If the management of organisational change is not conducted or communicated well, individuals can be confused or feel threatened by the change and this could lead to stress. Changes that cause the worker to feel their job or salary may be insecure due to re-organisation or redundancy can particularly have this effect. The absence of consultation of workers when change is considered can add to concerns about the change and lead to stress.

Effects of stress

Being exposed to stressful situations brings about changes in behaviour and also physical well-being.

Physical effects

- Increased heart rate.
- Increased sweating.
- Headache.
- Dizziness.
- Blurred vision.
- Aching neck and shoulders.
- Skin rashes.
- Lowered resistance to infection.

This can result in

- Lack of motivation.
- Lack of commitment.
- Poor timekeeping.
- Increase in mistakes.

Behavioural effects

- Increased anxiety.
- Irritability.
- Increased alcohol intake.
- Increased smoking.
- Erratic sleep patterns.
- Poor concentration.
- Feeling of inability to cope with everyday tasks.

- Increase in sickness absence.
- Poor decision making.
- Poor planning.

Stress is reflected in relationships at work as

- Tension between colleagues/supervisors.
- Poor service to clients.

- Deterioration in industrial relations.
- Increase in disciplinary problems.

Control measures

The Health and Safety Executive (HSE) Management Standards for stress at work set out the positive characteristics or culture of an organisation where stress is being managed effectively. Stress, like other risks should be subject to a risk assessment in order to identify the causes of pressure that can lead to stress and to evaluate the current controls.

The HSE Management Standards are based on the 6 main stress factors of demands, control, change, relationships, role and support. Each standard defines a desired state (best practice) to be achieved in order to minimise the risk of stress in the workplace.

DEMAND

The standard is - "employees indicate they can cope with the demands of the job and there are systems in place locally to respond to any individual concerns".

Control measures to meet this include:

- Balancing the demands of the work to the agreed hours of work, consider shift working, the amount of additional hours worked and unsocial hours.
- Provision of regular and suitable breaks from work and rest periods.
- Matching worker skills and abilities to the job demands.
- Designing jobs so they are within the capability of workers.
- Minimising the work environment risks, such as noise and temperature.

CONTROL

The standard is - "employees indicate that they are able to have a say about the way they do their work and there are systems in place locally to respond to any individual concerns".

Control measures to meet this include:

- Providing, where possible, workers with control over their pace and manner of work, consider reducing the effects of repetitive and monotonous work by job rotation.
- Encouraging workers to use their skills and initiative to do the work.
- Encouraging workers to develop to enable them to do more challenging or new work.
- Providing workers with opportunity to influence when breaks are taken.
- Consulting workers regarding work patterns.

SUPPORT

The standard is - "employees indicate that they receive adequate information and support from their colleagues and superiors and there are systems in place locally to respond to any individual concerns".

Control measures to meet this include:

- Establishing policies and procedures that provide support, particularly where workers may feel other factors are putting them under pressure.
- Provide systems that enable and encourage managers to identify where workers need support, consider where workers deal with the public in demanding environments, where new workers are introduced and times of high demand.
- Provide systems that enable and encourage managers to provide support to workers, consider particularly those working remotely by virtue of their location or time of working and new workers.
- Encourage co-workers to support each other.
- Ensure workers understand what resources and support is available and how they access it.
- Provide regular constructive feedback to workers.

WORK RELATIONSHIPS

Improving work relationships and attempting to modify people's attitudes and behaviour is a difficult and time-consuming process. Effective strategies include regular communication with staff, provision of accurate and honest information on the effect of organisational changes on them, adopting partnership approaches to problems, provision of support. The onus is on employers to promote a culture that respects the dignity of others - if it is left to employees to do this it will not happen.

The standard is - "employees feel able to indicate that they are not subjected to unacceptable behaviours, for example, bullying at work and there are systems in place locally to respond to any individual concerns".

Control measures to meet this include:

- Promote positive behaviour that avoids conflict and leads to fairness; consider co-workers, customers and suppliers.
- Establish policies and procedures that resolve unacceptable behaviour that leads to conflict.
- Encourage managers to deal with unacceptable behaviour, such as harassment, discrimination or bullying.
- Encourage workers to report unacceptable behaviour.
- Establish systems that ensure communication with managers and workers, consider timeliness of communication to those that work isolated by location or time.
- Establish systems that ensure involvement and consultation, such as regarding the process of conducting risk assessments.

ROLE

The standard is - "employees indicate that they understand their role and responsibilities and there are systems in place locally to respond to any individual concerns".

Control measures to meet this include:

- Ensure workers have the knowledge, skill and experience to conduct their role or are being supported appropriately; consider workers undertaking new or difficult work.
- Ensure role requirements are compatible, for example, that the need to manage costs does not conflict with health and safety.
- Ensure role requirements are clear.
- Ensure workers and their managers understand the roles and responsibilities.
- Provide systems to enable workers to raise concerns about role uncertainty or conflict, particularly consider the work life balance for those workers that provide care for others outside their work.

CHANGE

The standard is - "employees indicate that the organisation engages them frequently when undergoing organisational change and there are systems in place locally to respond to any individual concerns".

Control measures to meet this include:

- Provide workers with timely information to help them understand the change, reasons for it and timing of effects.
- Ensure worker consultation on proposed changes.
- Provide workers with information on likely impacts of change on their jobs.

- Provide training and support through the period of change.

In addition to the six specific factors that relate to the HSE management standards for stress at work there are a number of general control measures that should form part of a stress management strategy. These include:

- Introducing a stress policy and procedures to demonstrate to managers, workers, worker representatives and enforcing authorities that the organisation recognises stress as a serious issue worthy of a commitment to manage the risk.
- Providing training and support for workers and all levels of management in the form of stress awareness and stress management training, as appropriate.
- Addressing the issue of work-life balance, which may include consideration of job-share, part-time work, voluntary reduced hours, home-working, flexitime etc.
- Promoting general health and well-being awareness initiatives within the organisation, such as diet, exercise and fitness programmes.
- Providing access to occupational health practitioners, counselling support or assistance programmes for those that may be affected by stress.

Sample assessment questions

1. The Control of Noise at Work Regulations 2005 gives noise exposure action values.

    (a) **Identify** the lower **AND** the upper exposure action values. (2)

    (b) **Outline** the control measures an employer is required to take when employees are exposed to noise at or above an upper exposure action value. (6)

2. **Outline** the actions that management might consider in order to reduce levels of occupational stress amongst workers on site. (8)

3. As part of major road construction ground consolidation anchors are being installed by workers using hand-held powered percussive equipment that produce high levels of vibration.

    (a) **Identify** possible health effects due to exposure to vibration. (4)

    (b) **Outline** control measures that could be used to reduce the risk of such effects. (4)

Please refer to back of assessment section for answers.

Working at height - hazards and risk control

Learning outcomes

On completion of this element, candidates should be able to demonstrate understanding of the content through the application of knowledge to familiar and unfamiliar situations. In particular they should be able to:

10.1 Explain the hazards of working at height and outline the precautions necessary to control them.

10.2 Explain safe working practices for access equipment and roof work.

10.3 Outline control measures necessary to protect other persons not involved in the work at height.

10.4 Outline control measures to reduce risk when working over or near to water.

Content

Sources of reference

Essentials of Health and Safety at Work, HSE Books, ISBN 978-0-7176-6179-4

Health and Safety in Construction HSG150, 3rd Edition, HSE Books, ISBN 978-0-7176-6182-2

Health and safety in roof work, HSG33, HSE Books, ISBN 978-0-7176-6527-3

Personal Protective Equipment at Work (second edition), Personal Protective Equipment at Work Regulations 1992 (as amended), Guidance on Regulations, HSE Books, ISBN: 978-0-7176-6139-3

Protecting the public: Your next move, HSG151, HSE Books, ISBN 978-0-7176-6294-4

Safe use of work equipment, Provision and Use of Work Equipment Regulations 1998, ACOP and guidance, L22, HSE Books, ISBN 978-0-7176-6295-1

Inspection and reports, HSE Construction Information Sheet no 47 (rev1) Series Code, CIS47REV1

Work at Height Regulations 2005 (as amended) - A Brief Guide, INDG401 (rev1), HSE Books

Working on roofs, INDG284REV1, HSE, ISBN 978-07176-6288-3

Relevant statutory provisions

Construction (Design and Management) Regulations (CDM) 2007

Personal Protective Equipment at Work Regulations (PPER) 1992

Provision and Use of Work Equipment Regulations (PUWER) 1998

Work at Height Regulations (WAH) 2005

10.1 - Working at height hazards and risks

Work activities involving a risk of injury from falling from height

Falls are the most common cause of fatal injuries in the construction industry. They account for about half of those accidentally killed each year. The HSE reported in 2012/13 that construction accounted for ten of the 21 fatal injuries to the self-employed and 13 of the 25 to employees. Construction also had the most major injury falls, accounting for over a fifth of the total, 541 out of 2,522. On average 12 people a year die at work falling from ladders and over 1,200 suffer major injuries. Ladders remain the most common agent involved and account for more than a quarter of all falls from height. The most common injuries sustained as a result of falls from height are broken bones or permanent damage to the human body, leading to lack of mobility.

Much of the work carried out on a construction site is done above ground at heights of more than two metres. Typical activities that involve working at height are:

- Steel erecting.
- Fixing of cladding, roof work.
- Painting and decorating.
- Demolition and dismantling.
- Falls from ladders.

- Bricklaying.
- Scaffold erection.
- Electrical installation and maintenance.
- Bridge construction repairs.

Basic hazards and factors affecting the risk from working at height

Work at height is classified as anything above floor level. The nature and range of the hazards from work at height will depend on the location and work activity involved with the work at height.

There are four main types of hazard associated with work at height:

- Falls of persons.
- Falling objects.
- Contact with or crushed against structures.
- Access to normally inaccessible hazards, for example, overhead power cables.

Whether a fall is liable to cause injury may depend on:

- The height of the fall.
- Dangers associated with falling onto or into material below.
- Dangers associated with passing traffic.
- Whether there is rough or uneven ground.
- The type of structure and its security.

The risks of falls from height are substantial, however long or short the work. Risks related to work activities at height are increased by the presence of fragile roofs, roof lights, voids, deteriorating materials and the weather. Some jobs rarely involve the average worker needing to work above ground level, such as welding and machinery maintenance. This means that workers with little or no experience of work at height find themselves exposed to the dangers of working above ground level when carrying out their usual job in a construction setting. The main factors affecting the risk of work at height include:

- Effectiveness of design.
- Vertical distance that workers may fall.
- Fragile roofs, roof lights and deterioration of materials.
- Unprotected edges.
- Stability and condition of access equipment.
- Weather conditions.
- Falling materials.

EFFECTIVENESS OF DESIGN

Perhaps the biggest factor affecting the risk from working at height is the design of structures and equipment where access to height is required in order to work. For example, older buildings may not have parapet walls on their roof and structures were often designed without thought of access requirements beyond the construction period. Good design that prevents the need to approach edges or built in fall prevention measures will significantly affect the risk. If means of access is not built in to the design it means that access has to be provided by other methods and will involve risks related to erection and dismantling of means of access to height as well as working with temporary access arrangements.

The failure of design to anticipate the need for access may introduce overhanging canopies that prevent access equipment being positioned close to the building or structure, leading to more complex arrangements for access equipment and increased time exposed to work at height while arrangements are put in place or removed.

VERTICAL DISTANCE

Though some construction work involves work activities to be carried out at a significant height, for example on a roof or scaffold, it should not be assumed that work at less significant heights is without risk. Major injuries can occur if a fall results whilst carrying out tasks at height of less than 2 metres, for example, fitting false ceilings or installing utilities inside buildings. This remains a significant risk and many injuries result each year. Legislation, the Work at Height Regulations (WAH) 2005 (as amended in 2007), reflects this risk and requires controls to be in place to manage the risk of falling, whatever the height. This legislation applies to workplaces in general, and therefore includes construction activities. Under these regulations the interpretation of 'work at height' includes any place of work at, above, or below ground level that a person could fall a distance which would be liable to cause personal injury; including places for obtaining access or egress, except by staircase in a permanent workplace.

Where people are working at heights of greater than 2 metres the impact experienced having fallen this vertical distance to a lower level is significant and above this height it is very likely to result in major injury or a fatality.

WAH 2005 Regulation 6 states that work at height must only be carried out when it is not reasonably practicable to carry out the work otherwise. If work at height does take place, suitable and sufficient measures must be taken to prevent a fall of any distance, to minimise the distance and the consequences of any fall liable to cause injury. Employers must also make a risk assessment, as required by regulation 3 of the Management of Health and Safety at Work Regulations (MHSWR) 1999.

ROOFS

Working at height and on roofs carries a high risk of accidents, unless proper procedures and precautions are taken. The danger of people or materials falling affects the safety of those working at height and those working beneath.

Particular danger arises from two types of roof - fragile roofs and sloping roofs.

Fragile roofs

Fragile roofs can cause a hidden hazard, as it is not always obvious that there is potential problem. Skylights can be hidden under debris or moss, slates or roof supports may have unseen damage or may have become brittle which can lead to failure or collapse.

Materials such as asbestos, cement, glass or plastic are likely to be unable to bear the weight of a person. Asbestos sheet deteriorates over time leaving the remaining material in a particularly fragile state. Though the sheet looks intact it will only have a small fraction of its original strength. In a similar way plastic roof material, such as may be used in roof lights, will be affected by exposure to sunlight, leaving it brittle. It should not be assumed that it is safe to walk on newly installed roof material. Though the material may have some strength it may not be enough to bear the weight of a worker. All fragile roofs and/or access routes to them should be marked with an appropriate warning sign.

The WAH 2005 Regulation 9 states that every employer shall ensure that suitable and sufficient steps are taken to prevent any person at work falling through any fragile surface; and that no work may pass across or near, or work on, from or near, fragile surfaces when it is reasonably practicable to carry out work without doing so. If work has to be from a fragile roof then suitable and sufficient means of support must be provided that can sustain foreseeable loads. No person at work should be allowed to pass or work near a fragile surface unless suitable and sufficient guard rails and other means of fall protection is in place. Signs must be situated at a prominent place at or near to work involving fragile surfaces or persons must be made aware of the fragile roof by other means.

Sloping roofs

Sloping roofs are those with a pitch greater than 10 degrees. Falls from the edge of sloping roofs can cause serious injury even when the eaves are relatively low. The hazard of sloping roofs is less obvious when the pitch is small causing people to underestimate the possibility of workers sliding off the edge. The material and therefore the surface of the roof have a significant influence on the hazard, for example a smooth sheet metal surface can present a significant hazard even when the pitch is small.

The chances of an accident are increased when working on roofs that are wet or covered in moss growth and in extreme weather conditions such as high winds. The other significant influencing issue is the footwear used by the worker, smooth flat soled footwear may seem suitable in dry conditions but may not provide sufficient grip and deal with surface water in wet conditions. A build-up of dry particles or grit on a roof can present a surface that leads to a high risk of slipping as the particles become free to move and form a mobile layer between the roof and the worker's foot.

Roof-lights

Roof lights need to be identified before work commences; plastic domed roof lights or lead framed glass roof lights will deteriorate with age, exposure to sunlight (UV) and acid rain. Heavy bodily contact with them may cause them to shatter or collapse. Corrugated plastic lights designed to match the roof profile of metal or asbestos sheeting will have similar failure characteristics, but with the added problem that they may be covered with mould or moss growth obscuring them completely from the other sturdier parts of the roof. Obscured roof lights present a significant fall through risk to workers on the roof structure. Inspection of the roof from inside the building is essential to enable them to be identified and located before any roof work is considered.

VOIDS

Voids in ground works, for example, cellars, drains or old mine shafts could remain undetected which could lead to major hazards. A site survey should be completed prior to commencing any work to identify these hazards. Excavations, incomplete scaffolding/boards or guard rails, ladders should be inspected / checked on a daily basis for damage or unauthorised alterations to reduce any potential hazards. A variety of voids will be created during the construction phase of a multi storey building; these include holes in floors for services, spaces for stairwells and lifts. It is important at the planning stage to make provision for fall protection to include guard rails for stairwells and lift shafts, and hand rails on stairs; fixing covers over other holes in floors; providing adequate levels of lighting; and ensuring a good standard of housekeeping and a high level of supervision and control.

DETERIORATION OF MATERIALS

The condition of the structure on which people are working can deteriorate with time. The rate of deterioration will accelerate if the structure is exposed to adverse weather conditions (including extremes of temperature) or attack by chemicals, animals, insects etc. It may be too late before the evidence of deterioration is noticed. Asbestos cement, fibreglass and plastic deteriorate with age and become more fragile. Similarly, steel sheets may rust or may not be supported properly. This presents a serious risk to workers who work on these materials without means to prevent falls.

Accidental damage may have also occurred to structural parts of the building during the construction phase. There should be a formal way of reporting these incidents.

UNPROTECTED EDGES

Roofs, scaffolds, unfinished steel work and access platforms may sometimes have open sides. This increases the likelihood of someone or something falling, particularly if people have to approach them, work at them or pass by them repeatedly. It is very easy in these circumstances to lose perception of the hazard and forget that it is there. Errors, such as stepping back over an edge, overreaching, or being pushed over the edge whilst manoeuvring materials can easily lead to fatal falls.

UNSTABLE/POORLY MAINTAINED ACCESS EQUIPMENT

An employer, having committed to providing access to height by the provision of work equipment, needs to understand that employees using it are at risk from basic hazards relating to its stability and maintenance. Working with mobile elevated work platforms (MEWPs), ladders and scaffolds have their own specific stability and maintenance issues, the hazard of falling from height whilst using them being the common theme. Each is influenced by the problem of the stability of the ground conditions they are placed on and the height they are used at compared to their stability base. *See also - Mobile Elevating Work Platforms - later in this element.*

All equipment, access equipment being no exception, can fail if not properly maintained. Cracks may occur in the sides of ladders and loose rungs can lead to failure. They may warp or rot if left exposed to the elements. Defects in ladders may be hidden if they are painted or covered in plaster.

The effective working of the hydraulics of a MEWP is critical and failure to maintain this could lead to a sudden and catastrophic failure of the MEWP whilst it is extended. Scaffolds need periodic maintenance to ensure load-bearing parts are still secured and those critical items such as brakes on mobile scaffolds are in place and effective. Failure to maintain them can quickly undermine the strength, integrity and stability of the scaffold leading to collapse or overturning.

WEATHER

Adverse weather can have a significant effect on the safety of those working at height. Rain, snow and ice increase the risk of slips and falling from a roof. When handling large objects, such as roof panels, then high wind can be a serious problem and may cause the person to be blown off the roof. Extremely cold temperatures can increase the likelihood of brittle failure of materials and therefore increase the likelihood of failure of roof supports, scaffold components and plastic roof lights.

In addition, moisture can freeze; increasing the slipperiness of surfaces and on many occasions the presence of ice is not easily visible.

Figure 10-1: Working above ground level. *Source: RMS.*

Workers exposed to the cold can lose their dexterity and when hot, sweat may cause them to lose their grip.

FALLING MATERIALS

The risk of falling materials from work conducted at height is increased by:

- Poor housekeeping of people working above.
- Surplus materials incorrectly stacked.

- Absence of toe boards or edge protection.
- Incorrect hooking and slinging.
- Incorrect assembly of gin wheels for raising materials.

- Open, unprotected edges.
- Deterioration of structures causing crumbling masonry.

The risk of falling materials may be increased by work platforms becoming cluttered with loose materials resulting from the work activity being conducted. In addition, if methods like toe boards, solid barriers and brick guards are not provided to prevent materials or other objects rolling, or being kicked off the edges of platforms the risk becomes significant.

The lack of control over removing materials from workplaces at a height can have a big influence on the risk of falling materials. If there are no suitable prescribed methods of removing materials workers may be tempted to improvise and throw materials, such as old slates, tiles and scaffold clips, to the ground. Even if enclosed debris chutes are provided, if they or the container materials go into becomes full workers may resort to throwing materials from height to the ground, putting people at risk.

Methods of avoiding working at height

WAH 2005 sets out a hierarchy for safe work at height. This requires the duty holder to:

- Avoid work at height where they can.
- Use work equipment or other measures to prevent falls where they cannot avoid working at height.
- Where they cannot eliminate the risk of fall, use work equipment or other measures to minimise the distance and consequence of a fall should one occur.

WAH 2005, Regulation 6 - Avoidance of risks from work at height, sets out the following requirements for dealing with risks from work at height:

"1) In identifying the measures required by this regulation, every employer shall take account of a risk assessment under regulation 3 of the Management Regulations.

Figure 10-2: Using a pole to avoid work at height.
Source: HSE, HSG150

2) Every employer shall ensure that work is not carried out at height where it is reasonably practicable to carry out the work safely otherwise than at height.

3) Where work is carried out at height, every employer shall take suitable and sufficient measures to prevent, so far as is reasonably practicable, any person falling a distance liable to cause personal injury.

4) The measures required by paragraph (3) shall include:

a) His ensuring that the work is carried out:

i) From an existing place of work.

ii) (In the case of obtaining access or egress) using an existing means; which complies with Schedule 1, where it is reasonably practicable to carry it out safely and under appropriate ergonomic conditions.

b) Where it is not reasonably practicable for the work to be carried out in accordance with sub-paragraph (a), his providing sufficient work equipment for preventing, so far as is reasonably practicable, a fall occurring.

5) Where the measures taken under paragraph (4) do not eliminate the risk of a fall occurring, every employer shall:

a) So far as is reasonably practicable, provide sufficient work equipment to minimise:

i) The distance and consequences.

ii) Where it is not reasonably practicable to minimise the distance, the consequences, of a fall.

b) Without prejudice to the generality of paragraph (3), provide such additional training and instruction or take other additional suitable and sufficient measures to prevent, so far as is reasonably practicable, any person falling a distance liable to cause personal injury".

Where possible, work at height should be avoided by conducting the work at ground level. This could be achieved by using different equipment or methods of work, for example the pre-assembly of roof trusses, either before delivery or on the ground on site, instead of assembly at height.

Good planning arrangements, considering how fixtures/fittings, plant and services can be designed or installed can be utilised to avoid the need to work at height both during construction and in ongoing cleaning or maintenance.

Main precautions necessary to prevent falls and falling materials

GOOD DESIGN

Good design should prevent the need to approach edges or provide built in fall prevention measures in order to prevent falls and falling materials; this will significantly reduce risk. If design anticipates the need for work at height it is possible to provide means of access that is integral with the building or structure, for example the provision of cradles fitted to bridges to enable periodic inspection and maintenance. Similarly, a movable access system may be permanently fitted to the inside and outside of an atrium of an office block to enable cleaning and repair of the glass or other fittings. This not only provides a good work position for work to be carried out but also eliminates the time that workers may be exposed to risk while erecting and dismantling temporary means of access. Where possible, permanent means of access should be built into the design of buildings and structures to minimise risk. Good design for work at height may include consideration of access by means of a mobile elevating work platform (MEWP), which requires being stable when used. This might include providing a firm level surface around the building or structure and may cause the redesign of the layout of aesthetic features, such as ponds and shrubs, in order to achieve this.

Regulation 6 of WAH 2005 requires that, where reasonably practicable, work at height must be carried out from an existing place of work and the place of work must comply with the contents of Schedule 1 of WAH 2005 with regard to such things as its strength and prevention of people or materials falling through gaps. This will require designers to consider the provision of existing places of work that are suitable for work at height.

PROPER PLANNING AND SUPERVISION OF WORK

Fall of people

Regulation 4 of WAH 2005 states that all work at height must be properly planned, supervised and be carried out so far as is reasonably practicable safely. Planning must include the selection of suitable equipment; take account of emergencies and gives consideration to any weather conditions impacting on safety.

WAH 2005, Regulation 5, states that those engaged in any activity in relation to work at height must be competent; and, if under training, be supervised by a competent person.

WAH 2005, Regulation 6, states that work at height must only be carried out when it is not reasonably practicable to carry out the work otherwise. If work at height does take place, suitable and sufficient measures must be taken to prevent a fall of any distance, to minimise the distance and the consequences of any fall liable to cause injury. Employers must also make a risk assessment, as required by Regulation 3 of the Management of Health and Safety at Work Regulations (MHSWR) 1999.

This means that organisations should review work done to determine a response to the above requirements. This may affect those that fill equipment hoppers located at height manually, requiring consideration of bulk delivery and automatic feed systems. Where workers have to lubricate or adjust equipment set at height by hand, options to automate or route the lubrication/adjustment mechanisms to ground level should be considered. If materials are pre-painted or pre-drilled this can greatly reduce the work needed to be done at height. Long reach handling devices can be used to allow cleaning or other tasks to be conducted from the ground. Where equipment, such as light units, requires maintenance an option may be to lower it sufficiently to enable bulbs to be changed and cleaning to be conducted from the ground.

Fall of materials

WAH 2005, Regulation 10, states that every employer shall take reasonably practicable steps to prevent injury to any person from the fall of any material or object; and where it is not reasonably practicable to do so, to take similar steps to prevent any person being struck by any falling material or object that is liable to cause personal injury. Also, that no material is thrown or tipped from height in circumstances where it is liable to cause injury to any person. Materials and objects must be stored in such a way as to prevent risk to any person arising from the collapse, overturning or unintended movement of the materials or objects.

WAH 2005, Regulation 11, states that every employer shall ensure that where an area presents a risk of falling from height or being struck from an item falling at height that the area is equipped with devices preventing unauthorised persons from entering such areas and the area is clearly indicated.

AVOIDING WORKING IN ADVERSE WEATHER CONDITIONS

Adverse weather can include wind, rain, sun, cold, snow and ice. Each of these conditions, particularly in extreme cases, can present a significant hazard to construction work. When long term projects are planned methods are often adjusted to minimise the effects. For example, road and walk routes that could quickly be affected by rain are made up into formal structures by the use of hardcore, concrete and tarmac. Work areas can be covered over at an early stage to enable work to be conducted in relative comfort. In some cases it may be that work is organised in an order that predicts expected adverse weather, allowing tasks to be adjusted until short term weather conditions improve. In some cases, adverse weather must be considered formally and work may have to cease until conditions improve, for example, work on a roof in icy conditions or high winds. Similar approaches may have to be taken for operating a mobile elevating work platform (MEWP) in windy conditions or entering a sewer during a rain storm.

EMERGENCY RESCUE

Where an individual has fallen from height but has been protected by personal fall arrest equipment such as a harness, significant health effects known as suspension trauma may be experienced if they are not rescued quickly. This is mainly due to blood pooling in the legs, reducing the amount circulating through the rest of the body, which has consequential effects for vital organs such as the brain, heart and kidneys. Unless the individual is rescued very quickly the lack of oxygenated blood to vital organs can be fatal. Therefore, a rescue procedure and equipment must be available and practiced. The procedure should also take into account that a sudden transition from a vertical to a horizontal position when rescued and laid down, can lead to a massive amount of deoxygenated blood entering the heart, causing cardiac arrest. Steps must be taken to minimise the risk of injury due to the fall or contact with the safeguard. Even a short fall onto a net or other fall arresting safeguard could cause minor injuries or fractures. This should be anticipated and workers taught how to minimise the likelihood of injury.

Measures to minimise distance and consequences of a fall

Regulation 6 of WAH 2005 states a simple hierarchy for managing and selecting equipment for work at height. Duty holders must:

- Avoid work at height where they can.
- Use work equipment or other measures to prevent falls where they cannot avoid working at height.
- Where they cannot eliminate the risk of a fall, use work equipment or other measures to minimise the distance and consequences of a fall should one occur.
- Regulation 6 of WAH 2005, further requires that the employer or the self employed provide such additional training and instruction or take other additional suitable and sufficient measures to prevent, so far as is reasonably practicable, any person falling a distance liable to cause personal injury.

PROVISION OF WORK EQUIPMENT TO PREVENT FALLS

Careful consideration during the risk assessment and planning phases for work at height should establish which equipment is best suited for the working environment and work to be done. There are various types of fall protection that should be evaluated in relationship to the activity and environment. This could be edge protection in the form of scaffolding or barriers (temporary or fixed), or consideration of the building of temporary walls.

Collective measures must be given priority over personal measures and account needs to be taken of such factors as:

- Working conditions and the risks to the safety of persons at the place where the work equipment is to be used.
- In the case of work equipment for access and egress, the distance to be negotiated.
- Distance and consequences of a potential fall.
- Duration and frequency of use.
- Need for easy and timely evacuation and rescue in an emergency.
- Any additional risk posed by the use, installation or removal of that work equipment or by evacuation and rescue from it.

To maintain safe access and egress, temporary staircases should be considered before the use of ladders. Where ladders are used it is more difficult to maintain a 'three-point contact' as workers may have to use their hands to carry or move items to different levels.

MITIGATING DISTANCE AND CONSEQUENCES OF A FALL

This is the third aspect in the work at height protection hierarchy set out in WAH 2005 and applies to situations where work equipment and other measures have not been able to provide sufficient means to prevent likely falls. Regulation 6(5) of WAH 2005 states:

"5) *Where the measures taken under paragraph (4) do not eliminate the risk of a fall occurring, every employer shall:*

    a) *So far as is reasonably practicable, provide sufficient work equipment to minimise:*

        i) *The distance and consequences.*

        ii) *Where it is not reasonably practicable to minimise the distance, the consequences, of a fall".*

Figure 10-3: Regulation 6(5) of WAH 2005.   *Source: The Work at Height Regulations (WAH) 2005.*

In mitigating the distance and consequences of a fall, two principal systems are used and considered by WAH 2005:

- Fall arrest systems, for example, nets and air bags.
- Personal fall protection systems, for example, work positioning systems, rope access and positioning techniques.

Fall arresting systems

Fall arrest systems include equipment designed to minimise the distance and consequence of falls, such as nets and air bags. Fall arresting systems are preferred to personal protection systems because they provide collective protection and, unlike a fall arrest harness, they do not rely on individual user discipline to guarantee acceptable safety standards.

WAH 2005 requires that a fall arresting safeguard may only be used if:

■ A risk assessment has demonstrated that the work activity can, so far as is reasonably practicable, be performed safely while using it and without affecting its effectiveness.
■ Use of other, safer work equipment is not reasonably practicable.
■ A sufficient number of available persons have received adequate training specific to the safeguard, including rescue procedures.

A fall arresting safeguard must be suitable and of sufficient strength to arrest safely the fall of any person who is liable to fall. In addition, it must:

■ In the case of a safeguard that is designed to be attached, be securely attached to all the required anchor points.
■ The anchors and the means of attachment must be suitable and of sufficient strength and stability for the purpose of supporting the foreseeable loading in arresting the fall and during any subsequent rescue.
■ In the case of an airbag, landing mat or similar safeguard, be stable.
■ In the case of a safeguard that distorts in arresting a fall, afford sufficient clearance.

Suitable and sufficient steps must be taken to ensure that in the event of a fall the safeguard does not itself cause injury to that person. Fall arresting systems such as safety nets, air/bean bags or crash mats may be used to minimise the impact of falls. They can simplify systems of work and can protect not only workers, but others such as supervisors.

Where safety nets are used, they must be installed as close as possible beneath the surface that people can fall from, securely attached and able to withstand a person falling onto them. These must be installed and maintained by competent personnel. If the work height increases, the nets must be repositioned at each higher level to ensure the minimum fall distance is maintained as the work progresses.

Personal fall protection systems

Personal fall protection systems include work positioning systems, rope access and positioning techniques, fall arrest systems and work restraint systems. Schedule 5, Part 1, WAH 2005 requires that a personal fall protection system may only be used if:

■ A risk assessment has demonstrated that:
  • Work can, so far as is reasonably practicable, be performed safely while using that system.
  • Use of other safer work equipment is not reasonably practicable.
■ The user and a sufficient number of available persons have received adequate training specific to the operations envisaged, including rescue procedures.

In addition, Schedule 5, Part1, requires that a personal fall protection system must be:

■ Be suitable and of sufficient strength for the purposes for which it is being used, having regard to the work being carried out and any foreseeable loading.
■ Where necessary, fit the user.
■ Be correctly fitted.
■ Be designed to minimise injury to the user and, where necessary, be adjusted to prevent the user falling or slipping from it, should a fall occur.
■ Be so designed, installed and used as to prevent unplanned or uncontrolled movement of the user.

Each of the different personal fall protection systems (work positioning systems, rope access and positioning techniques, fall arrest systems and work restraint systems) has requirements related to their use set out in Schedule 5 of WAH 2005. Personal fall arrest systems (harnesses) are useful when other means of fall protection are not reasonably practicable. The harness itself may cause injury when the person comes to a sudden stop; therefore the use of an inertia reel harnesses (the same principle as a car seat belt) may be preferable.

In order to minimise the consequences of a fall when using personal fall arrest systems it is important to maintain a 'clear fall zone' that takes account of the likely movement of the person after the fall, including the pendulum effect. When using harnesses in a mobile elevating work platform (MEWP), the harness should always be fixed to the inside of the cradle.

INSTRUCTION AND TRAINING AND/OR OTHER MEANS

Where a risk of a fall remains, Regulation 6 of WAH 2005 requires that instruction, training and suitable and sufficient other measures must also be provided to prevent any person falling a distance liable to cause personal injury. This may include training workers in techniques that would limit the effect of the fall, controlling what equipment they use that might fall with them, ceasing processes in the area that may cause the worker to be disorientated/overcome leading to a fall, covering items that the person may fall onto and providing means to assist those that have fallen.

Workers should receive full training and instruction on the use of equipment and systems of working that will minimise the distance and consequences of a fall. Where harnesses are to be used, this should include how to wear the fall arrest harnesses, how to fit it to fixing points, what is a suitable fixing point and fixing at a height that minimises the fall (for example, above the head where possible).

Training should also include the checks that need to be made on fall arrest systems before they are used, this will include checks on the security of nets and the adequacy of airbags. Workers will also need to be trained in how to get off/out of this equipment safely when it has arrested a fall and on emergency arrangements for rescue, where workers cannot assist themselves.

This is supported by the general duty to provide training to those involved with work at height, set out in Regulation 5 of WAH 2005:

"Every employer shall ensure that no person engages in any activity, including organisation, planning and supervision, in relation to work at height or work equipment for use in such work unless he is competent to do so or, if being trained, is being supervised by a competent person".

Figure 10-4: Regulation 5 of WAH 2005. *Source: The Work at Height Regulations (WAH) 2005.*

Requirements for head protection

Introduced from 6 April 2014, the Personal Protective Equipment Regulations (PPER) 1992 applies to the provision and wearing of head protection on construction sites following the revocation of the Construction (Head Protection) Regulations (CHPR) 1989. Hard hats are required where there is a foreseeable risk of injury to the head other than by a person falling, for example the risk of being struck by falling materials or where people might hit their head.

Hazards to consider:

- Loose material kicked into an excavation.
- Material falling from a scaffold platform.
- Material falling off a load being lifted by a crane or goods hoist or carried on a site dumper or truck.
- Dropping a fitting while erecting or dismantling a scaffold.

Decide on the areas of the site where hats have to be worn. Make site rules and tell everyone in the area. Provide employees with hard hats and make sure hats are worn and worn correctly. It is useful to ensure that a wide range of hats is available and to let employees try a few and decide which is most suitable for the job and for them. Some hats have extra features, including a sweatband for the forehead and a soft, or webbing harness. Although these hats are slightly more expensive, they are much more comfortable and therefore more likely to be worn.

Inspection requirements for work equipment

Inspection requirements for work equipment specified for use for work at height are set out in Regulation 12 of WAH 2005.

Requirements are:

- Where safety depends on how it is installed or assembled in any position - before used in that position.
- Where exposed to conditions causing deterioration which is liable to result in dangerous situations, to ensure that health and safety conditions are maintained and that any deterioration can be detected and remedied in good time - at suitable intervals and each time that exceptional circumstances which are liable to jeopardise the safety of the work equipment have occurred.
- Work platforms used for construction work in which a person could fall 2 metres or more - inspected in position, or if a mobile work platform inspected on the site, within the previous 7 days.

Result of an inspection must be recorded and kept until the next inspection. An inspection report containing the particulars set out below must be prepared before the end of the working period within which the inspection is completed and, within 24 hours of completing the inspection, be provided to the person it was carried out for.

The report must be kept at the site where the inspection was carried out until the construction work is completed and afterwards at an office of the person it was carried out for, for 3 months.

Reports on inspections must include the following particulars:

1) Name and address of person for whom the inspection is carried out.
2) Location of the work equipment.
3) Description of the work equipment.
4) Date and time of inspection.
5) Details of any matter identified that could give rise to a risk to the health and safety of any person.
6) Details of any action taken as a result of 5 above.
7) Details of any further action considered necessary.
8) Name and position of the person making the report.

10.2 - Safe working practices for access equipment and roof work

Scaffolding

DESIGN FEATURES OF SCAFFOLDING

Independent tied

This type of scaffold typically uses two sets of standards; one near to the structure and the other set at the width of the work platform. It is erected so that it is independent from the structure and does not rely on it for its primary stability. However, as the name suggests, it is usual to tie the scaffold to the structure in order to prevent the scaffold falling towards or away from the structure.

Figure 10-5: Independent tied scaffold. *Source: RMS.*

Figure 10-6: Independent tied scaffold. *Source: RMS.*

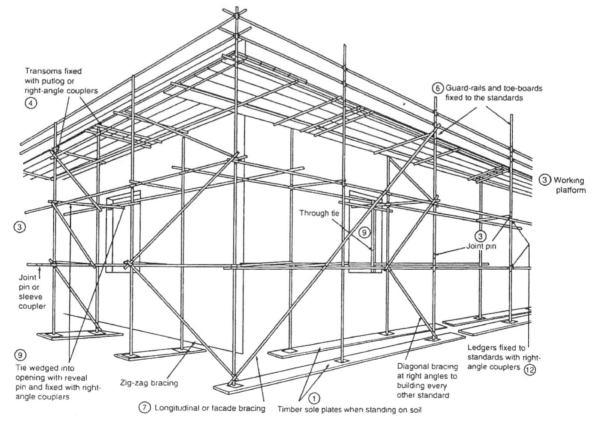

Figure 10-7: Independent tied scaffold. *Source: HSE, HSG150.*

Putlog

This type of scaffold has a single set of standards erected at the width required for the work platform. The transoms have a flat end that is inserted into the mortar gap in the wall. The structure effectively provides the inner support for the work platform and therefore an inner set of standards is not needed.

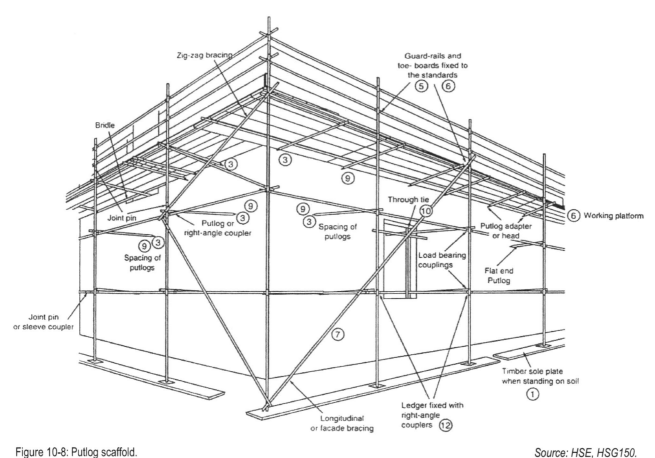

Figure 10-8: Putlog scaffold.

Source: HSE, HSG150.

Figure 10-9: Putlog scaffold.

Source: RMS.

Figure 10-10: Putlog scaffold.

Source: RMS.

Fan

Fans are scaffold boards fixed on scaffold tubes set at an upward angle out from a scaffold in order to catch debris that may fall from the scaffold.

They may be provided at the entrances to buildings to protect persons entering and leaving the building that the scaffold is erected against.

They are also used where a scaffold is erected alongside a pedestrian walkway where there is a need to have an increased confidence that materials that might fall cannot contact people below.

In some cases it may be necessary for horizontal barriers to be erected to direct pedestrians under the fan.

Figure 10-11: Fans.

Source: RMS.

Cantilevered

A cantilever scaffold is assembled in the normal way then continued outwards by erecting a cantilever section from the inner vertical columns.

Care must be taken to ensure the structure remains safe and stable. Adding stabilisers to the main scaffold or tying-in to the building are normally essential safety precautions. The use of adjustable bases either under the main scaffold or cantilever or both is usually helpful in ensuring the cantilever section rests firmly on the building.

Mobile tower scaffolds

Mobile scaffold towers are widely used as they are convenient for work which involves frequent access to height over a short period of time in a number of locations that are spaced apart.

Figure 10-12: Wheels with brakes.   *Source: RMS.*

However, they are often incorrectly erected or misused and accidents occur due to people/materials falling or the tower overturning/collapsing.

They must be erected and dismantled by trained, competent personnel, strictly in accordance with the supplier's instructions. All parts must be sound and from the same manufacturer.

- The height of an untied, independent tower must never exceed the manufacturer's recommendations. A 'rule of thumb' may be:
  - Outdoor use - 3 times the minimum base width.
  - Indoor use - 3.5 times the minimum base width.
- If the height of the tower is to exceed these maximum figures then the scaffold *must* be secured (tied) to the structure or outriggers used.
- Working platforms must only be accessed by safe means. Use internal stairs or fixed ladders only and never climb on the outside.
- Before climbing a tower the wheels must be turned outwards, the wheel brakes "on", locked and kept locked.
- Never move a tower unless the platform is clear of people, materials, tools etc.
- Towers must only be moved by pushing them at base level. Instruct operators not to pull the tower along whilst on it. Pay careful attention to obstructions at base level and overhead.
- Never use a tower near live overhead power lines or cables.
- Working platforms must always be fully boarded out. Guardrails and toe boards must be fitted if there is a risk of a fall of more than two metres. Inspections must be carried out by a competent person - before first use, after substantial alteration and after any event likely to have affected its stability.

Figure 10-13: Mobile tower scaffold. *Source: RMS.*

Figure 10-14: Mobile tower scaffold. *Source: RMS.*

Scaffolding terms

Base plate   Distributes the load from a standard or a raker (scaffold standard used as an outrigger).

Brace   A tube fixed diagonally across two or more members in a scaffold for stability.

Guard rail	A tube incorporated in the structure to prevent personnel from falling.
Ledger	A tube spanning horizontally and tying the scaffold longitudinally. It may act as a support for putlogs or transoms.
Putlog	A tube with a flattened end, spanning from a horizontal member to a bearing in or on a brick wall. It may support scaffold boards.
Reveal pin	A tube wedged by means of a reveal screw between two opposite surfaces (for example window reveals) to make a friction anchorage for tying a scaffold.
Standard/column	A vertical, or near vertical, supporting tube.
Tie	A tube used for fixing the scaffold to the building or other structure for stability.
Transom	A tube spanning across ledgers to tie a scaffold transversely. It may also support boards.

SAFETY FEATURES

Base plates and sole boards

- A base plate must be used under every standard - it spreads the load and helps to keep the standard vertical.
- Sole boards are used to spread the weight of the scaffold and to provide a firm surface on which to erect a scaffold, particularly on soft ground. Sole boards must be sound and sufficient, and should run under at least two standards at a time.

Figure 10-15: Base plates and sole boards. *Source: Lincsafe.*

Figure 10-16: Base plate and protection. *Source: RMS.*

Ties and bracing

Ensuring stability of a scaffold is critical. In the case of an independent tied scaffold the scaffold is set a small distance away from the structure and ties connect it to the structure and prevent the scaffold falling away from or towards the structure.

One of the ways to do this is to use a 'through tie' which is set into place through an opening in the structure such as a window. In addition to this, it is important that the scaffold is a rigid structure.

A scaffold comprising standards, transoms and ledgers alone may not be rigid enough, particularly in the case of tall scaffolds. In order to improve rigidity a system of braces, scaffold poles set at a diagonal angle, is used.

Figure 10-17: Tie through window. *Source: RMS.*

They are placed at the ends, in opposite diagonals for each level of scaffold, at intervals along the scaffold. In addition bracing is placed diagonally across the front of the scaffold.

Toe boards

These are scaffold boards placed against the standards at right angles to the surface of the working platform. They help prevent materials from falling from the scaffold and people slipping under rails. They must be suitable and sufficient to prevent the fall of any person or any material or object from a place of work.

- The toe boards should be fixed to the inside of the standards with toe board clips.
- Continuous around the platform where a guardrail is required.

- Typically a height of 150 mm is needed to be effective.
- Joints must be as near as possible to a standard.

- Any toe board that is removed temporarily for access or for any other reason must be replaced as soon as possible.

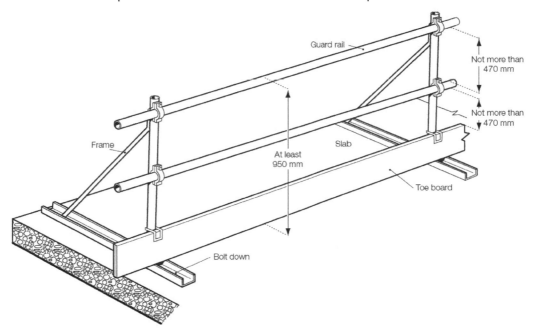

Figure 10-18: Guardrails and toeboards.   *Source: HSE, HSG150.*

Guardrails

These are horizontal scaffold tubes which help to prevent people falling from a scaffold.

- They must be fitted to any working platform that is two metres or more above ground level.
- They must be fixed to the *inside* of the standards, at least 950 mm from the platform.
- An intermediate guard rail must be no more than 470 mm between the top guardrail and the toe boards.
- Guardrails must always be fitted with load-bearing couplers.

- Joints in guardrails must be near to a standard.
- Joints must be secured with sleeve couplers.
- Guardrail must go all round the work platform.
- If the gap between the structures is 300 mm or more, then a guardrail must be fitted to the inside of the working platform as well as the outside.
- Guardrails must always be carried round the end of a scaffold, to make a "stop end".

Boarding

Boards provide the working platform of a scaffold and landings for access ladders. Boards supported by transoms or putlogs must be close fitting, free from cracks or splits or large knots, and must not be damaged in any way which could cause weakness.

Working platforms

However wide a working platform may be, if its height above ground or floor level is two metres or more, then it must be fitted with guardrails and toe boards. If it is also to carry materials, then the space between guardrails and toe boards must be reduced to a maximum 470 mm. This can be done with an intermediate rail, mesh or similar material. The following additional points will assist in minimising risks from working at height on working platforms:

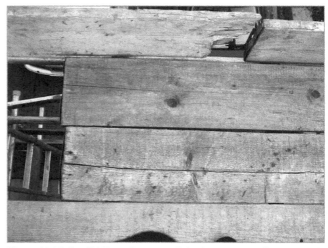

Figure 10-19: Scaffold boards - some defective.   *Source: RMS.*

- General access must not be allowed to any working platform until the scaffold has been fully erected. Access must be blocked off to any section of any scaffold that is not yet finished.
- If a gap or opening is created in a working platform for any reason, then it must immediately be blocked off and a warning notice displayed.
- Where a ladder passes through a working platform, the access must be as small as practicable.
- Any access point through a working platform must be covered when it is not being used, and clearly marked to show its purpose.
- Trestles *must not* be put up on any working platform.

- If a working platform becomes covered with ice, snow, grease or any other slippery material, then suitable action must be taken to reduce the hazard, by sprinkling sand, salt, sawdust, etc.
- Rubbish or unused materials must not be left on working platforms.
- Platforms must not be used for "storing" materials. All materials placed on a platform must be for immediate use only.
- Loadings must be evenly spread out over working platforms to the fullest extent possible.
- Where loading cannot be distributed evenly (as with bricklayers' materials) then the larger weights should be kept nearest to the standards.
- Any working platform positioned near to fragile items, such as glass, should be sheeted out to the full height of the guardrail.
- Everything loose must be taken off the working platforms before any start is made on dismantling.

Brick guards

Brick guards are designed to prevent material falling between the gaps in the guardrails and the toe board. Brick guards are not intended to protect against people falling. Therefore, brick guards should always be used in addition to the required fall protection, which consists of guard rails and toe boards or other similar barriers.

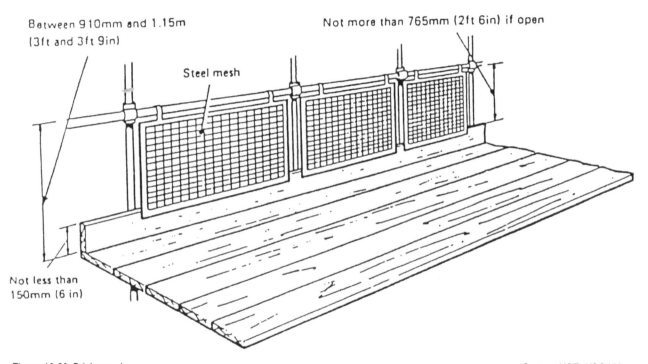

Between 910mm and 1.15m
(3ft and 3ft 9in)

Not more than 765mm (2ft 6in) if open

Steel mesh

Not less than
150mm (6 in)

Figure 10-20: Brick guards.   *Source: HSE, HSG150.*

Debris netting

Debris netting is often fixed to the sides of a scaffold to limit the amount of debris escaping from the scaffold that may come from work being done on it. It provides a tough, durable and inexpensive method of helping to provide protection from the danger of falling debris and windblown waste. It allows good light transmission and reduces the effects of adverse weather.

Figure 10-21: Nets and sheets.   *Source: RMS.*

Figure 10-22: Nets.   *Source: RMS.*

Debris netting may also be slung underneath steelwork or where roof work is being conducted to catch items that may fall. In this situation it should not be assumed that the debris netting is sufficient to hold the weight of a person who might fall.

REQUIREMENTS FOR SCAFFOLD ERECTORS

Scaffold erectors must erect and dismantle scaffold in a way that minimises the risk of falling. Where practicable they should erect intermediate platforms, with guardrails and toe boards, to enable them to build the next scaffold 'lift' safely. If a platform is not practicable, falls must be prevented (or their effects minimised) by other means, such as the use of a safety harness or similar fall arrest equipment.

The National Access and Scaffolding Confederation (NASC) provide guidance for scaffold workers on the safe erection of scaffolds.

MEANS OF ACCESS

Figure 10-23: Fitting advanced guardrail system. *Source: NASC.*

> *"So far as is reasonably practicable as regards any place of work under the employer's control, the maintenance of it in a condition that is safe and without risks to health and the provision and maintenance of means of access to and egress from it that are safe and without such risks".*

Figure 10-24: Means of access.   *Source: Health and Safety at Work Act (HASAWA) 1974 S2(2)(d).*

General access must not be allowed to any scaffold until its erection has been fully completed. Access must be prevented to any subsequent sections of scaffold that are not completed and a "scaffold incomplete" sign displayed. Ladders often provide access and egress to and from scaffolds where stairs cannot be provided.

Figure 10-25: Stair access.   *Source: RMS.*

Figure 10-26: Ladder access.   *Source: RMS.*

Factors to be considered in the safe use of ladders for access include:

- They should be free from defect and not painted.
- The correct length used to reduce manual handling risks, flexing in use.
- Placed on a firm footing, with each stile equally supported.
- Positioned so that there is sufficient space at each rung to give an adequate foothold.
- Positioned approximately at an angle of 75° (1 unit horizontally to 4 units vertically).
- Extended to a height of 1 metre above the working platform (unless there is another adequate hand hold).
- When more than 3 metres in length, must be securely tied at the top or footed at the bottom to prevent slipping.
- Not be so long that it extends excessively past the stepping off point as this can cause the ladder to pivot around the tie/stepping off point and cause the user to fall.
- Positioned so that the vertical height of the ladder running between landings does not exceed 9 metres.
- Both hands should be free when climbing a ladder.

DESIGN OF LOADING PLATFORMS

Scaffold platforms that are used for loading of materials or equipment will need to be designed to take into account any concentration of heavy loads that will be placed upon them (for example, bricks, blocks, mortar or timber).

A loading platform is designed to withstand a weight that would be excessive on the normal working area of a scaffold.

Often this will be a separate scaffold structure, assembled adjacent to the main working scaffold, tied to both the building and the main scaffold and will consist of additional braces and sections to provide extra support.

The platform must be correctly signed as a loading area with a safe working load specified.

Workers must not be allowed to access the area directly below the platform where the loading and unloading will take place.

Figure 10-27: Loading platform. *Source: RMS.*

SCAFFOLD HOISTS (PERSONS, MATERIALS)

The hoist should be protected by a substantial enclosure to prevent anyone from being struck by any moving part of the hoist or material falling down the hoist way. Gates must be provided at all access landings, including at ground level. The gates must be kept shut, except when the platform is at the landing.

The controls should be arranged so that the hoist can be operated from one position only. All hoist operators must be trained and competent. The hoist's safe working load must be clearly marked.

If the hoist is for materials only there should be a prominent warning notice on the platform or cage to stop people riding on it.

Figure 10-28: Loading platform. *Source: RMS.*

The hoist should be inspected weekly, and thoroughly examined every six months by a competent person and the results of inspection recorded.

Inclined hoists are often used to transport materials. Inclined hoists should be erected and used by competent personnel. Additionally, there would need to be arrangements for its inspection, testing and regular maintenance and for ensuring the guarding of dangerous parts of the machinery and the integrity of any electrical installation.

Protection would need to be provided at the base and top of the hoist and means provided to ensure the security of the load as it travels to the top of the hoist. Relocation and or dismantling should only be carried out by competent persons.

See also - Element 4 - Musculoskeletal hazards and control - 'Lifts and hoists' - for further information.

ENSURING STABILITY

Effects of materials

Scaffold systems are a means of providing safe access when work at height cannot be avoided. They are not designed for storage of materials for long periods. It is however, acceptable to situate materials on scaffolds in small quantities to reflect the usage rate of the materials by the people using the scaffold. Provided the safe working load specified for the scaffold is not exceeded materials may be distributed evenly on the working platform.

Care should be taken to ensure the working platform is not reduced to a width that compromises access around the scaffold, the materials are distributed evenly and the safe working load specified for the scaffold is not exceeded.

Materials (bricks, mortar, timber, etc) when placed on scaffold systems tend to be placed on the outer edge of the scaffold, creating an uneven balance and placing greater forces on the mechanical joints. These factors can contribute to failure of the joints, or buckling of the tube sections which may ultimately lead to a full or partial collapse of the structure. If this occurs, a host of other hazards become present (falls from height, falling materials).

All loading of scaffolds with materials should be well planned to prevent uneven loading and carried out under supervision. The scaffold should be checked to ensure the safe working load is adhered to at all times.

Weather

Adverse weather conditions not only affect the condition of structures and equipment but can also present dangers to those people who are exposed to them (cold weather can affect dexterity, awareness and morale). These need to be anticipated and suitable precautions taken. Rain, sleet or snow can make surfaces very slippery and in winter freeze to create ice or frost. Heavy rainfall can lead to soil being washed away from the base of the scaffold or the soil can subside leading to the scaffold becoming unstable. Scaffolds should always be inspected prior to work starting. If conditions have changed, checks should be made on whether it is safe to continue working.

A sudden gust of wind can cause loss of balance. This is usually exaggerated when working at height and handling large sheets of materials. In extreme circumstances, work should be stopped during windy weather as people can easily be thrown off balance while carrying out their work. When deciding whether to continue or suspend work consider:

- Wind speed.
- The measures which have already been taken to prevent falls from the scaffold.
- The position and height of the scaffold and the work being carried out.
- The relationship of the work to other large structures as wind may be tunnelled and amplified at certain points.

Sheeting

Sheeting can be used on the outside of scaffold systems as a means of preventing materials, dust and other debris being blown from the working areas of the scaffold onto the construction site or possibly a public area, and it can also provide a means of restricting and controlling access. It is not a means of fall protection.

Whilst sheeting is relatively light and causes little stress on the scaffold system, the additional forces created by wind, rain or snow spread over the surface of the sheeting could cause sufficient force to affect the safe stability of the scaffold. It is also important that sheeting is securely fixed to the structure and not allowed to flail loosely as this could be snagged on site mobile plant resulting in the scaffold being pulled and causing it to collapse.

Protection from impact of vehicles

Construction sites quite often involve numerous types of vehicles of varying size and weight all presenting hazards to other people carrying out work within the site. Protection from impact should be applied to all aspects of work carried out, not just to scaffold structures in particular.

Figure 10-29: Impact protection.   *Source: RMS.*

Figure 10-30: Lighting.   *Source: RMS.*

Measures that may be implemented in order to maintain a safe environment in relation to vehicles and scaffolds may include:

- Providing signs warning of the presence of scaffolds.
- Marking scaffolds with high-visibility tape or sheath around scaffold standards.
- Closing routes past scaffolds to vehicles.
- Ensuring adequate road width for the size of vehicle accessing the site.
- Provision of one-way systems around sites or turning points (away from scaffold) to minimise the need for reversing.
- Reversing vehicles properly controlled by trained banksmen. Competent drivers correctly trained.
- Concrete or wooden impact blocks strategically placed around scaffold perimeter to limit proximity.
- Providing lighting around the scaffold perimeter, scaffolds located near roads may be fitted with lighting to warn traffic of its presence.

Inspection requirements

Inspection requirements for scaffolds are set out in Regulation 12 of WAH 2005 Regulations. All scaffolds used for construction work must be inspected by a competent person before being taken into use for the first time, after any substantial addition, dismantling or other alteration, after any event likely to have affected its strength or stability and where a person could fall 2 metres or more at regular intervals not exceeding 7 days since the last inspection. The result of an inspection must be recorded and kept until the next inspection. A report on the inspection must be completed before the end of the work period and a copy provided to the person on whose behalf it was carried out within 24 hours.

Figure 10-31: Marking.   *Source: RMS.*

Figure 10-32: Inspection 'Scaftag'.   *Source: RMS.*

Reports on inspections to include the following details:

- Name and address of the person for whom the inspection was carried out.
- Location of the work equipment inspected.
- Description of the work equipment.
- Date and time of inspection.
- Details of any matter identified that could give rise to a risk to the health and safety of any person.
- Details of any action taken as a result of 5) above.
- Details of any further action considered necessary.
- Name and position of the person making the report.

It is useful to indicate to those using the scaffold that the inspection has been conducted by the addition of a tag to the scaffold that shows basic details of the inspection. Employers must keep a copy of the inspection report at the site where it was carried out, until construction work is complete. After this period they have to be kept at the employer's office for 3 months. It is useful to indicate to those using the scaffold that the inspection has been conducted by the addition of a tag to the scaffold that shows basic details of the inspection.

Mobile elevating work platforms

A mobile elevating work platform (MEWP) is, as the name suggests, a means of providing a work platform at height. The equipment is designed to be movable, under its own power or by being towed, so that it can easily be set up in a location where it is needed.

Various mechanical and hydraulic means are used to elevate the work platform to the desired height, including telescopic arms and scissor lifts.

The versatility of this equipment, enabling the easy placement of a platform at height, makes it a popular piece of access equipment. Often, to do similar work by other means would take a lot of time or be very difficult. They are now widely available and, like other equipment such as fork-lift trucks there is a tendency for people to oversimplify their use and allow people to operate them without prior training and experience.

Figure 10-33: Mobile elevated work platform (MEWPs).   *Source: RMS.*

They are now widely available and, like other equipment such as fork-lift trucks there is a tendency for people to oversimplify their use and allow people to operate them without prior training and experience.

This places users and others at high risk of serious injury. Some MEWPs can be used on rough terrain. This usually means that they are safe to use on uneven or undulating ground. The MEWP's limitations should always be checked in the manufacturer's handbook before moving on to unprepared or sloping ground and operates within the defined stability working area. Wearing a harness with a lanyard attached to the platform provides extra protection against falls especially when the platform is being raised or lowered.

Use of mobile elevating work platforms

Mobile elevating work platforms can provide excellent safe access to high level work. When using a MEWP make sure:

- Whoever is operating it is fully trained and competent.
- The work platform is fitted with guard rails and toe boards.
- It is used on suitable firm and level ground. The ground may have to be prepared in advance.
- Tyres are properly inflated.
- The work area is cordoned off to prevent access below the work platform.
- That it is well lit if being used on a public highway in poor lighting.
- Outriggers are extended and chocked as necessary before raising the platform.
- All involved know what to do if the machine fails with the platform in the raised position.

Figure 10-34: Mobile elevated work platform (MEWPs). *Source: RMS.*

Figure 10-35: Use of harness with a MEWP. *Source: HSE, HSG150.*

Figure 10-36: Scissor lift. *Source: RMS.*

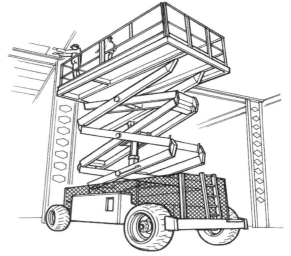

Figure 10-37: Scissor lift. *Source: HSE, HSG150.*

Do not

- Operate MEWPs close to overhead cables or dangerous machinery.
- Allow a knuckle, or elbow, of the arm to protrude into a traffic route when working near vehicles.
- Move the equipment with the platform in the raised position unless the equipment is especially designed to allow this to be done safely (check the manufacturer's instructions).
- Overload or overreach from the platform.

Ladders

USE OF LADDERS

Ladders are primarily a means of vertical access to a workplace. However, they are often used to carry out work and this frequently results in accidents. Many accidents involving ladders happen during work lasting 30 minutes or less. Ladders are often used for short jobs when it would be safer to use other equipment, for example mobile scaffold towers or MEWPs. Generally, ladders should be considered as access equipment and use of a ladder as a work platform should be discouraged. There are situations when working from a ladder would be inappropriate, for example:

■ When two hands are needed or the work area is large.
■ Where the equipment or materials used are large or awkward.
■ Excessive height.
■ Work of long duration.
■ Where the ladder cannot be secured or made stable.
■ Where the ladder cannot be protected from vehicles etc.
■ Adverse weather conditions.

Figure 10-38: Ladder as access and workplace. *Source: RMS.*

Figure 10-39: Improper use.   *Source: RMS.*

Before using a ladder to work from, consider whether it is the right equipment for the job. Ladders are only suitable as a workplace for light work of short duration, and for a large majority of activities a scaffold, mobile tower or MEWP is likely to be more suitable and safer.

■ Pre-use inspection. Make sure the ladder is in good condition. Check the rungs and stiles for warping, cracking or splintering, the condition of the feet, and for any other defects. Do not use defective or painted ladders.
■ Position the ladder properly for safe access and out of the way of vehicles. Do not rest ladders against fragile surfaces.
■ Ladders must stand on a firm, level base, be positioned approximately at an angle of 75° (1 unit horizontally to 4 units vertically) *(see figure ref 10-40)* (note means of securing omitted for clarity).
■ If the ladder is being used to gain access to a landing place it should extend about 1 metre above the landing place.
■ Ladders must be properly tied near the top, even if only in use for a short time, while being tied a ladder must be footed. If not tied, ladders must be secured near the bottom, footed or weighted. Footing is not considered effective on ladders longer than five metres.

Figure 10-40: Correct 1 in 4 angle. *Source: HSE, HSG150.*

■ Both hands should be free to grip the ladder when climbing or descending, with only one person on the ladder at any time. Beware of wet, greasy or icy rungs and make sure soles of footwear are clean.
■ Purpose designed roof ladders should be used to ensure safe access to sloping roofs.
■ Ladders should be returned to the correct, secure storage location when they are not in use.

Figure 10-41: Poor storage.   *Source: Lincsafe.*

Figure 10-42: Use of roof ladders. *Source: HSE, HSG150.*

STEP LADDERS

Stepladders require careful use. They are subject to the same general health and safety rules as ladders.

However, in addition, they will not withstand any degree of side loading and overturn very easily.

When using a step ladder over-reaching should be avoided at all times and care should be taken avoid side loading. Care should be taken to ensure it is placed on a firm level surface to minimise the possibility of it overturning sideways. Step ladder stays must be 'locked out' properly before use.

The top step of a stepladder should not be used as a working platform unless it has been specifically designed for that purpose.

Typically three clear steps should be left to ensure support and stability, depending on the size and design of the step ladder, *(see figure ref 10-44).*

Figure 10-43: Stepladder.   *Source: RMS.*

Figure 10-44: Three steps clear. *Source: HSE, HSG150.*

Figure 10-45: Step platform. *Source: HSE, HSG150.*

Figure 10-46: Incorrect use of a step ladder. *Source: HSE, HSG150.*

Figure 10-47: Correct use of a step ladder. *Source: HSE, HSG150.*

TRESTLES

Trestles are pre-fabricated steel, aluminium or wood supports, of approximately 500 mm to 1 metre width, that may be of fixed height or may be height adjustable by means of sliding struts with varying fixing points (pin method) or various cross bars to suit the height required. They are used to span scaffold boards from one to the other in order to make a work platform. *These can only be used where work cannot be carried out from the ground but where a scaffold would be impracticable.* A good example would be a plasterer who is installing and plastering a new ceiling.

Typical working heights when using a trestle system range from 300 mm to 1 metre, but can be up to above 4 metres. Edge protection should be fitted wherever practical.

As with any work carried out above ground level, a risk assessment, as required by the Management of Health and Safety at Work Regulations (MHSWR) 1999, should be carried out and consideration given to the application of the WAH Regulations 2005 and/or the Construction (Design and Management) Regulations (CDM) 2007 and/or the Workplace (Health, Safety and Welfare) Regulations (WHSWR) 1992.

Figure 10-48: Trestles and handrail system.   *Source: DSL.*

There are many configurations of locking and adjustable trestles. Platforms based on trestles should be fully boarded, adequately supported and provided with edge protection where appropriate. Safe means of access should be provided to trestle platforms, usually by stepladders.

Always

- Set up the equipment on a firm, level, non-slip surface.
- On soft ground, stand the equipment on boards to stop it sinking in.
- Place each trestle at 1.5m intervals which allows the scaffold boards to be adequately supported.
- Then open each up to the height required, ensure the locking pins are properly located.

Never

- Do anything that involves applying a lot of side force. The trestle could topple over.
- The maximum safe working load of a scaffold board is 150 Kg evenly spaced.
- The total weight of the user and tools must not exceed this.
- When moving to a new site, carry the equipment with care.
- Never use steps, boxes etc. to gain extra height.

STAGING PLATFORMS

Staging platforms can be made of metal alloy or wood and are often used for linking trestle systems or tower scaffolds together safely. They also provide a safe work platform for work on fragile roofs. They are produced in various lengths. The same rules apply for edge protection as with other scaffold platforms.

Ensure that the platform is:

- Of sufficient dimensions to allow safe passage and safe use of equipment and materials.
- Free from trip hazards or gaps through which persons or materials could fall.
- Fitted with toe boards and handrails. If toe boards and guardrails are not considered necessary for a specific platform, then this should be shown in the risk assessment, i.e. that not installing a toe board and/or a guard rail had been considered and why it was not necessary.
- Kept clean and tidy, for example mortar and debris should not be allowed to build-up on platforms.
- Not loaded to the extent that there is a risk of collapse or deformation that could affect its safe use. This is particularly relevant in relation to block work loaded on platforms.
- Erected on firm level ground to ensure equipment remains stable during use.

LEADING EDGE PROTECTION SYSTEMS

Leading edges are created as new roof sheets are laid, or old ones are removed. Falls from a leading edge need to be prevented. Work at the leading edge requires careful planning to develop a safe system of work. Nets are the preferred method for reducing the risk of injury from falls at the leading edge, as they provide protection to everyone on the roof. Nets should be erected by trained riggers and be strong enough to take the weight of people.

Debris nets are only rigged to trap lightweight debris - therefore it is important to know which type is in use at a workplace. Staging platforms fitted with guardrails or suitable barriers and toe boards, in advance of the leading edge, can provide protection in some circumstances.

Figure 10-49: Edge protection and staging platforms. *Source: RMS.*

Staging platforms will need to be used in conjunction with harnesses attached to a suitable fixing. Close supervision of this system of work will be needed as it is difficult for the harness to remain safely clipped at all times throughout the work activity.

Other techniques for working at height

Where it is not possible to work from the existing structure and the use of a scaffold working platform is not appropriate, a range of mobile access equipment including boatswain's chairs or seats, suspended cradles, rope access equipment and mobile elevating work platforms (MEWPs) can be used. Those using this type of equipment should be trained and competent to operate it.

They should learn emergency and evacuation procedures so that they know what to do if, for example, the power to the platform fails or fire breaks out in the building being worked on. With many pieces of equipment, more than one person will be needed to ensure safe operation.

MAST CLIMBING WORK PLATFORM

Mast climbing work platforms (MCWPs) are often used when carrying out repairs or refurbishment to high-rise buildings. They provide excellent access to work positions at a height and enable work to be carried out at different heights as the work progresses.

They are not designed as materials hoists though they have a capacity for some work material and people to be on the platform to carry out the work required.

A particular advantage of using MCWPs is that workers on the platform and their tools/materials can be protected from adverse weather conditions by the provision of an enclosed work platform.

Figure 10-50: Mast climbing work platforms. *Source: HSE, HSG150.*

When using MCWPs it is important to ensure that:

- It is erected/installed by a competent specialist who is aware of the purpose of use, likely loadings and weather conditions it will be exposed to.

- Masts are rigidly connected to the structures against which they are operating and outriggers are used when necessary.
- The area below the platform guarded to prevent people from being struck by the platform or by objects that may fall from the platform.
- Working platforms are provided with suitable guardrails and toe boards.
- The controls only operate from the working platform.
- A handover document is provided by the erector/installer. The document should state its safe working load; cover how to operate the equipment, what checks and maintenance is required and how to deal with emergencies.
- There is a current report of thorough examination for the equipment.

BOATSWAIN'S CHAIR

Boatswains' chairs (commonly known as Bosun's chair) and seats can be used for light, short-term work. The chair is distinguished from a climbing harness by the inclusion of a rigid seat, providing more comfort than padded straps for long-term use. The boatswains chair does not allow the freedom of movement necessary for climbing, and the occupant is generally hoisted or lowered into place using the rope alone. They should only be used where it is not practicable to provide a working platform.

Before use
- Installation and use of boatswain's chair to be supervised by trained, experienced and competent person.
- Chair and associated equipment carefully examined for defects.
- Confirm test/examination certificates are valid. Establish safe working load.
- Check that user is both trained and competent in the use of the chair.
- Warning notice displayed and notification of intention to carry out work given.
- Prohibit access to the area below the chair in case materials fall.

In use
- Free of material or articles which could interfere with user's hand-hold.

Figure 10-51: Boatswains chair. *Source: Photo, Pete Verdon.*

- The fall rope must be properly tied off in use and always under or around a cleat to act as a brake.

After use

Chairs and rope should be left in a safe condition:

- Top rope secured.
- Chair and rope secured to prevent swing.
- Raised when out of use or for overnight storage.
- Inspected for defects.
- Ropes (and chair, if timber) dried before storage.

CRADLES (INCLUDING SUSPENSION FROM CRADLES)

Before work starts, check that:

- Equipment is installed, modified and dismantled only by competent specialists.
- There is a current report of thorough examination for the equipment.
- A handover certificate is provided by the installer. The certificate should cover how to deal with emergencies, operate, check and maintain the equipment, and state its safe working load.
- Areas of the site where people may be struck by the cradle or falling materials have been fenced off or similar. Debris fans or covered walkways may also be required.
- Systems are in place to prevent people within the building being struck by the cradle as it rises or descends and prevent the cradle coming into contact with open windows or similar obstructions which could cause it to tip.

Figure 10-52: Suspended cradle. *Source: Harsco Infrastructure.*

■ Supports are protected from damage (for example, by being struck by passing vehicles or by interference from vandals).
■ The equipment should not be used in adverse weather. High winds will create instability. Establish a maximum safe wind speed for operation. Storms and snow falls can also damage platforms, so they should be inspected before use after severe weather.
■ Only trained personnel are to operate.

At the end of each day, check that:

■ All power has been switched off and, where appropriate, power cables have been secured and made dead.
■ The equipment is secured where it will not be accessible to vandals or trespassers.
■ Notices are attached to the equipment warning that it is out of service and must not be used.
■ Check the shift report for warnings of malfunction.

ROPE ACCESS

Often known as abseiling, this technique is usually used for inspection work rather than construction work.

Like a boatswain's chair, it should only be used when a working platform cannot be provided. If rope access is necessary, then check that:

■ A competent person has installed the equipment.
■ The user is fully trained.
■ There is more than one point securing the equipment.
■ Tools and equipment are securely attached or the area below cordoned off.
■ The main rope and safety rope are attached to separate points.

Figure 10-53: Personal suspension equipment. *Source: RMS.*

Fall arrest equipment

HARNESSES

There may be circumstances in which it is not practicable for guard rails etc to be provided, for example, where guard rails are taken down for short periods to land materials. In this situation if people approach an open edge from which they would be liable to fall two metres or more, a suitably attached harness and temporary horizontal lifeline could allow safe working. When using harnesses and temporary horizontal lifelines, ensure:

■ An emergency rescue system must be in place before a harness and lanyard is used to protect against a fall.
■ A harness will not prevent a fall - it can only minimise the injury if there is a fall. The person who falls may be injured by the impact load to the body when the line goes tight or when they strike against parts of the structure during the fall. An energy absorber fitted to the energy-absorbing lanyard can reduce the risk of injury from impact loads.
■ Where possible the energy-absorbing lanyard should be attached above the wearer to reduce the fall distance. Extra free movement can be provided by running temporary horizontal lifelines or inertia reels. Any attachment point must be capable of withstanding the impact load in the event of a fall. Consider how to recover anyone who does fall.
■ Anyone who needs to attach themselves should be able to do so from a safe position. They need to be able to attach themselves before they move into a position where they are relying on the protection provided by the harness.
■ To ensure that there is an adequate fall height to allow the system to operate and arrest the fall.

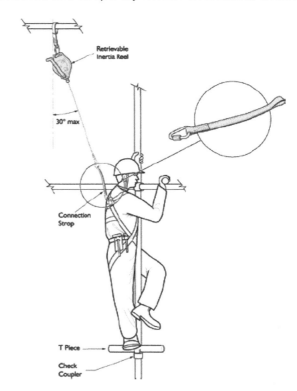

Figure 10-54: Scaffolder using personal fall arrest device. *Source: NASC.*

- A twin lanyard may be necessary in some cases where the wearer needs to move about. A twin lanyard allows the wearer to clip on one lanyard in a different position before unclipping the other lanyard.
- Installation of equipment to which harnesses will be fixed, for example a suitable anchor, must be inspected regularly.
- Everyone who uses a harness must be instructed in how to check, wear and adjust it before use and how to connect themselves to the structure or safety line as appropriate.
- They should be thoroughly examined at intervals of no more than every six months.
- Retractable type fall arresters tested against EN360 are tested with a 100 Kg mass and have to produce an arrest force of less than 6 kN. Therefore users greater than 100 Kg (15 stone 10 lbs.) should refer to the manufacturer's instruction for use and if not covered within the instruction should contact the manufacturer for information for users weighing greater than 100 Kg.

SAFETY NETS

Safety nets are used in a variety of applications where other forms of protection are not reasonably practicable - such as steel erecting and roof work where site personnel are at risk of falling through fragile roofs onto solid surfaces or structures (steel work) below.

Safety nets will arrest the fall of an individual preventing an impact that may cause injury or death. Safety nets must be installed beneath the work area, as a minimum, and consideration should be given to an extension of the protection to allow for people working outside the planned area. Safety nets are only to be installed under supervision by competent installers and are to be inspected weekly and checked daily as the build height progresses.

Figure 10-55: Safety nets. *Source: RMS.*

Relocation of the nets will be necessary if the build height increases to keep the fall distance to a minimum.

It should be remembered that nets are also used to collect debris that may fall. This may be rigged to take a lesser weight than that for protection of people. It is important to identify which type of net is in use in a workplace as reliance on the wrong type may have fatal consequences.

SOFT LANDING SYSTEMS

Soft landing systems normally consist of inflatable air bags or bean bags that are placed, prior to work commencing, under the work area.

Air bags

Airbags are shock absorption devices that can be employed to protect against the effects of falls from a height. They are made of a toughened nylon, or similar man-made material, and are usually inflated using a powered fan device.

They are designed so that should a person fall onto one, a volume of air is forced out of the bag creating a cushioning effect that does not bounce or deflect the person in another direction. This equipment must be matched to correspond to the fall height and as such must only be put into use by a competent person.

Figure 10-56: Soft fall arrest system. *Source: UK, HSE HSG150.*

Soft fall beanbags

Soft fall bean bags use a soft polymer bean to reduce the effect of a fall from up to two metres. The system is used in both traditional building and timber frame constructions.

CRASH DECKS

Collective fall prevention systems (including safety decking) are at the top of the HSE's hierarchy of controls for work at height.

Crash decks (passive, collective fall-protection) provide total protection from falls into the building for all trades at all build stages.

For example, bricklayers can work directly off the decking for topping out.

Because they can be set out at a variety of heights they can remove the need for trestles.

The decking can be installed concurrently with, or just before, external scaffold is lifted reducing build time.

Figure 10-57: Crash deck assembly. *Source: Bondeck Ltd.*

Figure 10-58: Passive, collective fall prevention. *Source: Bondeck Ltd.*

Figure 10-59: Crash deck designed for loading. *Source: Bondeck Ltd.*

EMERGENCY PROCEDURES INCLUDING RESCUE

It is essential that risk assessments are completed for work at height and they should include planned emergency procedures. Employees should be trained and competent in procedures. These procedures should be rehearsed, so that in the event of an actual incident, employees are competent. Emergency procedures should take account of the range of emergencies that may particularly affect those working at height, for example loss of power to powered access equipment, loss of power in areas that need to be illuminated to ensure safety (for example on a scaffold at night), possibilities of a fire or the occurrence of a fall of a person. In the case of equipment failure, the emergency procedures should include rescue from the work position. In situations where a person has fallen, emergency considerations should ensure that further injury is prevented by prompt rescue, using techniques that do not put the worker in further harm.

SUSPENSION TRAUMA IN THE USE OF ROPE AND HARNESSES

Use of harnesses and temporary horizontal lifelines; an emergency rescue system must be in place before a harness and lanyard is used to protect against a fall. The rescue team must be trained to carry out the rescue procedure and in how to deal with a person who is possibly unconscious. The rescue will need to be initiated rapidly (for example, within 15 minutes) to reduce the risk of suspension trauma, a postural hypertension which occurs when the blood pressure drops significantly (the trauma is primarily caused by gravity-induced blood pooling in the lower extremities, which in turn reduces venous return i.e. blood back to the heart, resulting in decreased cardiac output and subsequent lowering of arterial pressure).

Roof work

FLAT ROOFS

Work on a flat roof is high risk. People can fall:

- From the edge of a completed roof.
- From the edge where work is being carried out.
- Through openings or gaps.

Edge protection for flat roofs

Unless the roof parapet provides equivalent safety, temporary edge protection will be required during most work on flat roofs. Both the roof edge and any openings in it need to be protected. It will often be more appropriate to securely cover openings rather than put edge protection around them. Any protection should be:

- In place from start to finish of the work.
- Strong enough to withstand people and materials falling against it.

Where possible the edge protection should be supported at ground level, for example, by scaffold standards, so that there is no obstruction on the roof. If the building is too high for this, the roof edge up-stand can support the edge protection provided it is strong enough.

Edge protection can also be supported by frames, counterweights or scaffolding on the roof. The protection should be in place at all times. Guarding systems are widely available that enable roof repair work to carry on without removing any guard rails.

Short-duration work on flat roofs

Short-duration means a matter of minutes rather than hours. It includes such jobs as brief inspections or adjusting a television aerial. Work on a flat roof is dangerous even if it only lasts a short time. Appropriate safety measures are essential. It may not be reasonably practicable to provide edge protection during short-duration work. In such cases, anyone working nearer than 2 metres to any unguarded edge should be using a safety harness.

Where safety harnesses are used they need to be:

- Appropriate for the user and in good condition - full harnesses are essential, safety belts are not sufficient.
- Securely attached to an anchorage point of sufficient strength.
- Fitted with as short a lanyard as possible that enables wearers to do their work (significant management discipline is needed to ensure this).

Demarcating safe areas

Full edge protection may not be necessary if limited work on a larger roof involves nobody going any closer than 2 metres to an open edge. In such cases demarcated areas can be set up to limit the area where work can be conducted safely.

Demarcated areas should be:

- Limited to areas from which nobody can fall.
- Indicated by an obvious physical barrier (full edge protection is not necessary but a painted line or bunting is not sufficient).
- Subject to a high level of supervision to make sure that nobody strays outside them (demarcation areas are unacceptable if this standard is not achieved).

SLOPING ROOFS

On traditional pitched roofs most people fall:

- From eaves.
- By slipping down the roof and then over the eaves.
- Through the roof internally, for example during roof truss erection.
- From gable ends.

Edge protection for sloping roofs

Full edge protection at eaves level will normally be required for work on sloping roofs. The edge protection needs to be strong enough to withstand a person falling against it. The longer the slope and the steeper the pitch the stronger the edge protection needs to be. A properly designed and installed independent scaffold platform at eaves level will usually be enough. Less substantial scaffolding barriers (rather than platforms) may not be strong enough for work on larger or steeper roofs, especially slopes in excess of 30°.

On some larger roofs, the consequences of sliding down the whole roof and hitting the eaves edge protection may be such that intermediate platforms at the work site are needed to prevent this happening. If the work requires access within 2 metres of gable ends, edge protection will be needed there as well as at the eaves. Powered access platforms can provide good access as an alternative to fixed edge protection. They can be particularly useful in short-duration work.

Figure 10-60: Edge protection and access.   *Source: RMS.*

Figure 10-61: Edge protection and roof ladder.   *Source: RMS.*

MEANS OF ACCESS

Means of access for roof work is usually by means of a ladder or stair. Though, access may also be provided by using a scissor lift, which can also carry materials. If provided, a ladder should extend at least 1.05 metres above the edge of the roof, and it should be securely lashed in position, preferably with a wire bond or safety tie. All forms of access should enable workers to easily step onto a safe landing position on the roof or on a landing platform set to the side of the roof, for example a scaffold tower built for this purpose.

EDGE AND LEADING EDGE PROTECTION

When working on a roof it is essential that edge protection be provided, usually in the form of toe boards and guard rails. When doing work on a roof that requires the worker to lie, fit or remove roof materials, such as insulation and cladding, this can cause the worker to be working at a leading edge.

The leading edge is the limit of the roof structure, on one side of the leading edge is an open height hazard and the other is the relatively safer roof. In order to provide protection at the leading edge it is necessary to provide a system of crawling boards that both spread the weight of the worker and provide fall protection in the form of guardrails. The crawling boards must be repeatedly re-set at the new leading edge as the work progresses.

Figure 10-62: Stair access to roof and edge protection.
Source: RMS.

Figure 10-63: Leading edge protection and crawling boards.
Source: RMS.

CRAWLING BOARDS

On any fragile or angled roof (greater than 30°) or on any roof that is considered hazardous because of its condition or because of the weather; suitable crawling boards must be used. They must be correctly positioned and secure. If it is obvious that the job requires a progression along the roof, extra crawling boards must be provided and no fewer than two such boards shall be taken on any job.

10.3 - Protection of others

DEMARCATION

When working at height is being carried out it is important to protect others from the hazards of items or objects falling onto them. A simple way of doing this is to identify hazardous zones with hazard tape and barriers. Inform those that may be affected by the work that is being undertaken and warn of the possible dangers that may arise within the demarcated area.

Clear demarcation of areas where construction work is being undertaken and where it is not will assist those not involved in the work to keep out of the area and avoid exposure to hazards. The area should be demarcated at a distance that relates to the hazards, such as materials or tools falling. A safety margin should always be built into the demarcation to ensure risks are controlled.

BARRIERS

Barriers are a physical means of preventing access to an area that is required to be restricted, for example where work at height is being carried out. As such, they are particularly appropriate if people, such as the public, might stray past an area marked only with hazard tape.

These can be situated at a proximity that is relative to the hazards associated with the work being carried out. If necessary to ensure a demarcation zone the barriers may be 2 metre high fencing.

TUNNELS

Tunnels can be used to 'isolate' others from any surrounding hazards by enclosing an area (i.e. walkway) and thus preventing any contact with likely hazards until through the danger area.

An example of this could be the ground level of a scaffold on a shop front in a busy high street, being enclosed to form a tunnel that allows the public to pass through the works safely whilst allowing the work at height to continue above.

SIGNS

Safety signs are used to provide people with information relating to the works being carried out, to control or divert people and most importantly of any dangers or hazards.

Signs may be situated at a location in advance of the work area to give prior warning in addition to the works perimeter and actual work location. Signs may be used to prohibit public access to work areas where work at height is taking place.

MARKING

Where equipment used to gain access to height may be collided with it should carry hazard marking. For example, the standards of a scaffold at ground level on a street may be marked with hazard tape. *See also the sections - Demarcation and Signs - previously in this element.*

LIGHTING

Suitable and adequate lighting should be provided to allow the works being carried out and any possible hazards to be seen clearly in advance and allow people to take the required actions to avoid interference with the site.

Scaffolds located near roads may be fitted with lighting to warn traffic of its presence. MEWPs and similar equipment used in poor lighting conditions on or near roads and walkways must use standard vehicle lighting.

SHEETING, NETTING AND FANS

Sheeting can protect other people at risk by preventing dust, materials or tools being ejected from work activities conducted at height. Sheeting provides a solid barrier to particles and spray that may result from some work and may be preferred for processes where building surfaces are being cleaned.

However, for most construction activities the provision of fine netting is adequate, being lighter and offering less wind resistance it is often preferable to sheeting. Fans offer a robust means of collecting the material that may breach netting and fall onto the public, who would not be wearing head protection. The fans should extend sufficiently to provide protection over walk areas and be set at an angle that would deter material bouncing or rolling off the fan.

Fans add to the loading of the scaffold and consideration of this factor must be made at the time of scaffold design.

See also – 'Sheeting' - earlier in the section – 'Ensuring stability'.

HEAD PROTECTION

Figure 10-64: Nets, signs and head protection. *Source: RMS.*

Figure 10-65: Marking. *Source: RMS.*

Figure 10-66: Barriers, fans and netting. *Source: RMS.*

There is a need and legal duty to wear head protection on a construction site where there is a risk of injury from falling materials, this includes when people are working around people at height. This may necessitate the provision of head protection for people other than those involved in the work at height; this could include other workers, visitors to the site or client's workers.

However, it should be remembered that head protection, such as hard hats, provide the user with limited protection from objects falling from height. Therefore it is best, where practicable, to provide other collective means of protection from falling materials.

10.4 - Working over or near water

Prevention of drowning

CDM 2007, Part 4: Duties Relating to Health and Safety on Construction Sites, Regulation 35, states that:

"If there is a risk of persons falling into water and drowning, suitable steps should be taken to prevent a person from falling, and to ensure that suitable rescue equipment is provided".

Figure 10-67: Part 4, Regulation 35 of CDM 2007.   *Source: The Construction (Design and Management) Regulations (CDM) 2007.*

This means that prior to work above water being undertaken, a full risk assessment must be made that takes into account the conditions of the water being worked over or near (tidal, depth, temperature, fast flowing) and suitable control measures identified and implemented including emergency rescue plans and procedures.

Where possible and practicable, a scaffold system is the best method of safe working over water. Working above water brings an extra dimension to workplace safety and where the water is fast flowing additional risks need to be considered. Safety precautions will include protection for river traffic (advance warnings, lighting of obstructions and consultation with river authorities) and the need for the protection against the possibility of the structure being struck by such traffic.

There may also be the need for additional guardrails to working platforms or fall arrest equipment such as safety nets or harnesses; the provision of rescue equipment such as life belts and the availability of a rescue boat under the control of a competent person, should someone fall into the water. Scaffolds must be erected and inspected by competent persons with inspections required weekly. Workers who are required to work near to or over water are required to be properly trained with a provision made so that any person who does fall into water is able to float.

When working next to water in a MEWP, a harness should not be worn to prevent the risk of drowning by being pulled underwater if the MEWP falls into the water. Life jackets, however, should be worn *(see below - Buoyancy Aids)*. Workers that fall into water should be recovered as quickly as possible.

Additional means of preventing falls into water may include floating stages, safety nets, safety harnesses and barriers.

Additional control measures

BUOYANCY AIDS

Buoyancy aids must be provided and their use enforced when working on or near water. However, a distinction between buoyancy aids and lifejackets needs to be noted. Both lifejackets and buoyancy aids are designed to keep the wearer afloat with the main difference that a buoyancy aid will provide sufficient buoyancy to keep a conscious person afloat in a reasonable flotation position. A lifejacket will support an unconscious person in a face upright flotation position, therefore reducing the likelihood of the wearer drowning.

Buoyancy aids and lifejackets can be used with safety harnesses so long as the items do not interfere with each other and reduce effectiveness. It is possible to obtain a combined piece of equipment. All staff that are required to use this equipment must be properly trained in its use and be fully aware of its functions and limitations.

Management systems must be in place that considers the use, inspection and storage of lifejackets and buoyancy aids.

The majority of drowning occurs close to the bank or waters edge, and this should be taken into account at the planning stage. Other methods of equipment available to assist someone to remain afloat are life buoys or rescue lines. Life buoys are normally attached to approximately 30 metres of lifeline but can only be thrown a short distance of 6-8 metres. Rescue lines are available in various forms with life lines ranging from 25-40 metres in length. Rescue lines work by throwing a bag or capsule to the person in the water and the line deploying as the bag/capsule goes further out. The line, bag and capsule all stay afloat and allow the person in the water to grab the line and be pulled to safety. Care must be taken that the person deploying the line is secure at the bank and unable to be pulled into the water.

In fast flowing channels that have no water borne traffic, then 'safety nets' or 'safety lines' may be stretched across the width of the channel to allow the person in the water to hang on and wait for rescue. This is only effective if the person in the water remains conscious.

SAFETY BOATS

Where works are being carried out on fast flowing, or tidal waters then a rescue boat should be made available. Requirements state that it must have a reliable engine, carry oars, and the person that is operating the boat must be competent and experienced at handling small boats on flowing water.

It must be fitted with grab lines for persons who have fallen into the water and if any work is carried out in the hours of darkness, then the boat will be required to be fitted with high efficiency lighting. It may be a requirement to have two-way radio installed on the boat for communication between boat and shore.

Sample assessment questions

1. Scaffolding has been erected to the outside of a block of high-rise flats in order to undertake window replacement and repairs to external cladding.

    Outline factors that could affect the stability of the scaffold. (8)

2. A flat roof is to be repaired while a building remains occupied.

    Outline the issues that should be addressed to reduce the risk to the workers involved in the repair work and others who may be affected by the work. (8)

3. (a) **Identify FOUR** hazards associated with work at height above ground level. (4)

    (b) **Outline** factors to consider when conducting a working at height risk assessment. (8)

    (c) **Outline** safe working practices associated with the use of a mobile elevating working platform (MEWP). (8)

Please refer to back of assessment section for answers.

Excavation work and confined spaces - hazards and risk control

Learning outcomes

On completion of this element, candidates should be able to demonstrate understanding of the content through the application of knowledge to familiar and unfamiliar situations. In particular they should be able to:

11.1   Explain the hazards and risk assessment of excavation work.

11.2   Explain the control measures for excavation work.

11.3   Explain the hazards and risks associated with confined space working.

11.4   Outline the control measures for confined space working.

Content

Sources of reference

Essentials of health and safety at work, HSE Books, ISBN 978-0-7176-6179-4

Avoiding danger from underground services, HSG47, HSE Books, ISBN 978-0-7176-6584-6

Safe work in confined spaces. Confined Spaces Regulations 1997, ACoP and guidance, L101, HSE Books, ISBN 978-0-7176-6233-3

Protecting the public: Your next move, HSG151, HSE Books, ISBN 978-0-7176-6294-4

Avoidance of danger from overhead electric power lines, Guidance Note GS6 (Third Edition), HSE Books, ISBN 978-0-7176-1348-9

Relevant statutory provisions

Confined Spaces Regulations (CSR) 1997

Construction (Design and Management) Regulations (CDM) 2007

Personal Protective Equipment at Work Regulations (PPER) 1992

Work at Height Regulations (WAH) 2005

11.1 - Excavations hazards and assessment

The hazards of work in and around excavations

Work in excavations and trenches, basements, underground tanks, sewers, manholes etc., can involve high risks and each year construction workers are killed with some buried alive or asphyxiated.

Figure 11-1: Buried services.   *Source: RMS.*

Figure 11-2: Excavation hazards.   *Source: RMS.*

BURIED SERVICES

Although electricity cables provide the most obvious risk, gas pipes, water mains, drains and sewers can all release dangerous substances. Gas is particularly dangerous if there is a potential ignition source close by. Fibre-optic cables may carry laser light, which could be damaging to the eyes if severed accidentally and are very expensive to repair.

Buried services (electricity, gas, water, etc) may not be obvious at the time of site survey; this increases the likelihood of striking a service when excavating, drilling or piling. The results of striking an underground service are varied, and the potential to cause injury or a fatality is high. As with overhead power lines, any underground service should be treated as live until confirmed dead by an authority (utility provider). Incidents can include shock, electrocution, explosion and burns from power cables, explosion, burns or unconsciousness from gas, impact injury from dislodged stones or flooding from ruptured water mains.

FALLS OF PERSONS/EQUIPMENT/MATERIAL INTO THE EXCAVATION

When people are working below ground in excavations, the problems are very similar to those faced when people are working at a height - falls and falling objects. Particular problems arise when:

- Materials, including spoil, are stored too close to the edge of the excavation.
- The excavation is close to another building and the foundations may be undermined.
- The edge of the excavation is not clear, especially if the excavation is in a public area.
- Absence of barriers or lighting.
- Poor positioning or the absence of access ladders allowing people to fall.
- Absence of organized crossing points.
- Badly constructed ramps for vehicle access which can cause the vehicle to topple.
- No stop blocks for back filling.
- Routing of vehicles too close to the excavation.

COLLAPSE OF SIDES

Often, the soil and earth that make up the sides of the excavation cannot be relied upon to support their own weight, leading to the possibility of collapse. The risk can be made worse if:

- The soil structure is loose or made unstable by water logging.
- Heavy plant or materials are too close to the edge of the excavation.
- Machinery or vehicles cause vibration.
- There is inadequate support for the sides.

The consequences of even a minor collapse can be very serious. A minor fall of earth can happen at high speed and bring with it anything (plant and machinery) that may be at the edge. Even if the arms and head of a person are not trapped in the soil, the material pressing on the person can lead to severe crush injuries to the lower body and asphyxiation due to restriction of movement of the chest.

COLLAPSE OF ADJACENT STRUCTURES

Excavations that are carried out within close proximity to existing buildings or structures may result in their foundations becoming undermined and create the potential for significant settling damage to occur or worse still, collapse. Consideration should be given to the effects that excavation work might have on foundations of neighbouring buildings or structures, and control measures implemented to ensure that foundations are not disturbed or undermined. Building foundations that are at a distance of less than twice the excavation depth from the face of the excavation are more likely to be affected by ground movement; underpinning or shoring of such structures may be required to prevent structural damage.

WATER INGRESS

Ingress of water may occur through rainfall, flood (river, sea) or when an excavation extends below the natural groundwater level. In deep excavations, where access is not readily available, the combined effect of water and mud could lead to difficulty in escape and risk of drowning. In addition, this can lead to the sides of the trench becoming soft and the integrity of the supports can be undermined.

USE OF COFFERDAMS

A cofferdam is a retaining wall that is built into a river, lake, or other body of water and is commonly made of steel sheet piling, or concrete. The retaining wall is intended to provide a dry workplace in which work can be carried out.

Cofferdams are typically used in the construction of the foundations of bridges, docks, and piers. The principle hazard involved in the use of a cofferdam is the risk of failure of the retaining wall, allowing water ingress. If this happens gradually it can make the ground very wet and difficult to work in or travel around. Without the use of pumps to control water ingress slips and falls may become a major problem. If the failure of the wall is sudden, perhaps caused by severe tidal or storm water activity, there is a high risk of workers drowning.

Figure 11-3: Cofferdam.   *Source: USA Army Corps Library.*

The nature of the soil, depth of water, amount of water movement, depth of excavation and type of structure can all influence the stability and strength of the retaining wall and therefore its effectiveness in keeping water out.

USE OF CAISSONS

A caisson is a retaining, water tight structure that is constructed, floated or lowered into position where work needs to be conducted in a defined area, creating a type of 'box' to work in. Caissons are often made of concrete sections joined together to create the structure. When set in position, the water within the caisson is pumped out, providing a chamber as a workspace.

In the case of hollow caissons, if additional depth is required the earth can be mechanically excavated from the centre of the caisson and the weight of the caisson causes it to sink lower. This can be continued by adding additional caisson sections until a firm foundation is reached. Caissons are used for a wide variety of work, for example to create or work on the foundations of a bridge pier that may be submerged in water.

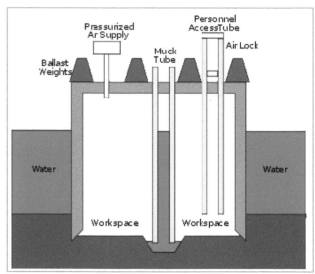

Figure 11-4: Pressurised caisson.   *Source: YK Times.*

Pressurised (Pneumatic) caissons are shaped like an open box, turned upside down. They are placed where the work is needed and the bottom edges of the caisson sink into the earth, creating a seal. The inside is pressurised by compressed air to remove the water and prevent water ingress. Workers enter through an air lock. They remove earth from the bottom of the caisson by hand and place it in a (muck) tube connected to the surface, where it is removed by a crane and bucket. As with the hollow caisson, removing the earth at the bottom allows the caisson to sink deeper. When great strain or pressure is likely to be encountered in the construction of foundations or piers deep in a body of water, the pressurised caisson is generally used.

The principal hazard of work within caissons is the risk of water or slurry ingress and drowning. With hollow caissons, this may be because of failure of the sealing of joints between the sections that comprise the caisson. This failure could be due to damage at the time of assembly, the effects of water over time or the pressure due to the depth it is operating at overcoming the seal. Because caissons are frequently used in rivers and the sea there is the further hazard of service vessels colliding with the caisson, causing leaks or catastrophic failure.

In the case of pressurised caissons, they have the additional possibility of failure of the system maintaining pressure within the structure; this could lead to failure of seals or in the case of a homogenous structure the collapse of the sides. Work in pressurised conditions can be strenuous and workers leaving a pressurised caisson after hours of working under high pressure may suffer from a form of decompression sickness unless they are given special decompression treatment to accustom them to the lower atmospheric pressure.

CONTAMINATED GROUND

Digging may uncover buried materials that have the potential to be hazardous to health. The history of the site should be examined to try to identify if substances have been buried on the site during its previous use. Sites that once were used as steel works may contain arsenic and cyanide dating back many years; farmyards may have been used as graves for animals and to dispose of pesticides and organo-phosphates. There is always the presence of vermin to consider - this can increase the risk of diseases such as leptospirosis.

TOXIC AND ASPHYXIATING ATMOSPHERES

Excavations can under different circumstances be subject to toxic, asphyxiating or explosive atmospheres. Chalk or limestone deposits when in contact with acidic groundwater can release carbon dioxide, and gases such as methane or hydrogen sulphide can seep into excavations from contaminated ground or damaged services in built-up areas. These atmospheres can accumulate at the bottom of an excavation and result in asphyxiation, poisoning, explosion or potential fatalities.

Excavations should be treated with similar caution to that applied to confined spaces, and an assessment should be carried out prior to work commencing in excavations to identify the risk of toxic gas, oxygen deficiency, and fire or explosion. It should also identify the appropriate risk control measures required, such as:

- Type of gas monitoring equipment to be provided.
- Testing of the atmosphere before entry into the excavation.
- Provision of suitable ventilation equipment.
- Training of employees.
- Use of a sufficient number of people, including one at ground level.
- Procedures and equipment needed for an emergency rescue.

Figure 11-5: Water in excavation. *Source: RMS.*

MECHANICAL HAZARDS

Mechanical hazards of excavation work relate mainly to the equipment used to create the excavation and to lay equipment/materials in place.

The principal mechanical hazard is the risk of being struck by this equipment as it moves its excavator arm or jib. The risk is greatly increased as people move close to the equipment, for example, workers or pedestrians passing by. People particularly at risk are those that place themselves in close proximity to the equipment when it is operating.

This would include people directing the equipment movement or those supervising the work, particularly if they stand in or close to the excavation at a position near to where work is going on.

Figure 11-6: Mechanical hazard from excavator. *Source: RMS.*

The closing movements of parts of this equipment, such as an excavator arm or bucket, present a significant crushing risk. In addition, as the plant is usually capable of mobility there is a risk of people working in close proximity receiving crush injuries to their feet.

OVERHEAD HAZARDS

The overhead hazards influencing excavation activities will depend upon where the excavation work is carried out. If the work is on a 'green field' site the only overhead hazards present are likely to be from overhead telephone and power lines or trees.

If the work is on an existing site, then the access and egress route, as well as the working area will need to be assessed for overhead hazards. Hazards may include overhead pipes and pipe racks/bridges, pedestrian walkways between buildings and power/telephone lines.

Work on or adjacent to the highway will present a number of overhead hazards, such as street lights, traffic signs/signal systems and bridges. The bridges may additionally carry utilities such as gas, water and sewage below them. Work near to water or railways will have similar overhead hazards to the highway.

Wherever the excavation is taking place, if the site is well developed there is the additional overhead hazard of scaffolds, MEWPS or parts of the structure.

Hazards of overhead power lines

Every year people are seriously hurt by coming into contact with overhead power lines. A high proportion, about one third, proves to be fatal. These fatalities occur at voltages ranging from 400 kV to 230 V. Any lines found on a site should always be treated as live until they are proved to be otherwise.

Overhead power lines usually consist of bare (uninsulated) conductors. These are often referred to as cables. They are supported overhead in a number of ways, the most common being wooden posts or metal towers. A common problem with the type supported by wooden posts is that they are mistaken for telephone cables, which may mean they are treated with less care than is deserved; an accidental contact with an excavators bucket could be fatal to the operator.

If the excavator comes into contact with an overhead line it may not discharge immediately to earth through the vehicle; this can be because the tyres offer some resistance. Operators of excavators have received fatal shocks in these circumstances when, on getting out of the vehicle, they make contact with the ground and provide a passage for the current to earth.

One of the other risks related with overhead power lines is that of arcing or, as it is sometimes called, a flashover. This occurs where the excavator approaches the conductor, but does not touch it. Instead, the electricity in the conductor bridges the air gap between the conductor and excavator as an arc; current then flows through the excavator. The risk of flashover increases significantly as the voltage applied to the conductor increases.

If excavators are brought closer than the following distances there is a significant risk of flashover:

- 15 m of overhead lines supported by steel towers.
- 9 m of overhead lines supported by wooden poles.

See also - Element 6 - Electrical safety – 'High risks associated with electricity' section.

Risk assessment

FACTORS TO CONSIDER

The depth of the excavation

Risks increase with the depth of excavation, risks from materials falling increase with the height they may fall and there is an increased risk of collapse at greater depths as the amount of material to support (comprising the excavation wall) increases. A collapse of an excavation deeper than the head height of a worker carries a high risk of suffocation.

It should be remembered that a worker may have to work low down in an excavation so a shallow excavation can present serious risks, depending on the work being carried out in it.

The type of soil being excavated

Clay presents specific risks of collapse due to it drying out or becoming more fluid when wet. If the soil is not compacted, for example because of a previous excavation near by, its strength may not be as higher as if it has had chance to settle and become compacted.

Soil changes its strength significantly when it becomes wet; presenting an added risk that water may make its way into the excavation and cause flooding. If the soil is chalky carbon dioxide may be liberated as part of the excavation process, similarly if it is in contaminated land there may be toxic substances and risks from methane.

The type of work being undertaken

If the work to be done to create and work in the excavation is to be done manually or mechanically the risks vary significantly. The task being conducted can increase the risks, for example, pipe jointing operations carried out manually will usually bring the head of the worker below the top of the excavation for a significant time. Additional risks may also be created by hot working or work in a confined space.

The use of mechanical equipment

Though this can reduce the risk to workers by not requiring them to enter the excavation to dig it they carry risks of their own. Where people work alongside this equipment there is a risk of contact or collision and as it carries a considerable amount of momentum major injuries or death would not be uncommon if contact was made.

Proximity of roadways and structures etc

Where excavations are within close proximity of roadways and structures, vehicles should be segregated and excluded from excavation areas wherever possible. Brightly painted baulks or barriers and or fencing should be used where necessary to protect and clearly identify the excavation area.

If vehicles have to unload materials into excavations, then the use of stop blocks to prevent such vehicles falling into the excavation as a result of over-running is recommended. Special consideration should be given to the reinforcement of the sides of the excavation, which may need extra support, especially when adjacent to busy roads.

Excavations should not be allowed to affect the footings of scaffolds or the foundations of nearby structures. Walls especially in older properties may have very shallow foundations, which could be undermined by small trenches, therefore some structures may need temporary support even before digging can commence. It is always best practice to conduct surveys of the foundations and gain the advice of a structural engineer in such cases.

Presence of public

Excavations in public areas should be fenced off, fitted with toe boards and stop block type barriers to prevent pedestrians and vehicles falling into them. Where children or trespassers might inadvertently get access to a site out of hours then certain precautions should be considered such as backfilling or securely covering excavations to reduce the potential of such people being injured. The excavation should have suitable and sufficient identification and signage, with any pedestrian routes or detours clearly marked, fenced off and lit (if appropriate).

Weather

Heavy rain or fast melting snow may undermine the stability of the ground and therefore of the supports or sides of the excavation. Hence, careful consideration should be given to the type of shoring used, depending on the site and sub-soils.

Services

The presence or likelihood of services in the area of an excavation carries high risks of a different type. For example, contact with an electrical service may be immediately fatal to a worker or damage to a gas service may cause a risk of major explosion.

Material and vehicles

If materials are placed too close to excavations or vehicles pass near by there is an increased risk of collapse or fall of materials/vehicle.

Required support equipment that may be needed

The risks from excavations may be reduced by using the correct support equipment. Care has to be taken to ensure that the right type and quantity is used if the risk is to be reduced effectively. For example, there may be a need to provide close shoring of the sides of an excavation to control a particular soil condition or where the effects of water are likely.

11.2 - Control measures for excavation work

Controls

IDENTIFICATION/DETECTION AND MARKING OF BURIED SERVICES

The Health and Safety Executive (HSE) guidance, HSG47; "Avoiding danger from underground services", outlines the dangers that can arise from work near underground services and gives advice on how to reduce the risk. The guidance defines 'service(s)' as all underground pipes, cables and equipment associated with the electricity, gas, water (including piped sewage) and telecommunications industries.

It also includes other pipelines that transport a range of petrochemical and other fluids. It does not include underground structures such as railway tunnels. The term 'service connection(s)' is used for pipes or cables between distribution mains and individual premises.

Identification

Excavation operations should not begin until all available service location drawings have been obtained and thoroughly examined to identify the location of services. Location drawings should not be considered as totally accurate, but do serve as an indication of the likelihood of the presence of services, their location and depth.

It is possible for the position of an electricity supply cable to alter if previous works have been carried out in the location. This can be due to the flexibility of the cable and movement of surrounding features since the original installation of the cable.

In addition, location drawings often show a proposed position for the services that does not translate to the ground, such that services are placed in position only approximately where the plan says.

Detection

The main types of detection and locating devices are:

Hum detectors, which detect the magnetic field radiated by electricity cables that have a current flowing through. They do not detect where there is little or no current flowing, for example, service connection cables to unoccupied premises or street lighting cables in the daytime.

Radio frequency detectors, which generate a low frequency radio signal into a cable or pipe placed very close to it. The receiver can then detect this signal and locate the cable or pipe run.

Metal detectors, which usually locate flat metal covers, joint boxes etc, but may not detect round cables or pipes.

Ground probing radar, which is a method that is capable of detecting anomalies in the ground. When plotted into a continuous line they may indicate a cable, duct or pipe.

Figure 11-7: Using a cable locator.   *Source: HSE, HSG47.*

Commercially available instruments use more than one of the techniques listed and may also include a depth-measuring facility.

It is important that 'service location devices', such as a cable avoidance tool (CAT) are used by competent, trained operatives to assist in the identification and marking of the actual location and position of buried services.

Marking

Markers may have been used to indicate the presence of services when they were laid, these include:

- Marker tiles, for example, to mark gas pipes when they have been laid at shallow depths.
- Coloured plastic, for example, tape laid to over an electric cable.
- Marker posts/plates, for example, to show the position and size of valves on gas mains or water mains.

Markers are useful in alerting caution with regard to excavation activities. However, these markers cannot be relied upon to accurately establish the position of the buried service, as they may have been disturbed in later work. Also, the absence of markers does not indicate that services are absent from the location.

Figure 11-8: Marking of services.   *Source: RMS.*

When it is uncovered, the type of service may be identified by markings in the form of a colour coding, for example, blue for water and yellow for gas.

When services are identified it is essential that physical markings be placed on the ground to show where the services are located. This can include waterproof, biodegradable paint, applied to solid surfaces, or wooden (not metal) pegs, for un-surfaced areas.

The colour coding of paint/pegs and addition of tape indicators can help to identify the type of service present.

SAFE DIGGING METHODS

Safe digging methods should be implemented within 0.5 metres of a buried service. This involves the use of insulated hand tools such as a spade or shovel with curved edges (to be used with light force and not sudden blows).

Mechanical, probing or piercing tools and equipment such as excavator's, forks, picks or drills should **not** be used when in the vicinity of buried services, as these may cause damage to any service if they strike it. Careful hand digging using a spade or shovel should be used instead.

Example of a permit to dig

Contract: ....   Contract No: ....

Principal Contractor: ....   Sub Contractor: ....

Permit No: ....   Date: ....

1.   Location: ....

2.   Size, detail and depth of excavation: ....

....

3.   Are Service Plans on site ?   YES / NO

Comments: ....

4.   Has cable locating equipment been used to identify services ?   YES / NO

Comments: ....

5.   Are all known services marked out ? (site inspection by relevant statutory bodies)   YES / NO

Comments: ....

6.   Are trial holes required ?   YES / NO

Comments: ....

7.   Have precautions been taken to prevent contact if overhead lines are in the vicinity of the operation or near approach to the operation?

YES / NO

8.   Additional precautions, i.e. Shoring/Fencing/Access/Storage/Fumes/Record of setting out points to re-establish services routes

Comments: ....

9.   Sketch details or attach copy of plans

10. Date and time of excavation: ....

Signed: ....   Accepted by: ....

For and on behalf of issuing party   (Work shall not commence unless all persons involved are aware of the safe systems of work)

A new permit will be required for any further excavations. This permit is for guidance only.

Persons carrying out work must take reasonable precautions when working around services.

Figure 11-9: Permit to dig.   *Source: Reproduced by kind permission of Lincsafe.*

METHODS OF SUPPORTING EXCAVATIONS

"(1) All practicable steps shall be taken, where necessary to prevent danger to any person, including, where necessary, the provision of supports or battering, to ensure that:

(a) Any excavation or part of an excavation does not collapse.

(b) No material from a side or roof of, or adjacent to, any excavation is dislodged or falls.

(c) No person is buried or trapped in an excavation by material which is dislodged or falls".

Figure 11-10: Methods of shoring and battering.   *Source: Regulation 31(1) of CDM 2007.*

Precautions must be taken to prevent collapse. An alternative method to the use of supports to prevent collapse is where soil and material is removed from the sides of the excavation so that steps or a shallow slope is created in the sides; this is called battering, *see figure ref 11-11*.

Battering relies on the material in the steps or slopes of the sides of the excavation creating minimal downward/sideways pressure, reducing the likelihood and effect of collapse.

The options available for providing support by shoring include closed boarding / sheeting *see figure refs 11-13 and 11-14*, open sheeting *see figure refs 11-14 and 11-16* and where the shoring needs to be repositioned frequently, such as where services are being laid, a trench box *see figure ref 11-12*.

The application of a particular method of prevention of collapse depends on the:

- Nature of the subsoil - for example wet may require close shoring with sheets.
- Projected life of the excavation - a trench box may give ready made access where it is only needed for short duration work.
- Work to be undertaken, including equipment used - for example the use of a trench box for shoring where pipe joints are made.
- Possibility of flooding from ground water and heavy rain - close shoring would be required.
- Depth of the excavation - a shallow excavation may use battering instead of shoring, particularly where shoring may impede access.
- Number of people using the excavation at any one time - a lot of space may be required so cantilever sheet piling may be preferred.

Figure 11-11: Battering.   *Source: RMS.*

Figure 11-12: Trench box - for shoring.   *Source: RMS.*

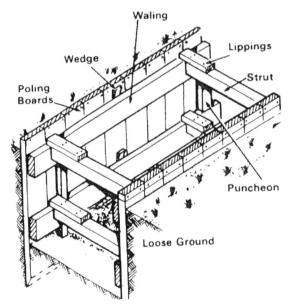

Figure 11-13: Close boarded excavation.   *Source: BS6031.*

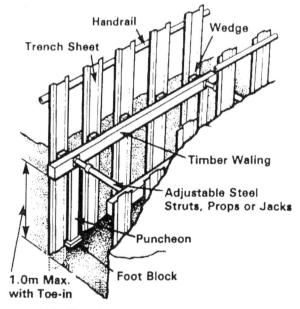

Figure 11-14: Open sheeting.   *Source: BS6031.*

Figure 11-15: Close sheeting.   *Source: RMS.*

Figure 11-16: Open sheeting.   *Source: RMS.*

MEANS OF ACCESS

Ladders are the usual means of access and egress to excavations. They must be properly secured, in good condition and inspected regularly. The ladder should extend about one metre or three rungs above ground level to give a good handhold.

To allow for emergency egress it is recommended that a minimum requirement of one ladder every 15 metres be provided.

CROSSING POINTS

Crossing excavations should only be allowed at predetermined points. The crossing point should be able to withstand the maximum foreseeable load and be provided with guardrails and toe boards. The spacing or location of crossing points should be such that workers and others are encouraged to use them, rather than to attempt other means of crossing the excavation.

BARRIERS, LIGHTING AND SIGNS

Where people or materials can fall from height a form of edge protection must be provided. In some cases the shoring method used can provide this barrier by ensuring the top of the shoring extends sufficiently above the edge of the excavation, *see figure ref 11-17*.

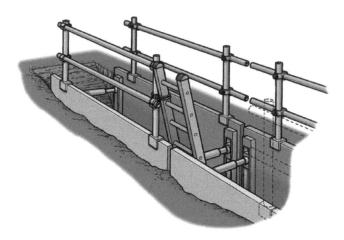

Figure 11-17: Access and guardrails.   *Source: HSE, HSG150.*

Guardrails that are provided must meet the same standards as those for working platforms used for work at height. It is also good practice to cover shallow trenches when they are left unattended.

"(2) Suitable and sufficient steps shall be taken to prevent any person, work equipment, or any accumulation of material from falling into any excavation".

Figure 11-18: Prevention of falls into excavation.   *Source: Regulation 31(2) of CDM 2007.*

The large pieces of mobile plant and equipment that are commonly used for excavation work have the potential to cause serious harm to site workers and members of the public. In order to keep people and vehicles apart, exclusion zones identified by barriers *see figure ref 11-17*, fencing *see figure ref 11-19*, warning signs and lights should be provided.

Concrete or wooden blocks (usually old railway sleepers) may be placed some distance from the edge of an excavation to prevent vehicles from getting too close, particularly when the excavation is being 'back filled'. In this case, the wooden blocks provide a 'stop block'.

Signs that comply with The Health and Safety (Signs and Signals) Regulations (SSSR) 1996 should be displayed to warn people of the excavation and any special measures to be taken. If working on a public highway, the police or the local authority must be consulted over the positioning of traffic lights. Appropriate lighting should be provided; it must provide sufficient illumination for those at work but should not create glare or other distractions for passers by, especially motorists. Battery operated headlamps (to avoid trailing cables) may be considered for individual use. If excavations are present in dark conditions they must be suitably lit to prevent vehicles or people colliding or falling into them.

SAFE STORAGE OF SPOIL

Excavated material (spoil), other materials, plant and vehicles should never be stored or parked close to the sides of any excavation. The additional pressure distributed on the ground from spoil, vehicles, etc significantly increases the likelihood of collapse occurring at the sides of the excavation. Though it will depend on the weight of the material, it would normally be kept to a minimum of 1 metre from the edge of the excavation. *See figure ref 11-19* which shows heavy pipes set away from the excavation and spoil set to the side.

In addition, spoil heaps consist of loose materials that have the risk of spilling into the excavation. A means of preventing spillage of spoil into an excavation is by positioning scaffold boards as toe boards, fixed along the outside of trench sheets. An alternative to this is to allow boards or sheeting to protrude above the top of the excavation sufficiently to act as toe boards and prevent materials falling. Head protection must be worn by workers working in excavations to provide protection from small pieces of material falling either from above or from the sides of the excavation.

If stored at a suitable distance away from an excavation and at a suitable height, spoil heaps can form an effective barrier against vehicles travelling around the construction site and assist in preventing falls of vehicles and plant into an excavation and onto workers.

Figure 11-19: Materials storage.   *Source: RMS.*

Figure 11-20: Preventing water ingress.   *Source: RMS.*

CONTROL OF WATER AND DEWATERING

Consideration must be given to the likelihood of water entering the excavation and the measures to be implemented in order to control water entering the excavation and water levels within it. Ingress of water may occur through rainfall, flood or when excavating below the natural groundwater level. When an excavation is liable to water ingress the stability of the excavation walls can be undermined, increasing the risk of collapse and possible drowning.

The first priority is to control the amount of water entering the excavation; this will influence the choice of shoring, for example, close sheeting may be used rather than open sheeting. In addition, it may be necessary to position flood or rain water barriers to direct water away from the excavation; this may include the use of sandbags or similar methods that provide a portable barrier, **see figure ref 11-20**.

Well points

Well point dewatering is often used to reduce the hydrostatic pressure from the back of a sheet pile wall, in conjunction with lowering the water table to the maximum excavation depth required for the construction site.

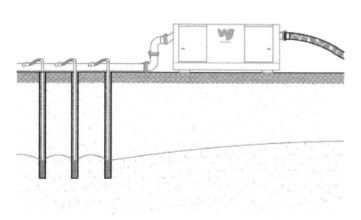

Figure 11-21: Well point schematic.   *Source: W J Groundwater Ltd.*

Figure 11-22: Well point trench installation.
Source: www.khansahebsykes.com.

Well point dewatering systems are installed around the perimeter of the site against excavation shoring and are coupled with a perimeter discharge line via a pump set. The system can effectively draw the water table down to between 3 and 8 metres depending on the type of pump set used and the type of soil conditions. For a well point dewatering system to be effective, the ground sub-strata generally needs to be permeable, to allow the well points to draw the groundwater.

Sump points

Usually water in excavations is drained to sumps, from where it can be pumped out for disposal. The sump should be at the lowest point where the water collects. Typically a sump will be a minimum of 0.6 metres deep, so that the pump is covered by the water. This allows the pump to cycle on and off with rising and falling water levels within the sump.

It is normally permissible to distribute pumped groundwater from within an excavation over grassy areas where any silt deposits can be absorbed and not have a detrimental effect on the environment. However, when works are within close proximity to a watercourse, i.e. within 10 metres, then advice should be sought on the disposal of groundwater and a 'Consent for Works Affecting Watercourses' should be obtained from the Environment Agency.

SUBSTANCES

Excavations should be treated with similar caution to that applied to confined spaces, and an assessment should be carried out prior to work commencing in excavations to identify the risk of toxic gas, oxygen deficiency and fire or explosion. It should also identify the appropriate risk control measures required, such as:

■ Type of gas monitoring equipment to be provided.
■ Testing of the atmosphere before entry into the excavation.
■ Provision of suitable ventilation equipment.
■ Training of employees.
■ Use of a sufficient number of people, including one at ground level.
■ Procedures and equipment needed for an emergency rescue.

Figure 11-23: Substances in excavation. *Source: RMS.*

POSITIONING AND ROUTING OF VEHICLES, PLANT AND EQUIPMENT

"(3) Without prejudice to paragraphs (1) and (2), suitable and sufficient steps shall be taken, where necessary, to prevent any part of an excavation or ground adjacent to it from being overloaded by work equipment or material".

Figure 11-24: Overloading of excavation by work equipment or material. *Source: Regulation 31(3) of CDM 2007.*

To prevent objects falling into excavations, the following precautions should be taken:

■ Spoil and construction materials must not be stacked near to the edge.
■ The weight of stacks should not be enough to cause the sides to collapse.
■ Designated operating areas for vehicles and equipment must be established.
■ Unnecessary vehicles and equipment should be routed away from the excavation.
■ Where vehicles have to approach the excavation, stop barriers must be provided to prevent overrunning.

PERSONAL PROTECTIVE EQUIPMENT

As well as the need for hard hats to limit the risks from falling materials, other personal protective equipment (PPE) may be necessary, such as:

■ Breathing apparatus.
■ Safety harnesses.
■ Hearing protection.
■ Clothing to protect from the rays of the sun.

■ Masks and respirators.
■ Face masks and gloves for welding and grinding.
■ Gloves for contaminated materials.
■ Footwear.

FILLING IN

On completion of use of the excavation, experienced people should remove support materials. A competent person should inspect the site to ensure that all people and materials have been removed. The excavation may need water pumping from it before filling.

Where vehicles approach the excavation to add materials it is essential that stop barriers are used at the edge of the excavation to avoid vehicles falling into it.

Materials added to the excavation must be sufficiently compacted to allow for the next use of the area, for example, as part of a roadway or to allow a scaffold to be placed on top of it. Only appropriate in-fill materials must be used. Uncontrolled tipping/burial is an offence.

Particular requirements for contaminated ground

Contaminated ground can give rise to various health hazards, including biological and chemical hazards. Exposure to the hazards can vary depending on the work to be carried out and assessments should be made to determine which controls are required.

Site preparation work which involves the removal of topsoil from land known to be contaminated with heavy metals will require specific arrangements in relation to personal protective equipment required and practices to be carried out. The work is likely to require the provision of gloves, overalls, eye protection and respirators. Additionally, the work will require campaigns of awareness training to ensure good levels of personal hygiene are maintained, with emphasis on ensuring that open cuts are covered with waterproof dressings whenever required. Consideration will need to be given to specific welfare facilities provision, for example a decontamination unit. There should be arrangements in place in order to prevent contamination when eating and smoking. First-aid and emergency decontamination facilities should be made available located near to the place of work.

SOIL TESTING

Surveys should be undertaken, and a soil-testing programme implemented prior to works beginning. As each site is different and may involve various contaminant types, the methods of testing and analysis used should be suitable to the particular local needs of each site.

Usually, specialist contractors are used to carry out this type of work. Historical information such as land deeds, maps, building plans and any other information relating to the site provide useful assistance. Contaminants will usually be found in the top 0.5 - 1m layer (strata) of ground and soil samples should be at least to the greatest depth of any excavation, remembering that contamination may seep from one part of a site to another. As a minimum precaution, any proposed control measures chosen should adequately protect against the highest concentrations of contaminant found on site.

WELFARE FACILITIES

Ensuring good hygiene standards is one of the more important elements of protective measures to be taken when working on construction sites and in particular with contaminated ground. Whilst the level of risk that is identified will establish the range of measures that are to be provided, the principles outlined should always be followed when working on a contaminated site.

Installation of a sufficiently ventilated and lit hygiene facility must be provided. This may be purpose built or a smaller standard unit may be sufficient depending upon the number of personnel involved at the site. The installation of the hygiene/decontamination unit should be situated at the most convenient point to or from the dirty zone.

The hygiene/decontamination facility should generally be in three stages, but prior to entering the unit a boot wash point should be provided that includes running water and fixed or hand brushes for removing contaminated matter.

The hygiene facility should then be arranged in its three stages as follows:

Stage 1   Should provide storage for ordinary clothing not used whilst at work.
Stage 2   A high standard washing facility. This includes the provision of hot and cold water with taps preferably operated by the elbow or foot, detergent, nail brushes and disposable towels. In certain circumstances (toxic or corrosive contamination) showers may be the necessary means of cleansing. Both men and women may use showers (at separate times) provided that it is in a separate room with a lock on the inside of the door.
Stage 3   Should provide storage for contaminated work wear such as overalls, boots, etc.

In addition to the hygiene facility, toilets should be provided. The location of toilet units on contaminated sites must be situated so workers are directed through the hygiene facility prior to reaching the toilet for use. Daily cleaning and decontamination must be carried out on toilet facilities. Everyone who works on construction sites must have access to adequate toilet and washing facilities, a place for warming up and a clean room set aside for taking meals and refreshment. Secure storage for clothing and facilities for drying wet clothing. First-aid facilities should also be provided.

HEALTH SURVEILLANCE

The employer should decide about the need for health surveillance as part of the Control of Substances Hazardous to Health Regulations (COSHH) 2002 assessment. Health surveillance is appropriate where:

■   A disease or adverse effect may be related to exposure.
■   It is likely that this could arise in the circumstances of the work.
■   There is valid techniques for detecting the disease or effect.

For example, work with cadmium, phenol, or arsenic, will normally need health surveillance including biological monitoring of workers.

Inspection requirements for excavation support systems

CDM 2007, Regulation 31, requires inspections and reports to be carried out for excavations.

A competent person must inspect excavations:

■   At the start of each shift in which the work is to be carried out.
■   After any event likely to have affected the strength or stability of the excavation.
■   After any material unintentionally falls or is dislodged and the person who carried out the inspection is satisfied that the work can be carried out there safely.

The competent person must:

■   Where the person who carried out the inspection has informed the person, on whose behalf the inspection was carried out, of any matter about which he or she is not satisfied work shall not be carried out in the excavation until the matters have been satisfactorily remedied.
■   Prepare a report and must, within 24 hours of completing the inspection to which the report relates, provide the report or a copy of it to the person on whose behalf the inspection was carried out.

The inspection report must include the following information:

1) Name and address of person on whose behalf the inspection was carried out.
2) Location of the workplace inspected.
3) Description of workplace or part of workplace inspected (including any plant and equipment and materials, if any).
4) Date and time of inspection.
5) Details of any matter identified that could lead to a risk to the health and safety of anyone.
6) Details of any action taken as a result of any matter identified in the last point.
7) Details of any more action considered necessary.
8) The name and position of the person making the report.

11.3 - Confined spaces hazards and risks

A failure to appreciate the dangers associated with confined spaces has led not only to the deaths of many workers, but also to the demise of some of those who have attempted to rescue them.

Meaning of the term 'confined space'

A confined space is a space that is substantially enclosed and where there will be a reasonably foreseeable risk of serious injury from substances or conditions. This therefore means not only a space that is small and difficult to enter, exit or work in, but one with limited or restricted access; or it can also be a space that is badly ventilated for example a tank or a large tunnel.

Typical confined spaces found during construction activities

The Confined Spaces Regulations (CSR) 1997 defines a confined space as any place, including:

Chamber Cellar, tunnel, caisson, cofferdam, water interception chamber or chamber for a pump.

Tank Storage tanks for solid or liquid chemical.

Vat Process vessels, which may be open, but by its depth confines a person.

Silo May be an above the ground structure for storing cement or mortar.

Pit Excavations.

Pipe Concrete, plastic steel etc, fabrication used to carry liquids or gases.

Sewer Brick or concrete structure for the carrying of liquid waste.

Flue Exhaust chimney for disposal of waste gases.

Well Deep source of water.

Cellar An enclosed low level room or space below ground level usually found in old buildings or public houses.

Trench A relatively shallow, narrow excavation, usually for utility laying provision or drainage facility.

Or other similar space, in which, by virtue of its enclosed nature, there is a foreseeable risk of a 'specified occurrence'.

Figure 11-25: Confined space - chamber.   *Source: RMS.*

Figure 11-26: Confined space - sewer.   *Source: RMS.*

"SPECIFIED OCCURRENCE"

The Confined Spaces Regulations (CSR) 1997 apply to situations where there is a risk of a "specified occurrence", this is defined as:

- Fire or explosion.
- Loss of consciousness or asphyxiation of any person at work arising from gas, fumes, vapour or lack of oxygen.
- Drowning of any person at work.
- Asphyxiation of any person at work arising from a free flowing solid.
- Loss of consciousness of any person arising from a high ambient temperature.

Figure 11-27: Confined space - cement silo.   *Source: RMS.*

Figure 11-28: Confined space - open tank.   *Source: RMS.*

Hazards and risks associated with confined spaces

EXPOSURE TO TOXIC, EXPLOSIVE AND OXYGEN DEFICIENT ATMOSPHERES

Air in the confined space is made unbreathable either by toxic gases, fumes or by lack of oxygen. There is not enough natural ventilation to keep the air fit to breathe. In some cases the gases may be flammable, so there may also be a fire or explosion risk.

Some confined spaces are naturally dangerous, for example, because of:

- Gas build-up in sewers and manholes and pits connected to them.
- Gases leaking into trenches and pits in contaminated land such as old refuse tips and old gas works.
- Rust inside tanks and vessels which eat up the oxygen.
- Liquids and slurries which can suddenly fill the space or release gases into it when disturbed.
- Chemical reaction between some soils and air causing oxygen depletion or the action of ground water on chalk and limestone producing carbon dioxide.

Some places are made dangerous by vapours from the work done in them. Where possible, it is important to keep hazards out of confined spaces, for example, do not use petrol or diesel engines in or near to confined spaces, because exhaust gases can cause asphyxiation. Because paints and glues used in construction work processes may give off hazardous vapours it is essential to ensure the confined space has enough ventilation to make the air fit to breathe; mechanical ventilation might be needed.

HEAT

Confined spaces have limited natural ventilation and depending on the tasks being undertaken within the area may become hot and uncomfortable to work in. In extreme cases this may cause heat exhaustion which may lead to loss of consciousness. It may be necessary to implement a forced ventilation system to refresh and cool the air within the confined space.

WATER

Many confined spaces do not allow for ease of exit. If a large volume of water were to enter a confined space the consequences could be the drowning of workers due to the restrictions on space preventing rapid exit.

FREE-FLOWING SOLIDS

The term "free flowing solid" means any substance consisting of solid particles and which is of, or is capable of being in, a flowing or running consistency. This includes flour, grain, sugar, sand or other similar material. These materials are usually stored in silos (enclosed tank), which are classed as a confined space. Silos are increasingly used on construction sites to store cement or mortar in bulk.

Asphyxiation can result as a consequence of falling into a free flowing solid such as grain, due to sinking into the material as it becomes displaced as weight is applied. Because the material can appear firm, possibly because a crust of material has formed, someone may be tempted to access and walk on the crust in order to dislodge it. It is common for such a crust to break up without warning causing the person to fall into the free-flowing solid.

RESTRICTED SPACE

Working space may be restricted, bringing workers into close contact with other hazards such as moving machinery, electricity or steam vents and pipes. The entrance to a confined space, for example a small access hole, may make escape or rescue in an emergency more difficult.

11.4 - Control measures for confined space working

Precautions for safe entry

AVOIDANCE WHERE POSSIBLE

Employers have a duty to prevent employees, or others who are to any extent within the employer's control, such as contractors, from entering or working inside a confined space where it is reasonably practicable to undertake the work without entering the space. Similarly, the self-employed should not enter or work inside a confined space where it is reasonably practicable to undertake the work without entering it.

In every situation, the employer or the self-employed must consider what measures can be taken to enable the work to be carried out without the need to enter the confined space. The measures might involve modifying the confined space itself to avoid the need for entry, or to enable the work to be undertaken from outside the space. In many cases it will involve modifying working practices.

The following are examples of modified working practices avoiding the need for entry:

- It is usually possible to test the atmosphere or sample the contents of confined spaces from outside.
- Using appropriate long tools and probes to do work.
- In some cases you can clean a confined space, or remove residues from it, from the outside using water jetting, steam or chemical cleaning, long-handled tools, or in-place cleaning systems.
- Blockages can be cleared in silos where grain or other flowing solids can 'bridge' or where voids can form by the use of remotely-operated rotating flail devices, vibrators and air purgers which avoid the need to enter the space.
- In some cases, it is possible to see what is happening inside without going in by looking in through a porthole, sight glass, grille or hole. If a sight glass tends to become blocked, it can be cleaned with a wiper and washer. Lighting can be provided inside or by shining a light in through a window. The use of closed circuit television (CCTV) systems may be appropriate in some cases.

RISK ASSESSMENT AND PLANNING

There should be a safe system of work for operations inside confined spaces, and everyone should know and follow the system. A permit-to-work system may be required.

If entry is essential:

- Identify what work must be done in the confined space and the hazards involved.
- Consider if the space could be altered to make it permanently safe or if the work could be changed to make entry to the dangerous area unnecessary.
- Make sure workers have been trained in the dangers and precautions, including rescue procedures.
- Make sure the entrance to the space is big enough to allow workers wearing all the necessary equipment to climb in and out easily.
- Before entry, ventilate the space as much as possible, test the air inside the space and only enter if the test shows it is safe.
- After entry, continue to test the air for toxic substances, flammable gases and oxygen deficiency as necessary.
- If there is a flammable risk, the space must be ventilated until it is safe. When selecting equipment, remember heat or sparks from electrical or other equipment could ignite flammable vapours, so air-powered tools may be required. The risk from flammable vapours is very high when work is carried out on the tanks of petrol service stations and similar sites. This is work that may be safer left to a specialist contractor.
- Disturbing deposits and slurries in pipes and tanks may produce extra vapour, resulting in a greater risk, so clear deposits before entry where possible.
- If the air inside the space cannot be made fit to breath because of the presence of a toxic risk or lack of oxygen, workers must wear breathing apparatus.
- Never try to 'sweeten' the air in a confined space with oxygen as this can produce a fire and explosion risk.
- Workers inside the confined space should wear rescue harnesses, with lifelines attached, which run back to a point outside the confined spaces.
- Someone should be outside to keep watch and to communicate with anyone inside, raise the alarm in an emergency and take charge of rescue procedures if it becomes necessary. It is essential those outside the space know what to do in an emergency. They need to know how to use breathing apparatus if they are to effect a rescue. *See also - Emergency Arrangements - later in this element.*

PERMIT-TO-WORK PROCEDURES AND REQUIREMENTS

Permit-to-work procedure

A permit-to-work procedure is a formal written system and is usually required where there is a reasonably foreseeable risk of serious injury in entering or working in the confined space. The permit-to-work procedure is an extension of the safe system to work, not a replacement for it. The use of a permit-to-work procedure does not, by itself, make the job safe. It supports the safe system, providing a ready means of recording findings and authorisations required to proceed with the entry. It also defines information on control measures, for example, time limits on entry, results of the gas testing, and other information that may be required during an emergency. When the job is completed, historical information on original entry conditions can also provided. A permit-to-work procedure is appropriate, for example:

- To ensure that the people working in the confined space are aware of the hazards involved and the identity, nature and extent of the work to be carried out.
- To ensure there is a formal check undertaken confirming elements of a safe system of work are in place. This needs to take place before people are allowed to enter or work in the confined space.
- Where there is a need to coordinate or exclude, using controlled and formal procedures, other people and their activities where they could affect work or conditions in the confined space.
- If the work requires the authorisation of more than one person, or there is a time-limit on entry. It may also be needed if communications with the outside are other than by direct speech, or if particular respiratory protective and/or personal protective equipment is required.

Permit-to-work document

Permit-to-work procedures will normally require a formal documented control system, including a permit-to-work document, to be used to:

- Describe (and restrict) the work to be done.
- Provide a process to determine the hazards.
- Define the controls to reduce the risk to an acceptable level.

EXAMPLE	*ENTRY INTO CONFINED SPACES*
Possible Lay-Out For A Permit-To-Work Certificate Permit-To-Work Certificate	
PLANT DETAILS (Location, identifying number, etc)	ACCEPTANCE OF CERTIFICATE Accepts all conditions of certificate
WORK TO BE DONE	Signed Date Time
WITHDRAWAL FROM SERVICE Signed Date Time	COMPLETION OF WORK All work completed - equipment returned for use
ISOLATION Dangerous fumes Electrical supply Sources of heat Signed Date Time	Signed Date Time
CLEANING AND PURGING Of all dangerous materials Signed Date Time	EXTENSION Signed Date Time
TESTING For contamination Contaminations tested Results Signed Date Time	
I CERTIFY THAT I HAVE PERSONALLY EXAMINED THE PLANT DETAILED ABOVE AND SATISFIED MYSELF THAT THE ABOVE PARTICULARS ARE CORRECT (1) THE PLANT IS SAFE FOR ENTRY WITHOUT BREATHING APPARATUS (2) BREATHING APPARATUS MUST BE WORN Other precautions necessary: Time of expiry of certificate: Signed Delete (1) or (2) Date Time	THIS PERMIT TO WORK IS NOW CANCELLED. A NEW PERMIT WILL BE REQUIRED IF WORK IS TO CONTINUE Signed Date Time RETURN TO SERVICE I accept the above plant back into service Signed Date Time

Figure 11-29: Example PTW document confined spaces. *Source: HSE Guidance note on permits to work.*

A permit-to-work document should be cancelled once the operations to which it applies have finished.

Lock-off

Where there are distinct hazards presented by stored energy, such as plant and machinery or civil utilities, which would need to be disconnected and isolated in order for work to be conducted safely, then a lock off tag out regime should be in place. For example, if there could be residual energy or potential of harm from electrical systems, gas mains, high pressure water mains, heat or chemical carrying lines, then it would be essential that these hazardous sources of danger should be locked off at distribution boxes, control valves and supply lines.

A useful approach would be to have a multiple hasp type of lock off method. In this method all workers and the person managing the work have a padlock and attach it to the hasp, which is used to lock off the source of energy. In this way, a unified decision would have to be made in order to reinstate the energy supplies. Along with the lock off there should also be identification in the form of a tag notifying that the main energy control points have been isolated and by whom.

TRAINING AND THE USE OF COMPETENT PERSONS

To be competent to work safely in confined spaces adequate training and experience in the particular work involved is essential. Training standards must be appropriate to the task, and to the individual's roles and responsibilities, so that work can be carried out safely.

Where the risk assessment indicates that properly trained individuals can work for periods without supervision, a periodic check will need to be made to ensure that they are competent to follow the established safe system of work and have been provided with adequate information and instruction about the work to be done. It is important that those that issue and work under a permit-to-work for entry into confined spaces are trained and competent to do so in general and that consideration is given to whether this training is sufficient for a specific confined space being worked in. If necessary, because of special features of the confined space, further training may be required. Anyone providing emergency rescue must be trained and competent to do so.

It is likely that general training will need to cover:

- Awareness of the Confined Spaces Regulations (CSR) 1997.
- An understanding of the work to be done, the hazards and the necessary precautions.
- An understanding of safe systems of work and permits to work, where appropriate.
- How emergencies arise and the dangers, and prepared emergency arrangements.

Specific training will relate to the type of equipment used and the circumstances of use. Refresher training should be planned and conducted in order to maintain knowledge and skills.

ATMOSPHERIC TESTING

Testing of the atmosphere may be needed where the atmosphere might be contaminated or abnormal. The appropriate choice of testing equipment will depend on particular circumstances. For example, when testing for toxic atmospheres, chemical detector tubes or portable atmospheric monitoring equipment is appropriate. However there may be cases requiring monitoring equipment specifically designed to measure for flammable atmospheres. Only persons experienced and competent in the practice should carry out testing and records should be kept of the results of the tests.

MEANS OF ACCESS

Openings into confined spaces need to be sufficiently large and free from obstruction to allow the passage of workers wearing the necessary protective clothing and equipment and to allow access and egress for rescue purposes. Practice drills will help to check that the size of openings and entry procedures are satisfactory.

Where entry to a confined space is necessary, employers will need to ensure that the necessary safety features are provided to enable safe access and egress. For example, alongside openings there might be a safety sign warning against unauthorised entry and platforms may be provided to enable safe working within the confined space. In some situations, a permanent hoist may be installed to enable access and egress. In other cases, the site of the confined space may be fitted with bearing points for locating a portable hoist system.

Here a worker wearing full breathing apparatus is also wearing a harness with a lanyard connected to a winch so that he can be hauled to the surface in an emergency without others having to enter the manhole to rescue him.

Figure 11-30: Confined space.   *Source: HSE, HSG150.*

Figure 11-31: Entrance to a confined space.   *Source: RMS.*

PERSONAL PROTECTIVE EQUIPMENT

So far as is reasonably practicable, it should be ensured that a confined space is safe to work in without the need for personal protective equipment (PPE) and respiratory protective equipment (RPE) which should be a last resort, except for rescue work (including the work of the emergency services). Use of PPE and RPE may be identified as necessary in your risk assessment, in which case it needs to be suitable and should be provided and used by those entering and working in confined spaces.

Such equipment is in addition to engineering controls and safe systems of work. The type of PPE provided will depend on the hazards identified, but might include safety lines, harnesses and suitable breathing apparatus. It is important to take account of foreseeable hazards that might arise, and the need for emergency evacuation.

Wearing respiratory protective equipment and personal protective equipment can contribute to heat stress. In extreme situations cooling air may be required for protective suits.

Monitoring arrangements

The system of work for confined space working must be monitored to ensure health and safety. This will include checking the permit-to-work document and the practical precautions related to it. It is important that the atmosphere be monitored to ensure it stays breathable; this can be done by using specific sampler equipment or personal sampler equipment. Personal gas detectors should be worn whenever appropriate to take account of the hazard of local pockets of contaminant.

The use of personal communication equipment or a communication line will assist with monitoring the progress of the activities within the confined space and the condition of the workers. This can help decide suitable breaks, the need to stop tasks or the need to instigate emergency rescue.

It is the duty of employers to ensure that any personal protective equipment provided to their employees is maintained (including replaced or cleaned as appropriate) in an efficient state, in efficient working order and in good repair. Arrangements should be in place to ensure that any PPE issued for confined space working is inspected, maintained and all findings recorded.

Emergency arrangements

The CSR 1997 prohibit any person to enter or carry out work in a confined space unless there are suitable and sufficient rescue arrangements in place. Emergency arrangements will be suitable and sufficient provided they:

- Require the provision and maintenance of resuscitation equipment.
- Require the provision and maintenance of such equipment as is necessary to enable the emergency rescue to be carried out effectively.
- Restrict, so far as is reasonably practicable, the risks to health and safety of any rescuer.
- Shall immediately be put into operation when circumstances arise requiring a rescue.

The arrangements for emergency rescue will depend on the nature of the confined space, the risks identified and consequently the likely nature of an emergency rescue.

The arrangements might need to cover:

- Rescue and resuscitation equipment.
- Special arrangements with local hospitals (for example for foreseeable poisoning).
- Raising the alarm and rescue.
- Safeguarding the rescuers.
- Safeguarding the third parties.
- Firefighting.
- Control of plant.
- First-aid.
- Public emergency services.

Sample assessment questions

1. **Identify:**

    (a)   **FOUR** hazards associated with work in a confined space. (4)

    (b)   **FOUR** examples of a confined space that may be encountered on a construction site. (4)

2. **Identify** the main hazards associated with excavation work on construction sites. (8)

3. A leaking underground concrete reservoir has been emptied so that it can be visually inspected prior to repair.

    Outline the features of a safe system of work for the inspection team in order to satisfy the requirements of the Confined Spaces Regulations 1997. (8)

Please refer to back of assessment section for answers.

Demolition and deconstruction - hazards and risk control

Learning outcomes

On completion of this element, candidates should be able to demonstrate understanding of the content through the application of knowledge to familiar and unfamiliar situations. In particular they should be able to:

12.1   Identify the main hazards of demolition and deconstruction work.

12.2   Outline the control measures for demolition and deconstruction work.

12.3   Identify the purpose and scope of a pre-demolition/refurbishment survey.

12.4   Outline the main control measures that a demolition/refurbishment method statement should include.

Content

Sources of reference

Code of practice for demolition, BS 6187, British Standards Institution, ISBN 978-0-5803-3206-7

Protecting the public: Your next move, HSG151, HSE Books, ISBN 978-0-7176-6294-4

Relevant statutory provisions

Construction (Design and Management) Regulations (CDM) 2007

Environmental Protection Act (EPA) 1990

Personal Protective Equipment at Work Regulations (PPER) 1992

Provision and Use of Work Equipment Regulations (PUWER) 1998

12.1 - Demolition and deconstruction hazards and risk

The meaning of terms

DECONSTRUCTION

The term deconstruction is used to describe the taking apart and removal of a structure in such away that it may be reused again. Reuse may be as before or in a different configuration. The term deconstruction may be related to any structure that is taken apart in an orderly way that enables reuse in part or whole, whether the structure was permanent or temporary.

The growth in environmental considerations has lead to more permanent structures being deconstructed when redevelopment is needed, enabling the reuse of their component parts. Some industrial units are built in such a way that lends them to be deconstructed and used again elsewhere if they have not reached the end of their useful life, for example, when an industrial site grows units may have to be changed or relocated.

Temporary structures are one particular group of structures that are designed for ease of construction and deconstruction. Temporary structures include those used at events, such as concerts and sporting events. This will include structures for spectator seating, hospitality gatherings, communication (large screens) and accommodation facilities for performers or athletes. The events may take place indoors in arenas, for example, like the National Exhibition Centre (NEC), Birmingham, or outdoors under temporary cover, such as in marquees, and in the open air on show grounds. In addition, temporary film/television sets and exhibitions are constructed and later deconstructed.

The risks of deconstruction include major risks related to managing and controlling an orderly deconstruction that does not cause overloading of a small number of load-bearing parts and the structure's sudden collapse. Particular difficulties may also be experienced in deconstructing parts that have been strained in use and resist being taken apart. Procedures need to be in place to deal with these anticipated difficulties without putting workers at risk.

The timing and order of deconstruction can have a significant bearing on the hazards and their control, for example, where more than one aspect of the structure is being deconstructed at the same time they can conflict with each other leading to increased risks. Similarly, it is important to organise the isolation of power sources in such a way that hazards workers are exposed to be controlled. It may be necessary to isolate all power sources from the structure and provide independent supplies to enable the safe deconstruction. Other than these issues, the general hazards of deconstruction are essentially the same as those that might be experienced in constructing structures.

Planning should also involve the recognition that some of the control measures within the structure may not be available for the protection of workers as deconstruction progresses, for example, smoke detection and fire alarm facilities may be disabled at an early point in deconstruction. This would mean that protection of workers would have to be provided by different means.

DEMOLITION

The term demolition is used to describe the tearing down, knocking down or blowing up of a structure that is no longer required. There are a number of techniques used in demolition processes, including piecemeal demolition, deliberate controlled collapse and explosive collapse.

Piecemeal demolition

Piecemeal demolition is done by hand using hand held tools and is sometimes a preliminary to other methods. It can be completed or begun by machines. For example, when demolishing a tall chimney with occupied buildings in close proximity, the job may commence with the painstaking task of dismantling by hand - brick by brick. When the structure has been reduced to about 10 metres, then conventional heavy equipment can be used.

Deliberate controlled collapse

Deliberate controlled collapse involves the pre-weakening of the structure or building. This involves removing key structural members so the remaining structure collapses under its own weight.

There are several problems associated with this method of demolition:

- The structure may collapse to a greater extent than was anticipated, affecting neighbouring buildings.
- The planned collapse may only be a partial collapse and could leave the structure hazardous and insecure.
- The resultant debris may be projected over a wider area than anticipated, particularly dust.
- The pile of debris that is left after the collapse of the structure may be in a dangerous condition, presenting a serious risk of injury to those who remove it, for example, contaminated with biological hazards or asbestos.

One method of removing the key structural members is overturning by wire rope pulling. Wires are attached to the main supports, which are pulled away using a heavy tracked vehicle or a winch to provide the motive power.

The area must be cleared of workers for this operation and there must be enough clearance for the vehicle to move the distance required to pull out the structural supports. Problems associated with this method arise when the wire becomes overstressed. If it breaks, then whiplash can occur which can have sufficient force to slice through the human body.

The forces applied may be enough to overturn the winch or the tracked vehicle. Another problem can occur when the action of pulling has begun and there is inadequate power to complete it.

Figure 12-1: Hydraulic demolition jaws. *Source: RMS.*

Figure 12-2: Hydraulic demolition grapple. *Source: RMS.*

Explosive collapse

The use of explosives requires the expertise of an experienced explosives engineer. Also, the Health and Safety Executive (HSE) should be consulted to ensure compliance with the Control of Explosives Regulations (CER) 1991 and HSE Construction information sheet No 45.

When designing for demolition using explosives it is important to plan for the risk of possible ejection of projectiles. An exclusion zone should be established at a distance from and surrounding any structure that is being demolished using explosives.

Everyone, with the possible exception of the shot-firer, should be outside the exclusion zone at the time of the blast. If the shot-firer needs to remain within the zone, a position of safety must be created.

An exclusion zone is built up from four areas:

■ Plan area - the plan area of the structure that is to be demolished.
■ Designed drop area - the area covered by the main debris pile.
■ Predicted debris area - the maximum area in which fragments can fall outside the designed debris area.
■ Buffer area - the area between the predicted debris area and the exclusion zone perimeter.

Consideration should also be given to services, for example, ground vibration which could damage services.

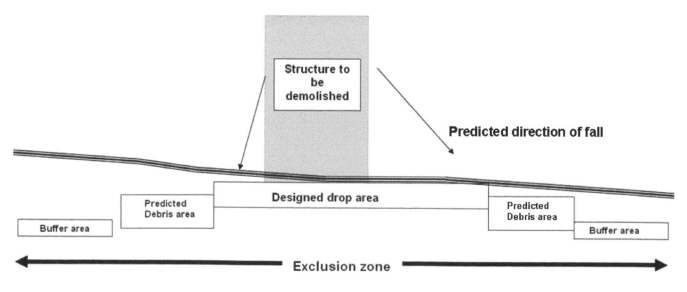

Figure 12-3: Demolition exclusion zone.

Source: Adapted from HSE construction sheet No 45.

There are a number of factors to be considered for safe demolition with the use of explosives, which include:

■ The local and structural conditions must be considered when fixing the size of the charges. The structure to be blasted can be divided into a number of sections and suitable charges applied to each section.

■ Shot holes should be drilled electrically. Drilling pneumatically could cause vibration, which could result in premature collapse.

■ Charges should not be placed near cast iron as it easily shatters into shrapnel.

■ The area around the structure being demolished and the firing point should be barricaded and unauthorised persons not allowed to enter.

■ The demolition engineer must be satisfied that no dangerous situation or condition has been left or created. The danger zone must be barricaded until rendered safe.

The selection of the appropriate method

A systematic approach to demolition and deconstruction projects is a team effort between many people, who all have responsibilities. Clients must appoint duty holders who are competent and adequately resourced. These will include structural engineers to survey the site and CDM coordinators to plan effective site management that keeps people (site workers and the public) as far as possible from the risks and principal contractors with as much information as possible.

The selection of an appropriate method will need to take into account the method of construction used for the original building and its proximity to other buildings, structures and the general public. These factors, together with location, the cost and availability of waste disposal and the desirability and economics of reuse, must also be considered.

"As built" drawings and structural details may often be unavailable or unreliable, consequently a site investigation will be necessary. This will ascertain the way in which the building was originally constructed, and identify the stresses and strains which exist within it.

Failure to establish these facts may result in risks to the safety of both those involved in the demolition and those in close proximity to the site.

Hazards relating to deconstruction and demolition

PREMATURE COLLAPSE

If a building selected for deconstruction or demolition comprises decaying materials and is unstable it may present an intrinsic hazard of premature collapse. In addition, the process of deconstruction or demolition can create a hazard of premature collapse or increase the risk if it is already there. Removal of part of a supporting wall could be sufficient to release cast concrete floor slabs to drop from one level to another, and the resultant kinetic energy can lead to the further collapse of floors below. The likelihood of premature collapse is a particular consideration when using the wrecking ball method or carrying out partial demolition. In some cases the façade of a building may be left intact for renovation and the rest of the structure removed. In these circumstances great care must be taken to avoid freestanding walls and in order to provide adequate support to the structure. When carrying out wrecking ball demolition the impact of the ball is designed to weaken the structure; if it is not used in a planned and careful manner the wrong parts of the structure or too much of it may be weakened leading to premature collapse.

Premature collapse can also be caused when carrying out systematic deconstruction or demolition by hand, particularly when load-bearing parts of the structure, such as beams, lintels, load-bearing walls and roof supports are removed. Premature collapse can occur in a similar way when carrying out building/structure undermining or dismantling.

FALLS AND FALLING MATERIALS

Depending on the type of building and method of deconstruction or demolition, workers may be expected to work at a significant height, for example, when demolishing a brick built structure by hand, and this can present a fall hazard. In the case of hand deconstruction/demolition it would be usual to remove parts of the structure in essentially the reverse order that it was erected. As such the same hazard of falling would exist as would be the case when constructing such a building. Fall hazards can often occur in the deconstruction/demolition process by the action of removing material, such as floors and stairs, or when access doors are not secured when part of the structure is removed. Part of the process may mean the removal of equipment built into the structure to prevent falls when in the structure was in normal use, thus exposing hazards, such as a rail and barrier around an atrium walkway. As with other construction work there is a risk of a worker falling outside the framework of a scaffold erected as part of the deconstruction/demolition process, particularly where workers over-reach. If the site is not well controlled there is a possibility of unauthorised people gaining access to the area, and in so doing they could be exposed to the risk of falling.

The process of deconstruction/demolition involves the movement of large quantities of material to ground level. If this is not done in an organised way and material is allowed to fall it may expose workers and passers by to the hazard. This is particularly the case where workers are carrying out demolition above other workers or near to access routes.

In addition, mechanical or explosive demolition may eject material, which could fall significant distances from the demolition process. Even small items of material represent a significant hazard when they are allowed to fall from a great height. In demolition processes, depending on how well they are conducted, material may fall in significant quantities and unexpectedly.

Figure 12-4: Risk of falling or premature collapse. *Source: RMS.*

Figure 12-5: Falling materials. *Source: RMS.*

PLANT, VEHICLES AND OTHER EQUIPMENT OVERTURNING

Demolition processes create large quantities of material that accumulate at low level. As this builds up, demolition equipment may be working on top of it to gain access to part of a structure. This can cause the centre of gravity of the equipment to be moved towards the edge of or outside its stability base. Sudden movement or an unexpected heavy load can cause it to overbalance and overturn.

Other ways in which the hazard of overturning may present itself are:

- Weak ground support, for example, cellars, sump covers, soft ground, causing one side of the equipment to be lower than another.
- Operating outside the machine's capability, for example, too large a load at too great a distance.
- Striking or getting caught up in fixed obstructions.

MANUAL HANDLING

In demolition processes there are large quantities of a wide variety of materials to be moved. This presents a potential manual handling hazard, though, in many cases, much of the manual handling hazards have been removed by the use of mechanical handling equipment. In situations where deconstruction/demolition is done by hand there is usually a lot of debris to move which may be done also by hand as the structure is reduced. In some cases the distance debris moved is limited by the provision of chutes. Where material is being salvaged this can mean an increase in manual handling is necessary in order to safeguard the condition of the material.

DUST AND FUME

Dust can be a nuisance and a risk to health to the public as well as to the workers. It may contain fungal and bacterial matter, which is pathogenic to humans, or asbestos. Structures that are being demolished may contain materials used in the construction of the structure which present a hazard as a dust or fume, for example, asbestos as fire insulation, and lead as a protective paint for metalwork. In addition, the use of the structure may lead to the presence of chemical deposits in the form of contaminated dusts; this may include toxic substances such as arsenic. As structures fall out of use it is not uncommon for pigeons to take up residence; their droppings contain a biological hazard that can lead to a lung disease called psittacosis if the dust from the droppings are breathed in. The process of demolition may liberate these materials such that they are present in the air where people are working or the public is passing by. If the process is conducted in dry conditions and windy conditions the dust may be more mobile and therefore presents more of a risk. Workers may carry out deconstruction/demolition work that creates large quantities of dust, which may be considered a nuisance in the open air, such as brick dust, but when encountered in a confined area may be a hazard because of the quantity of dust in the air.

Carbon monoxide fumes present a chemical asphyxiant hazard and may be given off by equipment used to support the demolition process, for example, demolition plant or generators used to provide temporary power supply.

NOISE AND VIBRATION

Much of the equipment used in the deconstruction/demolition process can present a noise hazard. Not surprisingly explosive charges present a noise hazard, as does impact equipment such as wrecking ball plant. Crusher and manipulation equipment can also present a noise hazard as the hydraulic system draws its power from the equipment's engine. Debris crusher plant can emit a large amount of noise as debris such as bricks is reduced.

Hand deconstruction/demolition may be supplemented by the use of electric or pneumatic chisels which emit high noise levels. On a busy site this cumulative noise can have an effect on workers and people nearby. Neighbours or other residents of an adjoining property may be affected by deconstruction/demolition work in the form of ground borne vibration, surface shock wave, or air overpressure from demolition work.

The use of hammer drills, pneumatic chisels, hammers and other similar equipment presents a vibration hazard that could lead to Hand Arm Vibration Syndrome (HAVS). The operation of demolition equipment such as manipulation and bucket equipment can expose the operator to Whole Body Vibration Syndrome (WBVS).

Figure 12-6: Noise and dust.　　*Source: Rollaston Council.*　　　　Figure 12-7: Siting of plant.　　　　*Source: RMS.*

EXISTENCE OF SERVICES SUCH AS GAS, ELECTRICITY AND WATER

Services that may be encountered during deconstruction/demolition present different hazards. Electricity may be still present in a building's mains supply because it had not been isolated and present a risk of electric shock. Sometimes there is a belief that mains circuits have been isolated but because it is fed from more than one route only part of the supply has been dealt with. Some buildings have backup systems in the form of batteries and/or capacitors which can present an unexpected electrical hazard when encountered. High voltage power supplies may pass underground or overhead, and these will present a significant hazard if not isolated before work commences.

Gas supplies routed into or under a building, if not isolated, may carry a risk of fire or explosion if they are disrupted. Residual quantities of gas left in isolated services within a building can present a lesser hazard but should not be ignored.

Water supplies that are damaged can present an indirect hazard in that they can lead to flooding of lower areas of a building where workers may be present. In addition, it may undermine part of the structure leading to premature collapse, increase the risk of slips trips and falls or aggravate a risk of electric shock.

HAZARDOUS SUBSTANCES

Hazardous substances may be present on the deconstruction/demolition site because they are left over from prior use. In industrial buildings this may mean such things as cadmium, arsenic, mercury, acids, alkalis and fuel oils and solvents (some of which may be prohibited by current good practices). In laboratory or hospital buildings that are to be demolished biological hazards may be present. Asbestos has been commonly used in buildings for many years and when the substance is broken up and fibres get into the air it can present a significant health risk. Asbestos fibres may get into the lungs and it can take many years (sometimes up to 40 years) before the symptoms of illnesses, like mesothelioma (cancer of the membrane lining the lungs), become apparent. The asbestos fibres may also be released into the air and contaminate clothing, which may pose an additional risk of harm to other workers and the public in the vicinity.

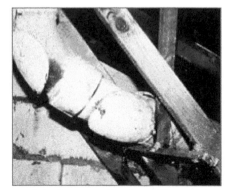

Asbestos cement drain pipe and cladding.　　　Decorative coating containing asbestos.　　　Asbestos cement flue in a ceiling void.

Figure 12-8: Asbestos use in buildings.　　　　　　　　　　　　　　　　　　　　　　*Source: HSE, HSG213.*

The type of asbestos fibre used in the manufacture of different products and present in buildings today has varied over time, for example, white asbestos was the main form used in the manufacture of asbestos cement; blue asbestos was used from 1950–69 and brown asbestos between 1945 to around 1980. Asbestos cement containing blue or brown asbestos is more hazardous than that which contains white asbestos alone. Asbestos may be present in lagging of boilers and pipework, fire proofing of structures, decorative ceiling materials and roofing materials. Pigeon infestation is common with derelict buildings and if dried pigeon droppings become disturbed and airborne they may present the risk of respiratory disease to workers, such as psittacosis. During deconstruction/demolition sewers may become exposed and present a risk of biological contamination from substances within them, for example, leptospirosis or hepatitis. In addition, hazardous substances from the site could contaminate sewers. Where vehicles are being used to transport the demolition waste material to a disposal site, they may inadvertently carry hazardous substances that may come off their wheels or drop off when travelling. Deconstruction/demolition work also possesses the potential to generate waste substances, such as oils, which can leak away into the soil.

DILAPIDATION

Dilapidation is the state of disrepair of a building. Dilapidation of structures and building may occur for a number of reasons, for example, a coal fired power station may no longer be required and abandoned, the owner of a house may no longer be in occupancy or a building may not be maintained for economic reasons, such as a non-profitable Victorian pleasure pier at a sea resort. Dilapidation develops over time through lack of maintenance, resulting in decay of the outer fabric of the structure leading to water ingress, wind damage and ultimate weakening of the whole structure. Dilapidation presents particularly high risks to those conducting deconstruction/demolition work and may influence the decision for the structure to be demolished, rather than deconstructed, as it may be possible to demolish it from a safe distance. Typical problems related to dilapidation include:

- Presence of weak/deteriorating materials and structural elements.
- Complex load paths, partial collapse may have caused additional load and stress on the remaining load-bearing parts.
- High levels of structural instability.
- Risk of premature collapse of part or the whole of the structure.
- Difficulty with access to the structure as normal access may be blocked by fallen parts of the structure.

Premature structural collapses can occur with dilapidated structures for a variety of reasons. It can result from a major structural fault arising from dilapidation or smaller faults can contribute to a chain of events that leads to a collapse while work is being conducted. Collapses may be:

- Localised collapse, for example, a collapse confined to a small part of the structure, without damage elsewhere.
- Progressive collapse, for example, the isolated failure of a critical member or section initiates a sequence of events, causing failure of the entire structure.

Figure ref 12-9 shows the result of a sudden collapse of a three storey building in Berkhamsted High Street, Hemel Hempstead in February 2011. It is believed a structural fault in the building caused the collapse.

Figure 12-9: Building collapse. *Source: The Gazette.*

12.2 - Control measures

Control measures for deconstruction and demolition work

The Construction (Design and Management) Regulations (CDM) 2007, Part 2, applies to all construction projects, of which demolition is a part. This focuses on management duties such as competence, co-operation, coordination, principles of prevention and duties of those involved in the project.

In addition, CDM 2007, Part 4, sets out duties related to health and safety on construction sites, including - good order and site security, stability of structures, demolition and dismantling, explosives, excavations, energy distribution installations, traffic routes and vehicles.

Regulation 29, of CDM 2007 requires that:

"(1) *The demolition or dismantling of a structure, or part of a structure, shall be planned and carried out in such a manner as to prevent danger or, where it is not practicable to prevent it, to reduce danger to as low a level as is reasonably practicable.*

> (2) *The arrangements for carrying out such demolition or dismantling shall be recorded in writing before the demolition or dismantling work begins".*

Figure 12-10: Regulation 29 of CDM 2007.   *Source: Construction (Design and Management) Regulations (CDM) 2007.*

AVOIDANCE OF PREMATURE COLLAPSE

Irrespective of which deconstruction/demolition process is used it is important that the deconstruction/demolition be conducted in a systematic way that prevents premature collapse of the structure. This will mean working with a good understanding of the building's strong and weak points. It is important that the deconstruction/demolition process does not leave unsupported walls or parts of a structure. Those controlling the deconstruction/demolition process should have a good understanding of building structure and mechanics, to avoid removing parts of the structure that can place an excessive load on other fragile parts. Modern machines can be fitted with scissor jaws that can break down a wall in small pieces. The use of this process reduces the likelihood of major structural damage or premature collapse. When the wrecking ball method or partial demolition is conducted, as these processes often leave free standing structures, it is important that a careful deconstruction/demolition plan is adhered to. As part of this plan it is important to leave the structure in its most stable condition when not working on it. This may mean not starting a phase of deconstruction/demolition because it cannot be completed before the end of the day or providing shoring to the structure that is left. If a part of a building, such as a façade is to be left intact for renovation it is important to provide adequate longer term support.

PROTECTION FROM FALLS AND FALLING MATERIAL

The technical advances in mechanical plant have considerably reduced the risk to deconstruction/demolition workers of working at a height. For example, modern equipment enables a lot of demolition to be conducted by agile high reach equipment. Where it is necessary for people to work at height the same standards of protection from falls must be provided to deconstruction/demolition workers as are provided to other construction workers. This will include provision of safe work platforms, use of mobile elevating work platforms (MEWPs), nets and fall arrest equipment.

In order to prevent debris falling on to passers-by, protective screens, and where appropriate fans, should be set up around scaffolds erected around structures undergoing deconstruction/demolition. In addition, brick guards, debris nets and sheeting will help to contain falling materials and prevent them falling outside the framework of a scaffold erected as part of the deconstruction/demolition process. Areas of a structure under deconstruction/demolition that present a risk from falling material must be clearly demarcated from other areas. Where buildings are being deconstructed/demolished by hand a safe access route to the workplace must be maintained, which may include demarcated routes and temporary erection of covered areas. The use of audible and visual warnings will assist in removing people from hazard areas at times that they are at risk from a particular demolition task. Head protection is an essential last line of defence for workers in this environment.

SITING AND USE OF PLANT, VEHICLES AND OTHER EQUIPMENT

Access to the site should be established to enable the large plant and appliances to be taken or driven there safely. It may also be necessary to get permission to close roads or pathways for the duration of the work.

Any plant and equipment if used in the manner for which it was designed should not fall over and injure any person at work. In order to prevent overturning care should be taken to:

- Identify weak ground conditions.
- Avoid operating outside the machine's capability.
- Create space sufficient to manoeuvre to avoid striking obstructions.
- Maintain safe access to work areas by the prompt removal of demolition debris.

The key to preventing plant overturning is planning and control. The appointment of a competent person to organise the operation of the plant, vehicles and machinery is essential. Care with siting of plant is essential in order to prevent accidental contact with nearby structures, the structure being deconstructed/demolished, power lines or other overhead obstructions. In restricted areas tight control of the use of plant and vehicles is essential; this may include physical barriers to restrict movement, where practicable.

It is important to restrict access to plant, vehicles and other machinery to prevent unauthorised use, by, for example, children. This will include securing plant in compounds, locking doors and securing keys effectively. Taking steps to prevent unauthorised access to the deconstruction/demolition site by using barriers, fencing, and increased security is the responsibility of the principal contractor.

DUST AND FUME

Large volumes of dust can be dissipated when deconstruction/demolition work is conducted. This can be in the form of brick dust asbestos or cement based materials. Asbestos is a special case, and the substance should be identified and removed by specialists who are authorised and registered by the Health and Safety Executive (HSE) to remove asbestos material. All asbestos should be removed before any deconstruction/demolition work takes place. The liberation of other dusts can be limited and restricted by the amount of deconstruction/demolition activities conducted at any one time.

Consideration of when to demolish and dismantle is also a key factor as wind direction can play a significant role, affecting the direction of travel of dust and materials. Exclusion of workers while a dust producing activity is conducted and subsequent clean up processes can also control the exposure of workers to dust.

The build-up of fume emissions, typically from diesel powered equipment, can be reduced by limiting the amount of plant and equipment activities conducted at any one time. This can be combined with control measures or restrictions imposed to segregate plant and equipment from any person who is likely to come into contact with such fume emissions. The use of modern plant and equipment significantly reduces the level of emissions as they possess more efficient engines with cleaner exhaust systems.

Where fume may be emitted form the actual deconstruction/demolition process, for example, when demolishing some form of storage vessel, such as in a chemical plant or hospital. Then potential emission should be restricted by draining any system or vessel holding fume producing substances in a controlled and planned manner.

MANUAL HANDLING

Most of the deconstruction/demolition process should, where possible, be done by using mechanical equipment to prevent or reduce any potential manual handling hazards. Chutes and conveyors should be used to transport debris from the upper floors of the building into skips, thereby eliminating any manual handling between floors.

NOISE AND VIBRATION

Noise and vibration can be a major cause of harm to workers; therefore it is important that suitable and sufficient risk assessments are produced. Exposure to noise and vibration should be minimised by the careful selection and maintenance of equipment such that levels emitted are kept to a minimum. For example, vibration damped seats for cab operated equipment, vibration mats for areas where workers stand to operate crusher plant, and vibration damped handles for power tools.

Exposure levels can be controlled by the careful use of task rotation such that those exposed to high noise and vibration levels are periodically moved to tasks that have low exposure levels. Where levels of noise are above the action values hearing protection must be made available or provided, as appropriate and it is the duty of the employer to enforce and ensure that such protection is worn. A noise protected refuge may be required in order to allow workers to move out of noisy areas to limit their exposure during rest breaks.

PROTECTION OF THE ENVIRONMENT

Where vehicles are being used to transport the demolition waste material to a disposal site, then provision should be made for wheel washes and the cleaning of the highway by a road sweeper. Waste substances, such as oils, must not be allowed to leak away into the soil and must be disposed of in a controlled manner. During demolition sewers may become exposed and be at risk of contamination from substances, so care should be taken to identify and protect them from entry of such materials. In the same way, it may be necessary to establish interceptor pits to control water run-off into water courses and/or fit temporary pressure drain covers.

Figure 12-11: Doubtful competence of workers. *Source: Lincsafe.*

Figure 12-12: Use of demolition equipment. *Source: RMS.*

COMPETENCE OF WORKFORCE

It is the client's responsibility to check the competence of the principal contractor. In turn, the principal contractor must ensure the competence of contractors appointed to conduct demolition and dismantling. Competence checks can include taking up references on past work and reviewing contractor's health and safety policies and procedures. It is important to recognise that deconstruction/demolition contractors may not be competent to act as principal contractors on larger or more complex projects. It is important that deconstruction/demolition work is controlled by someone with an understanding of buildings/structures and in turn that workers understand the effects on the building or structure that their work will make. In this way premature collapse may be prevented.

Operators of plant and equipment must be competent to operate the specific items they use, in demolition circumstances. Operation in deconstruction/demolition work can be quite different to operation in other building work and is particularly affected by the terrain of the demolition work area.

PRE-DECONSTRUCTION/DEMOLITION INVESTIGATION/SURVEY

Before any deconstruction/demolition work begins a survey is carried out to ensure that the deconstruction/demolition can go ahead safely and that property surrounding the site is protected from the deconstruction/demolition work as it progresses.

The survey should give special consideration to the location of the intended deconstruction/demolition work, for example, if it is near a place of worship, school, hospital, shopping area, leisure centre, or housing estate then the survey may identify the need for extra provisions to control risks to members of the public. It is important to know the previous use of the building/structure; it may still contain toxic or flammable materials, biological hazards or even radioactive materials or sources.

It is the client's responsibility to ensure that any building/structure to be deconstructed/demolished is adequately surveyed.

TYPE OF STRUCTURE

The survey should clearly identify the type of structure to be worked on, for example, high rise office blocks, chimneys or old buildings, as this will have a considerable impact on the method of deconstruction/demolition, the hazards present and the precautions to be taken.

METHOD OF CONSTRUCTION

The method of construction will also have a similar effect. The method of construction will particularly influence the method and order of deconstruction/demolition. Where buildings/structures contain pre-stressed or post-stressed concrete beams, this must be identified in the survey.

These buildings/structures have beams containing steel rods held under tension, which helps to bind the building/structure together. If part of the structure is deconstructed/demolished this may release the forces under tension and cause premature collapse.

Figure 12-13: Building structure.   *Source: RMS.*

Figure 12-14: Structural condition and substances. *Source: RMS.*

STRUCTURAL CONDITION

The structural condition of the building/structure should be surveyed in order to identify any degradation of materials that might influence the method and order of deconstruction/demolition. The structural condition might present such risks that it is not safe to carry out demolition by entering inside the building/structure and other means, such as the use of mechanical demolition equipment, may be required.

When deconstruction/demolition work is done by hand it involves the workers moving about at height on materials that may have degraded and are not able to sustain their weight. In this type of operation full scaffolding and other platforms should be provided and the building deconstructed/demolished in the reverse order of erection.

PRESENCE OF CELLARS

Basements, cellars, wells or storage tanks need to be identified in order to apply control measures to the risks they create, such as falls from a height and drowning. Workers may fall through into underground areas, while tanks pose a special risk if they have held or still hold toxic or flammable materials.

IDENTIFICATION OF SERVICES

Details and location of all the public utility services must be identified in order to identify the hazards they present and to take action to isolate, divert or otherwise protect them. This will involve the examination of service location drawings held by the utility service organisations.

Most of these will be buried services, including gas pipes, electricity cables, water pipes and sewerage. This will be supported by visual examination, test equipment and, in some cases, test digging to establish the specific location and status of the services.

Figure 12-15: Hazardous substances. *Source: Scaftag.*

Figure 12-16: Proximity of other structures. *Source: D Hitchen.*

PRESENCE OF HAZARDOUS SUBSTANCES

A particular health hazard that should be identified at time of survey is possible exposure to asbestos, which can present a significant risk, especially if workers are unaware of its presence and no precautions have been taken. It is important to obtain details of any prior survey conducted on the building/structure by the owner/occupier, for consideration as part of the pre-demolition survey.

The Control of Asbestos Regulations (CAR) 2012 prohibits the importation, supply and use of all forms of asbestos. They also prohibit the second-hand use of asbestos products such as asbestos cement sheets and asbestos tiles. If existing asbestos containing materials are in good condition they may be left in place and their condition monitored and managed. CAR 2012 sets out the following requirements:

■ The presence of asbestos must be identified and must be labelled.
■ An assessment must be done of work which exposes employees to asbestos.
■ Training is mandatory for those that may be exposed to asbestos fibres at work, including deconstruction/demolition workers or others that may come into contact with or disturb asbestos.
■ A written plan of work is required for work with asbestos.

Work with asbestos must be licensed unless the circumstances are that:

"(a) The exposure of employees to asbestos is sporadic and of low intensity.

(b) It is clear from the risk assessment that the exposure of any employee to asbestos will not exceed the control limit.

(c) The work involves:

(i) Short, non-continuous maintenance activities.

(ii) Removal of materials in which the asbestos fibres are firmly linked in a matrix.

(iii) Encapsulation or sealing of asbestos-containing materials which are in good condition, or

(iv) Air monitoring and control, and the collection and analysis of samples to ascertain whether a specific material contains asbestos".

■ Work with asbestos other than that listed above must be notified to the employer's enforcing authority.
■ Exposure must be prevented or reduced by controls.
■ Controls must be used and maintained.
■ The employer is responsible for the cleaning of personal protective clothing.

There may be other health hazards present that could affect the deconstruction/demolition worker or others, for example, Weil's disease from rats, breathing difficulties from the dust of disturbed pigeon droppings or chemicals from the previous use of the building.

WASTE MANAGEMENT – ON SITE SEGREGATION AND OFF SITE DISPOSAL

The construction industry is one of the largest producers of waste in the UK. Construction and deconstruction/demolition waste can be broken down into the following:

■ Concrete, bricks and tiles.
■ Asphalt, tar and tar by-products.
■ Metals.
■ Soil and rubble.
■ Wood.
■ Soil from ground works (which may be contaminated, through the sites previous use).

Work subject to CDM 2007 in England must also be compliant with the Site Waste Management Plans Regulations (SWMP) 2008. These require that all sites of a size where the project cost is greater than £300k prepare a site waste management plan before work commences.

The plan must:

■ Describe each waste type expected to be produced in the course of the project.
■ Estimate the quantity of each different waste type expected to be produced.
■ Identify the waste management action proposed for each different waste type, including re-using, recycling, recovery and disposal.
■ Contain a declaration that the client and the principal contractor will take all reasonable steps to ensure that:
  • All waste from the site is dealt with in accordance with the waste duty of care in section 34 of the Environmental Protection Act (EPA) 1990 (Part 1 pollution control) and the Environmental Protection (Duty of Care) Regulations (EPDOC) 1991(regulation 2 transfer notes).
  • Materials are handled efficiently and waste managed appropriately.

This means that waste products should be identified before disturbance and an action plan developed to regulate how these products should be handled. Waste should be segregated in terms of type, identifying waste that may be re-used, recycled and recovered and segregating it from waste for disposal.

All waste products and residues in containers must be identified and clearly labelled and steps taken to prevent the combined storage of incompatible materials prior to disposal.

Off site disposal must be carried out by a licensed contractor and taken to a licensed waste disposal site. If necessary, waste removal should be planned to avoid rush hour traffic and steps taken such as wheel washing to prevent contamination on public roads.

ACCESS AND EGRESS FROM THE SITE

Access and egress for site vehicles is an essential part of site planning.

Consideration should be given to:

■ The appropriateness of public roads in the proximity of the site. Select routes of suitable width and schedule access to avoid times when large numbers of domestic vehicles may be parked in the road whenever possible.
■ The nature of the surrounding buildings and their function, for example, the presence of schools or hospitals for which traffic and noise would be a problem.
■ The number and size of vehicles expected to enter and leave the site should be determined and their arrival and departures scheduled to avoid back-up of waiting vehicles onto public highways.
■ Speed limits should be imposed on site vehicles, limit signs should be displayed and the limit enforced.
■ Reversing from the site must be avoided or if reversing is necessary a banksman should be used to control the process.

PROXIMITY AND CONDITION OF OTHER STRUCTURES AND ROADWAYS

The survey should seek to identify the proximity and condition of other structures to determine the influence they may have on the deconstruction/demolition process. If a structure is close to the building/structure to be demolished and is in poor condition it may be necessary to shore it up and route demolition plant and equipment away from it.

The proximity and condition of roads to a site is an essential item to survey. If roads are good, and wide enough to take plant transport vehicles and debris vehicles, this will have a positive influence on the safety of the deconstruction/demolition activity. If restrictions exist, it may be necessary to obtain police co-operation to clear roads and to time the delivery of plant when least disruption will occur.

A new, dedicated access may be necessary to provide access to a larger road near by. This may influence the order of work to be conducted as part of the building/structure may need to be demolished to create better access. It is important to ensure that equipment and parts of equipment such as elbows of cranes, excavators, loaders etc do not swing into the path of vehicles or pedestrians. Early identification of risk and nuisance to adjoining land, buildings or road users will enable early notification to those affected.

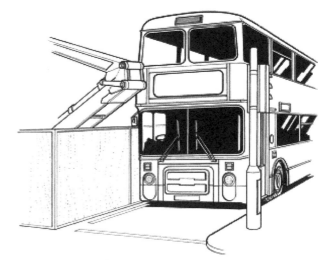

Figure 12-17: Risk of collision due to close proximity with public road. *Source: HSE, HSG151.*

12.3 - Pre-demolition, deconstruction or refurbishment surveys

Purpose and scope of surveys

The purpose of a pre-demolition, deconstruction or refurbishment survey is to ensure that before any work begins the structure to be worked on is assessed to determine inherent hazards related to the structure and those hazards that are likely to emanate from the proposed work on the structure.

The scope of the survey will include the following hazards:

- Premature collapse.
- Falls and falling materials.
- Plant, vehicles and other equipment overturning.
- Access and egress restrictions.
- Manual handling.
- Dust and fumes.
- Noise and vibration.
- Existence of services.
- Hazardous substances.
- Dilapidation.
- Presence of fragile and sharp materials.
- Weak surfaces, for example, cellars.
- Proximity of other structures, vehicles and people that might be affected.
- Likely waste issues.

Figure 12-18: Dilapidation of a structure.   *Source: RMS.*

The information determined by the survey will be used to determine a method of working that ensures satisfactory control measures are in place and an orderly work process.

Duties of the property owner for carrying out a pre-demolition survey

Clients of projects that are non-notifiable under CDM 2007 must provide contractors with specific information that will allow hazards to be identified. It is not sufficient to state that "asbestos might be present". The relevant information might be in an existing survey (for example, asbestos) or in an existing health and safety file. If clients do not have sufficient information available, then they must make arrangements to have the necessary surveys carried out by a competent person.

In the case of a notifiable project, the client must appoint a CDM coordinator and pass all the information discussed earlier to the CDM Coordinator, who must then in turn communicate it to the principal contractor in the form of a health and safety plan.

Competent person to carry out investigations

STRUCTURAL ENGINEERS

The structural engineer can play a crucial part in reducing the hazards associated with deconstruction, demolition, refurbishment, dismantling and decommissioning. Presenting the structural risks clearly at the beginning of a project reduces accidents and saves time and money. Good communication helps ensure that the potential hazards are understood by the client team, site managers, supervisors and the workforce.

ASBESTOS SURVEYORS

Occupiers must have an asbestos management plan, such as that provided by an asbestos survey conducted on any non-domestic property that is over 8 years old. Failure to do so could put the health of employees, visitors and, ultimately, deconstruction/demolition workers at risk.

Within an asbestos survey an asbestos surveyor must identify all materials either thought to contain asbestos or ones that could be mistaken for asbestos.

An independent expert/specialist organisation conducting asbestos surveys must:

- Have adequate training and be experienced in survey work.
- Be able to demonstrate independence, impartiality and integrity.
- Have an adequate quality management system.
- Carry out any asbestos survey work in accordance with recommended HSE guidance HSG264 "Asbestos: The survey".

HSG264 states that organisations offering an asbestos survey service should be able to demonstrate their competence by holding United Kingdom Accreditation Service (UKAS) accreditation to ISO/IEC 17020 and individuals to ISO/IEC 17024.

In considering competence for assessment the HSE guidance "Work with materials containing asbestos" states:

"Whoever carries out the assessment should:

Have adequate knowledge, competence, training and expertise in understanding the risks from asbestos and be able to make informed decisions about the risks and precautions that are needed. Know how the work activity may disturb asbestos; be familiar with the asbestos regulations and understand the requirements of the ACOP (Approved Code of Practice). Have the ability and the authority to collate all the necessary, relevant information. Be able to assess other non-asbestos risks on site".

Figure 12-19: "Work with materials containing asbestos".   Source: HSE guidance.

See also - Element 8 - Chemical and biological health - hazards and risk control – 'Health risks and controls associated with asbestos'.

Identification of features of the structure

IDENTIFICATION OF KEY STRUCTURAL ELEMENTS

It is important that the survey identify the key structural elements in order to evaluate the effects on the structure of the proposed work. The location and condition of lintels, beams and other load-bearing members will need to be taken into account when planning how the work is to be done. The structural elements may be made of steel beams or concrete, which may be reinforced, pre-stressed or post stressed.

Reinforced concrete is poured around rods of steel that are formed to the shape of the structure being created.

Pre-stressed concrete is a method of overcoming the concrete's natural weakness in tension. It is used to produce beams, floors or bridges with a longer span than is practical with ordinary reinforced concrete. Pre-stressed tendons (generally of high tensile steel cable or rods) are used to provide a clamping force that produces a compressive stress to offset the tensile stress that the concrete compression member would otherwise experience due to bending load. Pre-tensioned concrete is cast around already tensioned tendons.

Post-tensioned concrete is the descriptive term for a method of applying compression after pouring and curing concrete and is conducted in situ. Tendons are passed through the duct that provides the proposed shape of the member and the concrete is poured. Once the concrete has hardened, the tendons are tensioned by hydraulic jacks; when the tendons have stretched sufficiently they are locked in position and continue to transfer pressure to the concrete.

Demolishing reinforced concrete does not present any unusual hazards. However, demolishing pre-tensioned and post tensioned structures can be difficult because of the energy stored in the stressing tendons, which are under constant tensile stress. The uncontrolled release of this stored energy can cause a concrete component to fly through the air; care needs to be taken when they are cut. The tendons in tensioned structures are generally made of high tensile steel so there will be fewer to cut compared to standard reinforced concrete.

IDENTIFICATION OF LOCATION AND TYPE OF SERVICES

The location and type of services connected to the structure being worked on should be identified. Consideration should be given to both over ground, including, for example, pipe racks, power lines and telephone wires; and underground, such as pipes, cables and equipment associated with the electricity, gas, water (including piped sewage) and telecommunications industries. This will also includes the identification of other pipelines that may transport a range of petrochemical and other fluids through the site.

See also - Element 11.2 - Control measures for excavation work; Identification and detection of buried services.

IDENTIFICATION, SIGNIFICANCE AND EXTENT OF DILAPIDATION OF THE STRUCTURE

The state of dilapidation can cause a wide variety of problems during demolition/deconstruction of a structure.

The survey should determine the extent of the dilapidation and its significance to the health and safety of those that will be affected by the work to be conducted.

The dilapidation may mean that asbestos materials have become damaged and are exposed. Floors may have collapsed and stairs that could have been able to be used for access may have become rotten as they became affected by water ingress. If part of the roof has collapsed this may add stress to other members holding up the remainder of the roof. Fixtures and fittings may become damaged or parts stolen, leaving electrical services in a poor condition. Though power should have been removed from them this is not always the case.

Figure 12-20: Dilapidation of buildings.   Source: RMS.

Fungal and other harmful growth

Fungal growth occurs when there is moisture content in the walls of a structure. It flourishes in an environment of high humidity with lack of ventilation. Fungal growth may indicate the level of decline in the integrity of the structure. Harmful growth includes creeping ivy and plants that can grow either on walls, roofs or gutters. Roots can go deep into the existing holes causing cracks and water penetration that lead to the erosion of mortar joints and dampness, which weaken the structure.

Figure 12-21: Black mould. *Source: Premier preservation Ltd.*

Figure 12-22: Ivy.   *Source: Daily Mail.*

Cracking of walls and leaning walls

Vertical or diagonal cracks in the wall are common symptoms of structural instability. The survey should identify these cracks as symptoms and try to diagnose the cause.

This may be poor foundations, weak materials and joints; or any shrinkage or thermal movements such as those of timber window frames.

Diagonal cracks, usually widest at the foundations and terminating at the corner of a building, often occur when shallow foundations are laid on shrinkable sub-soil that is drier than normal. They may also be caused by a physical uplifting action of a large tree's main roots close to the walls.

Figure 12-23: Settlement diagonal wall cracking. *Source: diynot.com.*

Common causes of leaning walls include a spreading roof, which forces the weight of a roof down towards the walls, sagging due to soil movement, weak foundations due to the presence of dampness, shrinkable clay soil or decayed building materials; and disturbance of nearby mature trees with roots expanding to the local settlement.

Decayed floorboards

Timber floorboards were widely used in many older buildings including churches, schools, and railway stations. Some timber floorboards will have been subjected to surface abuse and subsequently deteriorated to the extent that they can no longer hold the weight of workers walking on them. The main natural causes of decay are pest attacks, such as dry rot or hidden cavities caused by death watch beetle.

Figure 12-24: Dry rot - characteristic cuboidal cracking.
Source: Safeguard Europe Ltd.

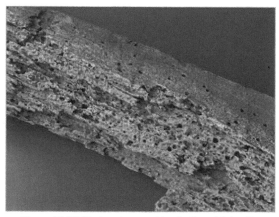

Figure 12-25: Timber damaged by death watch beetle.
Source: Rudders and Paynes Ltd.

Weakened or split boards may be caused by damage by occupants, loss of natural preservatives and the effects of corroded nails.

Roof defects

Common defects of roof tiles include corrosion of nails that fix the tiles to battens and rafters, the decay of battens, and the cracking of tiles caused by harmful growth. Another aspect to be considered is the mortar applied for ridge tiles, which tends to decay or flake off over the years. Roof light materials often deteriorate on exposure to sunlight and become brittle, lose structural strength and are easily fractured. Often they are covered with felt to prevent leaks or become obscured from the rest of the roof by the growth of moss. Hidden roof lights present a risk to workers of falling through.

Unstable foundations

Most of the common problems associated with foundations depend on the geology of the ground upon which a building stands. For example, settlement or subsidence may result if it is built prematurely on made up ground or the water table height is causing the ground to expand or contract.

The leaning Tower of Pisa is perhaps the most famous example of building subsidence. The tower began to sink after construction had progressed to the second floor in 1178. This was due to a shallow three-metre foundation, set in weak, unstable sandy subsoil, a design that was flawed from the beginning.

Unstable foundations may occur due to traffic vibrations, deterioration of building materials and through change of use, for example, increased floor loading. Problems with unstable foundations may lead to an unstable building structure, which increases the risks of premature collapse during deconstruction or demolition.

Figure 12-26: The leaning tower of Pisa, Italy. *Source: Marshaü.*

Review of factors affecting the structure

DRAWINGS, STRUCTURAL CALCULATIONS, HEALTH AND SAFETY

Before work commences every effort should be made to find the original design drawings, together with the calculations made by the architect. If the building is of recent construction these will be found in the health and safety file related to the structure.

This will provide information on how the structure was built, for example, reinforced concrete frame or steel frame. If it is a large structure, it will be important to identify any pre-stressed or post-stressed concrete beams present within the structure and whether any floor slabs or piles were involved in the build. It is also important to determine the age of the structure and its previous use.

It is the client's responsibility to provide such information to the contractor. Prior to deconstruction/demolition, any structural alterations that might affect the load-bearing capacity of walls and floors should be reviewed to avoid premature collapse.

STRUCTURAL ALTERATIONS CARRIED OUT ON THE STRUCTURE IN THE PAST

The pre-demolition survey should consider past alterations. This is particularly important to identify any changes, for example, the addition of doors or windows or the removal of walls, which may have compromised the building's original structural stability.

12.4 - Method statements

Control measures that a method statement should include

After completion of the survey it is possible to consider how the work is to be carried out and to establish a method statement to define and manage the work.

The method statement should include consideration of:

- Services.
- Soft strip requirements.
- Working at height.
- Protection of the public and neighbours.
- Emergency arrangements.
- Waste management.

- Asbestos.
- Control measures for identified hazards.
- Plant and equipment.
- Access and egress from site.
- Training and welfare arrangements.
- Named responsible person.

- Competence of workforce.
- Communications.

- Coordination of work activities.

SERVICES

Isolations

The method statement should define the actions necessary to establish isolations that are adequate and secure. It is important to isolate services at the furthest point practicable from the structure to be demolished, for example, at the site boundary.

This may include gas or water services isolated in the pavement outside the demolition site. This will help to remove the hazard at source and is preferable to local isolation of the services within the building. It should be remembered that some systems will store energy from services and should not be presumed safe merely by isolating the service. This includes electricity stored in capacitors and batteries, stored water in tanks, and compressed oils/air in pressure systems.

Temporary services

The method statement should set out any arrangements for temporary services that may be required. It may be necessary to install temporary services such as electricity, lighting and fresh air. These services must be installed by competent people and, in the case of fresh air supply; there must be an audible and visual warning of failure.

SOFT STRIP REQUIREMENTS

Often, the exterior of a building has to be preserved intact whilst the interior is completely stripped of partitioning, flooring and internal walls ready for refurbishment or redevelopment. The extent of soft strip should be clarified, as this work requires careful control and management because it often reveals unexpected aspects of the building's structural design, such as the presence of asbestos and weaknesses in the structure such as cracks that may have been hidden by plaster.

WORKING AT HEIGHT ACCESS INCLUDING SCAFFOLDING

If work at height cannot be avoided by the use of pusher arms or "nibblers", details of how those working at height will be protected will need to be determined and set out in the method statement. This will include details of competent scaffold erectors and the inspection arrangements for scaffolds to be used or other access equipment such as mobile elevating work platforms (MEWPS).

PROTECTION OF PUBLIC, THIRD PARTIES AND SURROUNDING STRUCTURES

The protection of the public, third parties and surrounding structures is an essential pre deconstruction/demolition or refurbishment control measure. The method statement should specify the measures to remove and prevent people accessing the building/structure, such as children, persons sleeping rough and those who wish to salvage materials, as well as people who are just passing by. The boundaries of the demolition site need to provide an effective barrier to persons not involved with the work, typically 2.5 metres high fencing with warning signs posted around it.

Fencing must be maintained to a good standard and checks made at the end of each day to ensure it is in place and continues to be effective. Where the work is close to where the public may pass they should be protected from falling materials by the use of sheeting, brick guards, nets, fans and covered areas. In some cases, work in such an area may have take place at a specified time and the public prevented from accessing the area.

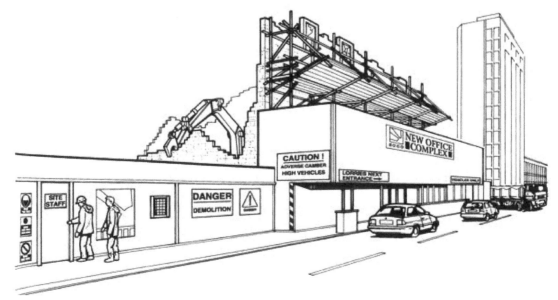

Figure 12-27: Demolition - separate entrance for workers and protected pedestrian route.   *Source: HSE, HSG151.*

Figure 12-28: Protection of public.   *Source: RMS.*

Figure 12-29: Disposal of waste.   *Source: RMS.*

EMERGENCY ARRANGEMENTS

The method statement should set out emergency procedures and arrangements. These should be sufficient for dealing with foreseeable emergencies, for example, fire, explosions, chemical leaks and premature collapse of the structure. Fire detection, fire alarms, fire-fighting equipment, first-aid provisions, site evacuation, and rescue plans should form part of these arrangements. The method statement should specify necessary training in the use of emergency techniques and equipment.

WASTE MANAGEMENT - ON-SITE SEGREGATION AND OFF SITE DISPOSAL

It is important that the method statement detail arrangements for waste management. Taking into account the size of the site, waste material must not be allowed to accumulate. This means controlling build-up of waste at local points around the site, particularly where they impede access and egress, as well as any major accumulation points. The disposal of building materials must be controlled by consignment certificates and taken to a recognised licensed landfill site. Asbestos waste should only be handled by trained and qualified workers and disposed of in accordance with current local environmental requirements.

COMPETENCE OF WORKFORCE

Details of the competencies of those involved in the work the method statement relates to should be clearly stated. The importance of adequate training in the demolition industry has been recognised by the introduction of the "Scheme for the Certification of Competence of Demolition Operatives" (CCDO). The CCDO scheme is for anyone whose job entails on-site demolition. The scheme applies to new entrants, temporary workers, and existing operatives with site experience. It is partly NVQ based, with the Demolition Site Operative and Demolition Operative 1 (Labourer) being the only jobs not requiring proof of an NVQ.

There are seven different cards available that confirm the holder of the card is competent. The appropriate card is issued under the scheme depending on qualifications and experience. All cards require a health and safety test in either demolition or demolition and plant in order to be issued or reissued, which takes place every five years.

Similar schemes operate through the CITB (provided by the Construction Skills organisation) and the ECITB (provided by the Client/Contractor National Safety Group) and may be relevant to refurbishment work.

COMMUNICATIONS

The method statement should include details of what meetings are planned (pre-start, weekly, progress, etc.) and who will attend.

ASBESTOS

Before work can begin an asbestos survey should be carried out by a qualified surveyor. The purpose of the survey is to help identify and manage any asbestos in the duty holder's premises. The survey has to provide sufficient information for:

- An asbestos register and plan to be prepared.
- A suitable risk assessment to be carried out.
- A written plan to manage the risks to be produced.

The duty to manage asbestos is covered by Regulation 4 of the Control of Asbestos Regulations (CAR) 2012.

The method statement should establish the way in which asbestos is to be managed. If refurbishment is to be carried out this may mean leaving it in place, ensuring it is identified and adding it to the register. If deconstruction or demolition is intended the method statement should set out the arrangements for removal and disposal.

CONTROL MEASURES FOR IDENTIFIED HAZARDS

Measures that will be taken to control hazards must be detailed, for example, noise nuisance, by the use of silencers, remote location of noisy equipment from neighbouring properties, avoidance of work at night. If dust nuisance is expected the method statement may set out arrangements for sheeting of the area, damping down of materials or avoidance of work on very windy days.

PLANT AND EQUIPMENT

The method statement should specify the type and capacity of equipment to be used at different stages in the demolition process, in order that it can be used within its capability and for the right purpose. The equipment specified should match the factors identified at time of survey. Due to the dangerous nature of demolition work all equipment should only be used by trained, competent and authorised workers. The method statement should take account of this and the availability of suitable operators at the demolition site.

ACCESS AND EGRESS FROM SITE

The method statement should give consideration to the movement of vehicles and people on and around the site. Arrangements for access and egress for loading and unloading materials should be considered. Segregation of vehicle and pedestrian traffic should be specified.

Access and egress routes should be kept clear of any obstructions, with traffic and pedestrian routes clearly marked and signed. Emergency routes may have unique signage. All routes should be inspected on a regular basis for compliance. Where possible, it is good practice to operate a one way traffic management system.

TRAINING AND WELFARE ARRANGEMENTS

Adequate training and information must be provided to visitors, new workers, transferred employees from another site and contractors. This should take the form of an induction course and include the following:

- Outline of the work.
- Key personnel and line managers.
- Site rules.
- Sites health and safety risks - for example, transport, any site contamination, hazardous substances and manual handling.
- Safe systems of work, permits to work systems.
- Security arrangements.
- Hearing protection zones.

- Personal protective equipment (PPE) provision, storage and cleaning stations.
- Housekeeping, material storage and waste.
- First-aid arrangements.
- Reporting of accidents or incidents.
- Emergency procedures.
- Welfare arrangements - for example, personal clothing storage, drying facilities, showers/toilets and rest areas.

The method statement should set out details of welfare facilities suitable for the work activity. This may include specialist decontamination facilities for workers dealing with contaminated materials or asbestos.

NAMED RESPONSIBLE PERSON

The client has the ultimate responsibility for the work being carried out. The principal contractor conducts the work on the client's behalf and should appoint a named responsible person (individual or agent) to control the work.

COORDINATION OF WORK ACTIVITIES

The method statement should specify measures for co-operation and coordination between people involved in the work, for example, client, CDM coordinator, principal contractor and contractors. The work process should follow the approved method statement produced in conjunction with the client, CDM coordinator and the principal contractor.

The site manager or agent of the principal contractor has overall control and coordination of the work. They take into account any changes or new hazards identified, liaising with employees or sub-contractors and updating any health and safety requirements.

Sample assessment questions

1. A three-storey office block is to be demolished.

    (a) **Identify** the possible hazards to the environment that could be caused by the demolition. (4)

    (b) **Outline** measures to reduce the risk to the environment during the demolition work. (4)

2. **Outline** the key issues to be addressed in a pre-demolition survey of a multi-storey block of flats in a city centre. (8)

3. A steel framed building is to be demolished.
    Identify the main areas to be included in a demolition method statement. (8)

Please refer to back of assessment section for answers.

Assessment

Content

Assessments of understanding

It is understood that those using this publication may be doing so to broaden their understanding of this important topic, management of health and safety in construction, and others will be studying in order to obtain a specific construction related award. The approach taken by those assessing such awards will vary.

This element provides information on how one such award is assessed, the NEBOSH National Certificate in Construction Health and Safety Management. The questions and related answers provided in this element may prove useful for those that want to assess their understanding for this award and for more general reasons. The inspection observation sheets and accompanying report, provided in the section 'construction health and safety review' below, will be of great use to those studying for the NEBOSH award and will prove particularly useful to those that wish to develop and use their own means of assessing construction management in their workplace.

Assessment questions

NEBOSH PAPER NCC1

To assist students understanding of the assessment requirements for the NEBOSH National Certificate in Construction Health and Safety award, paper NCC1, some short answer questions that are typical of the type used in an award at this level have been included at the end of each element. This is accompanied by the following observations related to the success of candidates taking examinations of this type.

At every examination a number of candidates - including some good ones - perform less well than they might because of poor examination technique. It is essential that candidates practice answering both essay-type and short answer questions and learn to budget their time according to the number of marks allocated to questions (and parts of questions) as shown on the paper.

A common fault is that candidates may fail to pay attention to the command word (e.g. outline, identify, explain, describe) in each question. The need to understand the meaning of the 'command word' and to read the question carefully is emphasised in the comments below that are taken from recent NEBOSH examiner's reports:

"... Many answers were too brief to satisfy the requirement for an outline or description. Points made should have been supported by sufficient reasoning to show their relevance to the question".

"Some candidates, even though they identified many of the relevant factors, could not be awarded the full range of marks available because they produced a truncated list that did not properly outline the relationship between each factor and the corresponding risks".

"...some candidates could not be awarded high marks as their responses did not include adequate and appropriate description of the practical measures...

"While answers to this question were generally to a reasonable standard, many were too brief to attract all the marks that were available".

"Some answers were extremely brief answers are expected to be proportionate to the marks available".

Answers to assessment questions

Typical answers are provided on pages 378-386.

General confirmation of understanding

Those not taking examinations related to health and safety may find the questions and answers useful to check and confirm their understanding of some of the issues covered by this publication.

Construction health and safety workplace review

NEBOSH UNIT NCC2

The aim of this unit is to assess a candidate's ability to complete successfully a construction health and safety review of their workplace and to provide a report to management with justified recommendations. The questionnaire has been produced by NEBOSH as part of their practical assessment of the above award, their origination and copyright is acknowledged. In order to understand how the questionnaire may be used and the type of report produced by candidates studying this award, a completed questionnaire and report is provided. In summary the proforma and report should clearly identify:

■ The nature, and if appropriate, the location of each health and safety at work issue.
■ Review findings with prioritisation and justification.

- Clear links to strengths and weaknesses in the way that health and safety at work is managed, with relevant prioritisation.

Creating workplace templates

The NEBOSH template is an excellent starting point for those wishing to develop and create their own templates to carry out reviews of their construction health and safety standards at work.

Procedure

The practical assessment is intended to test candidates' abilities to apply their knowledge of health and safety to a practical situation, to demonstrate their understanding of key issues and to communicate findings in an effective way. The assessment must take place within 14 days of (before or after) the date of the written paper (date of the examination). Please make sure you are clear about when you will carry out the assessment.

The time allowed by NEBOSH to complete the assessment is not restricted, but NEBOSH advise that candidates should aim to complete the inspection and report in two hours. This indicates an acceptable amount of time that could produce an acceptable result. The actual time taken will depend on the student, the type of workplace and the method used to produce the observations sheet and report, particularly if whether they are produced in hand written or word processed format.

You are advised to spend no more than 45 minutes making an inspection of the workplace in order to leave enough time to finish your observation notes and prepare the management report. NEBOSH advise that you should aim to complete the management report in one hour. If it is necessary to take longer than this time this is allowed. Once you have completed your practical assessment (observation sheets and management report) - you must sign a declaration that shows the submission is your own work. If this declaration is not submitted then your result may be declared void.

The whole assessment must be carried out under as near examination conditions as possible and you must not use anything previously prepared or gain assistance from other people while conducting the assessment.

The practical assessment must be completed using forms based on the NEBOSH forms provided and take place in a construction workplace of your choice. It must not contain extraneous material such as drawings and photographs.

When conducting the inspection of the workplace you are expected to recognise physical, health and environmental hazards. Good work practices as well as bad work practices should be observed, though the emphasis for this assessment should be on uncontrolled hazards. You should cover as wide a range of hazards as possible, but at least five different types. It is important that the candidate describes the hazard that they have observed; care should be taken as short general comments like "poor housekeeping in the store" does not convey what the hazard is.

The sample provided uses an approach that encourages a better description of the hazard, for example "**Risk of** trip in the walkway outside the office **due to** trailing electrical cables ....". Hazards that are well controlled should be observed and noted in a similar way, for example, "**Risk of** trip in walkway outside office **controlled by** ....".

While only short notes on each hazard are required, it is important that the assessor is able to identify from your notes in the observation column:

- Where the hazard was located.
- The type and nature of the hazard.
- In what way, if any, the hazard was being controlled.

Welfare and environmental issues may also be observed and noted, for example:

- Availability and standard of washing and toilet facilities.
- Adequacy of heating, lighting and ventilation.
- Condition of floors and gangways.
- Cleanliness of structures.
- If workers are present in the workplace, are they aware of the actions to take in the event of an emergency?

In the time advised for the inspection it should be possible to make 24 good observations and record what was seen. In order to gain good marks it is necessary to observe and describe at least 20 hazards that are not controlled.

For each observation you should comment on any actions necessary to control the hazards in the 'Control measures' column. Experience shows that some candidates do this part of the assessment in an inconsistent way. The addition of a column to the left of the 'Control measures' part of the observation form and the use of a key to remind you to consider immediate, medium and long term actions would be useful and improve consistency. This is not a NEBOSH requirement, but candidates have found that it prompts them to be more consistent.

It is important to consider each of the immediate, medium and long term actions for each observation to gain good marks. This will require the candidate to note actions to take immediate control of the hazard and control measures to deal with the causes of the hazard and improve the management of them to prevent a reoccurrence. Where hazards are currently controlled, medium and longer term actions should be considered in order to maintain or improve control.

Care should be taken to describe the action proposed sufficiently and avoid over simple statements like "Monitor"; you should indicate what should be monitored and perhaps how. Actions proposed should be practical and cost effective, in that they should relate to the level of risk. Candidates should remember that if observations noted are unclear it will not be possible to gain full credit for the actions suggested as their suitability in relation to the hazard cannot be determined by the assessor.

The 'Timescales' column should be completed for each action to indicate an acceptable completion date, for example, immediately, 1 week, 1 month, 3 months etc.

When completing the management report it should follow the structure set out by NEBOSH:

- Introduction, including overview of area inspected and activities taking place.
- Executive summary.
- Main findings of the inspection.
- Conclusions.
- Recommendations - action plan.

Deviation from this structure will make the report less effective and will usually lead to reduced marks. NEBOSH allows the candidate to consult reference books when preparing the management report, but plagiarism is treated seriously.

The report should be written persuasively, so that a manager would be encouraged and be able to take action. Only copying the notes from the observation sheet would not usually be persuasive enough and not gain good marks. NEBOSH advise that the report should be approximately 700 to 1,000 words. There is no penalty based on word count, but marks are available for the quality of interpretation of findings and persuasiveness. Experience shows that a word processor word count of approximately 2,000 words will be necessary to explain well and provide motivation for the reader, depending on the number and complexity of main findings.

The executive summary should be written after completion of the other parts of the report to enable an overview of the positive and negative findings, with a summary of the conclusions and indicate actions recommend. It can be difficult for the candidate to provide a concise executive summary, but they should keep in mind that it should only be long enough to indicate the outcome of the inspection and the content of the report.

The main findings are an important part of a report of this type and attract nearly a third of the marks. Observations from the observation sheets should be selected for specific comments in the findings. A large number of small risks may be a significant problem, if this is the case this should be made clear in the report. It would be common to find that four significant findings are necessary; care should be taken to ensure that the findings do not become just a copy of all the observations.

The notes in the observation sheet should further explain to ensure the manager understands the hazard, the significance of the risk and the likely outcomes, in terms of harm to people, cost and breach of legal standards. Where breaches of legal standards exist the candidate should explain what causes the breach and what the breach is. Stating the name of the legal standard alone will not be sufficient. The actions proposed should be explained and emphasis made of the cost effectiveness of the actions relative to the risk, reasonable practicability.

The conclusions and recommendations are also important and attract nearly one third of the available marks. The conclusions should be drawn from and reflect the findings of the report. Care should be taken not to introduce new items not discussed in the report. Conclusions should be clear, concise and convince management to take action.

Sample practical application (NCC2)

NEBOSH NATIONAL CERTIFICATE IN CONSTRUCTION HEALTH AND SAFETY

UNIT NCC2 - CONSTRUCTION HEALTH AND SAFETY PRACTICAL APPLICATION

Candidate's observation sheet

Sheet number 1 **of** 5

Student name:	A. N. Other	Student number:	XXXX
Place inspected:	*********** site	Date of Inspection:	01/06/20**

Observations Hazards and consequences		Control measures Immediate and longer-term actions	Timescale
1. Risk of falling from height due to missing edge protection	I	Stop work	1 hour
	M	Reinstall edge protection	1 day
	L	Instigate toolbox talk	One Week
2. Risk of person falling due to use of damaged step ladder by electrician	I	Stop work and remove ladder	1 hour
	M	Provide new ladder	1 day
	L	Set up a recorded system of testing, inspections labelling	1 week
3. Risk of being struck by moving objects due to lack of barriers around material lifting machine	I	Install barrier tape	1 hour
	M	Install permanent barrier	Week
	L	Inspect barrier weekly	1 month then weekly
4. Risk of falling controlled by secure ladder when accessing control room roof	I	None	N/A
	M	Commend good practice	Immediate
	L	Commend good practice at toolbox talks	one month
5. Risk of fall from height due to incorrect barrier between MCC room and corridor	I	Remove barrier and stop work in MCC room	1 hour
	M	Install correct barrier	1 day
	L	Install correct door	1 week

Key: I = Immediate   M = medium   L = Long term actions

NEBOSH NATIONAL CERTIFICATE IN CONSTRUCTION HEALTH AND SAFETY
UNIT NCC2 - CONSTRUCTION HEALTH AND SAFETY PRACTICAL APPLICATION

Candidate's observation sheet

Sheet number 2 **of** 5

Student name: A. N. Other   Student number: XXXX

Place inspected: ************ site   Date of Inspection: 01/06/20**

Observations Hazards and consequences		Control measures Immediate and longer-term actions	Timescale
6. Risk of electric shock or fire controlled by regular PAT testing	I	None	
	M	Continue regular testing	On going
	L	Ensure competence of electricians	6 months
7. Risk of falling loads due to damaged lifting sling	I	Remove sling from site	1 hour
	M	Replace with new sling	1 day
	L	Instigate system of regular checks	1 week
8. Risk of respiratory problems due to not wearing respirator when cutting ducting insulation board	I	Issue appropriate PPE to include dust mask/respirator	1 hour
	M	Implement recorded inspections to ensure PPE is being worn	1 day
	L	Review cutting process to determine if dust can be reduced at source	1 month
9. Risk of skin problems controlled by availability of clean washing facilities and provision of barrier creams	I	None	
	M	Instigate weekly inspections	1 day
	L	Review other welfare facilities	One Month
10. Risk of collision with vehicles due to pedestrian route not clearly signed	I	Stop pedestrian access	Immediately
	M	Install permanent demarcation barriers	1 day
	L	Erect clear signs	1 week

Key: I = Immediate   M = medium   L = Long term actions

NEBOSH NATIONAL CERTIFICATE IN CONSTRUCTION HEALTH AND SAFETY

UNIT NCC2 - CONSTRUCTION HEALTH AND SAFETY PRACTICAL APPLICATION

Candidate's observation sheet

Sheet number 3 **of** 5

Student name:	A. N. Other	Student number:	XXXX
Place inspected:	************ site	Date of Inspection:	01/06/20**

Observations Hazards and consequences	Control measures Immediate and longer-term actions		Timescale
11. Risk of fire/explosion due to incorrect storage of oxyacetylene bottles when in use. Wheel broken on trolley.	I	Stop using cutting gear	Immediate
	M	Inspect and repair trolley	One day
	L	Inspect other similar equipment	One month
12. Risk of fire/explosion due to wood and timber being stored where grinding work is being done	I	Remove timber to dedicated storage area	Immediate
	M	Remind employees of need for good housekeeping at next toolbox talk	One week
	L	Include item on workplace inspection checklist	One week
13. Risk of sprains due to poor storage of materials, uneven floor and poor lighting.	I	Move all excess materials to store or waste bin	One week
	L	Install more lights	One month
	M	Inspect light levels regularly and review floor condition	3 months
14. Risk of injury from fire due to alarm bell covered in concrete splashes making it in-audible in the event of a fire	I	Remove from use and clean	1 hour
	M	Replace with new bell	1 week
	L	Regular tests and inspection and record findings	1 month
15. Risk of building material falling from height controlled by good edge protection on scaffold	I	N/A	
	M	Commend good practice at next toolbox talk	One week
	L	Continue regular statutory inspections	Weekly

Key: I = Immediate   M = medium   L = Long term actions

NEBOSH NATIONAL CERTIFICATE IN CONSTRUCTION HEALTH AND SAFETY
UNIT NCC2 - CONSTRUCTION HEALTH AND SAFETY PRACTICAL APPLICATION

Candidate's observation sheet

Sheet number 4 **of** 5

Student name:	A. N. Other	Student number:	XXXX
Place inspected:	************ site	Date of Inspection:	01/06/20**

Observations		Control measures	Timescale
Hazards and consequences		Immediate and longer-term actions	
16. Risk of fire controlled by present use of fire extinguisher during hot work	I	None	
	M	Commend good practice	1 week
	L	Review permit to work system	2 weeks
17. Risk of cuts due to threaded bar protruding into walkway from cast section of concrete	I	Put tape barrier around protruding obstacle	1 day
	M	Ensure that rods are not cut too long in future	1 week
	L	Review design of clamp for concrete pouring	Annual
18. Risk of trips due to poor lighting in mezzanine area. 30% of lights not working	I	Provide temporary lighting in dark areas	2 days
	M	Repair broken lights	1 week
	L	Implement regular inspection	1 month
19. Risk of eye injury due to damaged socket on 22mm nut runner. Could cause flying debris	I	Remove tool from use	Immediate
	M	Replace with new tool	1 week
	L	Implement regular inspections	1 month
20. Risk of trips due to trailing electrical leads	I	Provide cable covers	1 day
	M	Review cable management systems	1 week
	L	Provide more power sockets	3 months

Key: I = Immediate   M = medium   L = Long term actions

NEBOSH NATIONAL CERTIFICATE IN CONSTRUCTION HEALTH AND SAFETY
UNIT NCC2 - CONSTRUCTION HEALTH AND SAFETY PRACTICAL APPLICATION

Candidate's observation sheet

Sheet number 5 **of** 5

Student name:	A. N. Other	Student number:	XXXX
Place inspected:	************ site	Date of Inspection:	01/06/20**

Observations	Control measures		Timescale
Hazards and consequences	Immediate and longer-term actions		
21. Risk of unauthorised access to the site controlled by signing and guarding	I	None	N/A
	M	Regular checks of fence line	Daily
	L	Review fencing requirements as project progresses	Monthly
22. Risk of delayed first aid treatment due to eye wash being out of date	I	Replace eye wash	1 day
	M	Implement system of weekly checks	1 week
	L	Toolbox talk on procedure for replacing first aid equipment	1 month
23. Risk of hearing damage when using disc cutter without protection.	I	Provide appropriate PPE	One day
	M	Implement regular inspections to ensure PPE is being worn	One week
	L	Set up regular audiometric tests	3 months
24. Risk of dermatitis from diesel fuel when refuelling vehicles	I	Provide suitable gloves	1 day
	M	Remind local supervisor of need to ensure staff wear PPE when refuelling vehicles	1 week
	L	Refresher training on personal hygiene	6 months

Key: I = Immediate   M = medium   L = Long term actions

Student number: XXXXX

Location: Site Inspection Report for **** Site, Anytown, Someplace.

Date of review: 01/06/20**

1. Introduction

This report is based on the findings by the author A. N. Other, during a recent workplace inspection that was completed on Thursday 1st June 20**. The workplace inspected was a construction site at **** Limited, Anytown, Someplace, where a new extension is being constructed.

The new building consists of two floors; the ground floor area is where all the services are being installed i.e., electrics, hydraulics and gas. The upper floor is where the main equipment is being installed. There is a new roof and side wall cladding on the new building. The roof is three meters high.

The work being carried out is moving very quickly, especially the sides of the building being installed and lots of concrete being poured inside the extension. There is a lot of activity in the basement (ground floor) with electricians and pipe fitters working to install new services which will supply all the new machinery.

In total, there are fifty eight people working on the site.

2. Executive Summary

Whilst carrying out this workplace inspection I was impressed to find that generally the construction site area was very tidy due to a good level of housekeeping. All inspections of portable appliances and scaffolding was in date and storage areas for gas bottles well maintained. All welfare facilities were in good order.

However, a number of items were noticed which, on further investigation, require your attention in order to prevent the risk of injury or ill-health. Immediate consideration should be given to matters such as the use of frayed lifting slings and the lack of edge protection when pouring concrete.

Further details can be found in the main body of this report and in the "observations" section.

3. Main Findings of the inspection

3.1. Observation No 1. Falling from height.

When pouring concrete to the south side of the main foundation, a part of the installed edge protection had been removed so that access could be gained for the concrete pour. After the work had been completed, the edge protection had not been replaced. All work was stopped until edge protection had been reinstalled and inspected. The immediate remedy to this problem was quite straightforward but, for a short period, ten people were standing idle.

This situation creates a breach of the Work at Height Regulations (WAH) 2005 which require the employer to take suitable and sufficient steps to prevent people falling from height. Employees must be reminded that the organisation will not tolerate unauthorised interference with safety equipment and that it is a possible breach of section 7 of the Health and Safety at Work Act (HASWA) 1974 if they do.

Further recommendations are that the situation should be discussed in toolbox talks, prominent signs erected and that the barriers are subject to a daily inspection by management.

There are no direct costs to these recommendations. However, failure to implement them could lead to a prosecution and civil action.

3.2. Observation No 7. Damaged lifting sling

The pipefitters installing the main six inch gas pipe were using a five ton capacity lifting sling which was clearly damaged and could have had very serious consequences had it failed whilst lifting a very heavy pipe. Employers have a duty under the Lifting Operations and Lifting Equipment (LOLER) Regulations 1998 to ensure that all lifting equipment and accessories are of adequate strength and regularly inspected.

The sling was immediately removed from site and replaced by a new, fully certified sling from stores. Regular inspection of lifting equipment is a legal requirement and must take place at approved intervals. I estimate that a new sling to replace the one damaged and calibration certificate will cost about £250.

3.3. Observation No 10. Traffic route demarcation

The concrete mixing wagons were being manoeuvred into an area which is a designated pedestrian area. HSE statistics show that collision with vehicles is one of the most common causes of death in the workplace. This is a possible breach of the Construction (Design and Management) Regulations (CDM) 2007 under which employers have a duty to ensure that all traffic routes are organised so that pedestrians can move safely without risk.

The pedestrian route was closed and re-routed away from the danger by using concrete blocks and warning tape. Drivers and pedestrians need to be reminded at toolbox talks of the dangers caused by site traffic.

The cost of moving the concrete blocks and erecting new signs is about £350.

3.4. Observation No 18. Poor lighting

The lighting level in the lower mezzanine basement was not very good on account of about 30% of the lights not working. As the project progresses, more and more people are working in this area. The poor quality of the lighting significantly increases the likelihood of accidents such as tripping.

CDM 2007 requires that all workplaces have suitable and sufficient lighting. Therefore, to avoid a breach, the lighting must be repaired as soon as possible. Some of the fittings will have to repositioned to prevent them being obscured by the new pipework.

The cost to reposition the light fittings will be about £550.

3.5. Observation No's 6, 9 and 15. Good practice

It must be stated that, whilst carrying out the inspection, several examples of good practice were identified. Notably, all portable appliances that were inspected had indate test stickers on them which assists with compliance with the Electricity at Work (EWR) Regulations 1989.

All welfare facilities were clean and in good order as required by CDM 2007.

Similarly, all scaffolds were clearly identified by a green "scafftag" to show that it was safe to use. This, again, suggests compliance with the WAH 2005.

4. Conclusions

The removal of edge protection is an indication that employees are not aware of their responsibilities to themselves and fellow workers. It also suggests a lax approach to health and safety on the part of site management. The inclusion of this subject in future toolbox talks is an immediate remedy but the message has to be consistently reinforced.

The damaged sling would have been identified and taken out of service much earlier if a system of regular inspections had been in place and records kept. To comply with the minimum requirements set out in LOLER 1998, the whole inspection system must be reviewed.

The concrete mixer encroaching on the pedestrian area was totally avoidable. Planning by the vehicle co-ordination team should have taken into account the long term development of the site and the constant evolution of the traffic routes as the project progressed. As stated in the main body, uncontrolled vehicle movements are one of the most common causes of fatal accidents in the workplace. The moral aspect of these serious incidents is something that should be at the forefront of everyone's mind.

The poor lighting levels are a concern. Once again, as building work has progressed, it has become apparent that there was a lack of planning when positioning the fittings. The present lights are only in place temporarily. So, when permanent lighting is installed, thought should be given to the layout of pipework and other fixtures to prevent a recurrence of the problem.

I suggest that my recommendations are implemented at the earliest opportunity according to the priority allocated to them in the next section of this report. By doing this, the organisation will openly demonstrate to all employees that their health and safety is being taken seriously at all levels of management. Also, it will show that, in the long term, a positive safety culture is being developed which will reduce the sizeable costs attributed to accidents and enhance the reputation of the business in a very competitive market place.

Several items of good practice were noted during the inspection. It is important that complacency does not creep into these areas and that the systems that have brought about these good standards are maintained and improved throughout the project.

5. Recommendations

Ref No	Recommendation	Likely resource implications	Priority	Target date
3.1	Display prominent warning signs	£20	Immediate	One week
	Regular inspection	30 minutes of management time	Immediate	One week
3.2	Inspect all lifting equipment and replace damaged items	£250	Medium	One month
3.3	Replace barriers and erect signs	£350	Immediate	One week
3.4	Redesign and move light fittings	£550	Low	One month
3.5	Review management system to ensure continued good practice	No immediate implications	Low	Six months

Candidate and course provider declarations:

For completion by the Candidate:

I declare that the work submitted for this practical application assessment i.e. the completed observation sheets and the report to management, is my own work. I recognise that contravention of this statement constitutes malpractice and may result in my being subject to the penalties set out in the NEBOSH Malpractice policy.

Name (Print) _____A N Other_____

Signature _____*A N Other*_____

Date _____01 / 06 / 20**_____

For completion by a course provider representative (eg, internal practical assessor):

I declare that the work marked is identical to that received from the candidate. I recognise that contravention of this statement constitutes malpractice and may result in my being subject to the penalties set out in the NEBOSH Malpractice policy.

Name (Print) _____B Bond_____

Signature _____*B Bond*_____

Date _____10 / 06 / 20**_____

For completion by the course provider's internal practical assessor:

I declare that I have marked this work and am both qualified and approved by NEBOSH to do so. I recognise that contravention of this statement constitutes malpractice and may result in my being subject to the penalties set out in the NEBOSH Malpractice policy.

Name (Print) _____ R Rice _____

Signature _____ *R Rice* _____

Date _____15 / 06 / 20**_____

Sample assessment questions - answers

NCC1 - Managing and controlling hazards in construction activities

ELEMENT 1

1. **Identify** the duties of the client for projects that are notifiable under the Construction (Design and Management) Regulations 2007(CDM). **(8)**

The duties of the client under the Construction Design and Management Regulations, include: appointing a principal contractor, a designer and a CDM coordinator and ensuring the competence of all appointees; ensuring that a construction phase plan is in place before construction starts and that adequate welfare facilities will be provided for the construction phase; providing pre-construction information to designers and contractors; allowing sufficient time and resources for all stages; ensuring management arrangements are in place for carrying out the work in a safe manner; cooperating with and coordinating the work of other duty holders; providing information to the CDM coordinator for the health and safety file; and after the completion of the construction phase, retaining, revising and providing access to the file.

2. **Identify** the duties placed upon the principal contractor under the Construction (Design and Management) Regulations (CDM) 2007. **(8)**

The duties placed upon the principal contractor by the Regulations include: being satisfied that a CDM coordinator has been appointed and that the client is aware of their duties under the Regulations; planning, managing and monitoring the construction phase to ensure it is carried out without risks to health and safety; preparing, developing and updating a construction phase plan; liaising with the CDM coordinator regarding the on-going design of the project; checking the competence of all appointees; ensuring the provision of welfare facilities to the required standard; developing and enforcing site rules for health and safety; providing access to other contractors to those parts of the construction phase plan relevant to the work to be carried out by them and informing them of the time allowed for planning and preparation; identifying to all contractors the information relating to their activities required by the CDM coordinator for inclusion in the health and safety file; taking steps to prevent access to the construction site by unauthorised persons; ensuring that all employees are given site induction and any further information and training they might need in relation to health and safety and consulting with employees or their representatives on health and safety issues.

3. **Identify** the designer's duties during a notifiable project under the Construction (Design and Management) Regulations 2007 (CDM). **(8)**

Identify duties such as: not commencing work unless the client is aware of their duties and a CDM co-ordinator has been appointed; eliminating hazards which might give rise to risks during design, reducing the risks from any hazards that might remain and providing information on the residual risks; taking account of the requirements of the Workplace (Health, Safety and Welfare) Regulations when designing a building to be used as a workplace; providing information to clients, contractors and other designers to assist them to comply with their duties under the Regulations; cooperating with the CDM coordinator and providing information for the health and safety file.

ELEMENT 2

1. A project involves the construction of an in situ concrete structure, including the installation of drains, on a brownfield site. Up to 60 people are likely to be involved in the work at any one time.

    Identify the welfare facilities that should be provided for such work. **(8)**

Identify that the welfare facilities that should be provided for employees include: washing facilities including showers with hot and cold or warm running water with soap and towels made available; a sufficient number of toilets and the provision of changing rooms with separate storage for dirty and clean clothing. Facilities for drying clothing would also be necessary as would a room set aside for taking meals and refreshment. This room should be equipped with means of boiling water and heating food and a clearly marked supply of drinking water. Marks are also available for identifying that provision for first aid treatment should be made and that an adequate standard of lighting, heating and ventilation should be provided for the facilities. If appropriate, separate facilities would be necessary for men and women.

2. **Identify** the factors to be considered when deciding upon adequate first-aid arrangements for a construction site. **(8)**

Identify the key factors including the maximum number of persons on site, the number and type of contractors involved and the types of hazard and level of risk present on site. Another important factor would be the number of first-aid personnel to be provided including those with specialist training, for example in the use of defibrillators and the first aid facilities to be provided in terms of the number and contents of first aid boxes and first-aid rooms, both of which could be dependent on the proximity to emergency medical services, and the ability to provide continued cover over different shifts and for sickness, leave and other absences.

3. An initial site assessment should be completed before a construction project commences in order to determine possible hazards that could be present on or near a site.

    Outline factors that should be addressed when carrying out the initial site assessment. **(8)**

An initial site assessment before the start of a construction project should address factors such as the previous and current use of the site which might indicate the presence of hazardous materials such as asbestos or chemical contaminants; the possibility of voids or cellars remaining from previous construction work; the area of the site and the existence of any natural obstacles; the nature of the surroundings taking into account the proximity of roads, railways, footpaths, schools and housing; the location of rivers, streams or other controlled waters; the possible presence of overhead or underground services; an assessment of the ground conditions; the means of access to the site; evidence of possible biological hazards caused by the presence of vermin and any history of trespass, vandalism or arson or evidence of drug use.

ELEMENT 3

1. Approximately one quarter of all accidents on construction sites are associated with plant, machinery and vehicles.

    Outline possible control measures which may prevent such accidents. **(8)**

In answering this question, outline control measures such as the proper selection of equipment for the task in hand; ensuring the competency of operators; the need to ensure that dangerous parts of machines were properly guarded, and that a regime of planned inspections and maintenance and procedures for reporting defects was put in place. Additionally, site control measures play an important part, including planning and maintenance of traffic routes to segregate pedestrians and vehicles, imposing and enforcing speed restrictions in respect of vehicles, preventing the unauthorised use or movement of plant and ensuring good standards of lighting and adequate signage. Finally it would be necessary to provide competent supervision to ensure equipment was used properly and for its proper purpose and to provide awareness training to all employees on the hazards associated with the use of plant, machinery and vehicles and the precautions that must be observed.

2. A dumper truck overturned whilst being driven across a construction site.

    (a) **Identify FOUR** reasons why the dumper truck may have overturned. **(4)**

    (b) **Outline** practical measures that could be taken to minimise the risk of a dumper truck overturn. **(4)**

There are a number of reasons which cause dumper trucks to overturn on site and these are generally connected with the nature of the ground over which they are being driven, the condition and loading of the trucks themselves and the competence and carelessness of the drivers. Overturn can occur if a truck is being driven over uneven or unstable ground, on or across slopes or too close to an excavation or embankment. As for the trucks themselves, they might be poorly maintained with tyres that are not inflated to the recommended pressure while overloading or uneven loading of the bucket could affect their stability. The competence of the driver is also an important factor and particularly if he is prone to drive or corner at excessive speeds and fail to avoid the many obstacles that are found on a construction site.

For part (b), outline practical measures that could be taken to minimise the risks identified in the first part of the question. These include the use of trucks with a wide wheel base and a low centre of gravity; carrying out regular maintenance with particular attention being given to brakes, steering and tyre pressures and arranging for drivers to carry out peruse checks; providing designated traffic routes which are kept free from obstructions; providing edge protection around excavations; setting and enforcing speed limits; ensuring that the loads carried by trucks are within their safe working loads; and using trained and competent drivers and monitoring their performance on a regular basis.

3. **Outline** features of pedestrian routes on a construction site that will help to minimise the risk of accidents to workers. **(8)**

Pedestrian routes should be kept separate from those for vehicular traffic and be wide enough to accommodate the number of workers likely to use them. They should be maintained in good condition, be well lit and clearly signed, kept free from obstruction, afford protection from falling materials and allow easy access to work areas. Where pedestrians have to cross main vehicle routes, precautions must be taken to ensure their safety such as, for example, erecting barriers and providing refuges where necessary and ensuring they have a clear view of traffic movement at the crossing points.

ELEMENT 4

1. A lifting operation is to be carried out with the use of a crane hired for the purpose. **Outline** the main items to be checked by the person appointed to have overall control of this operation. **(8)**

The person appointed to control the lifting operation would need to carry out an initial assessment of the operation to take account of the ground conditions. They would have to ensure that the lifting appliance and the associated equipment were suitable for lifting the load and were marked with their safe working loads and that there was documentary evidence to show that the required examinations, inspections and maintenance had been carried out. Following consultation with everyone involved, they should then ensure a plan was in place to enable effective coordination of the operation ensuring that all personnel concerned such as the crane driver, slinger and banksman were competent to carry out their duties and fully conversant with the hand signals or other means of communication that were to be used. They would also have to put in place systems for reporting incidents and defects. Finally they would have to take the prevailing weather conditions into account and especially the presence of high winds which would have an effect on the control of the load.

2. An audit by Senior Management on lifting operations identified that lifts were not planned, defective accessories were being used during lifting and the statutory testing of lifting equipment had not been carried out.

    (a) **Outline** the issues that could be included in a lifting plan. **(8)**

    (b) **Identify** factors relating to the condition of lifting accessories that could form part of a pre-use checklist. **(8)**

    (c) **Identify** the frequency of thorough examinations and inspections of lifting equipment required by the Lifting Operations and Lifting Equipment Regulations (LOLER). **(4)**

Issues that should be addressed in a lifting plan include the load to be lifted including its weight, shape and centre of gravity; the lifting equipment and accessories to be used ensuring that the statutory tests and examinations have been completed and that all items are marked with their safe working load; the proposed route to be taken for the load to be moved avoiding overhead cables and other obstructions; ground conditions, weather conditions and the provision of lighting if this is necessary; the demarcation of the site of the lift allowing entrance only to authorised personnel; the use of competent personnel to carry out the lift and ensuring an effective method of communication amongst those involved; setting up procedures to be followed in the event of an emergency; and making arrangements for the completion of the task including the dismantling and storage of lifting equipment.

For part (b), in regard to factors relating to the condition of lifting accessories that could be included in a pre-use check list, you should identify those such as abraded or cut slings; stretched fabric; broken wires or kinks in wire ropes and slings; deformed hooks and deformed and cracked links in chains; damaged or missing safety clips; evidence of corrosion or misalignment; evidence of alterations to accessories such as shortening or joining items together; and the marking of accessories with their safe working loads. The Lifting Operations and Lifting Equipment Regulations require that lifting equipment should be thoroughly examined before being put into use for the first time; after assembly and before being taken into use where the safety of the equipment depends on the installation conditions; every six months in the case of accessories or equipment for lifting persons; every twelve months for other lifting equipment; and when exceptional circumstances have occurred which could jeopardise the safety of the equipment.

3. Manual handling operations can cause injuries.

    (a) **Identify THREE** types of injury that may be caused by the incorrect manual handling of loads. **(3)**

    (b) With reference to the task, **identify** means of reducing the risk of injury during manual handling operations. **(5)**

In answering Part (a), you could choose from a list of potential injuries that include spinal disc compression or prolapsed disc; strains to tendons or muscles; hernia or ruptures; dislocation or fracture of bones; cuts and abrasions and crushing or impact injuries.

For Part (b), you could identify means of reducing the risk of injury during manual handling operations such as the use of mechanical means for lifting; splitting the load by breaking it into smaller units; the use of team handling; placing materials near to the working area and storing them at waist height; arranging the storage of materials to prevent the need for bending and twisting by the operatives; reducing the need for sustained holding, pushing or pulling of heavy loads and ensuring that the workforce were given breaks at frequent intervals.

ELEMENT 5

1. The Provision and Use of Work Equipment Regulations 1998 require that work equipment used in hostile environments is inspected at suitable intervals.

    Identify the items on a small dumper truck that should be the subject of such an inspection. **(8)**

Identify many of the items on a dumper truck that should be the subject of periodic inspection. Such items include: the provision and condition of roll over protection and driver restraints (e.g. seats belts); the condition of the bodywork and seats; the condition of the tyres; the effectiveness of the braking system, steering and warning devices; the performance of the bucket release and tilt mechanisms; the integrity of fuel, oil and hydraulic systems and the legibility of labels and signs.

2. **Outline** practical ways of reducing the risk to employees when using an electrical powered cement mixer on site. **(8)**

In answering this question, refer to control measures such as; ensuring the mixer is set up on level ground and secured against movement; ensuring guards are in place and the engine cover closed to provide protection against moving parts; using a reduced voltage of 110 volts for the mixer and connecting it to the supply through a residual current device (RCD); using heavy duty cables or cable covers to provide protection against moving vehicles; placing materials close to the mixer to minimise the amount of manual handling to be carried out; the use of appropriate personal protective equipment such as eye and hearing protection and gloves to counter the corrosive and irritant properties of cement; ensuring that the mixer is not overloaded and that the manufacturer's instructions with regard to loading are followed; the provision of training and information to employees on the health risks involved and the precautions to be taken and providing a good standard of monitoring and supervision to ensure the precautionary measures are followed.

3. **Outline** the control measures that should be adopted when cutting paving slabs with a petrol disc cutter. **(8)**

In answering this question, the measures that you should outline include the suitable selection of equipment and its inspection prior to use; the use of a competent person to change the disc when needed; the provision of an adequate top guard for the disc cutter; dust suppression by wet cutting and using the equipment in a ventilated area away from other operations; stopping the engine and applying the brake when the cutter was not being used or when it was being carried; protecting the operator against HAVS by, for example, the provision of insulation for the handle and introducing job rotation; ensuring a safe system of work for refuelling and keeping the minimum amount of fuel on site; the provision and use of appropriate personal protective equipment such as goggles, ear defenders, gloves, respiratory protection and boots and the provision of information on and training in manual handling.

ELEMENT 6

1. **Describe** how the following two protective measures reduce the risk of electric shock **AND**, in **EACH** case, give an example of their application.

    (a) Reduced low voltage. **(4)**

    (b) Double insulation. **(4)**

"Reduced low voltage" commonly used for portable electrical hand tools on construction sites, involves the reduction of mains voltage by a transformer to a lower safer voltage - typically 110 volts. Any shock voltage can be restricted to 55 volts by means of a transformer that is centre tapped to earth. Additionally, Safety Extra Low Voltage (SELV) - a voltage less than 50 volts - is used in low power tools such as hand lamps or soldering irons.

In "double insulation" internal live parts of a piece of equipment have two layers of insulation which prevent the exposure of live parts to exposed conductive parts such as the outer metal casing of the equipment. Consequently, an internal fault condition cannot make any part of the casing live. Double insulation is used on Class II appliances such as hand held portable appliances.

2. Ground works are being planned on a site crossed by high voltage overhead power lines. The work will involve the use of excavators and tipper lorries to remove spoil from the site.

    Outline control measures to reduce the risk from contact with the overhead power lines. **(8)**

For this question, reference to HSE Guidance Note GS6 would give you the information you need to provide a good answer prompting you initially to highlight the necessity of consulting the electricity supply company with a view to making the lines dead and obtaining written confirmation that isolation has been achieved. If isolation was not possible, advice should be obtained from the supply company on a safe working distance and precautions introduced such as the erection of goalpost barriers and warning signs; fitting plant with height restrictors coupled with audible warnings in the cab; ensuring that spoil heaps were kept away from the overhead lines; using competent banksmen; and communicating the safety precautions to the operatives by means of, for example, tool box talks.

3.   Hand-held electric drills are commonly used on construction sites.

    (a)   **Outline** the checks that should be carried out by the user of a drill to reduce the likelihood of electric shock. **(4)**

    (b)   Other than electricity, **identify FOUR** hazards associated with the use of hand-held electric drills. **(4)**

In answering part (a) of the question, you should refer to the need for the user of the equipment to check: the general condition of the drill for damage; the integrity of the connectors, both plug and socket, and evidence of over heating or burning; the integrity of the cables; the rating of the fuses; other protective measures such as the use of reduced low voltage where possible or the provision of residual current devices and evidence that a portable appliance test (PAT) has been carried out.

For part (b), other hazards associated with the use of the drill include entanglement with the chuck or bit, stabbing or puncture by the drill bit, noise, vibration, dust, hot surfaces and tripping hazards associated with trailing cables.

ELEMENT 7

1.   (a)   **Identify TWO** flammable gases contained in cylinders that might be found on a construction site. **(2)**

    (b)   **Outline** precautions that should be taken to prevent fires and explosions during the transport and use of flammable gases contained in cylinders. **(6)**

For part (a) of the question, refer to acetylene, propane and butane.

For Part (b), if flammable gases in cylinders are transported, they should be disconnected from any equipment, placed upright in a secure cage, rack or trolley, secured against movement and should not be laid down. When in use, they should be protected from mechanical shock and placed in well ventilated areas, out of direct sunlight and away from sources of ignition and combustible materials. Flash back arrestors should be fitted and hose connectors should be secure and hoses inspected regularly for damage. When cylinders are not in actual use, the valves should be shut to isolate the gas supply. If any cylinder is suspected of leaking, it should be stored in a safe place and immediate contact made with the supplier. The gases should be used only by competent persons and there may be occasions when a permit to work may be required.

2.   Arson on a construction site is a common cause of fire.

    (a)   **Give** reasons why some construction sites may be vulnerable to arson attacks. **(4)**

    (b)   **Identify** ways of reducing the risk of arson on a construction site. **(4)**

Reasons why some construction sites might be vulnerable to arson attacks include a lack of or damaged perimeter fencing; inadequate supervision of visitors to the site or a failure to provide CCTV or security guards during non-working hours; a poor standard of housekeeping with combustible materials allowed to remain on the ground and the use of open skips; a failure to store flammable materials in a secure store when work has finished for the day; the location of the site, perhaps in social deprivation areas or areas with a history of vandalism; and a failure to communicate with the local community and in particular schools to advise on the dangers present on a working construction site.

Identify ways of reducing the risk of arson such as erecting and maintaining perimeter fencing; providing security lighting and using security guards and CCTV during non-working hours; ensuring flammable materials were kept in a secure storage area; controlling the entry of persons to the site such as visitors and sub contractors; erecting warning signs and liaising closely with local police and neighbouring schools.

3.   A major hazard on a refurbishment project is fire.

    (i)   **Identify THREE** activities that represent an increased fire risk in such a situation. **(3)**

    (ii)   **Outline** the precautions that may be taken to reduce the risk of a fire occurring. **(5)**

In answering part (a) of the question, identify activities such as hot work, for example cutting and welding; the use of flammable or combustible materials; electrical work where defective equipment might be used or the electrical system overloaded; individuals smoking and burning rubbish on site.

For part (b), outline precautions such as the inspection and testing of electrical systems and equipment; the use of permits to work for hot work and inspection of the work area both during and after the completion of the work;

arranging for the regular clearing away of accumulated rubbish; the proper storage of flammable and combustible materials; prohibiting bonfires on site; the control of smoking particularly since this is now prohibited at a place of work; and avoiding the risk of fire by fabricating components off site.

ELEMENT 8

1. Insulation board tiles that contain asbestos are to be removed from the ceiling of a store room located within a primary school.

    Outline factors which should be taken into consideration when planning the work. **(8)**

In planning the removal of the insulation board tiles, factors that would have to be taken into consideration include: the type and condition of the tiles; the possibility that asbestos might be present in other parts of the building and the need for a management or refurbishment and demolition survey; measures to be taken to prevent access to the area by isolating the storeroom and locking the door; consideration of other risks involved in the removal such as working at height or contact with electricity; preparing a schedule for the removal of the tiles which preferably should be done outside of term time; the appointment of a licensed contractor for the removal of the asbestos; ensuring that, if the work is notifiable, HSE is given fourteen days notice of the work to be carried out; the need to erect sheeting to contain the asbestos during its removal and dependent on the removal method and the condition of the tiles, the need to maintain the sheeted enclosure under negative pressure; the arrangements for monitoring airborne fibre levels during the operation and for carrying out an air clearance test and the issue of a certificate when the work is completed; the arrangements for the safe disposal of the asbestos waste by means of a licensed carrier; the provision and siting of decontamination and welfare facilities and ensuring that the employees are made fully aware both of the risks involved in the removal operation and the precautions to be taken.

2. Silica can be found in various materials used in construction, and exposure to silica dust can lead to chronic health effects such as silicosis.

    (a) **Give** the meaning of the term 'workplace exposure limit'. **(2)**

    (b) **Outline** control measures that could be considered to control levels of silica dust in the workplace. **(6)**

A workplace exposure limit defines the maximum permitted concentration of an airborne hazardous substance averaged over a specified period of time and referred to as a time weighted average. Two time periods are used: long term (eight hours), intended to control effects by restricting the total intake by inhalation on a daily basis, and short term (fifteen minutes) the immediate limit of exposure which should not be exceeded.

One measure that could be adopted to control the level of silica dust in the workplace would be to have the process that produces the dust carried out off site in a controlled environment. This is not always possible and other means have to be considered such as using a wet instead of a dry process; suppressing the dust as it arises with water sprays; enclosing the whole process as might be possible with a large grinding operation; installing local exhaust ventilation and introducing a high standard of housekeeping using a vacuum cleaning system as opposed to hand sweeping.

3. **Identify FOUR** hazardous substances prevalent to the construction industry **AND give** the associated health risk for **EACH**. **(8)**

In identifying four hazardous substances prevalent to the construction industry and their associated health risks, you could choose from the following:

Wood dust - inhalation of the dust arising from sanding or cutting operations may cause allergic or non-allergic respiratory symptoms and cancer.

Silica - inhalation of silica may result in silicosis which is a fibrosis of the lung.

Cement - prolonged or repeated exposure to cement dust can lead to silicosis. Continuous contact with wet cement may cause burns or skin ulcers.

Solvents - inhalation of vapours from organic solvents such as trichloroethylene being used as a cleaning agent can cause drowsiness, can depress the central nervous system and may lead to liver failure.

Asbestos - asbestos fibres readily become airborne when disturbed and can enter the lungs where they cause fibrosis, involving scarring and thickening of the lung tissue, asbestosis or mesothelioma – a thickening of the pleural lining.

Lead - lead poisoning results from the inhalation of fumes produced from the heating of lead such as the oxyacetylene cutting of metal coated with lead paint.

ELEMENT 9

1. The Control of Noise at Work Regulations 2005 gives noise exposure action values.

   (a) **Identify** the lower **AND** the upper exposure action values. **(2)**

   (b) **Outline** the control measures an employer is required to take when employees are exposed to noise at or above an upper exposure action value. **(6)**

For part (a), you should identify that the lower exposure action value is 80 dB(A) and the upper 85 dB(A).

In answering part (b), measures that should be outlined include: the completion of a risk assessment (required at or above the lower action level); the elimination of noise at source or its reduction to as low a level as reasonably practicable; the control of exposure to noise by the implementation of organisational measures such as reducing the time of exposure, or technical measures such as the provision of engineering controls; the designation and marking of hearing protection zones; the provision and maintenance of hearing protection and ensuring that it was fully and properly used; the provision to employees of information, instruction and training on the risks of exposure to noise and the controls that had been introduced; and undertaking health surveillance where the assessment indicated that this was necessary.

2. **Outline** the actions that management might consider in order to reduce levels of occupational stress amongst workers on site. **(8)**

In answering this question, outline that the options that are available to management to reduce stress levels amongst their employees include those related to the environment and those associated with organisational, job and individual stress factors. In the former category, actions include reductions in noise levels, provision of adequate levels of lighting, the provision of adequate welfare facilities and the maintenance of a high standard of housekeeping. For the latter, actions might be those related to work/life balance such as discouraging the working of excessively long hours; introducing job rotation and increasing work variety; providing adequate resources and properly maintained equipment; providing good levels of communication, seeking the views of employees, involving them in decisions and recognising good performance when it occurs; introducing and implementing policies to cover harassment, discrimination, violence and the investigation of complaints and ensuring adequate levels of supervision with supervisors trained to recognise the symptoms of stress so that ameliorative action can be taken or, in extreme cases, so that those affected might be offered counselling.

3. As part of major road construction ground consolidation anchors are being installed by workers using hand-held powered percussive equipment that produce high levels of vibration.

   (a) **Identify** possible health effects due to exposure to vibration. **(4)**

   (b) **Outline** control measures that could be used to reduce the risk of such effects. **(4)**

In answering part (a) of the question, identify effects such as numbness, tingling and blanching of the fingers; swollen and painful joints; a reduction in strength, grip, dexterity and in sensory perception; and involuntary muscular movement.

For part (b), you should outline a hierarchy of control measures such as elimination by mechanisation or automation; substituting the tools with lower vibration equipment; reducing the time of exposure of the operatives by providing frequent breaks and/or job rotation; modifying the equipment to improve the grip on the tools; introducing a planned maintenance programme for the tools; providing appropriate personal protective equipment such as gloves to keep the hands warm; introducing a programme of health surveillance and providing the employees with information, instruction and training on the hazards associated with the use of the tools and the control measures that should be taken.

ELEMENT 10

1. Scaffolding has been erected to the outside of a block of high-rise flats in order to undertake window replacement and repairs to external cladding.

   Outline factors that could affect the stability of the scaffold. **(8)**

Recognise that the design of the scaffold could have an effect upon its stability such as for example the arrangements made for ground floor access points and the position of the hoist as could its erection on soft or inadequately consolidated ground or without sound foundations such as sole boards and base plates. Erection by incompetent workmen, the use of defective material and incorrect components, insufficient ties or their unauthorised removal and inadequate bracing, adverse weather conditions, overloading and the possibility of the scaffold being struck by vehicles and vandalism were among the other factors which were mentioned.

2. A flat roof is to be repaired while a building remains occupied.

    Outline the issues that should be addressed to reduce the risk to the workers involved in the repair work and others who may be affected by the work. **(8)**

In considering the reduction of the risk to the workers involved in the repair work you should refer to issues such as the condition of the roof vis-à-vis its safe working load and the possible presence of fragile materials; the provision of safe means of access to the working area and the protection to be provided at the roof edge such as double guard rails and toe boards; the provision of equipment to lift tools and materials on to the roof; precautions to be observed in the use of a LPG heated boiler and the possible contact with hazardous materials such as tar or asbestos; the provision and use of personal protective equipment such as that for the protection of head, eyes, hands and feet; the employment of competent personnel, fully aware of the risks associated with the work and the precautions that should be taken; the provisions for first aid, and the procedures to be followed in the event of an emergency.

Additional measures to ensure the health and safety of others who might be affected by the work include briefing the occupiers of the building on the likely duration of the work and on the risks and precautions to be observed and the erection of barriers and signs at ground level to prevent access to the working area by unauthorised persons.

3. (a) **Identify FOUR** hazards associated with work at height above ground level. **(4)**

    (b) **Outline** factors to consider when conducting a working at height risk assessment. **(8)**

    (c) **Outline** safe working practices associated with the use of a mobile elevating working platform (MEWP). **(8)**

In answering part (a), you should identify hazards such as falling over a vertical distance; working on fragile surfaces or on those whose material has deteriorated; unprotected edges; unsuitable, unstable or poorly maintained access equipment; falling objects; overhead obstructions such as cables; and severe weather conditions.

In carrying out a working at height risk assessment, factors to be considered include: determining whether the work at height could be avoided; the nature and duration of the task; arrangements for planning and supervising the work; the suitability and state of repair of the access equipment; the level of competence and training of the workers involved; the prevailing weather conditions; means of access and egress including the use of access boards or platforms provided with guard rails and toe boards or fencing; the use of personal protection such as harnesses and hard hats and fall arrest systems; the arrangements for emergency rescue; and any health conditions of the workers involved such as vertigo or heart or balance problems.

For part (c), in using a mobile elevating working platform (MEWP), safe working practices which should be adopted include: the involvement of competent persons both to operate and work from the platform; the completion of any statutory inspection requirements; its use only on firm level ground with checks being made on the presence of buried services, drains and overhead obstructions; the use of outriggers and the fitting of guard rails and toe boards to the platform; the use of harnesses by workers on the platform; the erection of barriers round the area where the platform is to be used; ensuring the platform is not overloaded and securing all tools and equipment before the platform is moved; and introducing emergency rescue procedures.

ELEMENT 11

1. **Identify:**

    (a) **FOUR** hazards associated with work in a confined space. **(4)**

    (b) **FOUR** examples of a confined space that may be encountered on a construction site. **(4)**

For part (a), you could identify a range of possible hazards including the presence of toxic, flammable or explosive fumes and vapours; the lack of oxygen or conversely oxygen enrichment; the ingress of fluids for example from sewer flows; falls of materials particularly during tunnelling work; the possibility of injury, particularly to the head, due to restricted space; claustrophobic effects; biological hazards arising from the presence of vermin; the low levels of lighting and access and egress issues.

For part (b) identify examples such as manholes, sewers, tunnels, excavations, tanks, chambers, pits and silos.

2. **Identify** the main hazards associated with excavation work on construction sites. **(8)**

Identify the main hazards associated with excavation work such as the collapse of the sides of the excavation; contact with buried services such as gas electricity and water; flooding following adverse weather conditions; build up of fumes and lack of oxygen; fire and explosion from flammable substances; the dangers associated with excavation machinery particularly contact with overhead lines; the effect of the excavation work on adjacent structures leading to collapse; the possibility of vehicles or people falling into unprotected excavations; biological hazards such as leptospirosis; coming into contact with contaminated land and even the possible presence of an unexploded bomb.

3. A leaking underground concrete reservoir has been emptied so that it can be visually inspected prior to repair.

    Outline the features of a safe system of work for the inspection team in order to satisfy the requirements of the Confined Spaces Regulations 1997. **(8)**

A safe system of work for the inspection of the underground reservoir would initially entail a preliminary remote inspection followed by the completion of a risk assessment and the preparation of a safety method statement which should require the utilisation of a permit to work system for entry; the provision of safe means of access and egress; the stipulation of a minimum gang size of at least three persons one of whom should always be outside the confined space; the selection and training of staff in confined space working; the isolation and locking off of valves to prevent the ingress of water into the reservoir; the provision of gas monitoring while the work was in progress; the provision of adequate lighting and ventilation; arrangements for the installation of an effective means of communication between those inside and outside the reservoir; the provision and use of personal protective equipment such as hard hats, goggles and overalls and the provision of rescue equipment such as breathing apparatus, resuscitation equipment and a tripod in the event of an emergency.

ELEMENT 12

1. A three-storey office block is to be demolished.

    (a) **Identify** the possible hazards to the environment that could be caused by the demolition. **(4)**

    (b) **Outline** measures to reduce the risk to the environment during the demolition work. **(4)**

For part (a) identify hazards such as airborne dust, fumes and fibres, noise, spilled fuel, silt affecting the drainage systems and mud and debris being deposited on adjacent roads.

For part (b), control measures to outline include damping down the structure to reduce the production of dust; washing down and sheeting disposal vehicles, using street cleaners and providing wheel wash facilities; noise controls such as barriers; fitting filters or stoppers to site drain gullies; bunding fuel tanks and introducing effective controls for waste including the prohibition of burning rubbish on site.

2. **Outline** the key issues to be addressed in a pre-demolition survey of a multi-storey block of flats in a city centre. **(8)**

The issues to be addressed in a pre-demolition survey include the location and nature of adjacent properties; methods used in the construction of the block of flats; the presence of underground cellars; the potential for asbestos to be present; the location of existing services; restrictions of means of access and egress to the site; the presence of retaining walls and attendant structural issues; the possibility of security issues such as unauthorised use of the site with visible evidence of drug use; environmental issues such as noise, vibration and dust caused by the demolition process and the presence of any protected species; evidence of biological hazards such as the presence of vermin; and the existence of a health and safety file.

3. A steel framed building is to be demolished.

    Identify the main areas to be included in a demolition method statement. **(8)**

In a demolition method statement, areas to include would initially be the demolition sequence and the methods of work to be used; the stability of adjacent buildings; the use of temporary propping to prevent premature collapse; the isolation of existing services; and the protection of the employees and the public by means, for example, of creating exclusion zones and erecting perimeter fencing. Other areas which would need attention include the provision of access and egress to the site; working at height; the provision of temporary services; the control of noise and dust; the precautions to be taken in dealing with hazardous or flammable materials such as asbestos, lead and paints and/or solvents; the temporary storage and removal of waste from the site; control and coordination on site and the competencies of the personnel to be involved in the demolition operation; and the procedures to be followed in the event of an emergency.

Relevant statutory provisions

Content

RMS technical publications refer to the principal legislation relevant to the subjects covered by the publication. This is provided in context in the sections that comprise the publication. In addition, an outline of the main points of the legislation is provided in this relevant statutory provisions section. Here the outline relates to the main points of the legislation relevant to construction health and safety issues. This is provided to aid understanding and 'signpost' further reading and research.

RMS publications are widely used by students to support their professional studies and by qualified practitioners to maintain their continual professional development or to develop new skills.

This section to the guide provides an excellent reference source for those undergoing the following learning programmes:

- To meet the requirements of the NEBOSH National Certificate in Construction Health and Safety syllabus, this award meets the key knowledge indicator when assessing Stage 1 competence for CDM co-ordinators referenced in the Approved Code of Practice for the Construction (Design and Management) Regulations 2007.
- To develop the knowledge of managers and supervisors working in construction.
- To develop and enhance competency and skills needed for facilities managers.
- To develop and enhance competency and skills needed for those who construct and disassemble temporary structures for outdoor events, music or theatre production and trade or other exhibitions.

The source documents used in this section may be obtained, free of charge, from www.legislation.gov.uk and www.hse.gov.uk/pubns/books.

Chemicals (Hazard Information and Packaging for Supply) Regulations (CHIP 4) 2009

Law considered in context/more depth in Element 8.

Arrangement of Regulations

PART 1 - INTRODUCTION
1) Citation, commencement and extent
2) Interpretation
3) Application

PART 2 - GENERAL REQUIREMENTS
4) Classification of dangerous substances and dangerous preparations
5) Safety data sheets for substances and preparations
6) Packaging of dangerous substances, dangerous preparations and certain specified preparations
7) Labelling of dangerous substances and dangerous preparations
8) Labelling of single receptacles and receptacles in outer packaging.
9) Particular labelling requirements for certain preparations
10) Methods of marking or labelling packages
11) Child resistant fastenings, tactile warning devices and other consumer protection measures
12) Retention of data for dangerous preparations
13) Transitional provisions for dangerous substances, dangerous preparations and certain specified preparations

PART 3 - MISCELLANEOUS
14) Enforcement
15) Defence
16) Extension outside Great Britain
17) Revocations and amendments

SCHEDULES
Schedule 1 - Classification of dangerous substances and dangerous preparations
Schedule 2 - Indications of danger and symbols for dangerous substances and dangerous preparations
Schedule 3 - Provisions for classifying dangerous preparations
Part 1 - General provisions
Part 2 - Concentration limits to be used in the evaluation of health hazards
Part 3 - Concentration limits to be used for the evaluation of environment hazards
Schedule 4 - Labelling particulars for dangerous substances, dangerous preparations and for certain other preparations
Part 1 - General provisions relating to labels
Part 2 - Particular provisions concerning certain preparations
Schedule 5 - British and international standards relating to child resistant fastenings and tactile warning devices
Schedule 6 - Amendments
Schedule 7 - Revocations

Outline of main points

CHIP refers to the Chemicals (Hazard Information and Packaging for Supply) Regulations 2009, which came into force on 6th April 2009. These regulations are also known as CHIP 4 and shall not extend to Northern Ireland.

CHIP is the law that applies to suppliers of dangerous chemicals. Its purpose is to protect people and the environment from the effects of those chemicals by requiring suppliers to provide information about the dangers and to package them safely.

CHIP requires the supplier of a dangerous chemical to:

- Identify the hazards (dangers) of the chemical. This is known as 'classification'.

- Give information about the hazards to their customers. Suppliers usually provide this information on the package itself (for example, a label).
- Package the chemical safely.

Safety data sheets (SDS) are no longer covered by the CHIP regulations. The laws that require a SDS to be provided have been transferred to the European REACH Regulation.

REACH

REACH is a new European Union regulation concerning the registration, evaluation, authorisation and restriction of chemicals. It came into force on 1st June 2007 and replaces a number of European Directives and Regulations with a single system to gather hazard information, assess risks, classify, label, and restrict the marketing and use of individual chemicals and mixtures. This is known as the REACH system:

R egistration of basic information of substances to be submitted by companies, to a central database.

E valuation of the registered information to determine hazards and risks.

A uthorisation requirements imposed on the use of high-concern substances.

CH emicals.

REACH covers both "new" and "existing" substances and puts the onus on Industry to prove that chemicals it uses are safe. REACH only applies to chemicals manufactured in or imported into the EU. It does not apply to the use of chemicals in finished products. So a product like a television, or computer or shampoo made outside the EU could contain chemicals that are not registered under REACH - providing they are not banned under specific safety regulations (such as lead).

'Supply' means making a chemical available to another person. Manufacturers, importers, distributors, wholesalers and retailers are all examples of suppliers.

CHIP applies to most chemicals but not all. The details of the scope are set out in the regulations. Some chemicals, such as cosmetics and medicines, are outside the scope and have their own specific laws.

CHIP 4 arises from the need to align national legislation with the new European regulation on the Classification, Labelling and Packaging of Substances and Mixtures, known as the CLP Regulation, which will directly apply in all member states of the European Union. CHIP 4 will also put in place the necessary legal provisions to allow regulators in Great Britain to enforce the CLP Regulation.

Source: HSE.

Confined Spaces Regulations (CSR) 1997

Law considered in context/more depth in Element 11.

Arrangement of Regulations

1) Citation, commencement and interpretation.
2) Disapplication of Regulations.
3) Duties.
4) Work in confined spaces.
5) Emergency arrangements.
6) Exemption certificates.
7) Defence in proceedings.
8) Extension outside Great Britain.
9) Repeal and revocations.

Outline of main points

The Confined Spaces Regulations (CSR) 1997 repeal and replace earlier provisions contained in s.30 of the Factories Act 1961.

A failure to appreciate the dangers associated with confined spaces has led not only to the deaths of many workers, but also to the demise of some of those who have attempted to rescue them. A confined space is not only a space which is small and difficult to enter, exit or work in; it can also be a large space, but with limited/restricted access. It can also be a space which is badly ventilated for example, a tank or a large tunnel.

The Confined Spaces Regulations (CSR) 1997, define a confined space as any place, including any chamber, tank, vat, silo, pit, pipe, sewer, flue, well, or other similar space, in which, by virtue of its enclosed nature, there is a foreseeable risk of a 'specified occurrence'.

The CSR 1997 sets out duties on employers and the self-employed in regard to work carried out in confined spaces. Entry into confined spaces is prohibited unless it is not reasonably practicable to do the work without entering. Work conducted must be done in accordance with a safe system of work and arrangements must be in place to deal with emergencies that may arise and to effect a rescue.

Construction (Design and Management) Regulations (CDM) 2007

Law considered in context/more depth in Element 1.

The CDM Regulations came into force on 6th April 2007 and revised and brought together the existing CDM 1994 and the Construction (Health Safety and Welfare) (CHSWR) Regulations 1996 into a single regulatory package. They are supported by an Approved Code of Practice (ACoP) and industry-approved guidance.

The CDM 2007 regulations offer an opportunity for a step change in health and safety performance and will be used to re-emphasise the health, safety and broader business benefits of a well-managed and co-ordinated approach to the management of health and safety in construction.

Arrangement of regulations

PART 1 - INTRODUCTION
1) Citation and commencement.
2) Interpretation.
3) Application.

PART 2 - GENERAL MANAGEMENT DUTIES APPLYING TO CONSTRUCTION PROJECTS
4) Competence.
5) Co-operation.
6) Co-ordination.
7) General principles of prevention.
8) Election by clients.
9) The client's duty in relation to arrangements for managing projects.
10) Client's duty in relation to information.
11) Duties of designers.
12) Designs prepared or modified outside Great Britain.
13) Duties of contractors.

PART 3 - ADDITIONAL DUTIES WHERE PROJECT IS NOTIFIABLE
14) Appointments by the client.
15) Client's duty in relation to information.
16) The client's duty in relation to the start of construction phase.
17) The client's duty in relation to the health and safety file.
18) Additional duties of designers.
19) Additional duties of contractors.
20) General duties of CDM co-ordinators.
21) Notification of project by CDM co-ordinator.
22) Duties of the principal contractor.
23) Principal contractor's duties in relation to the construction phase plan.
24) Principal contractor's duties in relation to co-operation and consultation with workers.

PART 4 - DUTIES RELATING TO HEALTH AND SAFETY ON CONSTRUCTION SITES
25) Application of regulations 26-44.
26) Safe places of work.
27) Good order and site security.
28) Stability of structures.
29) Demolition or dismantling.
30) Explosives.
31) Excavations.
32) Cofferdams and caissons.
33) Reports of inspections.
34) Energy distribution installations.
35) Prevention of drowning.
36) Traffic routes.
37) Vehicles.
38) Prevention of risk from fire etc.
39) Emergency procedures.
40) Emergency routes and exits.
41) Fire detection and fire-fighting.
42) Fresh air.
43) Temperature and weather protection.
44) Lighting.

PART 5 - GENERAL
46) Enforcement in respect of fire.
47) Transitional provision.
48) Revocation and amendments.

SCHEDULES
Schedule 1 (regulation 21(1), (2) and (4)) - Particulars to be notified to the Executive
Schedule 2 (regulation 11, 16(l) (b) and 19(4)) - Welfare facilities
1) Sanitary conveniences.
2) Washing facilities.
3) Drinking water.
4) Changing rooms and lockers.
5) Facilities for rest.

Schedule 3 (regulation 33(1) (b)) - Particulars to be included in a report of inspection

Schedule 4 (regulation 48(1)) - Revocation of instruments

Schedule 5 (regulation 48(2)) - Amendments

Outline of main points

PART 2 - GENERAL MANAGEMENT DUTIES

Competence

4(1)   No person on whom these regulations place a duty shall:

(a)   Appoint or engage a co-ordinator, designer, principal contractor or contractor unless he has taken reasonable steps to ensure that he is competent.

(b)   Accept such appointment or engagement unless he is competent.

(c)   Arrange for or instruct a worker to carry out or manage design or construction work unless he is:

(i) Competent.

(ii) Under the supervision of a competent person.

Co-operation

5(1)   Every person concerned in a project on whom a duty is placed by these regulations, including paragraph (2), shall:

(a)   Co-operate with any other person concerned in any project involving construction work at the same or an adjoining site so far as is necessary to enable the latter to perform any duty or function under these regulations.

(b)   Seek the co-operation of any other person concerned in any project involving construction work at the same or an adjoining site so far as is necessary to enable the former to perform any duty or function under these regulations.

(2)   Every person concerned in a project who is working under the control of another person shall report to him anything which he is aware is likely to endanger the health or safety of himself or others.

Co-ordination

All persons shall coordinate their activities with one another in a manner which ensures, so far as is reasonably practicable, the health and safety of persons affected by the work.

General principles of prevention

7.   Every person on whom a duty is placed by these regulations in relation to the design, planning and preparation of a project shall take account of the general principles of prevention in the performance of those duties during all the stages of the project.

Election by clients

8.   If, in relation to a project, one or more clients elect in writing to be treated for the purposes of these regulations as the only clients, other clients who have agreed in writing to such election shall not be subject to any duty owed by a client under these regulations after such election and consent, save the duties in regulations 5(1) (a), 10(1) so far as it relates to information in his possession, and 12(1).

The client's arrangements for managing projects

9(1)   The client shall take reasonable steps to ensure that arrangements are made, and maintained throughout the project, for managing it which are suitable to ensure:

(a)   That:

(i)   The construction work can be carried out.

(ii)   Any structure to which the construction work relates, and which is designed for use as a place of work, can be used, without risk to health or safety.

(b)   The welfare of the persons carrying out the construction work.

(2)   The arrangements referred to in paragraph (1) shall include:

(a)   The allocation of resources (including time) to:

(i)   The design of a structure.

(ii)   Planning and preparation for construction work.

(iii)   The construction work itself, which are, so far as the client in question can reasonably determine, adequate.

(b)   Arrangements for:

(i)   Review and revision of the arrangements.

(ii)   Review of the suitability and compatibility of designs and for any modification.

(iii)   Ensuring that persons arc appointed under regulation 8 or engaged as designers or contractors in a suitable sequence and in good time.

(iv)   The planning for and monitoring of construction work; (v) ensuring that the duties in regulations 5 and 16 are performed.

(vi)   Communication.

Client's duty in relation to information

10(1)   The client shall ensure that the persons specified in regulation 13(l) (f) (i) to (iii) are promptly provided by the co-ordinator with all the information in the client's possession, or prepared by the co-ordinator, or which is reasonably obtainable (or with such of the information as is relevant to the person to whom the co-ordinator provides it), including:

(a)   Any such information in a health and safety file.

(b)   Any such further information about or affecting the site or the construction work.

(c)   Information provided by a designer under regulation 14(5).

(d)   The minimum notice which will be allowed to the principal contractor, and the contractors directly appointed by the client, for planning and preparation for construction work, which is relevant to the purposes specified in paragraph (2).

(2)   The purposes referred to in paragraph (1) are:

    (a) To secure so far as is reasonably practicable the health, safety of persons engaged in the construction work and the health and safety of persons liable to be affected by the way in which it is carried out.

    (b) Without prejudice to sub-paragraph (a), to assist the persons to whom information is provided under this regulation:

        (i)   To perform their duties and functions under these regulations.

        (ii)   To determine the adequacy of the resources referred to in regulation 7(2) to be allocated by them.

Duties of designers

11.   No designer shall commence work in relation to a project unless any client for the project is aware of his duties under these regulations.

Every designer shall in preparing or modifying a design which may be used in construction work in Great Britain avoid foreseeable risks to the health and safety of any person liable to be affected by such construction work;

In discharging these duties, the designer shall:

- Eliminate hazards which may give rise to risks.
- Reduce risks from any remaining hazards, and in so doing shall give collective measures priority over individual measures.

In designing any structure for use as a workplace the designer shall take account of the provisions of the Workplace (Health, Safety and Welfare) Regulations 1992 which relate to the design of, and materials used in, the structure.

The designer shall take all reasonable steps to provide with his design sufficient information about aspects of the design of the structure or its construction or maintenance as will adequately assist clients, other designers and contractors to comply with their duties under these Regulations.

Designs prepared or modified outside Great Britain

12.   Where a design is prepared or modified outside Great Britain for use in construction work to which these Regulations apply:

    (a) The person who commissions it, if he is established within Great Britain.

    (b) If that person is not so established, the client shall ensure that Regulation 14 is complied with.

Duties of contractors

13.   No contractor shall carry out construction work in relation to a project unless any client for the project is aware of his duties under these Regulations.

Every contractor shall ensure that any contractor whom he appoints or engages in his turn in connection with a project is informed of the minimum amount of time which will be allowed to him for planning and preparation before he begins construction work

Every contractor shall provide every worker carrying out the construction work under his control with any information and training which he needs for the particular work to be carried out safely and without risk to health.

No contractor shall begin work on a construction site unless reasonable steps have been taken to prevent access by unauthorised persons to that site.

PART 3 - ADDITIONAL DUTIES FOR NOTIFIABLE PROJECTS

Appointments by the client

14(1)   The client shall:

    (a) Appoint a person ("the co-ordinator"), before design work, or planning or other preparation for construction work is begun, to perform the functions specified in regulation 13(1).

    (b) Ensure so far as is reasonably practicable that the functions are performed.

(2)   The client shall appoint one person (in these Regulations called "the principal contractor") as soon as is practicable after the client knows enough about the project to be able to select a suitable person for such appointment, to perform the functions specified in regulations 16 to 18.

(3)   The client shall ensure that appointments under paragraphs (1) and (2) are changed or renewed as necessary to ensure that there are at all times until the end of the construction phase a co-ordinator and a principal contractor, filling them.

(4)   The client shall:

    (a) Be deemed for the purposes of these Regulations, save paragraphs (1) and (2) and regulations 14(l)(b) and 19(1) (b), to have been appointed as the co-ordinator or principal contractor for any period for which no person (including himself) has been so appointed.

    (b) Accordingly be subject to the duty imposed by regulation 13(2) on a co-ordinator or, as the case may be, the duties imposed by regulations 16 to 18 on a principal contractor.

(5)   Any reference in this regulation to appointment is to appointment in writing.

Client's duty in relation to information where a project is notifiable

15.   Where the project is notifiable, the client shall provide the CDM co-ordinator with pre-construction information consisting of -

- Any information about or affecting the site or the construction work.
- Any information concerning the proposed use of the structure as a workplace.
- The minimum amount of time before the construction phase which will be allowed to the contractors appointed by the client for planning and preparation for construction work.
- Any information in any existing health and safety file.

The client's duty in relation to the start of construction phase

16. The client shall ensure that the construction phase does not start unless:

   (a) The principal contractor has prepared a construction phase plan which is sufficient to enable the construction work to start without undue risk to health or safety.
   (b) The requirements of Schedule 2 are complied with.

The client's duty in relation to the health and safety file

17(1) The client shall ensure that the co-ordinator is provided with all the health and safety information likely to be needed during any subsequent works for inclusion in a record ("the health and safety file").

(1) Where a single health and safety file relates to more than one project, site or structure, or where it includes other related information the client shall ensure that the information relating to each site or structure can be easily identified.

(2) The client shall take reasonable steps to ensure that after the construction phase the information in the health and safety file:

   (a) Is kept available for inspection by any person who may need it to comply with the relevant statutory provisions; and
   (b) Is revised as often as may be appropriate to incorporate any relevant new information, including information specified in regulation 4(9)(c) of the Control of Asbestos at Work Regulations 2012.

(3) It shall be sufficient compliance with paragraph (3)(a) by a client who disposes of his entire interest in the site if he delivers the health and safety file to the person who acquires his interest in it and ensures that he is aware of the nature and purpose of the file.

Additional duties of designers

18(1) No designer shall commence work in relation to a project unless:

   (a) The client is aware of his duties under these Regulations.
   (b) A co-ordinator has been appointed for the project.
   (c) Notice of the project has been given to the Executive under regulation 9.

(2) The duties in paragraphs (3) and (4) shall be performed so far as is reasonably practicable, taking due account of other relevant design considerations.

(3) Every designer shall in preparing or modifying a design which may be used in construction work in the United Kingdom avoid risks to the health and safety of any person:

   (a) Carrying out construction work.
   (b) Cleaning or maintaining the permanent fixtures and fittings of a structure.
   (c) Using a structure designed as a place of work.
   (d) Liable to be affected by such construction work.

(4) In discharging the duty in paragraph (3), the designer shall:

   (a) Eliminate hazards which may give rise to risks.
   (b) Reduce risks from any remaining hazards, and in doing so shall give collective measures priority over individual measures.

(5) The designer shall provide with the design sufficient information about aspects of the design of a structure or its construction or maintenance as will adequately assist:
   (a) Other designers to comply with their duties under this regulation.
   (b) Contractors to comply with their duties under regulation 19.

Additional duties of contractors

19. Where a project is notifiable, no contractor shall carry out construction work in relation to the project unless:

   - He has been provided with the names of the CDM co-ordinator and principal contractor.
   - He has been given access to such part of the construction phase plan as is relevant to the work to be performed by him, containing sufficient detail in relation to such work.
   - Notice of the project has been given to the Executive.

   Every contractor shall:

   - Provide the principal contractor with any information (including any relevant part of any risk assessment in his possession or control) which:
   - Might affect the health or safety of any person carrying out the construction work or of any person who may be affected by it.
   - Might justify a review of the construction phase plan.
   - Which has been identified for inclusion in the health and safety file in pursuance of regulation 22(1) (j).
   - Identify any contractor whom he appoints or engages in his turn in connection with the project to the principal contractor.

   Comply with:

   - Any directions of the principal contractor given to him under regulation 22(1) (e).
   - Any site rules.
   - Provide the principal contractor with the information in relation to any death, injury, condition or dangerous occurrence which the contractor is required to notify or report under the Reporting of Injuries, Diseases and Dangerous Occurrences Regulations 2013.

   Every contractor shall:

   - Take all reasonable steps to ensure that the construction work is carried out in accordance with the construction phase plan.
   - Notify the principal contractor of any significant finding which requires the construction phase plan to be altered or added to.

General duties of CDM co-ordinators

20(1)   The functions of a co-ordinator, referred to in regulation 8(l) (a), are to:

(a) Advise and assist the client in undertaking the measures he needs to take to comply with these Regulations (including in particular, in assisting the client in complying with regulations 9 and 16).

(b) Identify and extract the information specified in regulation 10.

(c) Advise on the suitability and compatibility of designs and on any need for modification.

(d) Co-ordinate design work, planning and other preparation.

(e) Liaise with the principal contractor in relation to any design or change to a design requiring a review of the construction phase plan, during the construction phase.

(f) Promptly provide, in a convenient form, to:
(i) Every person designing the structure.
(ii) The principal contractor.
(iii) Every contractor who has been or is likely to be appointed by the client, the information specified in regulation 10 (or such of it as is relevant to him).

(g) Prepare, where none exists, and otherwise review and update the health and safety file.

(h) At the end of the construction phase, pass the health and safety file to the client.

(2)   A co-ordinator shall so far as is reasonably practicable perform any function specified in paragraph (1) for which he is appointed.

Notification of the project by the CDM co-ordinator

21. The CDM co-ordinator shall as soon as is practicable after his appointment ensure that notice is given to the Executive containing such of the particulars specified in Schedule 1 as are available.

Duties of the principal contractor

22. The principal contractor for a project shall:

- Plan, manage and monitor the construction phase in a way which ensures that, so far as is reasonably practicable, it is carried out without risks to health or safety, including facilitating:
(i) Co-operation and co-ordination between persons concerned in the project in pursuance of regulations 5 and 6.
(ii) The application of the general principles of prevention in pursuance of regulation 7.
- Liaise with the CDM co-ordinator in performing his duties in regulation 20(2) (d) during the construction phase in relation to any design or change to a design.
- Ensure that sufficient welfare facilities are provided.
- Draw up rules which are appropriate to the construction site and the activities on it.
- Give reasonable directions to any contractor.
- Ensure that every contractor is informed of the minimum amount of time which will be allowed to him.
- Consult a contractor before finalising such part of the construction phase plan as is relevant to the work to be performed by him.
- Ensure that every contractor is given, access to such part of the construction phase plan as is relevant to the work to be performed by him.
- Ensure that every contractor is given, such further information as he needs to carry out the work to be performed by him without risk.
- Identify to each contractor the information relating to the contractor's activity which is likely to be required by the CDM co-ordinator for inclusion in the health and safety file.
- Ensure that the particulars required to be in the notice are displayed in a readable condition in a position where they can be read by any worker.
- Take reasonable steps to prevent access by unauthorised persons to the construction site.

The principal contractor shall take all reasonable steps to ensure that every worker carrying out the construction work is provided with:

- A suitable site induction.
- Any further information and training which he needs for the particular work to be carried out without undue risk to health or safety.

The principal contractor's duty in relation to the construction phase plan

The principal contractor shall:

- Prepare a construction phase plan.
- Update, review, revise and refine the construction phase plan.
- Arrange for the construction phase plan to be implemented in a way which will ensure so far as is reasonably practicable the health and safety of all persons carrying out construction work and all persons who may be affected by the work.

The principal contractor's duty in relation to co-operation and consultation with workers

The principal contractor shall:

- Consult those workers or their representatives on matters connected with the project which may affect their health, safety or welfare.
- Ensure that such workers or their representatives can inspect and take copies of any information except any information:
  - The disclosure of which would be against the interests of national security.
  - Which he could not disclose without contravening a prohibition imposed by or under an enactment.
  - Relating specifically to an individual, unless he has consented to its being disclosed.
  - The disclosure of which would, for reasons other than its effect on health, safety or welfare at work, cause substantial injury to his undertaking or, where the information was supplied to him by some other person, to the undertaking of that other person.
  - Obtained by him for the purpose of bringing, prosecuting or defending any legal proceedings.

Principal contractor's duties in relation to the construction phase plan

23(1)   The principal contractor shall before the start of the construction phase, prepare a sufficient health and safety plan to allow the construction phase to start, so far as is reasonably practicable, without risk to health and safety. Review, update, revise and refine the plan as necessary. Arrange for the construction phase to be implemented in such a way as to ensure, so far as is reasonably practicable, the health and safety of people carrying out the construction work.

(2)   Take reasonable steps to ensure that the construction phase plan identifies all the risks arising from the construction phase.

Principal contractor's duties in relation to co-operation and consultation with workers

24.   The principal contractor shall:

(a)   Make and maintain arrangements to ensure that workers co-operate in promoting and developing measures to ensure the health, safety and welfare of workers.

(b)   Consult with workers or their representatives in good time on matters that may affect their health, safety or welfare.

(c)   Ensure that relevant information is available to workers except any information which is specified in the Health and Safety (Consultation with Employees) Regulations 1996.

PART 4 - DUTIES RELATING TO HEALTH AND SAFETY ON CONSTRUCTION SITES

A general duty to ensure a safe place of work and safe means of access to and from that place of work, this Regulation sets out a general requirement which applies to all construction work. It applies equally to places of work in the ground, at ground level and at height. In essence it requires that 'reasonably practicable' steps should be taken to provide for safety and to ensure risks to health are minimised. This means that action to be taken should be proportionate to the risk involved.

Safe place of work, good order and site security (regulations 26 and 27)

■   Safe access to and egress from places of work, safe and healthy places of work.
■   The site should be kept in a reasonable state of cleanliness and in good order.
■   Site fencing and signage to be provided in accordance with the level of risk.
■   Removal of material with nails or similar objects that could be a source of danger.

Work on structures (regulations 28, 29 and 30)

■   Prevent accidental collapse of new or existing structures or those under construction.
■   Make sure any dismantling or demolition of any structure is planned and carried out in a safe manner under the supervision of a competent person.
■   Only fire explosive charges after steps have been taken to ensure that no one is exposed to risk or injury from the explosion.

Every year there are structural collapses which have the potential to cause serious accidents. Demolition or dismantling are recognised as high risk activities. In any cases where this work presents a risk of danger to anyone, it should be planned and carried out under the direct supervision of a competent person.

Excavations, cofferdams and caissons (regulations 31 and 32)

■   Prevent collapse of ground both in and above excavations.
■   Identify and prevent risk from underground cables and other services.
■   Ensure cofferdams and caissons are properly designed, constructed and maintained.

From the outset, and as work progresses, any excavation which has the potential to collapse unless supported, should have suitable equipment immediately available to provide such support. Underground cables and services can also be a source of danger. These should be identified before work starts and positive action taken to prevent injury.

Energy distribution installations (regulation 34)

■   Where necessary to prevent danger, energy distribution installations shall be suitably located, checked and clearly indicated.
■   Where there is a risk from electric power cables: they shall be directed away from the area of risk; or the power shall be cut off; or if it is not reasonably practicable to comply with these requirements:
   ●   Suitable warning notices.
   ●   Barriers suitable for excluding work equipment which is not needed.
   ●   Where vehicles need to pass beneath the cables, suspended protections.
   ●   In either case, measures providing an equivalent level of safety, shall be provided or (in the case of measures) taken.
■   No construction work which is liable to create a risk to health or safety from an underground service, or from damage to or disturbance of it, shall be carried out unless suitable and sufficient steps (including any steps required by this regulation) have been taken to prevent such risk, so far as is reasonably practicable.

Prevention or avoidance of drowning (regulation 35)

■   Take steps to prevent people from falling into water or other liquid so far as is reasonably practicable.
■   Ensure that personal protective and rescue equipment is immediately available for use and maintained, in the event of a fall.
■   Make sure safe transport by water is under the control of a competent person.

Traffic routes and vehicles (regulations 36 and 37)

■   Ensure construction sites are organised so that pedestrians and vehicles can both move safely and without risks to health.
■   Make sure routes are suitable and sufficient for the people or vehicles using them.
■   Prevent or control the unintended movement of any vehicle.
■   Make arrangements for giving a warning of any possible dangerous movement, for example, reversing vehicles.
■   Ensure safe operation of vehicles including prohibition of riding or remaining in unsafe positions.
■   Make sure doors and gates which could present danger, for example, trapping risk of powered doors, have suitable safeguards.

Prevention and control of emergencies (regulations 38, 39, 40 and 41)

■   Prevent risk from fire, explosion, flooding and asphyxiation.

- Provide emergency routes and exits.
- Make arrangements for dealing with emergencies, including procedures for evacuating the site.
- Where necessary, provide fire-fighting equipment, fire detectors and alarm systems.

These Regulations require the prevention of risk as far as it is reasonably practicable to achieve. However, there are times when emergencies do arise and planning is needed to ensure, for example, that emergency routes are provided and evacuation procedures are in place. These particular Regulations (as well as those on traffic routes, welfare, cleanliness and signing of sites) apply to construction work which is carried out on construction sites. However, the rest of the Regulations apply to all construction work.

The HSE continues to be responsible for inspection of means of escape and fire-fighting for most sites. However, fire authorities have enforcement responsibility in many premises which remain in normal use during construction work. This continues the sensible arrangement which ensures that the most appropriate advice is given.

Site-wide issues (regulations 27, 42, 43, and 44)

- Ensure sufficient fresh or purified air is available at every workplace, and associated plant is capable of giving visible or audible warning of failure.
- Make sure a reasonable working temperature is maintained at indoor work places during working hours.
- Provide facilities for protection against adverse weather conditions.
- Make sure suitable and sufficient emergency lighting is available.
- Make sure suitable and sufficient lighting is available, including providing secondary lighting where there would be a risk to health or safety if primary or artificial lighting failed.
- Keep construction sites in good order and in a reasonable state of cleanliness.
- Ensure the perimeter of a construction site to which people, other than those working on the site could gain access, is marked by suitable signs so that its extent can be easily identified.

Reports of inspections (regulation 33)

- The person who carries out an inspection under regulations 31 or 32 must:
  - Inform the person for whom the inspection was carried out if he is not satisfied that the construction work can be carried out safely at the place inspected.
  - Prepare a report which includes the particulars set out in Schedule 3 and within 24 hours of completion of the inspection, to which the report relates, provide a copy to the person for whom the inspection was carried out.
- The inspector's employer, or the person under whose control he works, shall ensure that the inspector performs his duty.
- The person for whom the inspection was carried out must keep the report or a copy of it available for inspection at the site of the place of work until that work is completed, and after that for 3 months, and send out extracts from or copies of it as required by an inspector appointed under section 19 of The Health and Safety at Work etc. Act 1974.
- No further inspection reports required within a 7 day period.

SCHEDULE 2 (REGULATIONS 9(1) (B), 13(7) AND 22(1) (C)) WELFARE FACILITIES

SANITARY CONVENIENCES

1. Suitable and sufficient sanitary conveniences shall be provided or made available at readily accessible places. So far as is reasonably practicable, rooms containing sanitary conveniences shall be adequately ventilated and lit.
2. So far as is reasonably practicable, sanitary conveniences and the rooms containing them shall be kept in a clean and orderly condition.
3. Separate rooms containing sanitary conveniences shall be provided for men and women, except where and so far as each convenience is in a separate room the door of which is capable of being secured from the inside.

Washing facilities

4. Suitable and sufficient washing facilities, including showers if required by the nature of the work or for health reasons, shall so far as is reasonably practicable be provided or made available at readily accessible places.

5. Washing facilities shall be provided:

    (a) In the immediate vicinity of every sanitary convenience, whether or not provided elsewhere.
    (b) In the vicinity of any changing rooms required by paragraph 5 whether or not provided elsewhere.

6. Washing facilities shall include:

    (a) A supply of clean hot and cold, or warm, water (which shall be running water so far as is reasonably practicable).
    (b) Soap or other suitable means of cleaning.
    (c) Towels or other suitable means of drying.

7. Rooms containing washing facilities shall be sufficiently ventilated and lit.

8. Washing facilities and the rooms containing them shall be kept in a clean and orderly condition.

9. Subject to paragraph 10 below, separate washing facilities shall be provided for men and women, except where and so far as they are provided in a room the door of which is capable of being secured from inside and the facilities in each such room arc intended to be used by only one person at a time.

10. Paragraph 9 above shall not apply to facilities which are provided for washing hands, forearms and face only.

Drinking water

11. An adequate supply of wholesome drinking water shall be provided or made available at readily accessible and suitable places.
12. Every supply of drinking water shall be conspicuously marked by an appropriate sign where necessary for reasons of health and safety.
13. Where a supply of drinking water is provided, there shall also be provided a sufficient number of suitable cups or other drinking vessels unless the supply of drinking water is in a jet from which persons can drink easily.

Changing rooms and lockers

14(1)   Suitable and sufficient changing rooms shall be provided or made available at readily accessible places if:

   (a)   A worker has to wear special clothing for the purposes of his work; and
   (b)   He cannot, for reasons of health or propriety, be expected to change elsewhere, being separate rooms for, or separate use of rooms by, men and women where necessary for reasons of propriety.

(2)   Changing rooms shall:

   (a)   Be provided with seating.
   (b)   Include, where necessary, facilities to enable a person to dry any such special clothing and his own clothing and personal effects.

(3)   Suitable and sufficient facilities shall, where necessary, be provided or made available at readily accessible places to enable persons to lock away:

   (a)   Any such special clothing which is not taken home.
   (b)   Their own clothing which is not worn during working hours.
   (c)   Their personal effects.

Facilities for rest

15(1)   Suitable and sufficient rest rooms or rest areas shall be provided or made available at readily accessible places.

(1)   Rest rooms and rest areas shall:

   (a)   Include suitable arrangements to protect non-smokers from discomfort caused by tobacco smoke.
   (b)   Be equipped with an adequate number of tables and adequate seating with backs for the number of persons at work likely to use them at any one time.
   (c)   Where necessary, include suitable facilities for any person at work who is a pregnant woman or nursing mother to rest lying down.
   (d)   Include suitable arrangements to ensure that meals can be prepared and eaten.
   (e)   Include the means for boiling water.

Control of Artificial Optical Radiation at Work Regulations (CAOR) 2010

Law considered in context/more depth in Element 9.

Arrangement of Regulations

1)   Citation, commencement and interpretation.
2)   Application of these Regulations.
3)   Assessment of the risk of adverse health effects to the eyes or skin created by exposure to artificial optical radiation at the workplace.
4)   Obligations to eliminate or reduce risks.
5)   Information and training.
6)   Health surveillance and medical examinations.
7)   Extension outside Great Britain.

Outline of main points

The Regulations came into force on 27 April 2010. The employer has duties to employees and any other person at work who may be affected by the work carried out.

ASSESSMENT OF THE RISK OF ADVERSE HEALTH EFFECTS TO THE EYES OR SKIN

The employer must make a suitable and sufficient assessment of risk for the purpose of identifying the measures it needs to take to meet the requirements of these Regulations where:

(a)   The employer carries out work which could expose any of its employees to levels of artificial optical radiation that could create a reasonably foreseeable risk of adverse health effects to the eyes or skin of the employee.
(b)   That employer has not implemented any measures to either eliminate or, where this is not reasonably practicable, reduce to as low a level as is reasonably practicable, that risk based on the general principles of prevention set out in Schedule 1 to the Ionising Radiation (IRR) Regulations 1999.

OBLIGATIONS TO ELIMINATE OR REDUCE RISKS

An employer must ensure that any risk of adverse health effects to the eyes or skin of employees as a result of exposure to artificial optical radiation which is identified in the risk assessment is eliminated or, where this is not reasonably practicable, reduced to as low a level as is reasonably practicable.

INFORMATION AND TRAINING

If the risk assessment indicates that employees could be exposed to artificial optical radiation which could cause adverse health effects to the eyes or skin of employees, the employer must provide its employees and representatives with suitable and sufficient information and training relating to the outcome of the risk assessment, and this must include the following:

(a)   The technical and organisational measures taken in order to comply with the requirements of regulation 4.
(b)   The exposure limit values.
(c)   The significant findings of the risk assessment, including any measurements taken, with an explanation of those findings.
(d)   Why and how to detect and report adverse health effects to the eyes or skin.
(e)   The circumstances in which employees are entitled to appropriate health surveillance.
(f)   Safe working practices to minimise the risk of adverse health effects to the eyes or skin from exposure to artificial optical radiation.
(g)   The proper use of personal protective equipment.

The employer must ensure that any person, whether or not that person is an employee, who carries out work in connection with the employer's duties under these Regulations has suitable and sufficient information and training.

HEALTH SURVEILLANCE AND MEDICAL EXAMINATIONS

If the risk assessment indicates that there is a risk of adverse health effects to the skin of employees, as a result of exposure to artificial optical radiation, the employer must ensure that such employees are placed under suitable health surveillance.

Control of Asbestos Regulations (CAR) 2012

Law considered in context/more depth in Element 8.

Arrangement of Regulations

PART 1 - PRELIMINARY

1) Citation and commencement.
2) Interpretation.
3) Application of these Regulations.

PART 2 - GENERAL REQUIREMENTS

4) Duty to manage asbestos in non-domestic premises.
5) Identification of the presence of asbestos.
6) Assessment of work which exposes employees to asbestos.
7) Plans of work.
8) Licensing of work with asbestos.
9) Notification of work with asbestos.
10) Information, instruction and training.
11) Prevention or reduction of exposure to asbestos.
12) Use of control measures etc.
13) Maintenance of control measures etc.
14) Provision and cleaning of protective clothing.
15) Arrangements to deal with accidents, incidents and emergencies.
16) Duty to prevent or reduce the spread of asbestos.
17) Cleanliness of premises and plant.
18) Designated areas.
19) Air monitoring.
20) Standards for air testing.
21) Standards for analysis.
22) Health records and medical surveillance.
23) Washing and changing facilities.
24) Storage, distribution and labelling of raw asbestos and asbestos waste.

PART 3 - PROHIBITIONS AND RELATED PROVISIONS

25) Interpretation of prohibitions.
26) Prohibitions of exposure to asbestos.
27) Labelling of products containing asbestos.
28) Additional provisions in the case of exceptions and exemptions.

PART 4 MISCELLANEOUS

29) Exemption certificates.
30) Exemptions relating to the Ministry of Defence.
31) Extension outside Great Britain.
32) Existing licences and exemption certificates.
33) Revocations and savings.
34) Defence.
35) Review.

SCHEDULE 1

Particulars to be included in a notification.

SCHEDULE 2

Appendix 7 to Annex XVII of the REACH Regulation – special provisions on the labelling of articles containing asbestos.

SCHEDULE 3

Amendments.

Outline of main points

SUMMARY

The **Control of Asbestos Regulations (CAR) 2012** place emphasis on assessment of exposure; exposure prevention, reduction and control; adequate information, instruction and training for employees; monitoring and health surveillance. The regulations also apply to incidental exposure. The section on prohibitions is now covered by REACH. The amendments in these regulations have introduced an additional category of work with asbestos. The three categories are: Licensed, Non-Licensed and a new category of Notifiable Non-Licensed (NNLW). A summary of the requirements of each category is detailed below:

Non-licenced work	Notifiable non-licenced work	Licenced work
■ Carry out and comply with a risk assessment. ■ Control exposure ■ Provide training and information	■ Notify before work starts ■ Provide medical examinations every three years ■ Keep health records of employees ■ Carry out and comply with a risk assessment. ■ Control exposure ■ Provide training and information	■ Licencing ■ Notify fourteen days in advance ■ Develop emergency arrangements ■ Designate of asbestos areas ■ Provide medical examination every two years ■ Keep health records of all employees ■ Carry out and comply with a risk assessment. ■ Control exposure ■ Provide training and information

In order to achieve the required changes the regulations provide a separate definition of licensable work and set out the scope of the work which is exempt from the various requirements as now. Several other amendments have also been necessary and as a result there are changes to the notification requirements and those relating to health records and medical surveillance to distinguish between licensed and non-licensed work and amendments to permit a wider range of medical professionals to carry out the required medical examinations. The work for which a licence is required is defined as "Licensable work with asbestos" and is work:

(a) Where the exposure to asbestos of employees is not sporadic and of low intensity; or

(b) In relation to which the risk assessment cannot clearly demonstrate that the control limit will not be exceeded; or

(c) On asbestos coating; or

(d) On asbestos insulating board or asbestos insulation for which the risk assessment:

    (i) Demonstrates that the work is not sporadic and of low intensity, or

    (ii) Cannot clearly demonstrate that the control limit will not be exceeded, or

    (iii) Demonstrates that the work is not short duration work.

Regulation 3(2) sets out the exemptions for non-licensable work as follows:

Regulations 9 (notification of work with asbestos), 18(1)(a) (designated areas) and 22 (health records and medical surveillance) do not apply where:

(a) The exposure to asbestos of employees is sporadic and of low intensity; and

(b) It is clear from the risk assessment that the exposure to asbestos of any employee will not exceed the control limit; and

(c) The work involves:

    (i) Short, non-continuous maintenance activities in which only non-friable materials are handled, or

    (ii) Removal without deterioration of non-degraded materials in which the asbestos fibres are firmly linked in a matrix, or

    (iii) Encapsulation or sealing of asbestos-containing materials which are in good condition, or

    (iv) Air monitoring and control, and the collection and analysis of samples to ascertain whether a specific material contains asbestos.

Whether a type of asbestos work is either licensable, NNLW or non-licensed work has to be determined in each case and will depend on the type of work being done, the type of material being worked on and its condition. The identification of the type of asbestos-containing material (ACM) to be worked on and an assessment of its condition are important parts of your risk assessment, which needs to be completed before work starts. It is the responsibility of the person in charge of the job to assess the ACM to be worked on and decide if the work is NNLW or non-licensed work. This will be a matter of judgement in each case, dependent on consideration of the above factors. A decision flow chart is available from the HSE at www.hse.gov.uk/asbestos/essentials/index.htm

Duty to manage asbestos in non-domestic premises (regulation 4)

The Regulations include the 'duty to manage asbestos' in non-domestic premises. Guidance on the duty to manage asbestos can be found in the Approved Code of Practice, Work with Materials Containing Asbestos, L143 (Second Edition), ISBN 9780717662067.

Information, instruction and training (regulation 10)

The Regulations require mandatory training for anyone liable to be exposed to asbestos fibres at work. This includes maintenance workers and others who may come into contact with or who may disturb asbestos (e.g. cable installers) as well as those involved in asbestos removal work.

Prevention or reduction of exposure to asbestos (regulation 11)

When work with asbestos or which may disturb asbestos is being carried out, the Control of Asbestos Regulations require employers and the self-employed to prevent exposure to asbestos fibres. Where this is not reasonably practicable, they must make sure that exposure is kept as low as reasonably practicable by measures other than the use of respiratory protective equipment. The spread of asbestos must be prevented. The Regulations specify the work methods and controls that should be used to prevent exposure and spread.

Control limits

Worker exposure must be below the airborne exposure limit (Control Limit). The Asbestos Regulations have a single Control Limit for all types of asbestos of 0.1 fibres per cm^3. A Control Limit is a maximum concentration of asbestos fibres in the air (averaged over any continuous 4 hour period) that must not be exceeded. In addition, short term exposures must be strictly controlled and worker exposure should not exceed 0.6 fibres per cm^3 of air averaged over any continuous 10 minute period using respiratory protective equipment if exposure cannot be reduced sufficiently using other means.

Respiratory protective equipment

Respiratory protective equipment is an important part of the control regime but it must not be the sole measure used to reduce exposure and should only be used to supplement other measures. Work methods that control the release of fibres such as those detailed in the **Asbestos Essentials task sheets** (available on the HSE website) for non-licensed work should be used. Respiratory protective equipment must be suitable, must fit properly and must ensure that worker exposure is reduced as low as is reasonably practicable.

Asbestos removal work undertaken by a licensed contractor

Most asbestos removal work must be undertaken by a licensed contractor but any decision on whether particular work is licensable is based on the risk. Work is only exempt from licensing if:

■ The exposure of employees to asbestos fibres is sporadic and of low intensity (but exposure cannot be considered to be sporadic and of low intensity if the concentration of asbestos in the air is liable to exceed 0.6 fibres per cm3 measured over 10 minutes).
■ It is clear from the risk assessment that the exposure of any employee to asbestos will not exceed the control limit.
■ The work involves:
  ● Short, non-continuous maintenance activities. Work can only be considered as short, non-continuous maintenance activities if any one person carries out work with these materials for less than one hour in a seven-day period. The total time spent by all workers on the work should not exceed a total of two hours*.
  ● Removal of materials in which the asbestos fibres are firmly linked in a matrix. Such materials include: asbestos cement; textured decorative coatings and paints which contain asbestos; articles of bitumen, plastic, resin or rubber which contain asbestos where their thermal or acoustic properties are incidental to their main purpose (e.g. vinyl floor tiles, electric cables, roofing felt) and other insulation products which may be used at high temperatures but have no insulation purposes, for example gaskets, washers, ropes and seals.
  ● Encapsulation or sealing of asbestos-containing materials which are in good condition.
  ● Air monitoring and control, and the collection and analysis of samples to find out if a specific material contains asbestos.

It is important that the amount of time employees spend working with asbestos insulation, asbestos coatings or asbestos insulating board (AIB) is managed to make sure that these time limits are not exceeded. This includes the time for activities such as building enclosures and cleaning.

Under the Asbestos Regulations, anyone carrying out work on asbestos insulation, asbestos coating or AIB needs a licence issued by HSE unless they meet one of the exemptions above.

Although you may not need a licence to carry out a particular job, you still need to comply with the rest of the requirements of the Asbestos Regulations.

Licensable work - additional duties

If the work is licensable there are a number of additional duties. The need to:

■ Notify the enforcing authority responsible for the site where you are working (for example HSE or the local authority).
■ Designate the work area (see regulation 18 for details).
■ Prepare specific asbestos emergency procedures.
■ Pay for your employees to undergo medical surveillance.

Non-notifiable licensable work - additional duties

If work is determined to be NNLW, the duties are:

■ To notify the enforcing authority responsible for the site where the work is before work starts. (There is no minimum period.)
■ By 2015 all employees will have to undergo medical examinations which are repeated every three years.
■ To have prepared procedures which can be put into effect should an accident, incident or emergency occur.
■ To keep a register of all NNLW work for all employees.
■ To record the significant findings of and comply with a risk assessment.
■ To prevent or reduce exposure so far as is reasonably practicable and to take reasonable steps that all control measures are used.
■ To ensure that adequate information, instruction and training is given to employees.

Air monitoring (regulation 19)

The Asbestos Regulations require any analysis of the concentration of asbestos in the air to be measured in accordance with the 1997 WHO recommended method.

Standards for air testing and site clearance certification (regulation 20)

From 06 April 2007, a clearance certificate for re-occupation may only be issued by a body accredited to do so. At the moment, such accreditation can only be provided by the United Kingdom Accreditation Service (UKAS). You can find more details of how to undertake work with asbestos containing materials, the type of controls necessary, what training is required and analytical methods in the following HSE publications:

■ Approved Code of Practice Work with Materials containing Asbestos, L143, ISBN 978 0 7176 6206 7.
■ Asbestos: the Licensed Contractors Guide, HSG 247, ISBN 978 0 7176 2874 2.
■ Asbestos: The analysts' guide for sampling, analysis and clearance procedures, HSG 248, ISBN 978 0 7176 2875 9.

- Asbestos Essentials, HSG 210, ISBN 978 0 7176 6263 0. (See also the 'Asbestos Essentials task sheets' available on the HSE website).

Other health and safety legislation must be complied with.

Source: HSE Website: www.hse.gov.uk.

Control of Noise at Work Regulations (CNWR) 2005

Law considered in context/more depth in Element 9.

Arrangement of Regulations

1) Citation and commencement.
2) Interpretation.
3) Application and transition.
4) Exposure limit values and action values.
5) Assessment of the risk to health created by exposure to noise at the workplace.
6) Elimination or control of exposure to noise at the workplace.
7) Hearing protection.
8) Maintenance and use of equipment.
9) Health surveillance.
10) Information, instruction and training.
11) Exemption certificates from hearing protection.
12) Exemption certificates for emergency services.
13) Exemption relating to the Ministry of Defence etc.
14) Extension outside Great Britain.
15) Revocations, amendment and savings.

Outline of main points

CHANGES TO THE ACTION LEVELS (REGULATION 4)

The values of the actions levels associated with noise at work have been lowered and their names have been changed. The first action level is reduced from *85 dB(A) down to 80 dB(A)* and is known as the *lower exposure action value*. Meanwhile, the section level is reduced from *90 dB(A) down to 85 dB(A)* and is known as the *upper exposure action value*. The Regulations also allow the employer to average out the exposure to noise over a one week period instead of the previous normal eight hour period, in situations where the noise exposure varies on a day-to-day basis. When determining noise levels for the purposes of determining exposure action levels, the noise exposure reducing effects of hearing protection may not be taken in to account.

Where exposure is at, or above, the *lower exposure action value* (80 dB(A)) the employer has a duty to provide hearing protection to those employees that request it. The employer also has a duty to information, instruction and training on the risks posed by exposure to noise and the control measures to be used.

Where the exposure is at, or above, the *upper exposure action value* (85 dB(A)) the employer is also required to introduce a formal programme of control measures. The measures to be taken as part of this programme of control measures will depend on the findings of the noise risk assessment (see below).

The Control of Noise at Work Regulations 2005 also introduces a new value known as the *exposure limit value*. These are limits set both in terms of daily (or weekly) personal noise exposure (LEP,d of 87 dB) and in terms of peak noise ($LCpeak$ of 140 dB). The exposure action values, take account of the protection provided by personal hearing protection (unlike the two exposure limit values). *If an employee is exposed to noise at or above the exposure limit value, then the employer must take immediate action to bring the exposure down below this level.*

SUMMARY OF EXPOSURE LIMIT VALUES AND ACTION VALUES

The lower exposure action values are:	A daily or weekly personal noise exposure of 80 dB (A-weighted)
	A peak sound pressure of 135 dB (C-weighted)
The upper exposure action values are:	A daily or weekly personal noise exposure of 85 dB (A-weighted)
	A peak sound pressure of 137 dB (C-weighted)
The exposure limit values are:	A daily or weekly personal exposure of 87 dB (A-weighted)
	A peak sound pressure of 140 dB (C-weighted)

NOISE RISK ASSESSMENT AND CONTROL MEASURES (REGULATIONS 5 AND 6)

The requirement for a noise risk assessment carries through from the Noise at Work Regulations 1989 into the Control of Noise at Work Regulations 2005. Employers are required (in accordance with the general risk assessment and general principles of prevention contained in Schedule 1 to the Management of Health and Safety at Work Regulation 1999) to ensure that the risks associated with employees' exposure to noise are eliminated where this is reasonably practicable. Where elimination is not reasonably practicable, then the employer must reduce the risks down to as low a level as is reasonably practicable.

Regulation 6(2) of the Control of Noise at Work Regulations 2005 introduces the requirement for a formal programme of control measures. If any employee is likely to be exposed to noise at or above an upper exposure action value, the employer shall reduce exposure to a minimum by establishing and implementing a programme of organisational and technical measures, excluding the provision of personal hearing protectors, which is appropriate to the activity and consistent with the risk assessment, and shall include consideration of:

(a) Other working methods which eliminate or reduce exposure to noise.
(b) Choice of appropriate work equipment emitting the least possible noise, taking account of the work to be done.
(c) The design and layout of workplaces, work stations and rest facilities.
(d) Suitable and sufficient information and training for employees, such that work equipment may be used correctly, in order to minimise their exposure to noise.
(e) Reduction of noise by technical means including:
   (i) In the case of airborne noise the use of shields, enclosures, and sound-absorbent coverings.
   (ii) In the case of structure-borne noise by damping and isolation.
(f) Appropriate maintenance programmes for work equipment, the workplace and workplace systems.
(g) Limitation of the duration and intensity of exposure to noise.
(h) Appropriate work schedules with adequate rest periods.

If the risk assessment indicates an employee is likely to be exposed to noise at or above an upper exposure action value, the employer shall ensure that

■ The area is designated a Hearing Protection Zone.
■ The area is demarcated and identified by means of the sign specified for the purpose of indicating "ear protection must be worn" (to be consistent with the Health and Safety (Safety Signs and Signals) Regulations 1996).
■ The sign shall be accompanied by text that indicates that the area is a Hearing Protection Zone and that employees must wear personal hearing protectors while in that area.
■ Access to the area is restricted where this is technically feasible and the risk of exposure justifies it and shall make every effort to ensure that no employee enters that area unless they are wearing personal hearing protectors.

MAINTENANCE AND USE OF EQUIPMENT (REGULATION 8)

There is a duty on the employer to maintain the control introduced to protect employees. This will include maintenance of acoustic enclosures, etc as well as the maintenance of machinery (as required under the Provision and Use of Work Equipment Regulations 1998) to control noise at source.

HEALTH SURVEILLANCE (REGULATION 9)

Under the Control of Noise at Work Regulations 2005, employees who are regularly exposed to noise levels of 85 dB(A) or higher must be subject to health surveillance, including audiometric testing. This constitutes a big change from the previous Regulations that only required an employer to carry out health surveillance where the employee was subject to noise levels of 95 dB(A) or higher. Where exposure is between 80 dB and 85 dB, or where employees are only occasionally exposed above the upper exposure action values, health surveillance will only be required if information comes to light that an individual may be particularly sensitive to noise induced hearing loss.

SUMMARY

The Control of Noise at Work Regulations 2005 became part of UK health and safety law in April 2006. They introduced levels for employees to control exposure down to, including a new exposure limit value, above which employers are obliged to take immediate action to reduce exposure. These new lower limits mean that about a further million workers will be afforded protection by these Regulations. The requirements for risk assessments, control measures and health surveillance have been updated, but are broadly similar to previous requirements.

Source: www.lrbconsulting.com and www.hse.gov.uk.

Control of Substances Hazardous to Health Regulations (COSHH) 2002

Law considered in context/more depth in Element 8.

Amendments to these Regulations were made by the Control of Substances Hazardous to Health (Amendment) Regulations 2004. The main change being that MELs and OESs were replaced by workplace exposure limits (WELs).

Arrangement of Regulations

1) Citation and commencement.
2) Interpretation.
3) Duties under these Regulations.
4) Prohibitions on substances.
5) Application of regulations 6 to 13.
6) Assessment of health risks created by work involving substances hazardous to health.
7) Control of exposure.
8) Use of control measures etc.
9) Maintenance of control measures.
10) Monitoring exposure.
11) Health surveillance.
12) Information etc.
13) Arrangements to deal with accidents, incidents and emergencies.
14) Exemption certificates.
15) Extension outside Great Britain.
16) Defence in proceedings for contravention of these Regulations.
17) Exemptions relating to the Ministry of Defence etc.
18) Revocations, amendments and savings.
19) Extension of meaning of "work".
20) Modification of section 3(2) of the Health and Safety at Work etc Act (HASAWA) 1974.

Schedule 1 - Other substances and processes to which the definition of "carcinogen" relates.

Schedule 2 - Prohibition of certain substances hazardous to health for certain purposes.

Schedule 3 - Special provisions relating to biological agents.

Schedule 4 - Frequency of thorough examination and test of local exhaust ventilation plant used in certain processes.

Schedule 5 - Specific substances and processes for which monitoring is required.

Schedule 6 - Medical surveillance.

Schedule 7 - Legislation concerned with the labelling of containers and pipes.

Schedule 8 - Fumigations excepted from regulation 14.

Schedule 9 - Notification of certain fumigations.

Appendix 1 - Control of carcinogenic substances.

Annex 1 - Background note on occupational cancer.

Annex 2 - Special considerations that apply to the control of exposure to vinyl chloride.

Appendix 2 - Additional provisions relating to work with biological agents.

Appendix 3 - Control of substances that cause occupational asthma.

NOTE the main impact to the latest version of the COSHH Regs concern the control of substances that cause occupational asthma.

Outline of main points

REGULATIONS

Reg. 2 **Interpretation**

"Substance hazardous to health" includes:

1) Substances which under The Chemicals (Hazard Information and Packaging) Regulations (CHIP 3) 2002 are in categories of very toxic, toxic, harmful, corrosive or irritant.

2) A substance listed in Schedule 1 to the Regulations or for which the HSE (*formerly HSC*) have approved a maximum exposure limit or an occupational exposure standard.

3) A biological agent.

4) Dust in a concentration in air equal to or greater than:

■ 10 mg/m3 inhalable dust as an 8hr TWA.

■ 4mg/m3 respirable dust as an 8hr TWA.

5) Any other substance which creates a health hazard comparable with the hazards of the substances in the other categories above.

Reg. 3 **Duties**

Are on employer to protect:

■ Employees.

Any other person who may be affected, except:

■ Duties for health surveillance do not extend to non-employees.

■ Duties to give information may extend to non-employees if they work on the premises.

Reg. 4 **Prohibitions on substances**

Certain substances are prohibited from being used in some applications. These are detailed in Schedule 2.

Reg. 5 **Application of regulations 6-13**

Regulations 6-13 are made to protect a person's health from risks arising from exposure. They do not apply if:

The following Regulations already apply:

■ The Control of Lead at Work Regulations (CLAW) 2002.

■ The Control of Asbestos at Work Regulations (CAWR) 2002.

The hazard arises from one of the following properties of the substance:

■ Radioactivity, explosive, flammable, high or low temperature, high pressure.

■ Exposure is for medical treatment.

■ Exposure is in a mine.

Reg. 6 **Assessment**

Employers must not carry out work that will expose employees to substances hazardous to health unless they have assessed the risks to health and the steps that need to be taken to meet the requirements of the Regulations. The assessment must be reviewed if there are changes in the work and at least once every 5 years.

A suitable and sufficient assessment should include:

■ An assessment of the risks to health.

■ The practicability of preventing exposure.

■ Steps needed to achieve adequate control.

An assessment of the risks should involve:

■ Types of substance including biological agents.

■ Where the substances are present and in what form.

■ Effects on the body.

■ Who might be affected?

■ Existing control measures.

Reg. 7 **Control of exposure**

1) Employer shall ensure that the exposure of employees to substances hazardous to health is either prevented or, where this is not reasonably practicable, adequately controlled.

2) So far as is reasonably practicable (1) above except to a carcinogen or biological agent shall be by measures other than personal protective equipment (PPE).

3) Where not reasonably practicable to prevent exposure to a carcinogen by using an alternative substance or process, the following measure shall apply:
- Total enclosure of process.
- Use of plant, process and systems which minimise generation of, or suppress and contain, spills, leaks, dust, fumes and vapours of carcinogens.
- Limitation of quantities of a carcinogen at work.
- Keeping of numbers exposed to a minimum.
- Prohibition of eating, drinking and smoking in areas liable to contamination.
- Provision of hygiene measures including adequate washing facilities and regular cleaning of walls and surfaces.
- Designation of areas/installations liable to contamination and use of suitable and sufficient warning signs.
- Safe storage, handling and disposal of carcinogens and use of closed and clearly-labelled containers.

4) If adequate control is not achieved, then employer shall provide suitable PPE to employees in addition to taking control measures.

5) PPE provided shall comply with The Personal Protective Equipment at Work Regulations (PPER), 2002 (dealing with the supply of PPE).

6&7) For substances which have a maximum exposure limit (MEL), control of that substance shall, so far as inhalation is concerned, only be treated if the level of exposure is reduced as far as is reasonably practicable and in any case below the MEL.

Where a substance has an occupational exposure standard (OES), control of that substance shall, so far as inhalation is concerned, only be treated as adequate if the OES is not exceeded or if it is, steps are taken to remedy the situation as soon as reasonably practicable.

8) Respiratory protection must be suitable and of a type or conforming to a standard approved by the HSE.

9) In the event of failure of a control measure which may result in the escape of carcinogens, the employer shall ensure:
- Only those who are responsible for repair and maintenance work are permitted in the affected area and are provided with PPE.
- Employees and other persons who may be affected are informed of the failure forthwith.

Reg. 8 Employer shall take all reasonable steps to ensure control measures, PPE, etc. are properly used/applied.

Employee shall make full and proper use of control measures, PPE etc. and shall report defects to employer.

Reg. 9 ### Maintenance of control measures

Employer providing control measures to comply with Reg.7 shall ensure that it is maintained in an efficient state, in efficient working order and in good repair and in the case of PPE in a clean condition, properly stored in a well-defined place checked at suitable intervals and when discovered to be defective repaired or replaced before further use.

- Contaminated PPE should be kept apart and cleaned, decontaminated or, if necessary destroyed.
- Engineering controls - employer shall ensure thorough examination and tests.
- Local exhaust ventilation (LEV) - Once every 14 months unless process specified in Schedule 4.
- Others - At suitable intervals.
- Respiratory protective equipment - employer shall ensure thorough examination and tests at suitable intervals.
- Records of all examinations, tests and repairs kept for 5 years.

Reg. 10 ### Monitoring exposure

Employer shall ensure exposure is monitored if:
- Needed to ensure maintenance of adequate control.
- Otherwise needed to protect health of employees.
- Substance/process specified in Schedule 5.

Records kept if:
- There is an identified exposure of identifiable employee - 40 years.
- Otherwise - 5 years.

Reg. 11 ### Health surveillance

1) Where appropriate for protection of health of employees exposed or liable to be exposed, employer shall ensure suitable health surveillance.

2) Health surveillance is appropriate if:
- Employee exposed to substance/process specified in Schedule 6.
- Exposure to substance is such that an identifiable disease or adverse health effect can result, there is a reasonable likelihood of it occurring and a valid technique exists for detecting the indications of the disease or effect.

3) Health records kept for at least 40 years.

4) If employer ceases business, HSE notified and health records offered to HSE.

5) If employee exposed to substance specified in Schedule 6, then health surveillance shall include medical surveillance, under Employment Medical Adviser (EMA) at 12 monthly intervals - or more frequently if specified by EMA.

6) EMA can forbid employee to work in process, or specify certain conditions for him to be employed in a process.

7) EMA can specify that health surveillance is to continue after exposure has ceased. Employer must ensure.

8) Employees to have access to their own health record.

9) Employee must attend for health/medical surveillance and give information to EMA.

10) EMA entitled to inspect workplace.

11) Where EMA suspends employee from work exposing him to substances hazardous to health, employer of employee can apply to HSE in writing within 28 days for that decision to be reviewed.

Reg. 12 **Information etc**

Employer shall provide suitable and sufficient information, instruction and training for him to know:
- Risks to health.
- Precautions to be taken.

This should include information on:
- Results of monitoring of exposure at workplace.
- Results of collective health surveillance.

If the substances have been assigned a maximum exposure limit, then the employee/Safety Representative must be notified forthwith if the MEL has been exceeded.

Reg. 13 **Arrangements to deal with accidents, incidents and emergencies**

To protect the health of employees from accidents, incidents and emergencies, the employer shall ensure that:

- Procedures are in place for first aid and safety drills (tested regularly).
- Information on emergency arrangements is available.
- Warning, communication systems, remedial action and rescue actions are available.
- Information made available to emergency services: external and internal.
- Steps taken to mitigate effects, restore situation to normal and inform employees.
- Only essential persons allowed in area.

These duties do not apply where the risks to health are slight or measures in place Reg 7(1) are sufficient to control the risk. The employee must report any accident or incident which has or may have resulted in the release of a biological agent which could cause severe human disease.

NOTE the main impact to the latest version of the COSHH Regs concern the control of substances that cause occupational asthma.

APPENDIX 3 CONTROL OF SUBSTANCES THAT CAUSE OCCUPATIONAL ASTHMA

This relates certain regulations specifically to substances with the potential to cause asthma.

- Regulation 6 - assessment of risk to health created by work involving substances hazardous to health, (i.e. substances that may cause asthma).
- Regulation 7 - prevention or control of exposure to substances hazardous to health, (i.e. substances that may cause occupational asthma).
- Regulation 11 - health surveillance, (for employees who are or may be exposed to substances that may cause occupational asthma).
- Regulation 12 - information, instruction and training for persons who may be exposed to substances hazardous to health, to include: typical symptoms of asthma, substances that may cause it, the permanency of asthma and what happens with subsequent exposures, the need to report symptoms immediately and the reporting procedures.

Training should be given, including induction training before they start the job.

SCHEDULE 3 ADDITIONAL PROVISIONS RELATING TO WORK WITH BIOLOGICAL AGENTS

Regulation 7(10)   Part I Provision of general application to biological agents

1) **Interpretation.**

2) **Classification of biological agents.**

The HSC shall approve and publish a "Categorisation of Biological Agents according to hazard and categories of containment" which may be revised or re-issued. Where no approved classification exists, the employer shall assign the agent to one of four groups according to the level of risk of infection.

Group 1 - unlikely to cause human disease.
Group 2 - can cause human disease.
Group 3 - can cause severe disease and spread to community.
Group 4 - can cause severe disease, spread to community and there is no effective treatment.

3) **Special control measures for laboratories, animal rooms and industrial processes**

Every employer engaged in research, development, teaching or diagnostic work involving Group 2, 3 or 4 biological agents; keeping or handling laboratory animals deliberately or naturally infected with those agents, or industrial processes involving those agents, shall control them with the most suitable containment.

4) **List of employees exposed to certain biological agents**

The employer shall keep a list of employees exposed to Group 3 or 4 biological agents for at least 10 years. If there is a long latency period then the list should be kept for 40 years.

5) **Notification of the use of biological agents**

Employers shall inform the HSE at least 20 days in advance of first time use or storage of Group 2, 3 or 4 biological hazards. Consequent substantial changes in procedure or process shall also be reported.

6) **Notification of the consignment of biological agents**

The HSE must be informed 30 days before certain biological agents are consigned.

Part II Containment measures for health and veterinary care facilities, laboratories and animal rooms.

Part III Containment measures for industrial processes.

Part IV Biohazard sign.

The biohazard sign required by regulation 7(6) (a) shall be in the form shown.

Part V Biological agents whose use is to be notified in accordance with paragraph 5(2) of Part I of this Schedule.

- Any Group 3 or 4 agent.
- Certain named Group 2 agents.

Figure RSP-1: Biohazard sign. *Source: COSHH 2002.*

Control of Vibration at Work Regulations (CVWR) 2005

Considered in context in Element 9.

Hand-arm vibration (HAV) and whole body vibration (WBV) are caused by the use of work equipment and work processes that transmit vibration into the hands, arms and bodies of employees in many industries and occupations. Long-term, regular exposure to vibration is known to lead to permanent and debilitating health effects such as vibration white finger, loss of sensation, pain, and numbness in the hands, arms, spine and joints. These effects are collectively known as hand-arm or whole body vibration syndrome. These Regulations introduce controls, which aim substantially to reduce ill health caused by exposure to vibration. These Regulations came into force on 6th July 2005.

Arrangement of Regulations

1) Citation and commencement.
2) Interpretation.
3) Application and transition.
4) Exposure limit values and action values.
5) Assessment of the risk to health created by vibration at the workplace.
6) Elimination or control of exposure to vibration at the workplace.
7) Health surveillance.
8) Information, instruction and training for persons who may be exposed to risk from vibration.
9) Exemption certificates for emergency services.
10) Exemption certificates for air transport.
11) Exemption relating to the Ministry of Defence etc.
12) Extension outside Great Britain.
13) Amendment.

Outline of main points

Regulation 3 makes provision for transition arrangements affecting equipment provided for use before 6th July 2007 and does not permit compliance with the exposure limits, taking into account technical advances and organisational measures to respond to the regulations, the regulations shall not apply until 6th July 2010. Duties under most of these regulations extend not only to employees but to others, whether or not at work, that may be affected. The duty does not include regulation 7 (health surveillance) or regulation 8 (information instruction and training), these are limited to employees.

Regulation 4 states the personal daily exposure limits and daily exposure action values normalised over an 8-hour reference period.

	Daily exposure action values	Daily exposure limits
Hand arm vibration	2.5 m/s^2	5 m/s^2
Whole body vibration	0.5 m/s^2	1.15 m/s^2

Regulation 5 requires the employer to make a suitable and sufficient assessment of the risk created by work that is liable to expose employees to risk from vibration. The assessment must observe work practices, make reference to information regarding the magnitude of vibration from equipment and if necessary measurement of the magnitude of the vibration.

Consideration must also be given to the type, duration, effects of exposure, exposures limit/action values, effects on employees at particular risk, the effects of vibration on equipment and the ability to use it, manufacturers' information, availability of replacement equipment, and extension of exposure at the workplace (for example, rest facilities), temperature and information on health surveillance. The risk assessment should be recorded as soon as is practicable after the risk assessment is made and reviewed regularly.

Regulation 6 states that the employer must seek to eliminate the risk of vibration at source or, if not reasonably practicable, reduce it to as low a level as is reasonably practicable. Where the personal daily exposure limit is exceeded the employer must reduce exposure by implementing a programme of organisational and technical measures. Measures include the use of other methods of work, ergonomics, maintenance of equipment, design and layout, rest facilities, information, instruction and training, limitation by schedules and breaks and the provision of personal protective equipment to protect from cold and damp. Measures must be adapted to take account of any group or individual employee whose health may be of particular risk from exposure to vibration.

Regulation 7 states that health surveillance must be carried out if there is a risk to the health of employees liable to be exposed to vibration. This is in order to prevent or diagnose any health effect linked with exposure to vibration. A record of health shall be kept of any employee who undergoes health surveillance. The employer shall, providing reasonable notice is given, provide the employee with access to their health records and provide copies to an enforcing officer on request. If health surveillance identifies a disease or adverse health effect, considered by a doctor or other occupational health professional to be a result of exposure to vibration, the employer shall ensure that a qualified person informs the employee and provides information and advice. The employer must ensure they are kept informed of any significant findings from health surveillance, taking into account any medical confidentiality. In addition the employer must also:

- Review risk assessments.
- Review the measures taken to comply.

- Consider assigning the employee to other work.
- Review the health of any other employee who has been similarly exposed and consider alternative work.

Regulation 8 states that employers must provide information, instruction and training to all employees who are exposed to risk from vibration and their representatives. This includes any organisational and technical measures taken, exposure limits and values, risk assessment findings, why and how to detect injury, entitlement to and collective results of health surveillance and safe working practices. Information instruction and training shall be updated to take account of changes in the employers work or methods. The employer shall ensure all persons, whether or not an employee, who carries out work in connection with the employer's duties has been provided with information, instruction and training.

Dangerous Substances and Explosive Atmospheres Regulations (DSEAR) 2002

Law considered in context/more depth in Element 7.

Arrangement of Regulations

1) Citation and commencement.
2) Interpretation.
3) Application.
4) Duties under these Regulations.
5) Risk assessment.
6) Elimination or reduction of risks from dangerous substances.
7) Places where explosive atmospheres may occur.
8) Arrangements to deal with accidents, incidents and emergencies.
9) Information, instruction and training.
10) Identification of hazardous contents of containers and pipes.
11) Duty of co-ordination.
12) Extension outside Great Britain.
13) Exemption certificates.
14) Exemptions for Ministry of Defence etc.
15) Amendments.
16) Repeals and revocations.
17) Transitional provisions.
Schedule 1 - General safety measures.
Schedule 2 - Classification of places where explosive atmospheres may occur.
Schedule 3 - Criteria for the selection of equipment and protective systems.
Schedule 4 - Warning sign for places where explosive atmospheres may occur.
Schedule 5 - Legislation concerned with the marking of containers and pipes.
Schedule 6 - Amendments.
Schedule 7 - Repeal and revocation.

Outline of main points

These regulations aim to protect against risks from fire, explosion and similar events arising from dangerous substances that are present in the workplace.

DANGEROUS SUBSTANCES

These are any substances or preparations that due to their properties or the way in which they are being used could cause harm to people from fires and explosions. They may include petrol, liquefied petroleum gases, paints, varnishes, solvents and dusts.

APPLICATION

DSEAR applies in most workplaces where a dangerous substance is present. There are a few exceptions where only certain parts of the regulations apply, for example:

- Ships.
- Medical treatment areas.
- Explosives/chemically unstable substances.
- Mines.

- Quarries.
- Boreholes.
- Offshore installations.
- Means of transport.

MAIN REQUIREMENTS

You must:

- Conduct a risk assessment of work activities involving dangerous substances.
- Provide measures to eliminate or reduce risks.
- Provide equipment and procedures to deal with accidents and emergencies.
- Provide information and training for employees.
- Classify places into zones and mark zones where appropriate.

The risk assessment should include:

- The hazardous properties of substance.
- The way they are used or stored.
- Possibility of hazardous explosive atmosphere occurring.

- Potential ignition sources.
- Details of zoned areas
- Co-ordination between employers.

SAFETY MEASURES

Where possible eliminate safety risks from dangerous substances or, if not reasonably practicable to do this, control risks and reduce the harmful effects of any fire, explosion or similar event.

Substitution - Replace with totally safe or safer substance (best solution).

Control measures - If risk cannot be eliminated apply the following control measures in the following order:

- Reduce quantity.
- Avoid or minimise releases.
- Control releases at source.
- Prevent formation of explosive atmosphere.
- Collect, contain and remove any release to a safe place, for example, ventilation.
- Avoid ignition sources.
- Avoid adverse conditions, for example, exceeding temperature limits.
- Keep incompatible substances apart.

Mitigation measures - Apply measures to mitigate the effects of any situation.

- Prevent fire and explosions from spreading to other plant, equipment or other parts of the workplace.
- Reduce number of employees exposed.
- Provide process plant that can contain or suppress an explosion, or vent it to a safe place.

ZONED AREAS

In workplaces where explosive atmospheres may occur, areas should be classified into zones based on the likelihood of an explosive atmosphere occurring. Any equipment in these areas should ideally meet the requirements of the Equipment and Protective Systems Intended for Use in Potentially Explosive Atmospheres Regulations (ATEX) 1996.

However equipment in use before July 2003 can continue to be used providing that the risk assessment says that it is safe to do so. Areas may need to be marked with an 'Ex' warning sign at their entry points. Employees may need to be provided with appropriate clothing, for example, anti static overalls. Before use for the first time, a person competent in the field of explosion protection must confirm hazardous areas as being safe.

ACCIDENTS, INCIDENTS AND EMERGENCIES

DSEAR builds on existing requirements for emergency procedures, which are contained in other regulations. These may need to be supplemented if you assess that a fire, explosion or significant spillage could occur, due to the quantities of dangerous substances present in the workplace. You may need to arrange for:

- Suitable warning systems.
- Escape facilities.
- Emergency procedures.
- Equipment and clothing for essential personnel who may need to deal with the situation.
- Practice drills.
- Make information, instruction and training available to employees and if necessary liaise with the emergency services.

Electricity at Work Regulations (EWR) 1989

Law considered in context/more depth in Element 6.

Arrangement of Regulations

PART I - INTRODUCTION

1) Citation and commencement.
2) Interpretation.
3) Persons on whom duties are imposed by these Regulations.

PART II - GENERAL

4) Systems, work activities and protective equipment.
5) Strength and capability of electrical equipment.
6) Adverse or hazardous environments.
7) Insulation, protection and placing of conductors.
8) Earthing or other suitable precautions.
9) Integrity of referenced conductors.
10) Connections.
11) Means for protecting from excess of current.
12) Means for cutting off the supply and for isolation.
13) Precautions for work on equipment made dead.
14) Work on or near live conductors.
15) Working space, access and lighting.
16) Persons to be competent to prevent danger and injury.

PART III - REGULATIONS APPLYING TO MINES ONLY

17) Provisions applying to mines only.
18) Introduction of electrical equipment.

19) Restriction of equipment in certain zones below ground.
20) Cutting off electricity or making safe where firedamp is found either below ground or at the surface.
21) Approval of certain equipment for use in safety-lamp mines.
22) Means of cutting off electricity to circuits below ground.
23) Oil-filled equipment.
24) Records and information.
25) Electric shock notices.
26) Introduction of battery-powered locomotives and vehicles into safety-lamp mines.
27) Storage, charging and transfer of electrical storage batteries.
28) Disapplication of section 157 of the Mines and Quarries Act 1954.

PART IV - MISCELLANEOUS AND GENERAL

29) Defence.
30) Exemption certificates.
31) Extension outside Great Britain.
32) Disapplication of duties.
33) Revocations and modifications.

Schedule 1   Provisions applying to mines only and having effect in particular in relation to the use below ground in coal mines of film lighting circuits.

Schedule 2   Revocations and modifications.

Outline of main points

SYSTEMS, WORK ACTIVITIES AND PROTECTIVE EQUIPMENT (REGULATION 4)

The system and the equipment comprising it must be designed and installed to take account of all reasonably foreseeable conditions of use.

- The system must be maintained so as to prevent danger.
- All work activities must be carried out in such a manner as to not give rise to danger.
- Equipment provided to protect people working on live equipment must be suitable and maintained.

STRENGTH AND CAPABILITY OF ELECTRICAL EQUIPMENT (REGULATION 5)

Strength and capability refers to the equipment's ability to withstand the effects of its load current and any transient overloads or pulses of current.

ADVERSE OR HAZARDOUS ENVIRONMENTS (REGULATION 6)

This regulation requires that electrical equipment is suitable for the environment and conditions that might be reasonably foreseen. In particular, attention should be paid to:

- Mechanical damage caused by for example; vehicles, people, vibration, etc.
- Weather, natural hazards, temperature or pressure. Ice, snow, lightning, bird droppings, etc.
- Wet, dirty, dusty or corrosive conditions. Conductors, moving parts, insulators and other materials may be affected by the corrosive nature of water, chemicals and solvents. The presence of explosive dusts must be given special consideration.
- Flammable or explosive substances. Electrical equipment may be a source of ignition for liquids, gases, vapours etc.

INSULATION, PROTECTION AND PLACING OF CONDUCTORS (REGULATION 7)

The purpose of this regulation is to prevent danger from direct contact. Therefore, if none exists, no action is needed. Conductors though will normally need to be insulated and also have some other protection to prevent mechanical damage.

EARTHING OR OTHER SUITABLE PRECAUTIONS (REGULATION 8)

The purpose of this regulation is to prevent danger from indirect contact. Conductors such as metal casings may become live through fault conditions. The likelihood of danger arising from these circumstances must be prevented by using the techniques described earlier in this section i.e. earthing, double insulation, reduced voltages etc.

INTEGRITY OF REFERENCED CONDUCTORS (REGULATION 9)

In many circumstances the reference point is earthed because the majority of power distribution installations are referenced by a deliberate connection to earth at the generators or distribution transformers. The purpose of this regulation is to ensure that electrical continuity is never broken.

CONNECTIONS (REGULATION 10)

As well as having suitable insulation and conductance, connections must have adequate mechanical protection and strength. Plugs and sockets must conform to recognised standards as must connections between cables. Special attention should be paid to the quality of connections on portable appliances.

MEANS FOR PROTECTING FROM EXCESS CURRENT (REGULATION 11)

Faults or overloads can occur in electrical systems and protection must be provided against their effects. The type of protection depends on several factors but usually rests between fuses and circuit breakers.

MEANS FOR CUTTING OFF THE SUPPLY AND FOR ISOLATION (REGULATION 12)

Means must be provided to switch off electrical supplies together with a means of isolation so as to prevent inadvertent reconnection.

PRECAUTIONS FOR WORK ON EQUIPMENT MADE DEAD (REGULATION 13)

Working dead should be the norm. This regulation requires that precautions be taken to ensure that the system remains dead and to protect those at work on the system. Any or all of the following steps should be considered:

- Identify the circuit. Never assume that the labelling is correct.
- Disconnection and isolation. These are the most common methods: isolation switches, fuse removal and plug removal.
- Proving dead. The test device itself must also be tested before and after testing.
- Earthing.
- Permits to work.
- Notices and barriers.

WORK ON OR NEAR LIVE CONDUCTORS (REGULATION 14)

Live work must only be done if it is unreasonable for it to be done dead. If live work must be carried out then any or all of the following precautions should be taken:

- Competent staff (see reg. 16).
- Adequate information.
- Suitable tools. Insulated tools, protective clothing.
- Barriers or screens.
- Instruments and test probes. To identify what is live and what is dead.
- Accompaniment.
- Designated test areas.

WORKING SPACE, ACCESS AND LIGHTING (REGULATION 15)

Space. Where there are dangerous live exposed conductors, space should be adequate to:

- Allow persons to pull back from the hazard.
- Allow persons to pass each other.

Lighting. The first preference is for natural lighting then for permanent artificial lighting.

PERSONS TO BE COMPETENT TO PREVENT DANGER AND INJURY (REGULATION 16)

The object of this regulation is to 'ensure that persons are not placed at risk due to a lack of skills on the part of themselves or others in dealing with electrical equipment'.

In order to meet the requirements of this regulation a competent person would need:

- An understanding of the concepts of electricity and the risks involved in work associated with it.
- Knowledge of electrical work and some suitable qualification in electrical principles.
- Experience of the type of system to be worked on with an understanding of the hazards and risks involved.
- Knowledge of the systems of work to be employed and the ability to recognise hazards and risks.
- Physical attributes to be able to recognise elements of the system, for example, colour blindness and wiring.

Advice and queries regarding qualifications and training can be directed to the IEE - Institute of Electrical Engineers, London.

DEFENCE (REGULATION 29)

In any Regulation where the absolute duty applies, a defence in any criminal proceedings shall exist where a person can show that: *"He took all reasonable steps and exercised due diligence to avoid the commission of the offence".* Is there a prepared procedure (steps), is the procedure being followed (diligence) and do you have the records or witness to prove it retrospectively?

Fire Safety (Scotland) Regulations (FSSR) 2006

Law considered in context/more depth in Element 7.

The Fire Safety (Scotland) Regulations 2006 ("FSSR") are regulations that were made by Scottish Ministers under the powers contained in the Fire (Scotland) Act 2005, and further build upon the requirements of that act.

Arrangement of regulations

PART 1 - PRELIMINARY

1) Citation and commencement
2) Interpretation

PART 2 - ASSESSMENTS

3) Duty to review
4) Duty in respect of young persons
5) Assessment and review duty in respect of young persons
6) Assessment and review duty in respect of dangerous substances
7) New work activities where dangerous substances are present
8) Duty to record information
9) Specified information

PART 3 - FIRE SAFETY

10) Fire safety arrangements
11) Elimination or reduction of risks from dangerous substances
12) Means for fighting fire and means for giving warning in the event of fire
13) Means of escape
14) Procedures for serious and imminent danger from fire and for danger areas
15) Additional emergency measures in respect of dangerous substances
16) Maintenance
17) Safety assistance
18) Provision of information to employees
19) Provision of information to employers and the self-employed from outside undertakings
20) Training
21) Co-operation and co-ordination
22) Duties of employees

PART 4 - MISCELLANEOUS

23) Maintenance of measures provided in relevant premises for protection of fire fighters
24) Maintenance of measures provided in the common areas of private dwellings for protection of fire-fighters
25) Arrangements with the Office of Rail Regulation
26) Nominated person's act or omission not to afford employer defence
27) Service of documents: further provision
28) Disapplication of certain provisions
Schedule - Measures to be taken in respect of dangerous substances

Please refer to the Regulatory Reform (Fire Safety) Order 2005 for the equivalent legislation for England and Wales.

Fire (Scotland) Act (FSA) 2005

Law considered in context/more depth in Element 7.

Arrangement of Act

PART 1 - FIRE AND RESCUE AUTHORITIES

1) Fire and rescue authorities.
2) Joint fire and rescue boards.
3) Meaning of "relevant authority".

PART 2 - FIRE AND RESCUE SERVICES

Chapter 1   Appointment of chief officer.
Chapter 2   Principal fire and rescue functions.
Chapter 3   Ancillary functions.
Chapter 4   Water supply.
Chapter 5   Powers of employees and constables.
Chapter 6   Mutual assistance etc.
Chapter 7   Assaulting or impeding employees and others.
Chapter 8   Central supervision and support.
Chapter 9   Employment.
Chapter 10   Interpretation.

PART 3 - FIRE SAFETY

Chapter 1   Fire safety duties.
Chapter 2   Enforcement.
Chapter 3   Miscellaneous.
Chapter 4   Offences.
Chapter 5   General.

PART 4 - MISCELLANEOUS

1) Inquiries.
2) Consultation requirements.
3) Pre-commencement consultation.
4) Advisory bodies.
5) Payments in respect of advisory bodies.
6) Abolition of Scottish Central Fire Brigades Advisory Council.
7) False alarms.
8) Disposal of land.

PART 5 - GENERAL

1) Ancillary provision.
2) Orders and regulations.
3) Minor and consequential amendments and repeals.
4) Commencement.
5) Short title.
Schedule 1   Joint fire and rescue boards: supplementary provision.
Schedule 2   Fire safety measures.
Schedule 3   Minor and consequential amendments.
Schedule 4   Repeals.

Outline of main points

The Act is targeted at reducing the number of workplace fires by imposing far reaching responsibilities on all employers, as well as those who have control to any extent of non-domestic premises, to assess and reduce the risks from fire.

Fire certificates were abolished under the Act and have been replaced by a new fire safety regime based upon the principles of risk assessment and the requirement to take steps to mitigate the detrimental effects of a fire on relevant premises.

The new regime applies to all employers as well as to anyone who has control of non-domestic premises to any extent including building owners, tenants, occupiers and factors.

The overriding duty is to ensure, so far as is reasonably practicable, safety in respect of harm caused by fire in the workplace and is supplemented by a number of prescriptive duties:

■ To carry out a fire safety risk assessment of the premises. If you have 5 or more employees, the risk assessment must be recorded in writing.
■ Not to employ a young person (a person under 18) unless an assessment of the risks of fire to young persons has been undertaking.
■ To appoint a competent person to assist with the discharge of fire safety duties.
■ To identify the fire safety measures necessary.
■ To put in place arrangements for the planning, organisation, control, monitoring and review of the fire safety measures that are put in place.
■ To implement these fire safety measures using risk reduction principles.
■ To inform employees of the fire safety risks and provide fire safety training.
■ To co-ordinate and co-operate with other duty holders in the same premises.
■ To review the risk assessment.

Hazardous Waste (England and Wales) Regulations (HWR) 2005 (as amended)

INTRODUCTION

These regulations replaced the Special Waste Regulations 1996 (as amended); the regulations came into force from 16th July 2005 and were subsequently amended by the Hazardous Waste (England and Wales) (Amendment) Regulations 2009 SI 507, which came into force in England on 6th April 2009. The regulations are outlined in their amended form.

Outline of main points

1) The term "special waste" has been replaced by "hazardous waste".
2) The European Waste Catalogue (EWC) and the Hazardous Waste List (part of the EWC) have been formally transposed into UK legislation. All wastes need to be characterised by their EWC code. *(See following section on the List of Wastes (England) Regulations 2005).*
3) Some wastes which were not classified as special waste will now be classified as hazardous waste by virtue of their EWC code, as a result more waste will need to be consigned.
4) Hazardous waste movements will continue to require a consignment note. However, additional information will be required.
5) 200 additional wastes have been added to the Hazardous Waste List. Among them are everyday items such as fluorescent tubes, fridges, TVs, computer monitors and end of life vehicles. There are new requirements on hazardous waste producers (registration, inspections, consignment notes, record keeping):
   ■ All producers of hazardous waste are required to annually register each of their sites with the Environment Agency, for which there is a fee.
   ■ Some sites will be exempt from registration such as those producing less than 500kg (200kg before amendment) of hazardous waste per annum.
   ■ The requirement to pre-notify the Environment Agency for every consignment of hazardous waste will be abolished, as will the consignment note charge.
   ■ Consignees, disposal and transfer sites, are required to provide quarterly returns that will form the basis of the new consignment charge.
6) Mixing of hazardous wastes with other hazardous wastes and with non-hazardous wastes is not permitted, except under license.
7) Fixed penalty charges of £300.00 for minor offences.

All Hazardous Waste producers must be registered; it will be an offence for companies to move the waste if the producers are not registered.

From 16th July 2005 all treated hazardous waste accepted into hazardous or special 'cells' of a non-hazardous landfill site must comply with the full Waste Acceptance Criteria (WAC), as required by the Landfill Regulations 2002.

EXCLUSIONS

The only hazardous waste type excluded from the regulations will be 'domestic wastes', arising from households. If you are a contractor dealing with asbestos waste from domestic premises the regulations affect you, but not the occupier.

THE NEED TO REGISTER WITH THE ENVIRONMENT AGENCY AS A HAZARDOUS WASTE PRODUCER

If hazardous waste is produced (as defined in the Hazardous Waste List of the EWC) the production site will be classed as a producer of hazardous waste. Each hazardous waste production site must be registered annually with the Environment Agency.

Registration applies to sites where separately collected fractions of domestic waste are bulked up (CA site, transfer station, etc).

These sites are classed as sites of production with appropriate notification fees.

THE RULES FOR NOTIFICATION AND RECORD KEEPING

1) Consignment Notes are used as before under the Special Waste Regulations, but a 72 hour pre-notification to the Environment Agency will be required before hazardous waste is moved.
2) Quarterly consignee returns have replaced the system of the consignee copying each Consignment Note to the Environment Agency. Electronic transfer is encouraged.
3) Sites exempt from waste management licensing need to send quarterly returns to the Environment Agency.
4) The consignee must send returns to waste producers notifying them of the receipt of their wastes. It is an offence to collect hazardous waste from non-notified premises if the producer is not exempt.

HOW THE CHANGES AFFECT THE COLLECTION OF WASTE

Waste producers cannot mix different categories of hazardous waste or mix hazardous waste with non-hazardous waste, except under license. If multiple hazardous waste streams from industrial or commercial premises are deposited within a single container, all the individual EWC codes must accompany the consignment note, which must contain the relevant EWC codes.

Both individual and multiple collections of hazardous wastes can be arranged. There is one consignment note for multiple collections with space in an annex for the details of individual loads rather than completely separate consignment notes for each collection. For waste collections using multi-lift vehicles and single compartment tankers, a transfer note will exist for each waste producer. Differences in the contents of the individual containers must be recorded in the individual written descriptions.

DUTIES RELATING TO THE WASTE ACCEPTANCE CRITERIA

From 16th July 2005 all hazardous and non hazardous wastes destined for disposal in landfill have to meet the WAC before they can be deposited. WAC contains the 'quality standards' wastes have to comply with before they are allowed to be placed in inert, non hazardous or hazardous landfills. The waste producer is under a duty of care to ensure the characterisation of the waste to establish its main characteristics as specified in the Regulations. That is, to assess the physical and chemical properties to identify if they classify as hazardous, non hazardous or inert waste. In particular, details of the chemical composition and leaching behaviour of the waste are required. This assessment takes the form of sample testing, whereby a representative sample of waste arising is sent away for scientific analysis.

THE INSPECTION REGIME

The Environment Agency will periodically inspect hazardous waste producing premises and assess the following:

(a) Does the site produce hazardous waste?

(b) Has the site been notified (i.e. registered)?

(c) Is mixing carried out?

(d) Are the Consignment Note records complete?

(e) Is the waste moved by a registered carrier…

(f) …and taken to a permitted consignee?

(g) If going to landfill how are the Waste Acceptance Criteria being met?

The Environment Agency issues fixed penalties (spot fines) for:

■ Failing to notify premises.

■ Failing to complete consignment notes.

■ Failing to apply for review of existing permit.

Source: www.sita.co.uk. Document code M141, Review of the Hazardous Waste (England) Regulations 2005 and the introduction of the Waste Acceptance Criteria.

List of Wastes (England) Regulations (LoWR) 2005

OUTLINE OF MAIN POINTS

Includes the European Waste Catalogue (EWC) and the Hazardous Waste List (part of the EWC); all wastes need to be characterised by their EWC code.

These regulations include Chapters of the List numbered 01-20. The Chapters are broken down into specific materials or substances which are further identified as 'wastes' or 'hazardous wastes'; *a waste marked with an asterisk in the List of Wastes is considered listed as a hazardous waste*, whereas those without an asterisk are considered as a waste.

The different types of wastes in the List of Wastes are fully defined by the six-digit code for the waste and the respective two-digit and four-digit chapter headings, and accordingly, for purposes connected with the regulation of waste or hazardous waste -

(a) Any reference to a waste by its six-digit code as specified in the List of Wastes is to be treated as a reference to that waste.

(b) A reference to wastes by the respective two-digit or four-digit chapter heading is a reference to the wastes listed in the List of Wastes under that chapter heading.

Source: The List of Wastes (England) Regulations 2005.

The regulations set out a list of hazardous waste properties, wastes on the List of Wastes are hazardous if they have one or more of the listed hazardous properties, for example:

H1	**Explosive:** substances and preparations which may explode under the effect of flame or which are more sensitive to shocks or friction than dinitrobenzene.
H2	**Oxidizing:** substances and preparations which exhibit highly exothermic reactions when in contact with other substances, particularly flammable substances.
H3A	**Highly flammable:** ■ Liquid substances and preparations having a flash point below 21C (including extremely flammable liquids). ■ Substances and preparations which may become hot and finally catch fire in contact with air at ambient temperature without any application of energy. ■ Solid substances and preparations which may readily catch fire after brief contact with a source of ignition and which continue to burn or to be consumed after removal of the source of ignition. ■ Gaseous substances and preparations which are flammable in air at normal pressure. ■ Substances and preparations which, in contact with water or damp air, evolve highly flammable gases in dangerous quantities.

Figure RSP-2: Hazardous properties.　　　　　　　　　　*Source: Environment Agency, HWR01, What is a Hazardous Waste?*

See the Regulations for specific details.

Health and Safety (Display Screen Equipment) Regulations (DSE) 1992 (as amended)

See also – Health and Safety (Miscellaneous Amendments) Regulations (MAR) 2002.

Arrangement of Regulations

2)   Every employer shall carry out suitable and sufficient analysis of workstations.

3)   Employers shall ensure that equipment provided meets the requirements of the schedule laid down in these Regulations.

4)   Employers shall plan activities and provide such breaks or changes in work activity to reduce employees' workload on that equipment.

5)   For display screen equipment (DSE) users, the employer shall provide, on request, an eyesight test carried out by a competent person.

6 & 7) Provision of information and training.

Outline of main points

WORKSTATION ASSESSMENTS (REG 2)

Workstation assessments should take account of:

- Screen   -   positioning, character definition, character stability etc.
- Keyboard   -   tilt able, character legibility etc.
- Desk   -   size, matt surface etc.
- Chair   -   adjustable back and height, footrest available etc.
- Environment -   noise, lighting, space etc.
- Software   -   easy to use, work rate not governed by software.

INFORMATION AND TRAINING (REGS 6 & 7)

Information and training should include:

- Risks to health.
- Precautions in place (for example, the need for regular breaks).

- How to recognise problems.
- How to report problems.

Health and Safety (First-Aid) Regulations (FAR) 1981 (as amended)

See also – Health and Safety (Miscellaneous Amendments) Regulations (MAR) 2002.

Law considered in context/more depth in Element 2.

Arrangement of Regulations

1)   Citation and commencement.
2)   Interpretation.
3)   Duty of employer to make provision for first-aid.
4)   Duty of employer to inform his employees of the arrangements.
5)   Duty of self-employed person to provide first-aid equipment.
6)   Power to grant exemptions.
7)   Cases where these Regulations do not apply.
8)   Application to mines.
9)   Application offshore.
10) Repeals, revocations and modification.

Schedule 1 - Repeals.

Schedule 1 - Revocations.

Outline of main points

1)   Regulation 2 defines first aid as: '…treatment for the purpose of preserving life and minimising the consequences of injury or illness until medical (doctor or nurse) help can be obtained. Also, it provides treatment of minor injuries which would otherwise receive no treatment, or which do not need the help of a medical practitioner or nurse'.

2)   Requires that every employer must provide equipment and facilities which are adequate and appropriate in the circumstances for administering first-aid to his employees.

3)   Employer must inform their employees about the first-aid arrangements, including the location of equipment, facilities and identification of trained personnel.

4)   Self-employed people must ensure that adequate and suitable provision is made for administering first-aid while at work.

Health and Safety (Miscellaneous Amendments) Regulations (MAR) 2002

See also - FAR 1981, DSE 1992, MHOR 1992, PPER 1992, WHSWR 1992, PUWER and LOLER.

These Regulations made minor amendments to UK law to come into line with the requirements of the original Directives and came into force on 17ᵗʰ September 2002. In relation to this publication, the Regulations that are affected by the amendments are:

- Health and Safety (First-Aid) Regulations (FAR) 1981.
- Health and Safety (Display Screen Equipment) Regulations (DSE) 1992.
- Manual Handling Operations Regulations (MHOR) 1992.
- Personal Protective Equipment at Work Regulations (PPER) 1992.
- Workplace (Health, Safety and Welfare) Regulations (WHSWR) 1992.
- Provision and Use of Work Equipment Regulations (PUWER) 1998.
- Lifting Operations and Lifting Equipment Regulations (LOLER) 1998.

Arrangement of Regulations

1) Citation and commencement.
2) Amendment of the Health and Safety (First-Aid) Regulations 1981.
3) Amendment of the Health and Safety (Display Screen Equipment) Regulations 1992.
4) Amendment of the Manual Handling Operations Regulations 1992.
5) Amendment of the Personal Protective Equipment at Work Regulations 1992.
6) Amendment of the Workplace (Health, Safety and Welfare) Regulations 1992.
7) Amendment of the Provision and Use of Work Equipment Regulations 1998.
8) Amendment of the Lifting Operations and Lifting Equipment Regulations 1998.
9) Amendment of the Quarries Regulations 1999.

Outline of main points

REGULATION 3 - AMENDMENT OF THE HEALTH AND SAFETY (FIRST AID) REGULATIONS 1981

The Health and Safety (First Aid) Regulations 1981 are amended by adding the additional requirements that any first-aid room provided under requirements of these regulations must be easily accessible to stretchers and to any other equipment needed to convey patients to and from the room and that the room be sign-posted by use of a sign complying with the Health and Safety (Safety Signs and Signals) Regulations 1996.

REGULATION 3 - AMENDMENT OF THE HEALTH AND SAFETY (DISPLAY SCREEN EQUIPMENT) REGULATIONS 1992

The Health and Safety (Display Screen Equipment) Regulations 1992 were amended to cover workstations "used for the purposes of" an employer's undertaking, which includes workstations provided by the employer and others.

The Health and Safety (Display Screen Equipment) Regulations 1992 were amended to provide for people that are users of display screen equipment in an employers undertaking but are not employees of the employer, for example staff provided through an employment agency. This extension of duty relates to requests for eye site tests from the person. The employer who carries on the undertaking must ensure an eyesight test is carried out, as soon as is practicable after the request for those currently a user and before they become a user for those who become users.

The Health and Safety (Display Screen Equipment) Regulations 1992 were similarly amended with regard to health and safety training for users.

REGULATION 4 - AMENDMENT OF THE MANUAL HANDLING OPERATIONS REGULATIONS 1992

Regulation 4 of the Manual Handling Operations Regulations 1992 were amended by adding the requirement to, when determining whether manual handling operations at work involve a risk of injury and the appropriate steps to reduce that risk, have regard to:

- Physical suitability of the employee to carry out the operations.
- Clothing, footwear or other personal effects they are wearing.
- Knowledge and training.
- Results of any relevant risk assessment conducted for the Management of Health and Safety at Work Regulations.
- Whether the employee is within a group of employees identified by that assessment as being especially at risk.
- Results of any health surveillance provided under the Management of Health and Safety Regulations.

REGULATION 5 - AMENDMENT OF THE PERSONAL PROTECTIVE EQUIPMENT AT WORK REGULATIONS 1992

The Personal Protective Equipment at Work Regulations 1992 were amended so that personal protective equipment (PPE) must also be suitable for the period for which it is worn and account is taken of the characteristics of the workstation of each person.

Provision of personal issue of PPE needs to take place in situations where it is necessary to ensure it is hygienic and free of risk to health. Where an assessment of PPE is made this must consider whether it is compatible with other personal protective equipment that is in use and which an employee would be required to wear simultaneously.

The amendments require that information provided to satisfy regulation 9 for the provision of information, instruction and training must be kept available to employees. A new, additional duty is created requiring the employer, where appropriate, and at suitable intervals, to organise demonstrations in the wearing of PPE.

REGULATION 6 - AMENDMENT OF THE WORKPLACE (HEALTH, SAFETY AND WELFARE) REGULATIONS 1992

The Workplace (Health, Safety and Welfare) Regulations 1992 have been amended to improve clarity, include additional regulations and make provision for the disabled.

An additional regulation (4A) sets out a requirement where a workplace is in a building, the building shall have a stability and solidity appropriate to the nature of the use of the workplace. The range of things requiring maintenance under these regulations is extended to equipment and devices intended to prevent or reduce hazards. A new duty requires workplaces to be adequately thermally insulated where it is necessary, having regard to the type of work carried out and the physical activity of the persons carrying out the work. In addition, excessive effects of sunlight on temperature must be avoided.

The regulations were amended with regard to facilities for changing clothing in that the facilities need to be easily accessible, of sufficient capacity and provided with seating. Requirements were amended such that rest rooms and rest areas must include suitable arrangements to protect non-smokers from discomfort caused by tobacco smoke. They also must be equipped with an adequate number of tables and adequate seating with backs for the number of persons at work likely to use them at any one time and seating which is adequate for the number of disabled persons at work and suitable for them.

A new regulation (25A) was added requiring, where necessary, those parts of the workplace (including in particular doors, passageways, stairs, showers, washbasins, lavatories and workstations) used or occupied directly by disabled persons at work to be organised to take account of such persons.

AMENDMENT OF THE PROVISION AND USE OF WORK EQUIPMENT REGULATIONS 1998

The regulations have a small number of amendments affecting 3 main regulations. Regulation 10, which deals with equipment's conformity with community requirements, is amended such that the requirement to conform to 'essential requirements' is no longer limited to the point at which the equipment was designed and constructed - equipment must now conform at 'all times'. The 'essential requirements' are those that were applicable at the time it was put into first service. Regulation 11 was amended to remove the opportunity of reliance on information, instruction, training and supervision as a separate option in the hierarchy of control of dangerous parts of machinery. The requirement to provide information, instruction, training and supervision is now amended to apply to each stage of the dangerous parts of machinery control hierarchy. Regulation 18, which deals with control systems, carries a small but important amendment which means the requirement that all control systems of work equipment are "chosen making due allowance for the failures, faults and constraints to be expected in the planned circumstances of use" is modified from an absolute duty to one of so far as is reasonably practicable.

AMENDMENT OF THE LIFTING OPERATIONS AND LIFTING EQUIPMENT REGULATIONS 1998

Minor changes to the definitions in the Lifting Operations and Lifting Equipment Regulations 1998 were made by these regulations.

(a) In the definition of "accessory for lifting" in regulation 2(1), by substituting for the word "work" the word "lifting".

(b) In regulation 3(4), by substituting for the words "(5) (b)" the words "(3) (b)".

Health and Safety (Miscellaneous Repeals, Revocations and Amendments) Regulations (MRRA) 2013

See also – PPER 1992 and WHSWR 1992.

These Regulations repeal one Act and revoke twelve instruments (plus a related provision in the Factories Act 1961) and came into force on 6th April 2013. The Regulations, applicable to this award, that are affected by the amendments are detailed below.

Arrangement of Regulations

1) Citation and commencement.
2) Repeals and revocations.
3) Consequential amendments to the Dangerous Substances (Notification and Marking of Sites) Regulations (NAMOS) 1990.
4) Consequential amendments to the Workplace (Health, Safety and Welfare) Regulations (WHSWR) 1992.

Outline of main points

CONSEQUENTIAL AMENDMENTS TO THE PERSONAL PROTECTIVE EQUIPMENT AT WORK REGULATIONS (PPE) 1992

The Personal Protective Equipment at Work Regulations 1992 have been amended so that they cover the provision and use of head protection on construction sites thus maintaining the level of legal protection when the Construction (Head Protection) Regulations were revoked as part of The Health and Safety (Miscellaneous Repeals, Revocations and Amendments) Regulations 2013.

These measures are being removed because they have either been overtaken by more up to date Regulations, are redundant or do not deliver the intended benefits.

AMENDMENT OF THE WORKPLACE (HEALTH, SAFETY AND WELFARE) REGULATIONS (WHSWR) 1992

The Workplace (Health, Safety and Welfare) Regulations 1992 have been amended to include the requirement for adequate lighting and safe access for workers on ships in a shipyard or harbour undergoing construction, repair or maintenance.

Health and Safety (Safety Signs and Signals) Regulations (SSSR) 1996

Law considered in context/more depth in Element 2.

Arrangement of Regulations

1) Citation and commencement.
2) Interpretation.
3) Application.
4) Provision and maintenance of safety signs.
5) Information, instruction and training.
6) Transitional provisions.
7) Enforcement.
8) Revocations and amendments.

Outline of main points

The Regulations require employers to provide specific safety signs whenever there is a risk which has not been avoided or controlled by other means, for example, by engineering controls and safe systems of work. Where a safety sign would not help to reduce that risk, or where the sign is not significant, there is no need to provide a sign.

They require, where necessary, the use of road traffic signs within workplaces to regulate road traffic.

They also require employers to:

■   Maintain the safety signs which are provided by them.
■   Explain unfamiliar signs to their employees and tell them what they need to do when they see a safety sign.

The Regulations cover 4 main types of signs:

1) **Prohibition** - circular signs, prime colours red and white, for example, no pedestrian access.
2) **Warning** - triangular signs, prime colours black on yellow, for example, overhead electrics.
3) **Mandatory** - circular signs, prime colours blue and white, for example, safety helmets must be worn.
4) **Safe condition** - oblong/square signs, prime colours green and white, for example, fire assembly point, first aid etc.

Supplementary signs provide additional information.

Supplementary signs with yellow/black or red/white diagonal stripes can be used to highlight a hazard, but must not substitute for signs as defined above.

Fire fighting, rescue equipment and emergency exit signs have to comply with a separate British Standard.

Ionising Radiations Regulations (IRR) 1999

Arrangement of Regulations

PART I - INTERPRETATION AND GENERAL

1) Citation and commencement.
2) Interpretation.
3) Application.
4) Duties under the Regulations.

PART II - GENERAL PRINCIPLES AND PROCEDURES

5) Authorisation of specified practices.
6) Notification of specified work.
7) Prior risk assessment etc.
8) Restriction of exposure.
9) Personal protective equipment.
10) Maintenance and examination of engineering controls etc. and personal protective equipment.
11) Dose limitation.
12) Contingency plans.

PART III - ARRANGEMENTS FOR THE MANAGEMENT OF RADIATION PROTECTION

13) Radiation protection adviser.
14) Information, instruction and training.
15) Co-operation between employers.

PART IV - DESIGNATED AREAS

16) Designation of controlled or supervised areas.
17) Local rules and radiation protection supervisors.
18) Additional requirements for designated areas.
19) Monitoring of designated areas.

PART V - CLASSIFICATION AND MONITORING OF PERSONS

20) Designation of classified persons.
21) Dose assessment and recording.
22) Estimated doses and special entries.
23) Dosimetry for accidents etc.
24) Medical surveillance.
25) Investigation and notification of overexposure.
26) Dose limitation for overexposed employees.

PART VI - ARRANGEMENTS FOR THE CONTROL OF RADIOACTIVE SUBSTANCES, ARTICLES AND EQUIPMENT

27) Sealed sources and articles containing or embodying radioactive substances.
28) Accounting for radioactive substances.
29) Keeping and moving of radioactive substances.
30) Notification of certain occurrences.
31) Duties of manufacturers etc. of articles for use in work with ionising radiation.
32) Equipment used for medical exposure.
33) Misuse of or interference with sources of ionising radiation.

PART VII - DUTIES OF EMPLOYEES AND MISCELLANEOUS

34) Duties of employees.
35) Approval of dosimetry services.
36) Defence on contravention.
37) Exemption certificates.
38) Extension outside Great Britain.
39) Transitional provisions.
40) Modifications relating to the Ministry of Defence.
41) Modification, revocation and saving.

SCHEDULES

Schedule 1 - Work not required to be notified under regulation 6.

Schedule 2 - Particulars to be provided in a notification under regulation 6(2).

Schedule 3 - Additional particulars that the Executive may require.

Schedule 4 - Dose limits.

Schedule 5 - Matters in respect of which radiation protection adviser must be consulted by a radiation employer.

Schedule 6 - Particulars to be entered in the radiation passbook.

Schedule 7 - Particulars to be contained in a health record.

Schedule 8 - Quantities and concentrations of radionuclides.

Schedule 9 - Modifications.

Outline of main points

The Regulations supersede and consolidate the Ionising Radiations Regulations 1985 and the Ionising Radiation (Outside Workers) Regulations 1993.

They impose duties on employers to protect employees and other persons against ionising radiation arising from work with radioactive substances and other sources of ionising radiation; and also impose certain duties on employees.

Lifting Operations and Lifting Equipment Regulations (LOLER) 1998 (as amended)

See also – Health and Safety (Miscellaneous Amendments) Regulations (MAR) 2002.

Law considered in context/more depth in Element 4.

Arrangements of Regulations

1) Citation and commencement.
2) Interpretation.
3) Application.
4) Strength and stability.
5) Lifting equipment for lifting persons.
6) Positioning and installation.
7) Marking of lifting equipment.
8) Organisation of lifting operations.
9) Thorough examination and inspection.
10) Reports and defects.
11) Keeping of information.
12) Exemption for the armed forces.
13) Amendment of the Shipbuilding and Ship-repairing Regulations 1960.
14) Amendment of the Docks Regulation 1988.
15) Repeal of provisions of the Factories Act 1961.
16) Repeal of section 85 of the Mines and Quarries Act 1954.
17) Revocation of instruments.

Schedule 1 - Information to be contained in a report of a thorough examination.

Schedule 2 - Revocation of instruments.

Outline of main points

The Lifting Operations and Lifting Equipment Regulations (LOLER) 1998 impose health and safety requirements with respect to lifting equipment (as defined in regulation 2(1)). They are not industry specific and apply to almost all lifting operations.

The Regulations place duties on employers, the self-employed, and certain persons having control of lifting equipment (of persons at work who use or supervise or manage its use, or of the way it is used, to the extent of their control (regulation 3(3) to (5)).

The Regulations make provision with respect to:

- The strength and stability of lifting equipment (regulation 4).
- The safety of lifting equipment for lifting persons (regulation 5).
- The way lifting equipment is positioned and installed (regulation 6).
- The marking of machinery and accessories for lifting, and lifting equipment which is designed for lifting persons or which might so be used in error (regulation 7).
- The organisation of lifting operations (regulation 8).
- The thorough examination (defined in (regulation 2(1)) and inspection of lifting equipment in specified circumstances, (regulation 9(1) to (3)).
- The evidence of examination to accompany it outside the undertaking (regulation 9(4)).
- The exception for winding apparatus at mines from regulation 9 (regulation 9(5)).
- Transitional arrangements relating to regulation 9 (regulation 9(6) and (7)).
- The making of reports of thorough examinations and records of inspections (regulation 10 and Schedule 1).
- The keeping of information in the reports and records (regulation 11).

Management of Health and Safety at Work Regulations (MHSWR) 1999

Law considered in context/more depth in Element 1.

Arrangement of Regulations

1) Citation, commencement and interpretation.
2) Disapplication of these Regulations.
3) Risk assessment.
4) Principles of prevention to be applied.
5) Health and safety arrangements.
6) Health surveillance.
7) Health and safety assistance.
8) Procedures for serious and imminent danger and for danger areas.
9) Contacts with external services.
10) Information for employees.
11) Co-operation and co-ordination.
12) Persons working in host employers' or self-employed persons' undertakings.
13) Capabilities and training.
14) Employees' duties.
15) Temporary workers.
16) Risk assessment in respect of new or expectant mothers.
17) Certificate from a registered medical practitioner in respect of new or expectant mothers.
18) Notification by new or expectant mothers.
19) Protection of young persons.
20) Exemption certificates.
21) Provisions as to liability.
22) Exclusion of civil liability.
23) Extension outside Great Britain.
24) Amendment of the Health and Safety (First-Aid) Regulations 1981.
25) Amendment of the Offshore Installations and Pipeline Works (First-Aid) Regulations 1989.
26) Amendment of the Mines Miscellaneous Health and Safety Provisions Regulations 1995.
27) Amendment of the Construction (Health, Safety and Welfare) Regulations 1996.
28) Regulations to have effect as health and safety regulations.
29) Revocations and consequential amendments.
30) Transitional provision.

Schedule 1 - General principles of prevention.

Schedule 2 - Consequential amendments.

Outline of main points

Management of Health and Safety at Work Regulations (MHSWR) 1999 set out some broad general duties that apply to almost all kinds of work. They are aimed mainly at improving health and safety management. The Regulations work in a similar way to the broad health and safety requirements set out in the Health and Safety at Work Act (HASAWA) 1974, and can be seen as a way of fleshing out what is already in the HASAWA 1974. The 1999 Regulations replace the Management of Health and Safety at Work Regulations 1992, the Management of Health and Safety at Work (Amendment) Regulations 1994, the Health and Safety (Young Persons) Regulations 1997 and Part III of the Fire Precautions (Workplace) Regulations 1997. The principal Regulations are discussed below.

RISK ASSESSMENT (REGULATION 3)

The regulations require employers (and the self-employed) to assess the risk to the health and safety of their employees and to anyone else who may be affected by their work activity. This is necessary to ensure that the preventive and protective steps can be identified to control hazards in the workplace. Where an employer is employing or about to employ young persons (under 18 years of age) he must carry out a risk assessment which takes particular account of:

- The inexperience, lack of awareness of risks and immaturity of young persons.
- The layout of the workplace and workstations.
- Exposure to physical, biological and chemical agents.
- Work equipment and the way in which it is handled.
- The extent of health and safety training to be provided.
- Risks from agents, processes and work listed in the Annex to Council Directive 94/33/EC on the protection of young people at work.

Where 5 or more employees are employed, the significant findings of risk assessments must be recorded in writing (the same threshold that is used in respect of having a written safety policy). This record must include details of any employees being identified as being especially at risk.

PRINCIPLES OF PREVENTION TO BE APPLIED (REGULATION 4)

Regulation 4 requires an employer to implement preventive and protective measures on the basis of general principles of prevention specified in Schedule 1 to the Regulations. These are:

1) Avoiding risks.
2) Evaluating the risks which cannot be avoided.

3) Combating the risks at source.

4) Adapting the work to the individual, especially as regards the design of workplaces, the choice of work equipment and the choice of working and production methods, with a view, in particular, to alleviating monotonous work and work at a predetermined work-rate and to reducing their effect on health.

5) Adapting to technical progress.

6) Replacing the dangerous by the non-dangerous or the less dangerous.

7) Developing a coherent overall prevention policy which covers technology, organisation of work, working conditions, social relationships and the influence of factors relating to the working environment.

8) Giving collective protective measures priority over individual protective measures.

9) Giving appropriate instructions to employees.

HEALTH AND SAFETY ARRANGEMENTS (REGULATION 5)

Appropriate arrangements must be made for the effective planning, organisation, control, monitoring and review of preventative and protective measures (in other words, for the management of health and safety).

Again, employers with five or more employees must have their arrangements in writing.

HEALTH SURVEILLANCE (REGULATION 6)

In addition to the requirements of other specific regulations, consideration must be given to carrying out health surveillance of employees, where there is a disease or adverse health condition identified in risk assessments.

HEALTH AND SAFETY ASSISTANCE (REGULATION 7)

The employer must appoint one or more competent persons to assist him in complying with the legal obligations imposed on the undertaking. The number of persons appointed should reflect the number of employees and the type of hazards in the workplace.

If more than one competent person is appointed, then arrangements must be made for ensuring adequate co-operation between them. The competent person(s) must be given the necessary time and resources to fulfil their functions. This will depend on the size the undertaking, the risks to which employees are exposed and the distribution of those risks throughout the undertaking.

The employer must ensure that competent person(s) who are not employees are informed of the factors known (or suspected) to affect the health and safety of anyone affected by business activities.

Competent people are defined as those who have sufficient training and experience or knowledge and other qualities to enable them to perform their functions. Persons may be selected from among existing employees or from outside. Where there is a suitable person in the employer's employment, that person shall be appointed as the 'competent person' in preference to a non-employee.

PROCEDURES FOR SERIOUS AND IMMINENT DANGER AND FOR DANGER AREAS (REGULATION 8)

Employers are required to set up emergency procedures and appoint **competent persons** to ensure compliance with identified arrangements, to devise control strategies as appropriate and to limit access to areas of risk to ensure that only those persons with adequate health and safety knowledge and instruction are admitted. The factors to be considered when preparing a procedure to deal with workplace emergencies such as fire, explosion, bomb scare, chemical leakage or other dangerous occurrence should include:

- The identification and training requirements of persons with specific responsibilities.
- The layout of the premises in relation to escape routes etc.
- The number of persons affected.
- Assessment of special needs (disabled persons, children etc.).
- Warning systems.
- Emergency lighting.
- Location of shut-off valves, isolation switches, hydrants etc.
- Equipment required to deal with the emergency.
- Location of assembly points.
- Communication with emergency services.
- Training and/or information to be given to employees, visitors, local residents and anyone else who might be affected.

CONTACTS WITH EXTERNAL SERVICES (REGULATION 9)

Employers must ensure that, where necessary, contacts are made with external services. This particularly applies with regard to first-aid, emergency medical care and rescue work.

INFORMATION FOR EMPLOYEES (REGULATION 10)

Employees must be provided with relevant information about hazards to their health and safety arising from risks identified by the assessments. Clear instruction must be provided concerning any preventative or protective control measures including those relating to serious and imminent danger and fire assessments. Details of any competent persons nominated to discharge specific duties in accordance with the regulations must also be communicated as should risks arising from contact with other employer's activities (see Regulation 11).

Before employing a child (a person who is not over compulsory school age) the employer must provide those with parental responsibility for the child with information on the risks that have been identified and preventative and protective measures to be taken.

CO-OPERATION AND CO-ORDINATION (REGULATION 11)

Employers who work together in a common workplace have a duty to co-operate to discharge their duties under relevant statutory provisions. They must also take all reasonable steps to inform their respective employees of risks to their health or safety which may arise out of their work. Specific arrangements must be made to ensure compliance with fire legislation.

PERSONS WORKING IN HOST EMPLOYERS' OR SELF EMPLOYED PERSONS' UNDERTAKINGS (REGULATION 12)

This regulation extends the requirements of regulation 11 to include employees working as sole occupiers of a workplace under the control of another employer. Such employees would include those working under a service of contract and employees in temporary employment businesses under the control of the first employer.

CAPABILITIES AND TRAINING (REGULATION 13)

Employers need to take into account the capabilities of their employees before entrusting tasks. This is necessary to ensure that they have adequate health and safety training and are capable enough at their jobs to avoid risk. To this end, consideration must be given to recruitment including job orientation when transferring between jobs and work departments. Training must also be provided when other factors such as the introduction of new technology and new systems of work or work equipment arise. Training must:

- Be repeated periodically where appropriate.
- Be adapted to take account of any new or changed risks to the health and safety of the employees concerned.
- Take place during working hours.

EMPLOYEES' DUTIES (REGULATION 14)

Employees are required to follow health and safety instructions by using machinery, substances, transport etc. in accordance with the instructions and training that they have received.

They must also inform their employer (and other employers) of any dangers or shortcoming in the health and safety arrangements, even if there is no risk of imminent danger.

TEMPORARY WORKERS (REGULATION 15)

Consideration is given to the special needs of temporary workers. In particular to the provision of particular health and safety information such as qualifications required to perform the task safely or any special arrangements such as the need to provide health screening.

RISKS ASSESSMENT IN RESPECT OF NEW OR EXPECTANT MOTHERS (REGULATION 16)

Where the work is of a kind which would involve risk to a new or expectant mother or her baby, then the assessment required by regulation 3 should take this into account. If the risk cannot be avoided, then the employer should take reasonable steps to:

- Adjust the hours worked.
- Offer alternative work.
- Give paid leave for as long as is necessary.

CERTIFICATE FROM A REGISTERED MEDICAL PRACTITIONER IN RESPECT OF NEW OR EXPECTANT MOTHERS (REGULATION 17)

Where the woman is a night shift worker and has a medical certificate identifying night shift work as a risk then the employer must put her on day shift or give paid leave for as long as is necessary.

NOTIFICATION BY NEW OR EXPECTANT MOTHERS (REGULATION 18)

The employer need take no action until he is notified in writing by the woman that she is pregnant, has given birth in the last six months, or is breastfeeding.

PROTECTION OF YOUNG PERSONS (REGULATION 19)

Employers of young persons shall ensure that they are not exposed to risk as a consequence of their lack of experience, lack of awareness or lack of maturity.

No employer shall employ young people for work which:

- Is beyond his physical or psychological capacity.
- Involves exposure to agents which chronically affect human health.
- Involves harmful exposure to radiation.
- Involves a risk to health from extremes of temperature, noise or vibration.
- Involves risks which could not be reasonably foreseen by young persons.

This regulation does not prevent the employment of a young person who is no longer a child for work:

- Where it is necessary for his training.
- Where the young person will be supervised by a competent person.
- Where any risk will be reduced to the lowest level that is reasonably practicable.

(Note: Two HSE publications give guidance on these topics. HSG122 - New and expectant mothers at work: a guide for employers and HSG165 - Young people at work: a guide for employers).

EXEMPTION CERTIFICATES (REGULATION 20)

The Secretary of State for Defence may, in the interests of national security, by a certificate in writing exempt the armed forces, any visiting force or any headquarters from certain obligations imposed by the Regulations.

PROVISIONS AS TO LIABILITY (REGULATION 21)

Employers cannot submit a defence in criminal proceedings that contravention was caused by the act or default either of an employee or the competent person appointed under Regulation 7.

EXCLUSION OF CIVIL LIABILITY (REGULATION 22)

As amended by Health and Safety at Work etc. Act 1974 (Civil Liability) (Exceptions) Regulations 2013:

Regulation 22 specifies:

"(1) Breach of a duty imposed by regulation 16, 16A, 17 or 17A shall, so far as it causes damage, be actionable by the new or expectant mother.

(2) Any term of an agreement which purports to exclude or restrict any liability for such a breach is void."

REVOCATIONS AND AMENDMENTS (REGULATIONS 24-29)

The Regulations:

- Revoke regulation 6 of the Health and Safety (First-Aid) Regulations (FAR) 1981 which confers power on the Health and Safety Executive to grant exemptions from those Regulations.
- Amend the Offshore Installations and Pipeline Works (First-Aid) Regulations 1989.
- Amend the Mines Miscellaneous Health and Safety Provisions Regulations 1995.

The Regulations also make amendments to the statutory instruments as specified in Schedule 2.

Manual Handling Operations Regulations (MHOR) 1992 (as amended)

See also – Health and Safety (Miscellaneous Amendments) Regulations (MAR) 2002.

Law considered in context/more depth in Element 4.

Arrangement of Regulations

1) Citation and commencement.
2) Interpretation.
3) Disapplication of Regulations.
4) Duties of employers.
5) Duty of employees.
6) Exemption certificates.
7) Extension outside Great Britain.
8) Repeals and revocations.

Outline of main points

CITATION AND COMMENCEMENT (1)

INTERPRETATION (2)

"Injury" does not include injury caused by toxic or corrosive substances which:

- Have leaked/spilled from load.
- Are present on the surface but not leaked/spilled from it.
- Are a constituent part of the load.

"Load" includes any person or animal.

"Manual Handling Operations" means transporting or supporting a load including:

- Lifting and putting down.
- Pushing, pulling or moving by hand or bodily force.
- Shall as far as is reasonably practicable.

DISAPPLICATION OF REGULATIONS (3)

DUTIES OF EMPLOYERS (4)

AVOIDANCE OF MANUAL HANDLING (4) (1) (A)

The employer's duty is to avoid the need for manual handling operations which involve a risk of their employees being injured - as far as is reasonably practicable.

ASSESSMENT OF RISK (4) (1) (B) (I)

Where not reasonably practicable make a suitable and sufficient assessment of all such manual handling operations.

REDUCING THE RISK OF INJURY (4) (1) (B) (II)

Take appropriate steps to reduce the risk of injury to the lowest level reasonably practicable.

THE LOAD - ADDITIONAL INFORMATION (4) (1) (B) (III)

Employers shall provide information on general indications or where reasonably practicable precise information on:

- The weight of each load.
- The heaviest side of any load whose centre of gravity is not central.

REVIEWING THE ASSESSMENT (4) (2)

Assessment review:

- Where there is reason to believe the assessment is no longer valid.
- There is sufficient change in manual handling operations.

DUTY OF EMPLOYEES (5)

Employees shall make full and proper use of any system of work provided for his use by his employer.

EXEMPTION CERTIFICATES (6)

EXTENSION OUTSIDE GREAT BRITAIN (7)

REPEALS AND REVOCATIONS (8)

SCHEDULES

Schedule 1 - Factors to which the employer must have regard and questions he must consider when making an assessment of manual handling operations.

Schedule 2 - Repeals and revocations.

Appendix 1 - Numerical guidelines for assessment.

Appendix 2 - Example of an assessment checklist.

Thus the Regulations establish a clear hierarchy of measures:

1) Avoid hazardous manual handling operations so far as is reasonably practicable.
2) Make a suitable and sufficient assessment of any hazardous manual handling operations that cannot be avoided.
3) Reduce the risk of injury so far as is reasonably practicable.

New Roads and Street Works Act (NRSWA) 1991

Arrangement of Act

PART I - NEW ROADS IN ENGLAND AND WALES
- Concession agreements.
- Toll orders.
- Further provisions with respect to tolls.
- Annual report.
- Miscellaneous.
- General.

PART II - NEW ROADS IN SCOTLAND
- Toll Roads.
- Further provision with respect to tolls.
- Report.
- Supplementary provisions.

PART III - STREET WORKS IN ENGLAND AND WALES
- Introductory provisions.
- The street works register.
- Notice and co-ordination of works.
- Streets subject to special controls.
- General requirements as to execution of street works.
- Reinstatement.
- Charges, fees and contributions payable by undertakers.
- Duties and liabilities of undertakers with respect to apparatus.
- Apparatus affected by highway, bridge or transport works.
- Provisions with respect to particular authorities and undertakings.
- Power of street authority or district council to undertake street works.
- Supplementary provisions.

PART IV - ROAD WORKS IN SCOTLAND
- Introductory provisions.
- The road works register.
- Notice and co-ordination of works.
- Roads subject to special controls.
- General requirements as to execution of road works.
- Reinstatement.
- Charges, fees and contributions payable by undertakers.
- Duties and liabilities of undertakers with respect to apparatus.
- Apparatus affected by road, bridge or transport works.
- Provisions with respect to particular authorities and undertakings.
- Power of road works authority or district council to undertake road works.
- Supplementary provisions.

PART V - GENERAL

SCHEDULES

Schedule 1   Supplementary provisions as to termination of concession.
Schedule 2   Procedure in connection with toll orders.
Schedule 3   Street works licences.
Schedule 4   Streets with special engineering difficulties.
Schedule 5   Procedure for making certain orders under Part III.
Schedule 6   Roads with special engineering difficulties.
Schedule 7   Procedure for making certain orders under Part IV.
Schedule 8   Minor and consequential amendments.
Schedule 9   Repeals.

Outline of main points

One of the most important elements of the street works legislation is the duty on street authorities to co-ordinate all works in the highway. As important is the parallel duty on undertakers to co-operate in this process. It is essential that both street authorities and undertakers take these responsibilities seriously.

The New Roads and Street Works Act 1991 spells out the objectives of the co-ordination function.

They are to:

- Ensure safety.
- Minimise inconvenience to people using a street, including a specific reference to people with a disability.
- Protect the structure of the street and apparatus in it.

These objectives should be taken into account by everyone responsible for planning and carrying out works in the highway.

The NRSWA 1991 sets out three requirements for a successful co-ordination framework:

- The notice system - the notices themselves provide vital information to aid the co-ordination process, while the notice periods provide time within which appropriate steps can be taken. The best method of exchanging notices is electronically.
- Streets subject to special controls - these designation procedures provide a mechanism by which attention can be focused on particularly sensitive streets.
- The co-ordination tools - the Act provides a range of tools to facilitate the co-ordination process. These include: the power to direct the timing of street works, the power to restrict street works following substantial road works and the requirement on undertakers to avoid unnecessary delay and obstruction.

There are three important principles to which undertakers and street authorities must adhere if co-ordination is to be effective. They are:

- The need to balance the potentially conflicting interests of road users and undertakers' customers.
- The importance of close co-operation and liaison between street authorities and undertakers.
- An acknowledgement on all sides of the fact that works programmes and practices may have to be adjusted in order to ensure that the objectives of the co-ordination provisions are achieved.

In carrying out their responsibilities under the NRSWA 1991 street authorities and undertakers should endeavour to ensure that their works are planned in such a way as to minimise inconvenience to all road users including disability groups.

Authorities and undertakers are expected to work particularly closely in relation to 'urgent work', which is that work that falls short of emergencies as defined by the NRSWA 1991. These works will need to be executed in circumstances where planning and co-ordination time is limited. Where work is needed in traffic sensitive streets considerable disruption may result and both parties are expected to take an objective but balanced view on the necessity of the work and arrangements surrounding it.

Personal Protective Equipment at Work Regulations (PPER) 1992 (as amended)

See also – Health and Safety (Miscellaneous Amendments) Regulations (MAR) 2002 and Health and Safety (Miscellaneous Repeals, Revocations and Amendments) Regulations (MRRA) 2002.

Law considered in context/more depth in Element 2.

Arrangement of Regulations

1) Citation and commencement.
2) Interpretation.
3) Disapplication of these Regulations.
4) Provision of personal protective equipment.
5) Compatibility of personal protective equipment.
6) Assessment of personal protective equipment.
7) Maintenance and replacement of personal protective equipment.
8) Accommodation for personal protective equipment.
9) Information, instruction and training.
10) Use of personal protective equipment.
11) Reporting loss or defect.
12) Exemption certificates.
13) Extension outside Great Britain.
14) Modifications, repeal and revocations directive.

Schedule 1 - Relevant Community

Schedule 2 - Modifications

Part I Factories Act 1961.

Part II The Coal and Other Mines (Fire and Rescue) Order 1956.

Part III The Shipbuilding and Ship-Repairing Regulations 1960.

Part IV The Coal Mines (Respirable Dust) Regulations 1975.

Part V The Control of Lead at Work Regulations 1980.

Part VI The Ionising Radiations Regulations 1985.

Part VII The Control of Asbestos at Work Regulations 1987.

Part VIII The Control of Substances Hazardous to Health Regulations 1988.

Part IX The Noise at Work Regulations 1989.

Part X The Construction (Head Protection) Regulations 1989.

Schedule 3 - Revocations

Outline of main points

2)   Personal protective equipment (PPE) means all equipment (including clothing provided for protection against adverse weather) which is intended to be worn or held by a person at work and which protects him against risks to his health or safety.

3)   These Regulations do not apply to:
- Ordinary working clothes/uniforms.
- Offensive weapons.
- Portable detectors which signal risk.
- Equipment used whilst playing competitive sports.
- Equipment provided for travelling on a road.

The Regulations do not apply to situations already controlled by other Regulations i.e.
- Control of Lead at Work Regulations 2002.
- Ionising Radiation Regulations 1999.
- Control of Asbestos at Work Regulations 2002.
- CoSHH Regulations 2002 (as amended).
- Noise at Work Regulations 2005.
- Construction (Head Protection) Regulations 1989.

4)   Suitable PPE must be provided when risks cannot be adequately controlled by other means. Reg. 4 requires that PPE will not be suitable unless it:
- Is appropriate for the risk and conditions.
- It takes account of ergonomic requirements.
- It takes account of the state of health of users.
- It takes account of the characteristics of the worker's workstation.
- Is capable of fitting the wearer, if required after adjustment.
- Is effective in controlling risks, without increase in overall risk.
- Complies with EU directives.

Where it is necessary to ensure hygiene or prevention of health risk personal issue will be made.

5)   Equipment must be compatible with any other PPE which has to be worn.

6)   Before issuing PPE, the employer must carry out a risk assessment to ensure that the equipment is suitable.
- Assess risks not avoided by other means.
- Define characteristics of PPE and of the risk of the equipment itself.
- Compare characteristics of PPE to defined requirement.
- Repeat assessment when no longer valid, or significant change has taken place.

7)   PPE must be maintained.
- In an efficient state.
- In efficient working order.
- In good repair.

8)   Accommodation must be provided for equipment when it is not being used.

9)   Information, instruction and training must be given on:
- The risks PPE will eliminate or limit.
- Why the PPE is to be used.
- How the PPE is to be used.
- How to maintain the PPE.

Information and instruction must be comprehensible to the wearer/user and kept available to them.

10)   Employers shall take reasonable steps to ensure PPE is worn.
- Every employee shall use PPE that has been provided.
- Every employee shall take reasonable steps to return PPE to storage.

11)   Employees must report any loss or defect.

The Guidance on the Regulations points out:

"Whatever PPE is chosen, it should be remembered that, although some types of equipment do provide very high levels of protection, none provides 100%".

Provision and Use of Work Equipment Regulations (PUWER) 1998 (as amended)

See also – Health and Safety (Miscellaneous Amendments) Regulations (MAR) 2002.

Law considered in context/more depth in Elements 3 and 5.

Arrangement of Regulations

PART I - INTRODUCTION
1)   Citation and commencement.
2)   Interpretation.
3)   Application.

PART II - GENERAL

4) Suitability of work equipment.
5) Maintenance.
6) Inspection.
7) Specific risks.
8) Information and instructions.
9) Training.
10) Conformity with Community requirements.
11) Dangerous parts of machinery.
12) Protection against specified hazards.
13) High or very low temperature.
14) Controls for starting or making a significant change in operating conditions.
15) Stop controls.
16) Emergency stop controls.
17) Controls.
18) Control systems.
19) Isolation from sources of energy.
20) Stability.
21) Lighting.
22) Maintenance operations.
23) Markings.
24) Warnings.

PART III - MOBILE WORK EQUIPMENT

25) Employees carried on mobile work equipment.
26) Rolling over of mobile work equipment.
27) Overturning of fork-lift trucks.
28) Self-propelled work equipment.
29) Remote-controlled self-propelled work equipment.
30) Drive shafts.

PART IV - POWER PRESSES

31) Power presses to which Part IV does not apply.
32) Thorough examination of power presses, guards and protection devices.
33) Inspection of guards and protection devices.
34) Reports.
35) Keeping of information.

PART V - MISCELLANEOUS

36) Exemption for the armed forces.
37) Transitional provision.
38) Repeal of enactment.
39) Revocation of instruments.

Schedule 1 - Instruments which give effect to Community directives concerning the safety of products.

Schedule 2 - Power presses to which regulations 32 to 35 do not apply.

Schedule 3 - Information to be contained in a report of a thorough examination of a power press, guard or protection device.

Schedule 4 - Revocation of instruments.

Outline of main points

GENERAL REQUIREMENTS

These Regulations impose health and safety requirements with respect to the provision and use of work equipment, which is defined as 'any machinery, appliance, apparatus, tool or installation for use at work (whether exclusively or not)'. These regulations:

- Place general duties on employers.
- Certain persons having control of work equipment, of persons at work who use or supervise or manage its use or of the way it is used, to the extent of their control.
- List minimum requirements for work equipment to deal with selected hazards whatever the industry.
- 'Use' includes any activity involving work equipment and includes starting, stopping, programming, setting, transporting, repairing, modifying, maintaining, servicing and cleaning.

The general duties require the employer to:

- Make sure that equipment is suitable for the use that will be made of it.
- Take into account the working conditions and hazards in the workplace when selecting equipment.
- Ensure equipment is used only for operations for which, and under conditions for which, it is suitable.
- Ensure that equipment is maintained in an efficient state, in efficient working order and in good repair.
- Ensure the inspection of work equipment in specified circumstances by a competent person; keep a record of the result for specified periods; and ensure that evidence of the last inspection accompany work equipment used outside the undertaking.
- Give adequate information, instruction and training.

- Provide equipment that conforms to EU product safety directives.

SPECIFIC REQUIREMENTS COVER

- Guarding of dangerous parts of machinery.
- Protection against specified hazards i.e. articles and substances falling/ejected, rupture/disintegration of work equipment parts, equipment catching fire or overheating, unintended or premature discharge of articles and substances, explosion.
- Work equipment parts and substances at high or very low temperatures.
- Control systems and control devices.
- Isolation of equipment from sources of energy.
- Stability of equipment.
- Lighting.
- Maintenance operations.
- Warnings and markings.

MOBILE WORK EQUIPMENT

Mobile work equipment must have provision as to:

- Its suitability for carrying persons and its safety features.
- Means to minimise the risk to safety from its rolling over.
- Means to reduce the risk to safety from the rolling over of a fork-lift truck.
- The safety of self-propelled work equipment and remote-controlled self propelled work equipment.
- The drive shafts of mobile work equipment.

POWER PRESSES

The Regulations provide for:

- The thorough examination (defined in regulation 2(1)) of power presses and their guards and protection devices (regulation 32).
- Their inspection after setting, re-setting or adjustment of their tools, and every working period (regulation 33).
- The making (regulation 34 and Schedule 3) and keeping (regulation 35) of reports.
- The regulations implement an EU directive aimed at the protection of workers. There are other directives setting out conditions which new equipment (especially machinery) will have to satisfy before it can be sold in EU member states.

Regulatory Reform (Fire Safety) Order (RRFSO) 2005

Law considered in context/more depth in Element 7.

INTRODUCTION

The amount of legislation covering the risk of fire has grown considerably over time. The situation was identified as unwieldy; many different regulations existed, often with conflicting definitions and requirements. In order to simply this and remove confusion the Regulatory Reform (Fire Safety) Order 2005 was introduced. There were 4 principal pieces of legislation that covered fire safety in the workplace that have been affected by the RRFSO:

- Fire Precautions Act (FPA).
- Fire Precautions (Workplace) Regulations (FPWR).
- Management of Health and Safety at Work Regulations (MHSWR).
- Dangerous Substances & Explosive Atmosphere Regulations (DSEAR).

FIRE PRECAUTIONS ACT

This legislation is has been repealed by the RRFSO 2005.

FIRE PRECAUTIONS WORKPLACE REGULATIONS

These regulations outlined the fire safety measures that need to be achieved via the risk assessment of fire and management of fire safety within a workplace. These regulations have been repealed by the implementation of the RRFSO, however their content has been incorporated within the RRFSO 2005.

MANAGEMENT OF HEALTH AND SAFETY AT WORK REGULATIONS

It is this regulation that makes the legal requirement for risk assessments. In addition, it made various requirements for the management of fire safety within workplaces, which have now been revoked. This regulation will continue as a stand alone health and safety regulation as the relevant fire aspects of this regulation have been incorporated within the RRFSO 2005.

DANGEROUS SUBSTANCES AND EXPLOSIVE ATMOSPHERE REGULATIONS

This regulation outlines the safety and control measures that need to be taken if dangerous or flammable/explosive substances are present. This regulation will continue as a stand alone health and safety regulation. Again the relevant fire aspects of this regulation have been incorporated within the RRFSO 2005.

REGULATORY REFORM (FIRE SAFETY) ORDER 2005

This is a new, all encompassing, fire safety order, which came into force in England and Wales on 01 October 2006. As shown above it has aspects of other legislation within it and has been compiled in such a way as to present a cohesive structure for fire safety legislation. The order is split into 5 parts, each part is then subdivided into the individual points, or articles as they are called in the order:

- Part 1   General.
- Part 2   Fire Safety Duties.
- Part 3   Enforcement.
- Part 4   Offences and appeals.
- Part 5   Miscellaneous.

Outline of main points

PART 1 - GENERAL

This part covers various issues such as the interpretation of terminology used, definition of responsible person, definition of general fire precautions, duties under the order, and its application.

PART 2 - FIRE SAFETY DUTIES

This part imposes a duty on the responsible person to carry out a fire risk assessment to identify what the necessary general fire precautions should be. It also outlines the principles of prevention that should be applied and the necessary arrangements for the management of fire safety.

The following areas are also covered:

- Fire-fighting and fire detection.
- Emergency routes and exits.
- Procedures for serious and imminent danger and for danger areas.
- Additional emergency measures re dangerous substances.
- Maintenance.
- Safety assistance.
- Provision of information to employees, employers and self employed.
- Capabilities and training.
- Co-operation and co-ordination.
- General duties of employees.

PART 3 - ENFORCEMENT

This part details who the enforcing authority is, (which in the main is the Fire Authority), and it states they must enforce the order. It also details the powers of inspectors. It also details the different types of enforcement that can be taken:

- Alterations notice.
- Enforcement notice.
- Prohibition notice.

PART 4 - OFFENCES AND APPEALS

This part details the 13 offences that may occur and the subsequent punishments and appeals procedure. It also explains that the legal onus for proving that an offence was not committed is on the accused. A new disputes procedure is also outlined within this part.

PART 5 - MISCELLANEOUS

Various matters are covered within this part, the principal points being:

- 'Fire-fighters switches' for luminous tube signs etc.
- Maintenance of measures provided for the protection of fire-fighters.
- Civil liability.
- Duty to consult employees.
- Special provisions for licensed premises.
- Application to crown premises.

There is then a schedule that covers the risk assessment process.

Road Traffic Act (RTA) 1991

Law considered in context/more depth in Element 3.

Arrangement of main part of Act

PART 1 - GENERAL

DRIVING OFFENCES

1) Offences of dangerous driving.
2) Careless, and inconsiderate, driving.

DRINK AND DRUGS

3) Causing death by careless driving when under influence of drink or drugs.
4) Driving under influence of drink or drugs.

MOTORING EVENTS

5) Disapplication of sections 1 to 3 of the Road Traffic Act 1988 for authorised motoring events.

DANGER TO ROAD-USERS

6) Causing danger to road-users.

CYCLING

7) Cycling offences.

CONSTRUCTION AND USE

8) Construction and use of vehicles.
9) Vehicle examiners.
10) Testing vehicles on roads.
11) Inspection of vehicles.
12) Power to prohibit driving of unfit vehicles.
13) Power to prohibit driving of overloaded vehicles.
14) Unfit and overloaded vehicles: offences.
15) Removal of prohibitions.
16) Supply of unroadworthy vehicles etc.

LICENSING OF DRIVERS

17) Requirement of licence.
18) Physical fitness.
19) Effects of disqualification.

INSURANCE

20) Exception from requirement of third-party insurance.

INFORMATION

21) Information as to identity of driver etc.

TRIAL

22) Amendment of Schedule 1 to the Road Traffic Offenders Act 1988.
23) Speeding offences etc: admissibility of certain evidence.
24) Alternative verdicts.
25) Interim disqualification.

PENALTIES

26) Amendment of Schedule 2 to the Road Traffic Offenders Act 1988.
27) Penalty points to be attributed to offences.
28) Penalty points to be taken into account on conviction.
29) Disqualification for certain offences.
30) Courses for drink-drive offenders.
31) Experimental period for section 30.
32) Disqualification until test is passed.
33) Short periods of disqualification.
34) Conditional offer of fixed penalty.

MISCELLANEOUS

35) Disabled persons' badges.
36) Forfeiture of vehicles.
37) Forfeiture of vehicles: Scotland.
38) Disqualification where vehicle used for assault.
39) Disqualification in Scotland were vehicle used to commit offence.
40) Power to install equipment for detection of traffic offences.
41) Variation of charges at off-street parking places.
42) Variation of charges at designated parking places.
43) Permitted and special parking areas outside London.
44) Parking attendants.
45) Variable speed limits.
46) Tramcars and trolley vehicles.
47) Application for licences to drive hackney carriages etc.

Outline of main points

SECTION 2 - CARELESS, AND INCONSIDERATE, DRIVING

"If a person drives a vehicle on a road or other public place without due care and attention, or without reasonable consideration for other persons using the road or place, he is guilty of an offence".

SECTION 3 - DRINK AND DRUGS

Causing death by careless driving when under influence of drink or drugs - if a person causes the death of another person by driving a vehicle on a road or other public place without due care and attention, or without reasonable consideration for other persons using the road or place:

- At the time of driving is unfit to drive through drink or drugs.
- Has consumed so much alcohol that the proportion of it in his breath, blood or urine at that time exceeds the prescribed limit.
- Is within 18 hours after that time, required to provide a specimen in pursuance of section 7 of this Act, but without reasonable excuse fails to provide it, he is guilty of an offence.

For the purposes of this section a person shall be taken to be unfit to drive at any time when his ability to drive properly is impaired.

SECTION 6 - DANGER TO ROAD-USERS

Causing danger to road-users - a person is guilty of an offence if he intentionally and without lawful authority or reasonable cause.

- Causes anything to be on or over a road.
- Interferes with a motor vehicle, trailer or cycle.
- Interferes (directly or indirectly) with traffic equipment, in such circumstances that it would be obvious to a reasonable person that to do so would be dangerous.

SECTION 8 - CONSTRUCTION AND USE OF VEHICLES

A person is guilty of an offence if he uses, or causes or permits another to use, a motor vehicle or trailer on a road when:

- The condition of the motor vehicle or trailer.
- Its accessories or equipment.

- The purpose for which it is used.
- The number of passengers carried by it, or the manner in which they are carried.
- The weight, position or distribution of its load, or the manner in which it is secured.

…..is such that the use of the motor vehicle or trailer involves a danger of injury to any person.

Breach of requirement as to weight (goods and passenger vehicles) - a person who:

- Contravenes or fails to comply with a construction and use requirement as to any description of weight applicable to:
- A goods vehicle.
- A motor vehicle or trailer adapted to carry more than eight passengers.
- Uses on a road a vehicle which does not comply with such a requirement, or causes or permits a vehicle to be so used, is guilty of an offence.

SECTION 21 - INFORMATION AS TO THE DRIVER ETC

Where the driver of a vehicle is alleged to be guilty of an offence to which this section applies:

- The person keeping the vehicle shall give such information as to the identity of the driver as he may be required to give by or on behalf of a chief officer of police.
- Any other person shall if required as stated above give any information which it is in his power to give and may lead to identification of the driver.

Special Waste Regulations (SWR) 1996

Arrangement of Regulations

1) Citation, commencement, extent, application and interpretation.
2) Meaning of special waste.
3) Certain radioactive waste to be special waste.
4) Coding of consignments.
5) Consignment notes: standard procedure.
6) Consignment notes: cases in which pre-notification is not required.
7) Consignment notes: procedure where pre-notification is not required.
8) Consignment notes: carrier's rounds.
9) Consignment notes: removal of ships' waste to reception facilities.
10) Consignment notes etc.: duty of consignee not accepting delivery of a consignment.
11) Consignment notes: duties of the Agencies.
12) Consignment notes: provisions as to furnishing.
13) Consignment notes: importers and exporters.
14) Fees.
15) Registers.
16) Site records.
17) Restrictions on mixing special waste.
18) Offences.
19) Responsibilities of the Agencies.
20) Transitional provisions for certificates of technical competence.
21) Amendment of regulations relating to the assessment of environmental effects.
22) Amendment of the Controlled Waste (Registration of Carriers and Seizure of Vehicles) Regulations 1991.
23) Amendment of the Environmental Protection (Duty of Care) Regulations 1991.
24) Amendment of the Controlled Waste Regulations 1992.
25) Amendment of the Waste Management Licensing Regulations 1994.
26) Revocations and savings.

SCHEDULES

1) Forms of consignment note and schedule.
2) Special waste.
3) Amendments to the Waste Management Licensing Regulations 1994.

Outline of main points

The Special Waste Regulations 1996 were used to implement the European Hazardous Waste Directive 91/689/EEC. They provide an effective system of control for wastes that are dangerous and have special requirements placed on their handling. The Regulations ensure sound management of waste from production to final disposal or recovery.

Special Waste Amendment (Scotland) Regulations (SWASR) 2004

The Special Waste Amendment (Scotland) Regulations amend the Special Waste Regulations 1996 SI 972 as it relates to storing and disposing of 'special waste' in Scotland.

Special waste is hazardous waste which may be harmful to human health or the environment. Examples include asbestos, lead acid batteries, electrical equipment containing hazardous components such as cathode ray tubes, oily sludge, solvents, fluorescent light tubes, chemical wastes and pesticides. The regulations apply in Scotland only.

Arrangement of Regulations

CITATION AND COMMENCEMENT

1) These Regulations may be cited as the Special Waste Amendment (Scotland) Amendment Regulations 2004 and shall come into force on 21st May 2004.

AMENDMENT OF THE SPECIAL WASTE AMENDMENT (SCOTLAND) REGULATIONS 2004

2) In regulation 2(10) of the Special Waste Amendment (Scotland) Regulations 2004(2), in regulation 15A (5) (Registers: special waste producers) as inserted Into the Special Waste Regulations 1996(3), omit, "together with the producer return detailing that consignment".

Outline of main points

These Regulations amend the Special Waste (Scotland) Regulations 1996 (S.I. 1996/972) ("the principal Regulations"), which make provision for handling special waste and for implementing Council Directive 91/689/EEC on hazardous waste (O.J. No. L 377, 31.12.1991, p.20) ("the Hazardous Waste Directive").

Supply of Machinery (Safety) Regulations (SMSR) 2008

Law considered in context/more depth in Element 5.

Outline of main points

Previously the Supply of Machinery (Safety) Regulations 1992 as amended by the Supply of Machinery (Safety) (Amendment) Regulations 1994 and the Supply of Machinery (Safety) (Amendment) Regulations 2005.

The SMSR 2008 imposes duties upon those who place machinery and safety components onto the market, or put them into service (this includes second-hand machinery which is "new" to Europe). They set out the essential requirements which must be met before machinery or safety components may be placed on the market or put into service in the UK. They implement the latest version of the Machinery Directive 2006/42/EC and came into force on 29 December 2009, replacing the previous Supply of Machinery (Safety) Regulations 1992, as amended in 1994 and 2005.

MEETING THE REQUIREMENTS

The duty to meet the requirements mainly falls to the 'responsible person' who is defined as the manufacturer or the manufacturer's representative. If the manufacturer is not established in the EEA, the person who first supplies the machinery in the EEA may be the responsible person, which can be a user who manufactures or imports a machine for their own use.

Conformity assessment

The responsible person should ensure that machinery and safety components satisfy the ***Essential Health and Safety Requirements (EHSRs)***, see Schedule 2, Part 1 of the Regulations, and that appropriate conformity assessment procedures have been carried out. These requirements are intended to ensure that all machinery throughout the EC is constructed to the same safety standards. In addition, the responsible person must draw up a technical file (see below).

For certain classes of dangerous machine and safety component, a more rigorous procedure is required.

The new SMSR place even greater emphasis on the EHSR requirements. However, still extant are the requirements of primary legislation by way of the Health and Safety at Work Act 1974 (HASAWA), which makes a specific reference to the duties of manufacturers and suppliers of workplace machinery (including second hand machinery).

Section 6 of HASAWA (general duties of manufacturers) states:
"It shall be the duty of any person who designs, manufactures, imports or supplies any article for use at work....
(a) To ensure , so far as is reasonably practicable, that the article is so designed and constructed that it will be safe and without risks to health at all times when it is being set, used, cleaned or maintained by a person at work".

HASAWA is reinforced by the duties under Part 3 of SMSR 2008 (general prohibitions and obligations), which states:
"No responsible person shall place machinery on the market or put it into service unless it is safe; and "before machinery is placed on the market or put into service, the responsible person must-
(a) Ensure that the applicable essential health and safety requirements are satisfied in respect of it...".

Declaration procedure

The responsible person must issue one of two forms of declaration.

Declaration of conformity

This declaration should be issued with the finished product so that it is available to the user. It will contain various details such as the manufacturer's address, the machinery type and serial number, and Harmonised European or other Standards used in design.

Declaration of Incorporation

Where machinery is intended for incorporation into other machinery, the responsible person can draw up a declaration of incorporation. This should state that the machinery must not be put into service until the machinery into which it is to be incorporated has been given a Declaration of Conformity. A CE mark is not affixed at this intermediate stage.

Marking

When the first two steps have been satisfactorily completed, the responsible person or the person assembling the final product should affix the CE mark.

ENFORCEMENT

In the UK the Health and Safety Executive is responsible for enforcing these Regulations in relation to machinery and safety components designed for use at work. Trading Standards Officers are responsible for enforcing these Regulations in relation to consumer goods.

DETAILED ADVICE FOR THE DESIGNER AND MANUFACTURER

Technical file contents

The responsible person (defined above) is required to draw up a technical file for all machinery and safety components covered by these Regulations. The file or documents should comprise:

a) An overall drawing of the product together with the drawings of the control circuits.

b) Full detailed drawings, accompanied by any calculation notes, test results etc. required to check the conformity of the product with the essential health and safety requirements.

c) A list of the essential health and safety requirements, transposed harmonised standards, national standards and other technical specifications which were used when the product was designed.

d) A description of methods adopted to eliminate hazards presented by the machinery or safety component.

e) If the responsible person so desires, any technical report or certificate obtained from a component body or laboratory.

f) If the responsible person declares conformity with a transposed harmonised standard, any technical report giving the results of tests.

g) A copy of the instructions for the product.

For series manufacture, the responsible person must also have available documentation on the necessary administrative measures that the manufacturer will take to ensure that the product meets requirements.

Technical file procedure

The technical file document need not be on a permanent file, but it should be possible to assemble and make them available to an enforcement authority. The technical file documents should be retained and kept available for at least ten years following the date of manufacture of the product or of the last unit produced, in the case of a series manufacture. If the technical file documents are drawn up in the United Kingdom, they should be in English unless they are to be submitted to an Approved/Notified Body in another Member State, in which case they should be in a language acceptable to that approved Body. In all cases the instructions for the machinery should be in accordance with the language requirements of the EHSRs.

Work at Height Regulations (WAH) 2005

Law considered in context/more depth in Elements 5 and 10. See also - PUWER 1998 and WHSWR 1992.

Arrangement of Regulations

1) Citation and commencement.
2) Interpretation.
3) Application.
4) Organisation and planning.
5) Competence.
6) Avoidance of risks from work at height.
7) Selection of work equipment for work at height.
8) Requirements for particular work equipment.
9) Fragile surfaces.
10) Falling objects.
11) Danger areas.
12) Inspection of work equipment.
13) Inspection of places of work at height.
14) Duties of persons at work.
15) Exemption by the Health and Safety Executive.
16) Exemption for the Armed Forces.
17) Amendment to the Provision and Use of Work Equipment Regulations (PUWER) 1998.
18) Repeal of section 24 of the Factories Act 1961.
19) Revocation of instruments.

SCHEDULES

Schedule 1   Requirements for existing places of work and means of access or egress at height.
Schedule 2   Requirements for guard-rails, toe-boards, barriers and similar collective means of protection.
Schedule 3   Requirements for working platforms.
        Part 1   Requirements for all working platforms.
        Part 2   Additional requirements for scaffolding.
Schedule 4   Requirements for collective safeguards for arresting falls.
Schedule 5   Requirements for personal fall protection systems.
        Part 1   Requirements for all personal fall protection systems.
        Part 2   Additional requirements for work positioning systems.
        Part 3   Additional requirements for rope access and positioning techniques.
        Part 4   Additional requirements for fall arrest systems.
        Part 5   Additional requirements for work restraint systems.
Schedule 6   Requirements for ladders.
Schedule 7   Particulars to be included in a report of inspection.

Schedule 8   Revocation of instruments.

Outline of main points

The final version of the regulations, designated the *Work at Height Regulations (WAH) 2005* came into force 6th April 2005. Under these regulations the interpretation of 'work at height' includes any place of work at ground level, above or below ground level that a person could fall a distance liable to cause personal injury and includes places for obtaining access or egress, except by staircase in a permanent workplace.

AMENDMENTS TO OTHER REGULATIONS AS A RESULT OF THE WORK AT HEIGHT REGULATIONS 2005

WAH 2005 makes an amendment to the Provision and Use of Work Equipment Regulations 1998; they also replace certain regulations in the Workplace (Health and Safety) Regulations; and amend definitions in the Construction (Health, Safety and Welfare) Regulations:

Regulation 17 - amendment of the Provision and Use of Work Equipment Regulations (PUWER) 1998. There shall be added to regulation 6(5) of the Provision and Use of Work Equipment Regulations 1998 the following sub-paragraph:

(f)   "Work equipment to which regulation 12 of the Work at Height Regulations 2005 applies".

Schedule 8 - revocation of instruments

Workplace (Health and Safety) Regulations 1992 - extent of revocation: regulation 13(1) to (4).

Construction (Health, Safety and Welfare) Regulations 1996 - extent of revocation: in regulation 2(1), the definitions of "fragile material", "personal suspension equipment" and "working platform"; regulations 6 to 8; in regulation   29(2)   the   word   "scaffold" in both instances; regulation 30(5) and (6) (a); Schedules 1 to 5; and the entry first mentioned in columns 1 and 2 of Schedule 7.

WORK AT HEIGHT (AMENDMENT) REGULATIONS 2007

These regulations amended WAH 2005 to remove the dis-application of WAH 2005 to certain work concerning the provision of instruction or leadership to people engaged in caving or climbing by way of sport, recreation, team building or similar activities. They introduce a new duty under Regulation 14A that takes into account the special circumstances of work at height in caving and climbing.

Under these regulations the interpretation of 'work at height' includes any place of work at ground level, above or below ground level that a person could fall a distance liable to cause personal injury and includes places for obtaining access or egress, except by staircase in a permanent workplace.

Regulation 4 states that all work at height must be properly planned, supervised and be carried out so far as is reasonably practicable safe. Planning must include the selection of suitable equipment, take account of emergencies and give consideration to weather conditions impacting on safety.

Regulation 5 states that those engaged in any activity in relation to work at height must be competent; and, if under training, are supervised by a competent person.

Regulation 6 states that work at height must only be carried out when it is not reasonably practicable to carry out the work otherwise. If work at height does take place, suitable and sufficient measures must be taken to prevent a fall of any distance, to minimise the distance and the consequences of any fall liable to cause injury. Employers must also make a risk assessment, as required by regulation 3 of the Management of Health and Safety at Work Regulations.

Regulation 7 states that when selecting equipment for use in work at height the employer shall take account of working conditions and any risk to persons in connection with the place where the equipment is to be used. The selection of work equipment must have regard in particular to the purposes specified in regulation 6.

Regulation 8 sets out requirements for particular equipment to conform to standards expressed in schedules to the regulations. It includes guard-rails, toe-boards, working platforms, nets, airbags, personal fall arrest equipment rope access and ladders.

Regulation 9 states that every employer shall ensure that suitable and sufficient steps are taken to prevent any person at work falling through any fragile surface; and that no work may pass across or near, or work on, from or near, fragile surfaces when it is reasonably practicable to carry out work without doing so. If work has to be from a fragile roof then suitable and sufficient means of support must be provided that can sustain foreseeable loads. No person at work should be allowed to pass or work near a fragile surface unless suitable and sufficient guard rails and other means of fall protection is in place. Signs must be situated at a prominent place at or near to works involving fragile surfaces, or persons are made aware of the fragile roof by other means.

Regulation 10 states that every employer shall take reasonably practicable steps to prevent injury to any person from the fall of any material or object; and where it is not reasonably practicable to do so, to take similar steps to prevent any person being struck by any falling material or object which is liable to cause personal injury. Also, that no material is thrown or tipped from height in circumstances where it is liable to cause injury to any person. Materials and objects must be stored in such a way as to prevent risk to any person arising from the collapse, overturning or unintended movement of the materials or objects.

Regulation 11 states that every employer shall ensure that where an area presents a risk of falling from height or being struck from an item falling at height that the area is equipped with devices preventing unauthorised persons from entering such areas and the area is clearly indicated.

Regulation 12 states that every employer shall ensure that, where the safety of work equipment depends on how it is installed or assembled, it is not used after installation or assembly in any position unless it has been inspected in that position.

Also, that work equipment is inspected at suitable intervals and each time that exceptional circumstances which are liable to jeopardise the safety of the work equipment occur. Specific requirements exist for periodic (every 7 days) inspection of a working platform where someone could fall 2 metres or more.

Regulation 13 states that every employer shall ensure that fall protection measures of every place of work at height are visually inspected before use.

Regulation 14 states the duties of persons at work to report defects and use equipment in accordance with training/instruction.

Workplace (Health, Safety and Welfare) Regulations (WHSWR) 1992

See also – Health and Safety (Miscellaneous Amendments) Regulations (MAR) 2002 and Health and Safety (Miscellaneous Repeals, Revocations and Amendments) Regulations (MRRA) 2002.

Law considered in context/more depth in Element 2.

Arrangement of Regulations

1) Citation and commencement.
2) Interpretation.
3) Application of these Regulations.
4) Requirements under these Regulations.
5) Maintenance of workplace, and of equipment, devices and systems.
6) Ventilation.
7) Temperature in indoor workplaces.
8) Lighting.
9) Cleanliness and waste materials.
10) Room dimensions and space.
11) Workstations and seating.
12) Condition of floors and traffic routes.
13) Falls or falling objects (*Revoked in part by WAH 2005*).
14) Windows, and transparent or translucent doors, gates and walls.
15) Windows, skylights and ventilators.
16) Ability to clean windows etc. safely.
17) Organisation etc. of traffic routes.
18) Doors and gates.
19) Escalators and moving walkways.
20) Sanitary conveniences.
21) Washing facilities.
22) Drinking water.
23) Accommodation for clothing.
24) Facilities for changing clothing.
25) Facilities for rest and to eat meals.
26) Exemption certificates.
27) Repeals, saving and revocations.

Schedule 1 - Provisions applicable to factories which are not new workplaces, extensions or conversions.
Schedule 2 - Repeals and revocations.

Outline of main points

SUMMARY

The main requirements of the Workplace (Health, Safety and Welfare) Regulations (WHSWR) 1992 are:

1) **Maintenance** of the workplace and equipment.
2) **Safety** of those carrying out maintenance work and others who might be at risk (for example, segregation of pedestrians and vehicles, provision of handrails etc).
3) Provision of **welfare** facilities (for example, rest rooms, changing rooms etc).
4) Provision of a safe **environment** (for example, lighting, ventilation etc).

ENVIRONMENT

Reg 1   New workplaces, extensions and modifications must comply.

Reg 4   Requires employers, persons in control of premises and occupiers of factories to comply with the regulations.

Reg 6   Ventilation - enclosed workplaces should be ventilated with a sufficient quantity of fresh or purified air (5 to 8 litres per second per occupant).

Reg 7   Temperature indoors - This needs to be reasonable and the heating device must not cause injurious fumes. Thermometers must be provided. Temperature should be a minimum of 16°C or 13°C if there is physical effort.

Reg 8   Lighting - must be suitable and sufficient. Natural light if possible. Emergency lighting should be provided if danger exists.

Reg 10   Room dimensions and space - every room where persons work shall have sufficient floor area, height and unoccupied space (min 11 cu. m per person).

Reg 11   Workstations and seating have to be suitable for the person and the work being done.

SAFETY

Reg 12   Floors and traffic routes must be of suitable construction. This includes absence of holes, slope, uneven or slippery surface. Drainage where necessary. Handrails and guards to be provided on slopes and staircases.

Reg 13   Tanks and pits containing dangerous substances to be covered or fenced where people could fall into them and traffic routes fenced.

Reg 14   Windows and transparent doors, where necessary for health and safety, must be of safety material and be marked to make it apparent.

Reg 15   Windows, skylights and ventilators must be capable of opening without putting anyone at risk.

Reg 17   Traffic routes for pedestrians and vehicles must be organised in such a way that they can move safely.

Reg 18   Doors and gates must be suitably constructed and fitted with any necessary safety devices.

Reg 19   Escalators and moving walkways shall function safely, be equipped with any necessary safety devices and be fitted with emergency stop.

HOUSEKEEPING

Reg 5   Workplace and equipment, devices and systems must be maintained in efficient working order and good repair.

Reg 9   Cleanliness and waste materials - workplaces must be kept sufficiently clean. Floors, walls and ceilings must be capable of being kept sufficiently clean. Waste materials shall not be allowed to accumulate, except in suitable receptacles.

Reg 16   Windows etc. must be designed so that they can be cleaned safety.

FACILITIES

Reg 20   Sanitary conveniences must be suitable and sufficient and in readily accessible places. They must be adequately ventilated, kept clean and there must be separate provision for men and women.

Reg 21   Washing facilities must be suitable and sufficient. Showers if required (a table gives minimum numbers of toilets and washing facilities).

Reg 22   Drinking water - an adequate supply of wholesome drinking water must be provided.

Reg 23   Accommodation for clothing must be suitable and sufficient.

Reg 24   Facilities for changing clothes must be suitable and sufficient, where a person has to use special clothing for work.

Reg 25   Facilities for rest and eating meals must be suitable and sufficient.

The WHSWR 1992 were amended by the Health and Safety (Miscellaneous Amendments) Regulations 2002 to establish specific requirements that rest rooms be equipped with:

An adequate number of tables and adequate seating with backs for the number of persons at work likely to use them at any one time. Seating which is adequate for the number of disabled persons at work and suitable for them.

In addition, WHSWR 1992 were amended to take account of disability arrangements. Where necessary, those parts of the workplace used or occupied directly by disabled persons at work, including in particular doors, passageways, stairs, showers, washbasins, lavatories and workstations, must be organised to take account of such persons.

This page is intentionally blank

Index

X

Z